# Mathematics III

## Volume 2

Randall I. Charles
Basia Hall
Dan Kennedy
Laurie E. Bass
Allan E. Bellman
Sadie Chavis Bragg
William G. Handlin
Art Johnson
Stuart J. Murphy
Grant Wiggins

PEARSON

Boston, Massachusetts • Chandler, Arizona • Glenview, Illinois • Upper Saddle River, New Jersey

Acknowledgments appear on page Z54, which constitutes an extension of this copyright page.



PEARSON

ISBN-13: 978-0-13-323479-4
ISBN-10: 0-13-323479-7
9 17

# *From the* **Authors**

## Welcome

Math is a powerful tool with far-reaching applications throughout your life. We have designed a unique and engaging program that will enable you to tap into the power of mathematics and mathematical reasoning. This award-winning program has been developed to align fully to the Common Core State Standards.

Developing mathematical understanding and problem-solving abilities is an ongoing process—a journey both inside and outside the classroom. This course is designed to help make sense of the mathematics you encounter in and out of class each day and to help you develop mathematical proficiency.

You will learn important mathematical principles. You will also learn how the principles are connected to one another and to what you already know. You will learn to solve problems and learn the reasoning that lies behind your solutions. You will also develop the key mathematical practices of the Common Core State Standards.

Each chapter begins with the "big ideas" of the chapter and some essential questions that you will learn to answer. Through this question-and-answer process you will develop your ability to analyze problems independently and solve them in different applications.

Your skills and confidence will increase through practice and review. Work through the problems so you understand the concepts and methods presented and the thinking behind them. Then do the exercises. Ask yourself how new concepts relate to old ones. Make the connections!

Everyone needs help sometimes. You will find that this program has built-in opportunities, both in this text and online, to get help whenever you need it.

The problem-solving and reasoning habits and problem-solving skills you develop in this program will serve you in all your studies and in your daily life. They will prepare you for future success not only as a student, but also as a member of a changing technological society.

Best wishes,

# **Series** *Authors*

**Randall I. Charles, Ph.D.,** is Professor Emeritus in the Department of Mathematics at San Jose State University, San Jose, California. He began his career as a high school mathematics teacher, and he was a mathematics supervisor for five years. Dr. Charles has been a member of several NCTM committees including the writing team for the Curriculum Focal Points. He is the former Vice President of the National Council of Supervisors of Mathematics. Much of his writing and research has been in the area of problem solving. He has authored more than 90 mathematics textbooks for kindergarten through college.

**Dan Kennedy, Ph.D.,** is a classroom teacher and the Lupton Distinguished Professor of Mathematics at the Baylor School in Chattanooga, Tennessee. A frequent speaker at professional meetings on the subject of mathematics education reform, Dr. Kennedy has conducted more than 50 workshops and institutes for high school teachers. He is coauthor of textbooks in calculus and precalculus, and from 1990 to 1994 he chaired the College Board's AP Calculus Development Committee. He is a 1992 Tandy Technology Scholar and a 1995 Presidential Award winner.

**Basia Hall** currently serves as Manager of Instructional Programs for the Houston Independent School District. With 33 years of teaching experience, Ms. Hall has served as a department chair, instructional supervisor, school improvement facilitator, and professional development trainer. She has developed curricula for Algebra 1, Geometry, and Algebra 2 and co-developed the Texas state mathematics standards. A 1992 Presidential Awardee, Ms. Hall is past president of the Texas Association of Supervisors of Mathematics and is a state representative for the National Council of Supervisors of Mathematics (NCSM).

# **Consulting** *Authors*

**Stuart J. Murphy** is a visual learning author and consultant. He is a champion of helping students develop visual learning skills so they become more successful students. He is the author of MathStart, a series of children's books that presents mathematical concepts in the context of stories, and *I See I Learn*, a Pre-Kindergarten and Kindergarten learning initiative that focuses on social and emotional skills. A graduate of the Rhode Island School of Design, he has worked extensively in educational publishing and has been on the authorship teams of a number of elementary and high school mathematics programs. He is a frequent presenter at meetings of the National Council of Teachers of Mathematics, the International Reading Association, and other professional organizations.

**Grant Wiggins, Ed.D.,** is the President of Authentic Education in Hopewell, New Jersey. He earned his B.A. from St. John's College in Annapolis and his Ed.D. from Harvard University Dr. Wiggins consults with schools, districts, and state education departments on a variety of reform matters; organizes conferences and workshops; and develops print materials and web resources on curricular change. He is perhaps best known for being the coauthor, with Jay McTighe, of *Understanding by Design* and *The Understanding by Design Handbook*[1], the award-winning and highly successful materials on curriculum published by ASCD. His work has been supported by the Pew Charitable Trusts, the Geraldine R. Dodge Foundation, and the National Science Foundation.

[1]ASCD, publisher of the "Understanding by Design Handbook" co-authored by Grant Wiggins and registered owner of the trademark "Understanding by Design", has not authorized or sponsored this work and is in no way affiliated with Pearson or its products.

# **Program** *Authors*

## *Algebra Topics*

**Allan E. Bellman, Ph.D.,** is an Associate Professor of Mathematics Education at the University of Mississippi. He previously taught at the University of California, Davis for 12 years and in public school in Montgomery County, Maryland for 31. He has been an instructor for both the Woodrow Wilson National Fellowship Foundation and the Texas Instruments' $T^3$ program. Dr. Bellman has expertise in the use of technology in education and assessment-driven instruction and speaks frequently on these topics. He is a recipient of the Tandy Award for Teaching Excellence and has twice been listed in Who's Who Among America's Teachers.

**Sadie Chavis Bragg, Ed.D.,** is Senior Vice President of Academic Affairs and professor of mathematics at the Borough of Manhattan Community College of the City University of New York. She is a past president of the American Mathematical Association of Two-Year Colleges (AMATYC). In recognition for her service to the field of mathematics locally, statewide, nationally, and internationally, she was awarded AMATYC's most prestigious award, The Mathematics Excellence Award for 2010. Dr. Bragg has coauthored more than 60 mathematics textbooks for kindergarten through college.

**William G. Handlin, Sr.,** is a classroom teacher and Department Chair of Mathematics and former Department Chair of Technology Applications at Spring Woods High School in Houston, Texas. Awarded Life Membership in the Texas Congress of Parents and Teachers for his contributions to the well-being of children, Mr. Handlin is also a frequent workshop and seminar leader in professional meetings.

## *Geometry Topics*

**Laurie E. Bass** is a classroom teacher at the 9–12 division of the Ethical Culture Fieldston School in Riverdale, New York. A classroom teacher for more than 30 years, Ms. Bass has a wide base of teaching experiences, ranging from Grade 6 through Advanced Placement Calculus. She was the recipient of a 2000 Honorable Mention for the Radio Shack National Teacher Awards. She has been a contributing writer for a number of publications, including software-based activities for the Algebra 1 classroom. Among her areas of special interest are cooperative learning for high school students and geometry exploration on the computer. Ms. Bass is a frequent presenter at local, regional, and national conferences.

**Art Johnson, Ed.D.,** is a professor of mathematics education at Boston University. He is a mathematics educator with 32 years of public school teaching experience, a frequent speaker and workshop leader, and the recipient of a number of awards: the Tandy Prize for Teaching Excellence, the Presidential Award for Excellence in Mathematics Teaching, and New Hampshire Teacher of the Year. He was also profiled by the Disney Corporation in the American Teacher of the Year Program. Dr. Johnson has contributed 18 articles to NCTM journals and has authored over 50 books on various aspects of mathematics.

# Using **Your Book** with Success

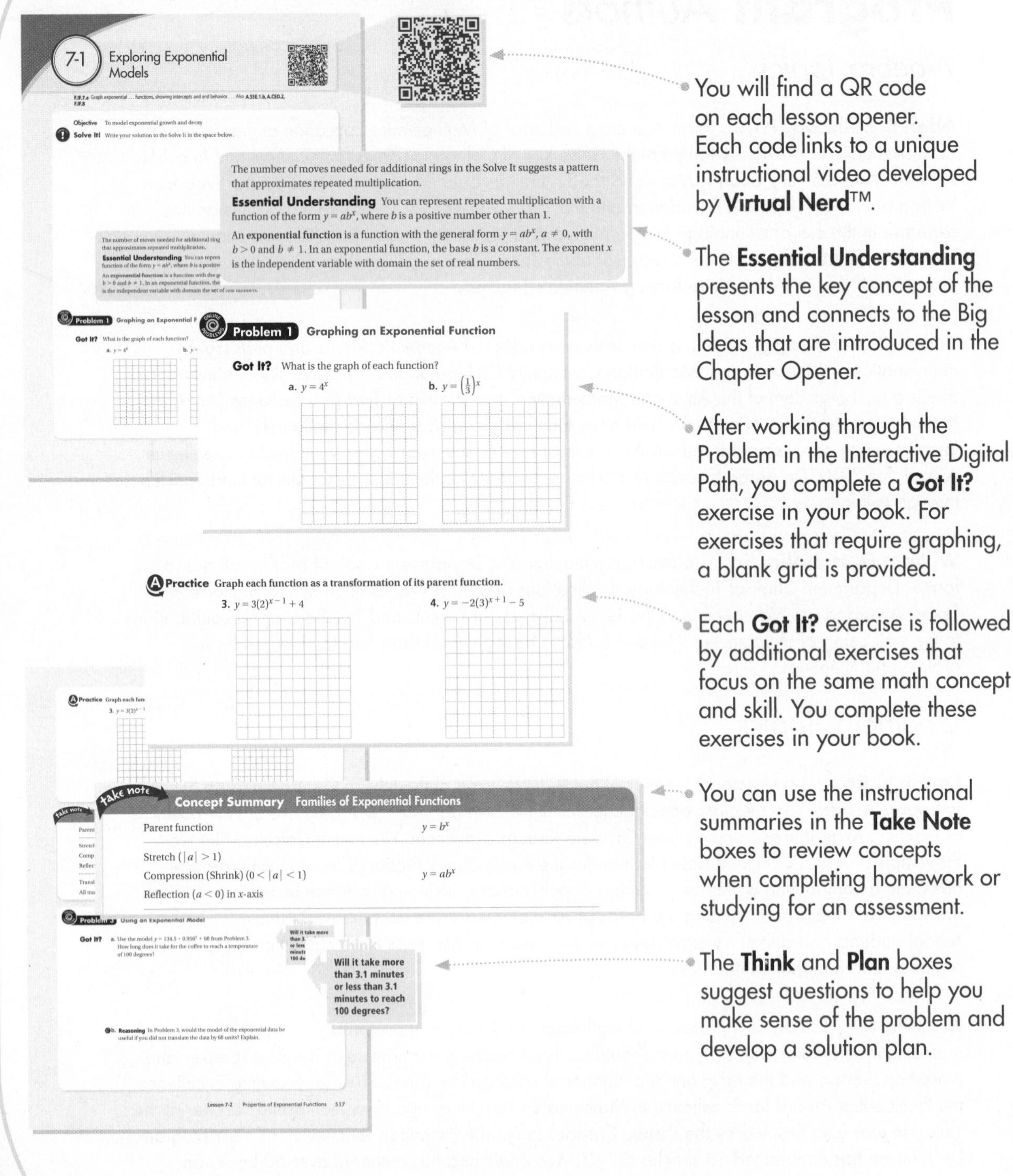


- You will find a QR code on each lesson opener. Each code links to a unique instructional video developed by **Virtual Nerd**™.
- The **Essential Understanding** presents the key concept of the lesson and connects to the Big Ideas that are introduced in the Chapter Opener.
- After working through the Problem in the Interactive Digital Path, you complete a **Got It?** exercise in your book. For exercises that require graphing, a blank grid is provided.
- Each **Got It?** exercise is followed by additional exercises that focus on the same math concept and skill. You complete these exercises in your book.
- You can use the instructional summaries in the **Take Note** boxes to review concepts when completing homework or studying for an assessment.
- The **Think** and **Plan** boxes suggest questions to help you make sense of the problem and develop a solution plan.

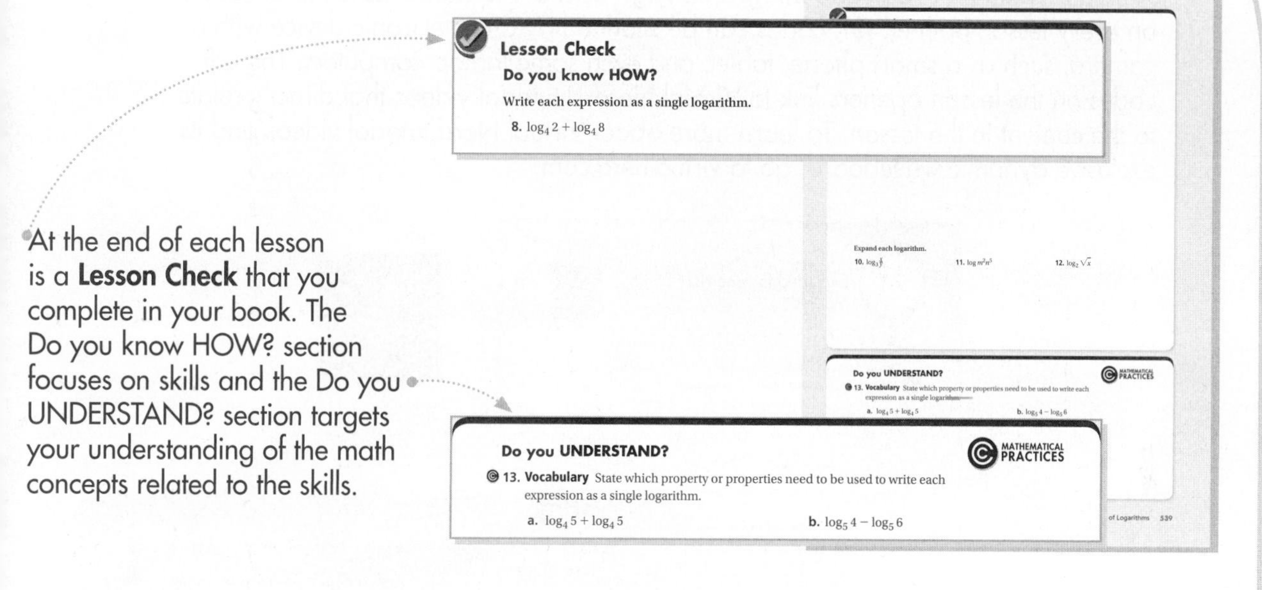

**Lesson Check**

**Do you know HOW?**

Write each expression as a single logarithm.

**8.** $\log_4 2 + \log_4 8$

Expand each logarithm.

**10.** $\log_3 \frac{x}{y}$ **11.** $\log m^2n^3$ **12.** $\log_2 \sqrt{x}$

**Do you UNDERSTAND?** MATHEMATICAL PRACTICES

**13. Vocabulary** State which property or properties need to be used to write each expression as a single logarithm.

**a.** $\log_4 5 + \log_4 5$ **b.** $\log_5 4 - \log_5 6$

At the end of each lesson is a **Lesson Check** that you complete in your book. The Do you know HOW? section focuses on skills and the Do you UNDERSTAND? section targets your understanding of the math concepts related to the skills.

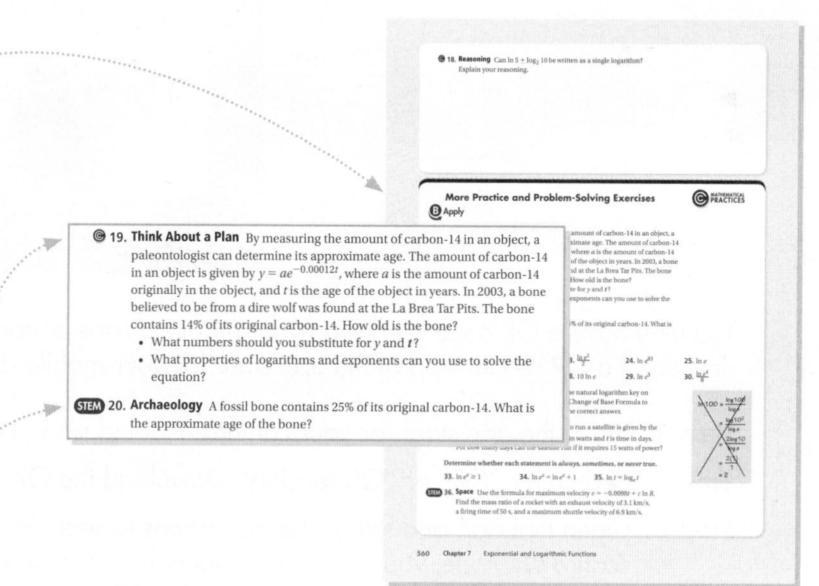

**18. Reasoning** Can $\ln 5 + \log_2 10$ be written as a single logarithm? Explain your reasoning.

**More Practice and Problem-Solving Exercises**

**B** Apply

**19. Think About a Plan** By measuring the amount of carbon-14 in an object, a paleontologist can determine its approximate age. The amount of carbon-14 in an object is given by $y = ae^{-0.00012t}$, where $a$ is the amount of carbon-14 originally in the object, and $t$ is the age of the object in years. In 2003, a bone believed to be from a dire wolf was found at the La Brea Tar Pits. The bone contains 14% of its original carbon-14. How old is the bone?

- What numbers should you substitute for $y$ and $t$?
- What properties of logarithms and exponents can you use to solve the equation?

STEM **20. Archaeology** A fossil bone contains 25% of its original carbon-14. What is the approximate age of the bone?

Each lesson ends with **More Practice and Problem Solving** Exercises. You will complete these exercises in your homework notebook or on a separate sheet of paper.

The exercises with the **Common Core logo** help you become more proficient with the Standards for Mathematical Practice. Those with **STEM** logo provide practice with science, technology, or engineering topics.

# What is a **QR code** and how do I use it?

A unique feature of Pearson's ***Integrated High School Mathematics*** is the QR code on every lesson opener. QR codes can be scanned by any electronic device with a camera, such as a smart phone, tablet, and even some laptop computers. The QR codes on the lesson openers link to Virtual Nerd™ tutorial videos that directly relate to the content in the lesson. To learn more about Virtual Nerd tutorial videos and its exclusive dynamic whiteboard, go to virtualnerd.com.

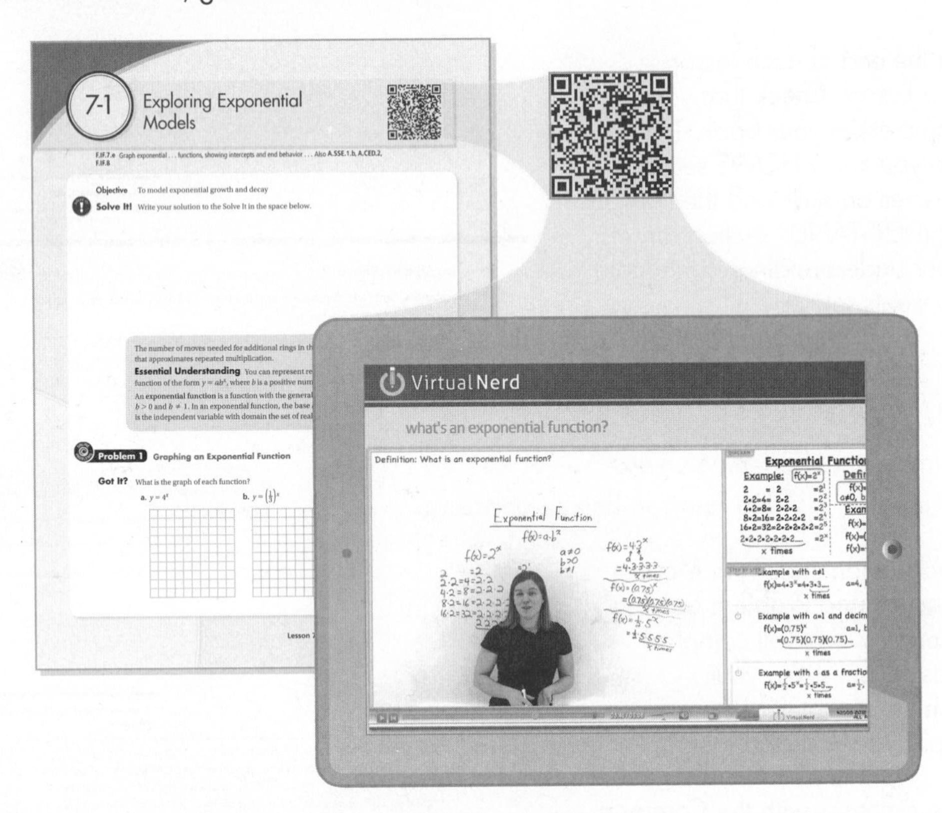


You must have a QR code reader on your mobile device or computer. You can download a QR reader app at the app store for your mobile device.

**Step 1:** Go to the app store for your camera-enabled smart phone or tablet.

**Step 2:** Search for "QR" or "QR readers". Download the QR reader app.

**Step 3:** Open that app and follow the instructions to scan. Whenever you want to scan a QR code, you will need to open the QR reader app first, otherwise you will just end up taking a picture of a QR code.

**Step 4:** After scanning the QR code, the appropriate Virtual Nerd tutorial video will play.

# *What* **Resources** *can I use when studying?*

Pearson's ***Integrated High School Mathematics*** offers a range of resources that you can use out of class.

**Student Worktext** Your book is more than a textbook. Not only does it have important summaries of key math concepts and skills, it will also have your worked-out solutions to the *Got It?* and *Practice* exercises and your own notes for each lesson or problem. Use your book to:

- Refer back to your worked-out solutions and notes.
- Review the key concepts of each lesson by rereading the *Essential Understanding* and *Take Note* boxes.
- Access video tutorials of the concepts addressed in the lesson by scanning the QR codes.

**Pearson SuccessNet** You have full access to all of the resources on Pearson SuccessNet, including the **Interactive Digital Path** where you will find all of the *Solve Its!* and Problems presented in class. Revisit the animated, stepped-out problems presented in-class to clarify and solidify your math knowledge. Additional resources available to you include:

- Interactive Student Worktext
- Homework Video Tutors in English and Spanish
- Online Glossary with audio in English and Spanish
- MathXL for School Interactive Math Practice
- Math Tools and Online Manipulatives
- Multilingual Handbook
- Assessments with immediate feedback

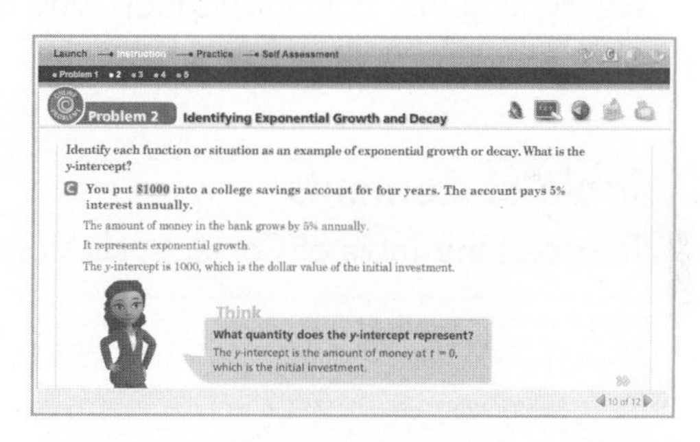


**Mobile eText** You may wish to access your student book on the go, either online or offline via download. Pearson's ***Integrated High School Mathematics*** also offers you a complete mobile etext of the Student Worktext.

- Use the notes, highlight, and bookmark features to personalize your eText.
- Watch animated problem videos with step-by-step instruction for every lesson.

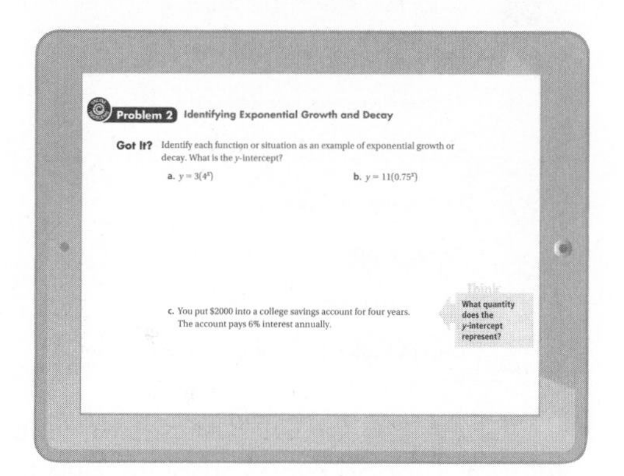

# Pearson SuccessNet

**Pearson SuccessNet** is the gateway to all of the digital components of the program. You can use the online content to review the day's lesson, complete lessons independently, get help with your homework assignments, and prepare for and/or take an assessment. You will be given a username and password to log into www.pearsonsuccessnet.com.

## The Homepage

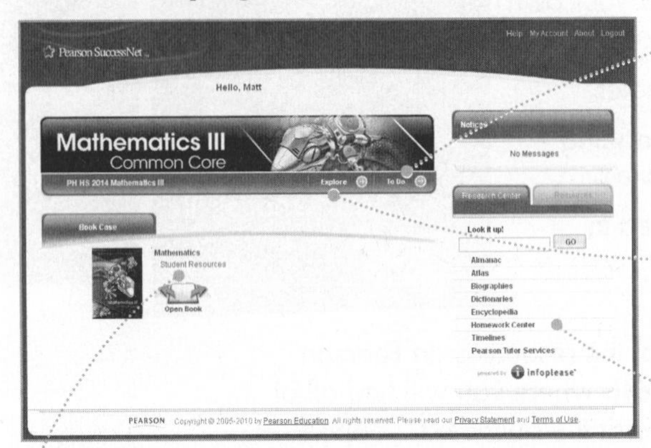


The **To Do** tab contains a list of assignments that you need to complete. You can also access your gradebook and review past assignments.

The **Explore** tab provides you access to the Table of Contents and all of the digital content for the program.

You can also access the following student resources: Practice Worksheets, Homework Video Tutors, and a Multilingual Handbook

Your eText includes links to animated lesson videos, highlighting and note taking tools, and a visual glossary with audio.

## Table of Contents

To access the Table of Contents, click on *Explore* from your Homepage.

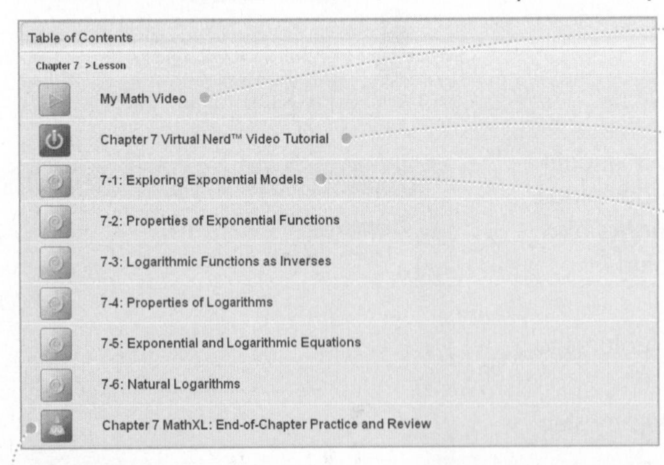


Student-developed videos bring real-life context to mathematics.

Step-by-step video tutorials offer additional support for every lesson.

Digital lessons include access to animated problems, math tools, homework exercises, and self-assessments.

**MathXL for School** exercises provide additional practice. Examples and tutorials support every problem, and instant feedback is provided as you complete each exercise.

## Interactive Digital Path

To access the **Interactive Digital Path**, click on the appropriate lesson from the Table of Contents.

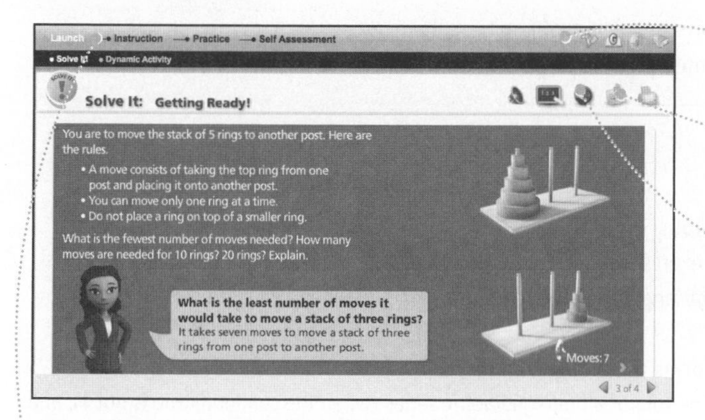


**Math Tools** help you explore and visualize concepts.

You'll find opportunities to review formulas, properties, and other key concepts.

**Interactive Glossary** is available in English and Spanish with audio.

Every lesson includes the following:

**Launch:** Interactive lesson opener connects the math to real-world applications.

**Instruction:** All lesson problems are stepped out with detailed instruction. You can complete the subsequent *Got It?* exercises in your Student Worktext.

**Practice:** Exercises from your Student Worktext are available for view.

**Self-Assessment:** You can take the self-check lesson quiz, and then check your answers on the second screen.

## MathXL for School

To access *MathXL for School*, click on the Chapter Review and Practice link from the Table of Contents.

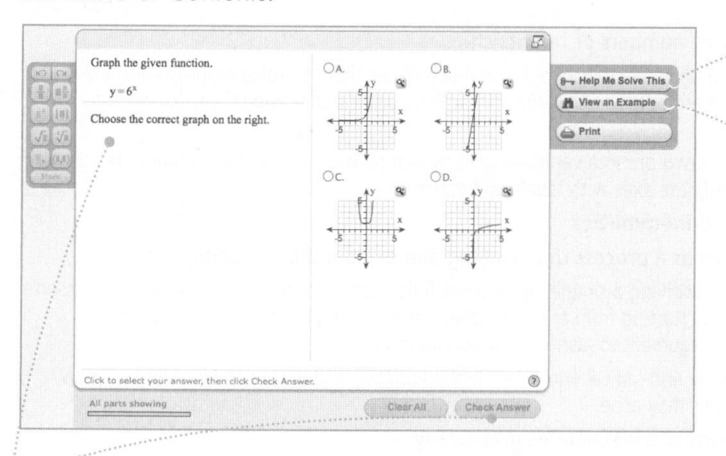


Select **Help Me Solve This** for an interactive step-by-step tutorial.

Select **View an Example** to see a similar worked out problem.

Input your answer and select **Check Answer** to get immediate feedback. After completing the exercise, a new exercise automatically regenerates, so you have unlimited practice opportunities.

# Common Core *State Standards*

## Mathematics III

### Number and Quantity

**Quantities**

**Reason quantitatively and use units to solve problems**

N.Q.2 Define appropriate quantities for the purpose of descriptive modeling.

### Algebra

**Seeing Structure in Expressions**

**Interpret the structure of expressions**

A.SSE.2 Use the structure of an expression to identify ways to rewrite it. *For example, see* $x^4 - y^4$ *as* $(x^2)^2 - (y^2)^2$*, thus recognizing it as a difference of squares that can be factored as* $(x^2 - y^2)(x^2 + y^2)$.

**Write expressions in equivalent forms to solve problems**

A.SSE.4 Derive the formula for the sum of a finite geometric series (when the common ratio is not 1), and use the formula to solve problems. *For example, calculate mortgage payments.* ★

**Arithmetic with Polynomials and Rational Expressions**

**Understand the relationship between zeros and factors of polynomial**

A.APR.2 Know and apply the Remainder Theorem: For a polynomial $p(x)$ and a number $a$, the remainder on division by $x - a$ is $p(a)$, so $p(a) = 0$ if and only if $(x - a)$ is a factor of $p(x)$.

A.APR.3 Identify zeros of polynomials when suitable factorizations are available, and use the zeros to construct a rough graph of the function defined by the polynomial.

**Use polynomial identities to solve problems**

A.APR.4 Prove polynomial identities and use them to describe numerical relationships. *For example, the polynomial identity* $(x^2 + y^2)^2 = (x^2 - y^2)^2 + (2xy)^2$ *can be used to generate Pythagorean triples.*

**Rewrite rational expressions**

A.APR.6 Rewrite simple rational expressions in different forms; write $a(x)/b(x)$ in the form $q(x) + r(x)/b(x)$, where $a(x)$, $b(x)$, $q(x)$, and $r(x)$ are polynomials with the degree of $r(x)$ less than the degree of $b(x)$, using inspection, long division, or, for the more complicated examples, a computer algebra system.

**Creating Equations★**

**Create equations that describe numbers or relationships**

A.CED.1 Create equations and inequalities in one variable and use them to solve problems. *Include equations arising from linear and quadratic functions, and simple rational and exponential functions.* ★

A.CED.2 Create equations in two or more variables to represent relationships between quantities; graph equations on coordinate axes with labels and scales.★

**Reasoning with Equations and Inequalities**

**Understand solving equations as a process of reasoning and explain the reasoning**

A.REI.1 Explain each step in solving a simple equation as following from the equality of numbers asserted at the previous step, starting from the assumption that the original equation has a solution. Construct a viable argument to justify a solution method.

A.REI.2 Solve simple rational and radical equations in one variable, and give examples showing how extraneous solutions may arise.

**Represent and solve equations and inequalities graphically**

A.REI.11 Explain why the $x$-coordinates of the points where the graphs of the equations $y = f(x)$ and $y = g(x)$ intersect are the solutions of the equation $f(x) = g(x)$; find the solutions approximately, e.g., using technology to graph the functions, make tables of values, or find successive approximations. Include cases where $f(x)$ and/or $g(x)$ are linear, polynomial, rational, absolute value, exponential, and logarithmic functions.★

## Functions

### Interpreting Functions

#### Interpret functions that arise in applications in terms of the context

F.IF.4 For a function that models a relationship between two quantities, interpret key features of graphs and tables in terms of the quantities, and sketch graphs showing key features given a verbal description of the relationship. *Key features include: intercepts; intervals where the function is increasing, decreasing, positive, or negative; relative maximums and minimums; symmetries; end behavior; and periodicity.*★

F.IF.6 Calculate and interpret the average rate of change of a function (presented symbolically or as a table) over a specified interval. Estimate the rate of change from a graph.★

#### Analyze functions using different representations

F.IF.7.c Graph functions expressed symbolically and show key features of the graph, by hand in simple cases and using technology for more complicated cases. Graph polynomial functions, identifying zeros when suitable factorizations are available, and showing end behavior.

F.IF.7.e Graph functions expressed symbolically and show key features of the graph, by hand in simple cases and using technology for more complicated cases. Graph exponential and logarithmic functions, showing intercepts and end behavior, and trigonometric functions, showing period, midline, and amplitude.

F.IF.9 Compare properties of two functions each represented in a different way (algebraically, graphically, numerically in tables, or by verbal descriptions). *For example, given a graph of one quadratic function and an algebraic expression for another, say which has the larger maximum.*

### Building Functions

#### Build new functions from existing functions

F.BF.3 Identify the effect on the graph of replacing $f(x)$ by $f(x) + k$, $k\,f(x)$, $f(kx)$, and $f(x + k)$ for specific values of $k$ (both positive and negative); find the value of $k$ given the graphs. Experiment with cases and illustrate an explanation of the effects on the graph using technology. *Include recognizing even and odd functions from their graphs and algebraic expressions for them.*

F.BF.4.a Find inverse functions. Solve an equation of the form $f(x) = c$ for a simple function $f$ that has an inverse and write an expression for the inverse. *For example,* $f(x) = 2x^3$ *or* $f(x) = (x + 1)/(x - 1)$ *for* $x \neq 1$.

### Linear, Quadratic, and Exponential

#### Construct and compare linear and exponential models and solve problems

F.LE.4 For exponential models, express as a logarithm the solution to $abct = d$ where $a$, $c$, and $d$ are numbers and the base $b$ is 2, 10, or $e$; evaluate the logarithm using technology.

### Trigonometric Functions

#### Extend the domain of trigonometric functions using the unit circle

F.TF.1 Understand radian measure of an angle as the length of the arc on the unit circle subtended by the angle.

F.TF.2 Explain how the unit circle in the coordinate plane enables the extension of trigonometric functions to all real numbers, interpreted as radian measures of angles traversed counterclockwise around the unit circle.

#### Model periodic phenomena with trigonometric functions

F.TF.5 Choose trigonometric functions to model periodic phenomena with specified amplitude, frequency, and midline.★

#### Prove and apply trigonometric identities

F.TF.8 Prove the Pythagorean identity $\sin^2(\theta) + \cos^2(\theta) = 1$ and use it to find $\sin(\theta)$, $\cos(\theta)$, or $\tan(\theta)$ given $\sin(\theta)$, $\cos(\theta)$, or $\tan(\theta)$ and the quadrant of the angle.

## Geometry

**Congruence**

**Make Geometric Constructions**

G.CO.12 Make formal geometric constructions with a variety of tools and methods (compass and straightedge, string, reflective devices, paper folding, dynamic geometric software, etc.). *Copying a segment; copying an angle; bisecting a segment; bisecting an angle; constructing perpendicular lines, including the perpendicular bisector of a line segment; and constructing a line parallel to a given line through a point not on the line.*

G.CO.13 Construct an equilateral triangle, a square, and a regular hexagon inscribed in a circle.

**Circles**

**Understand and apply theorems about circles**

G.C.1 Prove that all circles are similar.

G.C.2 Identify and describe relationships among inscribed angles, radii, and chords. *Include the relationship between central, inscribed, and circumscribed angles; inscribed angles on a diameter are right angles; the radius of a circle is perpendicular to the tangent where the radius intersects the circle.*

G.C.3 Construct the inscribed and circumscribed circles of a triangle, and prove properties of angles for a quadrilateral inscribed in a circle.

**Find arc lengths and areas of sectors of circles**

G.C.5 Derive using similarity the fact that the length of the arc intercepted by an angle is proportional to the radius, and define the radian measure of the angle as the constant of proportionality; derive the formula for the area of a sector.

**Expressing Geometric Properties with Equations**

**Translate between the geometric description and the equation for a conic section**

G.GPE.1 Derive the equation of a circle of given center and radius using the Pythagorean Theorem; complete the square to find the center and radius of a circle given by an equation.

G.GPE.2 Derive the equation of a parabola given a focus and directrix.

**Use coordinates to prove simple geometric theorems algebraically**

G.GPE.4 Use coordinates to prove simple geometric theorems algebraically. *For example, prove or disprove that a figure defined by four given points in the coordinate plane is a rectangle; prove or disprove that the point $(1, \sqrt{3})$ lies on the circle centered at the origin and containing the point $(0, 2)$.*

G.GPE.5 Prove the slope criteria for parallel and perpendicular lines and use them to solve geometric problems (e.g., find the equation of a line parallel or perpendicular to a given line that passes through a given point).

G.GPE.6 Find the point on a directed line segment between two given points that partitions the segment in a given ratio.

G.GPE.7 Use coordinates to compute perimeters of polygons and areas of triangles and rectangles, e.g., using the distance formula.★

**Geometric Measurement and Dimension**

**Visualize relationships between two-dimensional and three-dimensional objects**

G.GMD.4 Identify the shapes of two-dimensional cross-sections of three-dimensional objects, and identify three-dimensional objects generated by rotations of two-dimensional objects.

**Modeling with Geometry**

**Apply geometric concepts in modeling situations**

G.MG.1 Use geometric shapes, their measures, and their properties to describe objects (e.g., modeling a tree trunk or a human torso as a cylinder).★

G.MG.2 Apply concepts of density based on area and volume in modeling situations (e.g., persons per square mile, BTUs per cubic foot).★

G.MG.3 Apply geometric methods to solve design problems (e.g., designing an object or structure to satisfy physical constraints or minimize cost; working with typographic grid systems based on ratios).★

## Statistics and Probability

### Interpreting Categorical and Quantitative Data

#### Summarize, represent, and interpret data on a single count or measurement variable

S.ID.4 Use the mean and standard deviation of a data set to fit it to a normal distribution and to estimate population percentages. Recognize that there are data sets for which such a procedure is not appropriate. Use calculators, spreadsheets, and tables to estimate areas under the normal curve.

#### Summarize, represent, and interpret data on two categorical and quantitative variables

S.ID.6a Represent data on two quantitative variables on a scatter plot, and describe how the variables are related. Fit a function to the data; use functions fitted to data to solve problems in the context of the data. Use given functions or choose a function suggested by the context. *Emphasize linear, quadratic, and exponential models.* ★

S.ID.6.b Represent data on two quantitative variables on a scatter plot, and describe how the variables are related. Informally assess the fit of a function by plotting and analyzing residuals.

### Making Inferences and Justifying Conclusions

#### Understand and evaluate random processes underlying statistical experiments

S.IC.1 Understand statistics as a process for making inferences about population parameters based on a random sample from that population.

S.IC.2 Decide if a specified model is consistent with results from a given data-generating process, e.g., using simulation. *For example, a model says a spinning coin falls heads up with probability 0.5. Would a result of 5 tails in a row cause you to question the model?*

#### Make inferences and justify conclusions from sample surveys, experiments, and observational studies

S.IC.3 Recognize the purposes of and differences among sample surveys, experiments, and observational studies; explain how randomization relates to each.

S.IC.4 Use data from a sample survey to estimate a population mean or proportion; develop a margin of error through the use of simulation models for random sampling.

S.IC.5 Use data from a randomized experiment to compare two treatments; use simulations to decide if differences between parameters are significant.

S.IC.6 Evaluate reports based on data.

# BIG ideas

These Big Ideas are the organizing ideas for the study of important areas of mathematics: algebra, geometry, and statistics.

## Algebra

### Properties

- In the transition from arithmetic to algebra, attention shifts from arithmetic operations (addition, subtraction, multiplication, and division) to the use of the properties of these operations.
- All of the facts of arithmetic and algebra follow from certain properties.

### Variable

- Quantities are used to form expressions, equations, and inequalities.
- An expression refers to a quantity but does not make a statement about it. An equation (or an inequality) is a statement about the quantities it mentions.
- Using variables in place of numbers in equations (or inequalities) allows the statement of relationships among numbers that are unknown or unspecified.

### Equivalence

- A single quantity may be represented by many different expressions.
- The facts about a quantity may be expressed by many different equations (or inequalities).

### Solving Equations & Inequalities

- Solving an equation is the process of rewriting the equation to make what it says about its variable(s) as simple as possible.
- Properties of numbers and equality can be used to transform an equation (or inequality) into equivalent, simpler equations (or inequalities) in order to find solutions.
- Useful information about equations and inequalities (including solutions) can be found by analyzing graphs or tables.
- The numbers and types of solutions vary predictably, based on the type of equation.

### Proportionality

- Two quantities are proportional if they have the same ratio in each instance where they are measured together.
- Two quantities are inversely proportional if they have the same product in each instance where they are measured together.

### Function

- A function is a relationship between variables in which each value of the input variable is associated with a unique value of the output variable.
- Functions can be represented in a variety of ways, such as graphs, tables, equations, or words. Each representation is particularly useful in certain situations.
- Some important families of functions are developed through transformations of the simplest form of the function.
- New functions can be made from other functions by applying arithmetic operations or by applying one function to the output of another.

### Modeling

- Many real-world mathematical problems can be represented algebraically. These representations can lead to algebraic solutions.
- A function that models a real-world situation can be used to make estimates or predictions about future occurrences.

## Statistics and Probability

### Data Collection and Analysis

- Sampling techniques are used to gather data from real-world situations. If the data are representative of the larger population, inferences can be made about that population.
- Biased sampling techniques yield data unlikely to be representative of the larger population.
- Sets of numerical data are described using measures of central tendency and dispersion.

### Data Representation

- The most appropriate data representations depend on the type of data—quantitative or qualitative, and univariate or bivariate.
- Line plots, box plots, and histograms are different ways to show distribution of data over a possible range of values.

### Probability

- Probability expresses the likelihood that a particular event will occur.
- Data can be used to calculate an experimental probability, and mathematical properties can be used to determine a theoretical probability.
- Either experimental or theoretical probability can be used to make predictions or decisions about future events.
- Various counting methods can be used to develop theoretical probabilities.

## Geometry

### Visualization

- Visualization can help you see the relationships between two figures and help you connect properties of real objects with two-dimensional drawings of these objects.

### Transformations

- Transformations are mathematical functions that model relationships with figures.
- Transformations may be described geometrically or by coordinates.
- Symmetries of figures may be defined and classified by transformations.

### Measurement

- Some attributes of geometric figures, such as length, area, volume, and angle measure, are measurable. Units are used to describe these attributes.

### Reasoning & Proof

- Definitions establish meanings and remove possible misunderstanding.
- Other truths are more complex and difficult to see. It is often possible to verify complex truths by reasoning from simpler ones using deductive reasoning.

### Similarity

- Two geometric figures are similar when corresponding lengths are proportional and corresponding angles are congruent.
- Areas of similar figures are proportional to the squares of their corresponding lengths.
- Volumes of similar figures are proportional to the cubes of their corresponding lengths.

### Coordinate Geometry

- A coordinate system on a line is a number line on which points are labeled, corresponding to the real numbers.
- A coordinate system in a plane is formed by two perpendicular number lines, called the $x$- and $y$-axes, and the quadrants they form. The coordinate plane can be used to graph many functions.
- It is possible to verify some complex truths using deductive reasoning in combination with the distance, midpoint, and slope formulas.

# Exponential and Logarithmic Functions

| | | |
|---|---|---|
| **Get Ready!** | | **503** |
| **Chapter Opener** | | **504** |
| 7-1 | Exploring Exponential Models | 505 |
| 7-2 | Properties of Exponential Functions | 515 |
| 7-3 | Logarithmic Functions as Inverses | 525 |
| 7-4 | Properties of Logarithms | 535 |
| 7-5 | Exponential and Logarithmic Equations | 542 |
| | **Technology Lab:** Using Logarithms for Exponential Models | 551 |
| 7-6 | Natural Logarithms | 553 |
| | **Lesson Lab:** Exponential and Logarithmic Inequalities | 562 |
| **Chapter Review** | | **567** |
| **Pull It All Together** | | **570** |

Chapter 7

**Algebra**

**Seeing Structure in Expressions**
Interpret the structure of expressions

**Creating Equations**
Create equations that describe numbers and relationships

**Reasoning with Equations and Inequalities**
Represent and solve equations and inequalities graphically

**Functions**

**Interpreting Functions**
Interpret functions that arise in applications in terms of the context
Analyze functions using different representations

**Building Functions**
Build new functions from existing functions

**Linear, Quadratic, and Exponential Functions**
Construct and compare linear and exponential models and solve problems

# Trigonometric Functions


| | | |
|---|---|---|
| **Get Ready!** | | **571** |
| **Chapter Opener** | | **572** |
| 8-1 | Exploring Periodic Data | 573 |
| 8-2 | Angles and the Unit Circle | 581 |
| 8-3 | Radian Measure | 589 |
| 8-4 | The Sine Functions | 597 |
| | **Technology Lab:** Graphing Trigonometric Functions | 607 |
| 8-5 | The Cosine Function | 610 |
| 8-6 | The Tangent Function | 619 |
| 8-7 | Translating Sine and Cosine Functions | 628 |
| | **Technology Lab:** Plotting and Analyzing Residuals | 638 |
| 8-8 | Reciprocal Trigonometric Functions | 641 |
| 8-9 | Trigonometric Identities | 651 |
| 8-10 | Area and the Law of Sines | 660 |
| | **Lesson Lab:** The Ambiguous Case | 668 |
| 8-11 | The Law of Cosines | 670 |
| **Chapter Review** | | **679** |
| **Pull It All Together** | | **684** |

Chapter 8

**Functions**

**Interpreting Functions**
- Interpret functions that arise in applications in terms of the context
- Analyze functions using different representations

**Functions**

**Trigonometric Functions**
- Extend the domain of trigonometric functions using the unit circle
- Model periodic phenomena with trigonometric functions
- Prove and apply trigonometric identities

# Sequences and Series


| | | |
|---|---|---|
| **Get Ready!** | | **685** |
| **Chapter Opener** | | **686** |
| 9-1 | Mathematical Patterns | 687 |
| 9-2 | Arithmetic Sequences | 696 |
| 9-3 | Geometric Sequences | 703 |
| 9-4 | Arithmetic Series | 711 |
| | **Activity Lab:** Geometry and Infinite Series | 720 |
| 9-5 | Geometric Series | 722 |
| **Chapter Review** | | **731** |
| **Pull It All Together** | | **734** |

Chapter 9

**Algebra**

**Seeing Structure in Expressions**
Write expressions in equivalent forms to solve problems

**Functions**

**Building Functions**
Build new functions from existing functions

# Applying Geometric Concepts


**Get Ready!** 735

**Chapter Opener** 736

10-1 Applying Constructions 737

10-2 Solving Density and Design Problems 747

10-3 Perimeters and Areas of Similar Figures 755

10-4 Geometric Probability 765

10-5 Space Figures and Cross Sections 774

10-6 Areas and Volumes of Similar Solids 785

10-7 Locus: A Set of Points 794

**Chapter Review** 802

**Pull It All Together** 806

Chapter 10

**Geometry**

**Geometric Measurement and Dimension**
Visualize relationships between two-dimensional and three-dimensional objects

**Geometry**

**Modeling with Geometry**
Apply geometric concepts in modeling situations

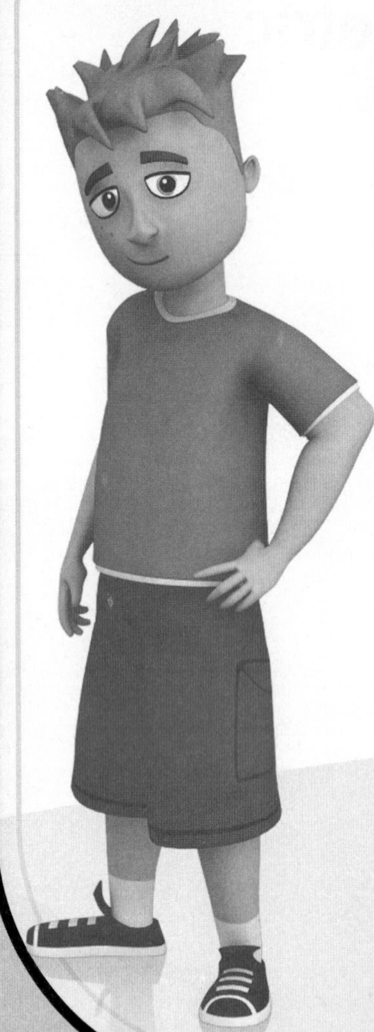

# Connecting Algebra and Geometry


**Get Ready!** **807**

**Chapter Opener** **808**

11-1 Perimeter and Area in the Coordinate Plane 809

**Lesson Lab:** Partitioning a Segment 821

11-2 Areas of Parallelograms and Triangles 823

11-3 Areas of Trapezoids, Rhombuses, and Kites 832

**Activity Lab:** Proving Slope Criteria for Parallel and Perpendicular Lines 839

11-4 Polygons in the Coordinate Plane 843

**Chapter Review** **850**

**Pull It All Together** **852**

Chapter 11

**Geometry**

**Expressing Geometric Properties with Equations**

Use coordinates to prove simple geometric theorems algebraically

# Circles


**Get Ready!** **853**

**Chapter Opener** **854**

12-1 Circles and Arcs 855

12-2 Areas of Circles and Sectors 865

**Activity Lab:** Circles and Radians 873

12-3 Tangent Lines 876

12-4 Chords and Arcs 886

12-5 Inscribed Angles 897

12-6 Angle Measures and Segment Lengths 906

**Chapter Review** **915**

**Pull It All Together** **918**

Chapter 12

**Geometry**

**Circles**

Understand and apply theorems about circles

Find arc lengths and areas of sectors of circles

**Statistics and Probability**

**Using Probability to Make Decisions**

Use probability to evaluate outcomes of decisions

# Get Ready!

## Evaluating Expressions

**Evaluate each expression for $x = -2, 0,$ and $2$.**

**1.** $10^{x+1}$ **2.** $\left(\frac{3}{2}\right)^{x}$ **3.** $-5^{x-2}$ **4.** $-(3)^{0.5x}$

## Using Linear Models

**Draw a scatter plot and find the line of best fit for each set of data.**

**5.** (0, 2), (1, 4), (2, 6.5), (3, 8.5), (4, 10), (5, 12), (6, 14)

**6.** (3, 100), (5, 150), (7, 195), (9, 244), (11, 296), (13, 346), (15, 396)

## Simplifying Rational Exponents

**Simplify each expression.**

**7.** $\left(x^{\frac{1}{5}}\right)^{10}$ **8.** $\left(-8x^{3}\right)^{\frac{4}{3}}$

## Finding Inverses

**Find the inverse of each function. Is the inverse a function?**

**9.** $y = 10 - 2x^2$ **10.** $y = (x + 4)^3 - 1$

## Looking Ahead Vocabulary

**11.** In advertising, the *decay factor* describes how an advertisement loses its effectiveness over time. In math, would you expect a decay factor to increase or decrease the value of $y$ as $x$ increases?

**12.** The word *asymptote* comes from a Greek word meaning "not falling together." When looking at the end behavior of a function, do you expect the graph to intersect its asymptote?

# Exponential and Logarithmic Functions

## Big Ideas

**1 Modeling**
**Essential Question:** How do you model a quantity that changes regularly over time by the same percentage?

**2 Equivalence**
**Essential Question:** How are exponents and logarithms related?

**3 Function**
**Essential Question:** How are exponential functions and logarithmic functions related?

## Domains

- Linear and Exponential Models
- Creating Equations that Describe Numbers
- Interpreting Functions

## Chapter Preview


7-1 Exploring Exponential Models
7-2 Properties of Exponential Functions
7-3 Logarithmic Functions as Inverses
7-4 Properties of Logarithms
7-5 Exponential and Logarithmic Equations
7-6 Natural Logarithms


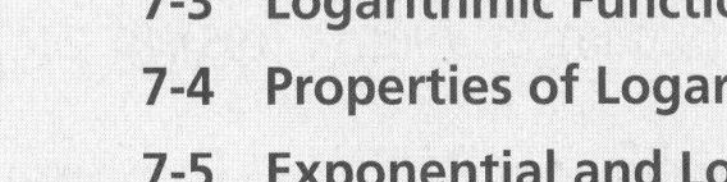

**Interactive Digital Path**
Log in to **pearsonsuccessnet.com** and click on Interactive Digital Path to access the Solve Its and animated Problems.

## Vocabulary

**English/Spanish Vocabulary Audio Online:**

| English | Spanish |
|---|---|
| asymptote, *p. 506* | asíntota |
| Change of Base Formula, *p. 537* | fórmula de cambio de base |
| common logarithm, *p. 527* | logaritmo común |
| exponential equation, *p. 542* | ecuación exponencial |
| exponential function, *p. 505* | función exponencial |
| exponential growth, *p. 506* | incremento exponencial |
| logarithm, *p. 525* | logaritmo |
| logarithmic equation, *p. 546* | ecuación logarítmica |
| logarithmic function, *p. 528* | función logarítmica |
| natural logarithmic function, *p. 553* | función logarítmica natural |

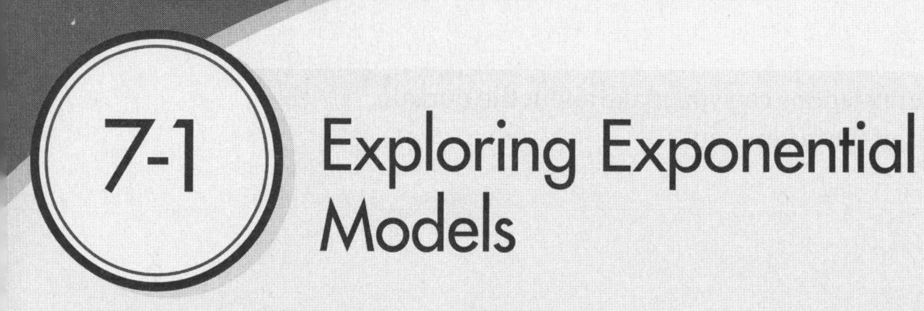

# 7-1 Exploring Exponential Models

**F.IF.7.e** Graph exponential . . . functions, showing intercepts and end behavior . . . Also **A.SSE.1.b, A.CED.2, F.IF.8**

**Objective** To model exponential growth and decay

**Solve It!** Write your solution to the Solve It in the space below.

The number of moves needed for additional rings in the Solve It suggests a pattern that approximates repeated multiplication.

**Essential Understanding** You can represent repeated multiplication with a function of the form $y = ab^x$, where $b$ is a positive number other than 1.

An **exponential function** is a function with the general form $y = ab^x$, $a \neq 0$, with $b > 0$ and $b \neq 1$. In an exponential function, the base $b$ is a constant. The exponent $x$ is the independent variable with domain the set of real numbers.

## Problem 1 Graphing an Exponential Function

**Got It?** What is the graph of each function?

**a.** $y = 4^x$

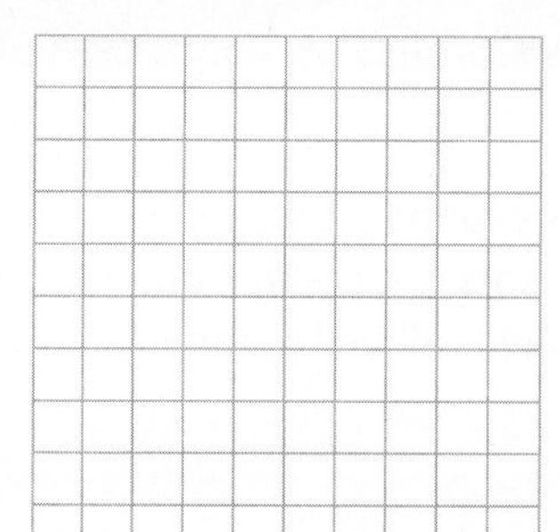

**b.** $y = \left(\frac{1}{3}\right)^x$

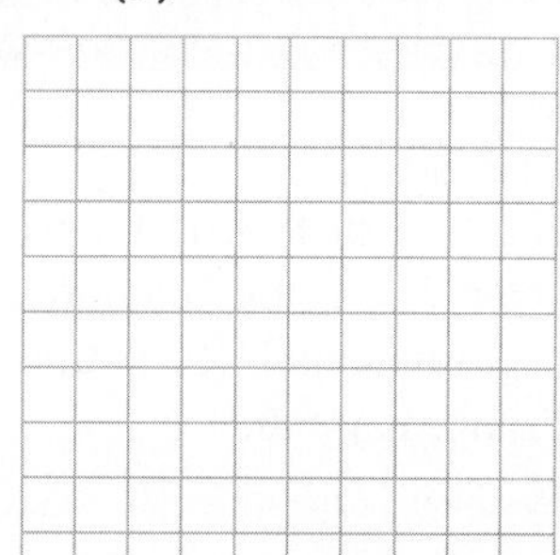

**c.** $y = 2(3)^x$

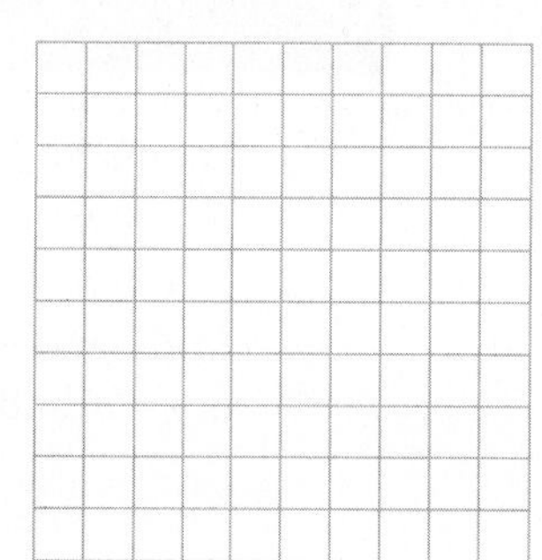

**d. Reasoning** What generalizations can you make about the domain, range, and $y$-intercepts of these functions?

**Practice** Graph each function.

**1.** $y = 1000(2)^x$

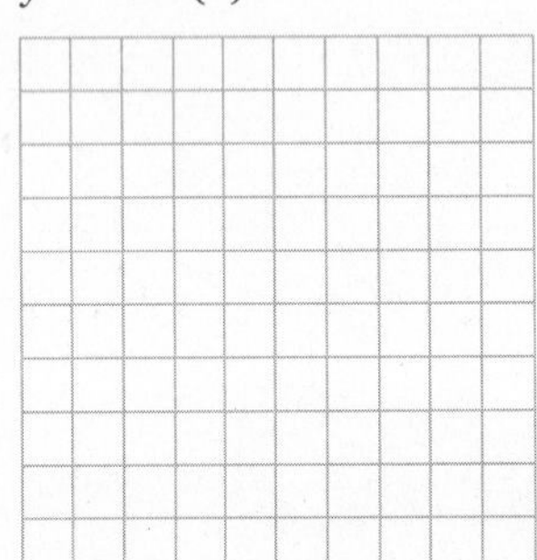

**2.** $y = 2^{2x}$

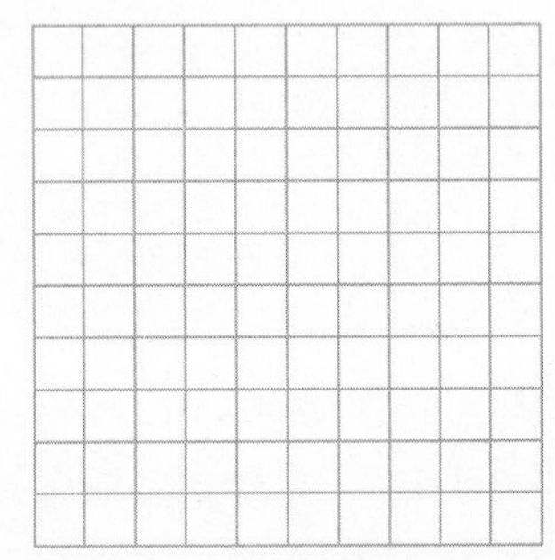

Two types of exponential behavior are *exponential growth* and *exponential decay*.

For **exponential growth**, as the value of $x$ increases, the value of $y$ increases. For **exponential decay**, as the value of $x$ increases, the value of $y$ decreases, approaching zero.

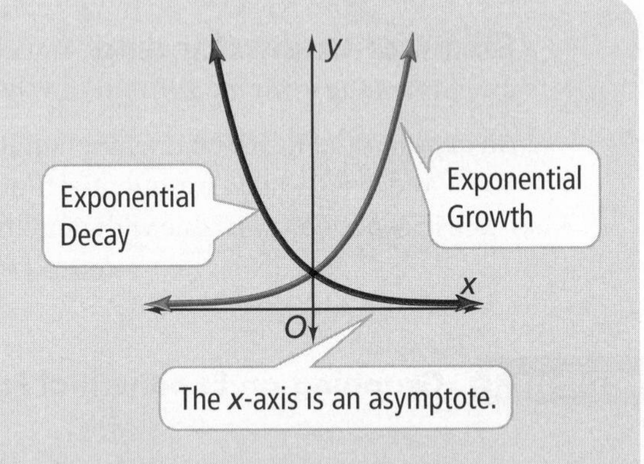


The exponential functions shown here are *asymptotic* to the $x$-axis. An **asymptote** is a line that a graph approaches as $x$ or $y$ increases in absolute value.

take note

## Concept Summary Exponential Functions

For the function $y = ab^x$,

- if $a > 0$ and $b > 1$, the function represents exponential growth.
- if $a > 0$ and $0 < b < 1$, the function represents exponential decay.

In either case, the $y$-intercept is $(0, a)$, the domain is all real numbers, the asymptote is $y = 0$, and the range is $y > 0$.

ONLINE PROBLEMS

## Problem 2 Identifying Exponential Growth and Decay

**Got It?** Identify each function or situation as an example of exponential growth or decay. What is the $y$-intercept?

**a.** $y = 3(4^x)$

**b.** $y = 11(0.75^x)$

**c.** You put $2000 into a college savings account for four years. The account pays 6% interest annually.

**Think**
**What quantity does the $y$-intercept represent?**

**A Practice** **Without graphing, determine whether the functions in Exercises 3 and 4 represent exponential growth or exponential decay. Then find the $y$-intercept.**

**3.** $y = 12\left(\frac{17}{10}\right)^x$

**4.** $f(x) = 4\left(\frac{5}{6}\right)^x$

For exponential growth $y = ab^x$, with $b > 1$, the value $b$ is the **growth factor.** A quantity that exhibits exponential growth increases by a constant percentage each time period. The percentage increase $r$, written as a decimal, is the *rate of increase* or *growth rate*. For exponential growth, $b = 1 + r$.

For exponential decay, $0 < b < 1$, and $b$ is the **decay factor**. The quantity decreases by a constant percentage each time period. The percentage decrease, $r$, is the *rate of decay*. Usually a rate of decay is expressed as a negative quantity, so $b = 1 + r$.

take note

## Key Concept Exponential Growth and Decay

You can model exponential growth or decay with this function.

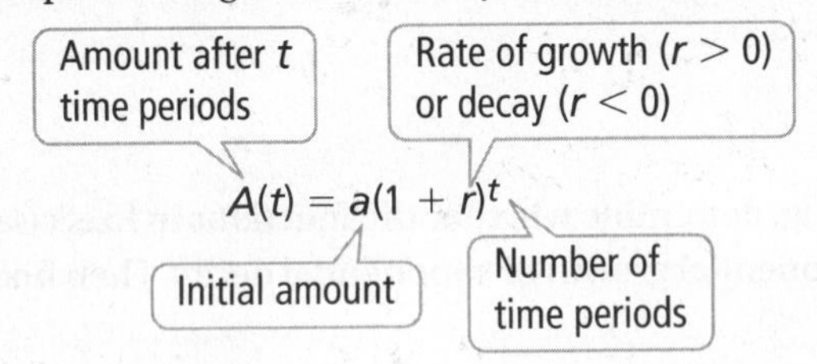


For growth or decay to be exponential, a quantity changes by a fixed percentage each time period.

## Problem 3 Modeling Exponential Growth

**Got It?** Suppose you invest \$500 in a savings account that pays 3.5% annual interest. How much will be in the account after five years?

**5. Interest** Suppose you deposit $2000 in a savings account that pays interest at an annual rate of 4%. Answer the following questions, supposing that no money is added to or withdrawn from the account.

a. How much will be in the account after 3 years?

b. How much will be in the account after 18 years?

## Problem 4 Using Exponential Growth

**Got It?** a. Suppose you invest $500 in a savings account that pays 3.5% annual interest. When will the account contain at least $650?

**Plan**
How can you make a table to solve this problem?

b. **Reasoning** Use the table in Problem 4 to determine when that account will contain at least $1650. Explain.

6. **Interest** Suppose you deposit \$2000 in a savings account that pays interest at an annual rate of 4%. Answer the following questions, supposing that no money is added to or withdrawn from the account.

   **a.** How many years will it take for the account to contain \$2500?

   **b.** How many years will it take for the account to contain \$3000?

Exponential functions are often discrete. In Problem 4, interest is paid only once a year. So the graph consists of individual points corresponding to $t = 1, 2, 3$, and so on. It is not continuous. Both the table and the graph show that there is never *exactly* \$1500 in the account and that the account will not contain more than \$1500 until the ninth year.

To model a discrete situation using an exponential function of the form $y = ab^x$, you need to find the growth or decay factor $b$. If you know $y$-values for two consecutive $x$-values, you can find the rate of change $r$, and then find $b$ using $r = \frac{(y_2 - y_1)}{y_1}$ and $b = 1 + r$.

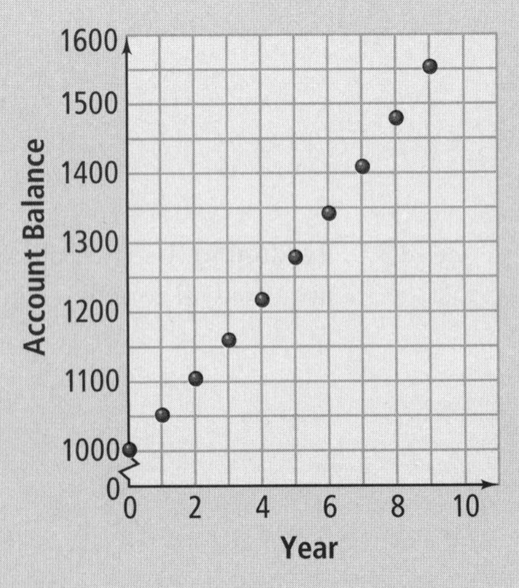

## Problem 5 Writing an Exponential Function

**Got It?** **a.** For the model in Problem 5, what will the world population of Iberian lynx be in 2020?

**b. Reasoning** If you graphed the model in Problem 5, would it ever cross the $x$-axis? Explain.

**Practice** **Write an exponential function to model each situation. Find each amount after the specified time.**

**7.** A population of 120,000 grows 1.2% per year for 15 years.

**8.** A population of 1,860,000 decreases 1.5% each year for 12 years.

## Lesson Check

### Do you know HOW?

**Without graphing, determine whether the function represents exponential growth or exponential decay. Then find the $y$-intercept.**

**9.** $y = 10(0.45)^x$

**10.** $y = 0.75(4)^x$

**11.** $y = 3^x$

**12.** $y = 0.95^x$

**Graph each function.**

**13.** $A(t) = 3(1.04)^t$

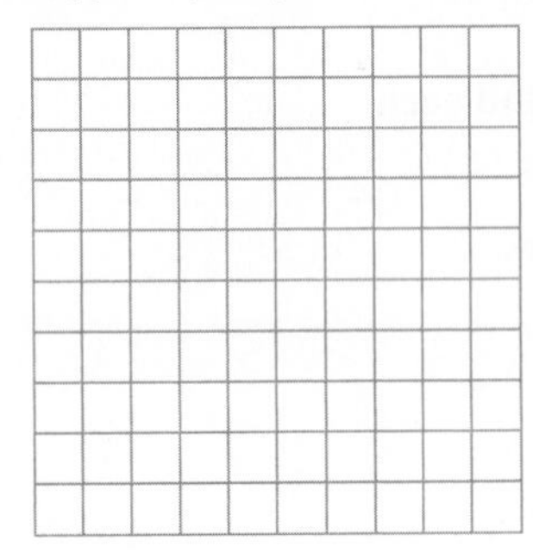

**14.** $A(t) = 7(0.6)^t$

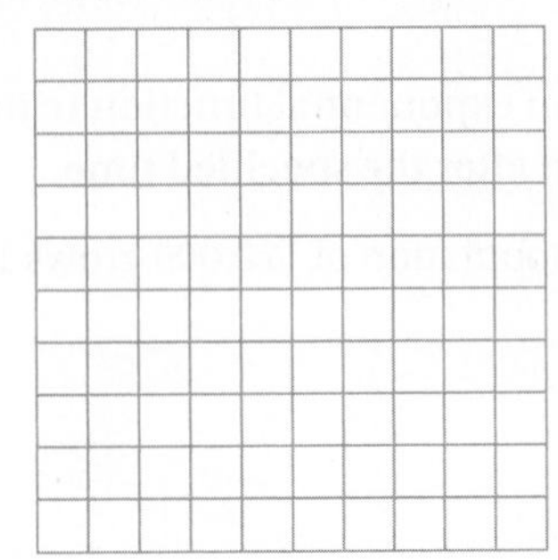

### Do you UNDERSTAND?

**15. Vocabulary** Explain how you can tell if $y = ab^x$ represents exponential growth or exponential decay.

16. **Reasoning** Identify each function as *linear, quadratic,* or *exponential.* Explain your reasoning.

a. $y = 3(x + 1)^2$

b. $y = 4(3)^x$

c. $y = 2x + 5$

d. $y = 4(0.2)^x + 1$

17. **Error Analysis** A classmate says that the growth factor of the exponential function $y = 15(0.3)^x$ is 0.3. What is the student's mistake?

## More Practice and Problem-Solving Exercises

### B Apply

18. **Think About a Plan** Your friend invested $1000 in an account that pays 6% annual interest. How much interest will your friend have after her college graduation in 4 years?
- Is an exponential model reasonable for this situation?
- What equation should you use to model this situation?
- Is the solution of the equation the final answer to the problem?

STEM **19. Oceanography** The function $y = 20(0.975)^x$ models the intensity of sunlight beneath the surface of the ocean. The output $y$ represents the percent of surface sunlight intensity that reaches a depth of $x$ feet. The model is accurate from about 20 feet to about 600 feet beneath the surface.

**a.** Find the percent of sunlight 50 feet beneath the surface of the ocean.

**b.** Find the percent of sunlight at a depth of 370 feet.

**20. Population** The population of a certain animal species decreases at a rate of 3.5% per year. You have counted 80 of the animals in the habitat you are studying.

**a.** Write a function that models the change in the animal population.

**b. Graphing Calculator** Graph the function. Estimate the number of years until the population first drops below 15 animals.

**21. Sports** While you are waiting for your tennis partner to show up, you drop your tennis ball from 5 feet. Its rebound was approximately 35 inches on the first bounce and 21.5 inches on the second. What exponential function would be a good model for the bouncing ball?

**For each annual rate of change, find the corresponding growth or decay factor.**

| | | | |
|---|---|---|---|
| **22.** +70% | **23.** +500% | **24.** −75% | **25.** −55% |
| **26.** +12.5% | **27.** −0.1% | **28.** +0.1% | **29.** +100% |

## Challenge

**30. Manufacturing** The value of an industrial machine has a decay factor of 0.75 per year. After six years, the machine is worth \$7500. What was the original value of the machine?

**31. Zoology** Determine which situation best matches the graph.

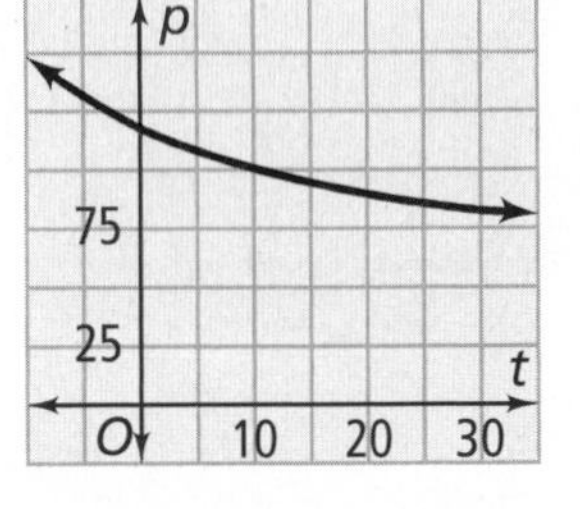


Ⓐ A population of 120 cougars decreases 98.75% yearly.

Ⓑ A population of 120 cougars increases 1.25% yearly.

Ⓒ A population of 115 cougars decreases 1.25% yearly.

Ⓓ A population of 115 cougars decreases 50% yearly.

**32. Open-Ended** Write a problem that could be modeled with $y = 20(1.1)^x$.

**33. Reasoning** Which function does the graph represent? Explain. (Each interval represents one unit.)

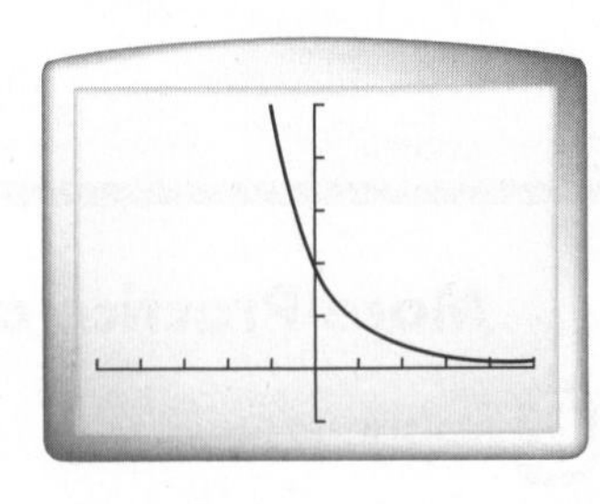

Ⓐ $y = \left(\frac{1}{3}\right)2^x$

Ⓑ $y = 2\left(\frac{1}{3}\right)^x$

Ⓒ $y = -2\left(\frac{1}{3}\right)^x$

# Properties of Exponential Functions

**F.IF.7.e** Graph exponential and logarithmic functions, showing intercepts and end behavior, . . . and amplitude. . . .
Also **A.SSE.3.c, F.IF.8, F.IF.8.b**

**Objectives** To explore the properties of functions of the form $y = ab^x$
To graph exponential functions that have base $e$

**Solve It!** Write your solution to the Solve It in the space below.

You can apply the four types of transformations—stretches, compressions, reflections, and translations—to exponential functions.

**Essential Understanding** The factor $a$ in $y = ab^x$ can stretch or compress, and possibly reflect the graph of the parent function $y = b^x$.

The graphs of $y = 2^x$ (in red) and $y = 3 \cdot 2^x$ (in blue) are shown. Each $y$-value of $y = 3 \cdot 2^x$ is 3 times the corresponding $y$-value of the parent function $y = 2^x$.

| $x$ | $y = 2^x$ | $y = 3 \cdot 2^x$ |
|---|---|---|
| −2 | $\frac{1}{4}$ | $\frac{3}{4}$ |
| −1 | $\frac{1}{2}$ | $\frac{3}{2}$ |
| 0 | 1 | 3 |
| 1 | 2 | 6 |
| 2 | 4 | 12 |

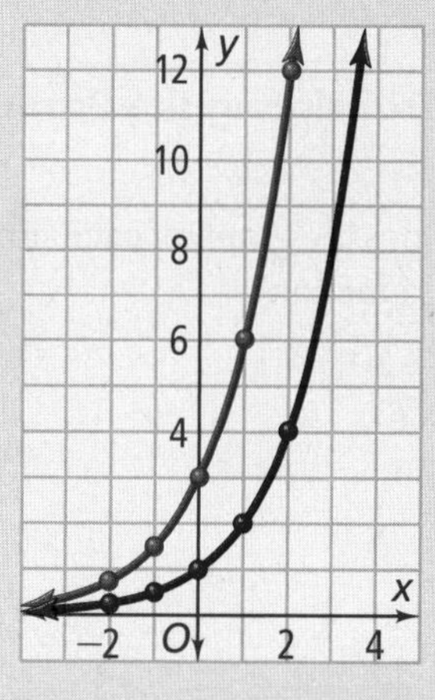


$y = 3 \cdot 2^x$ stretches the graph of the parent function $y = 2^x$ vertically by the factor 3.

## Problem 1 Graphing $y = ab^x$

**Got It?** How does the graph of $y = -0.5 \cdot 5^x$ compare to the graph of its parent function?

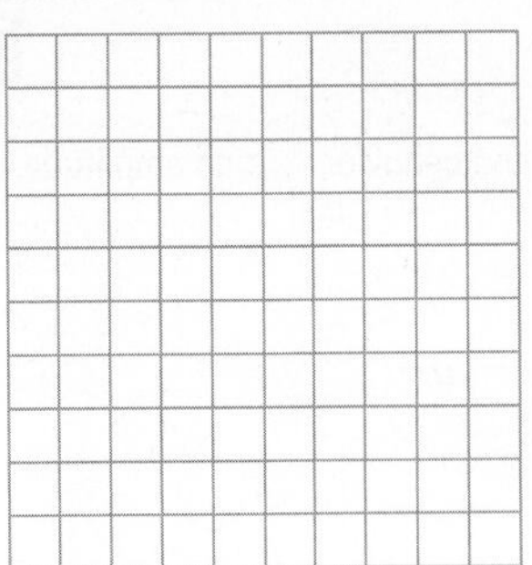

**Practice** Graph each function.

**1.** $y = -5^x$

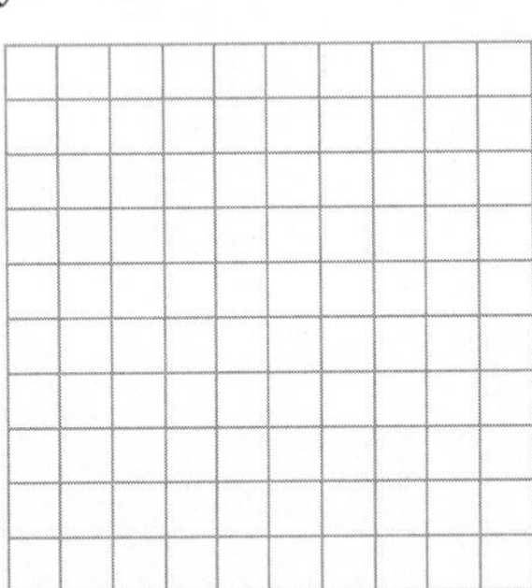

**2.** $y = 24\left(\frac{1}{2}\right)^x$

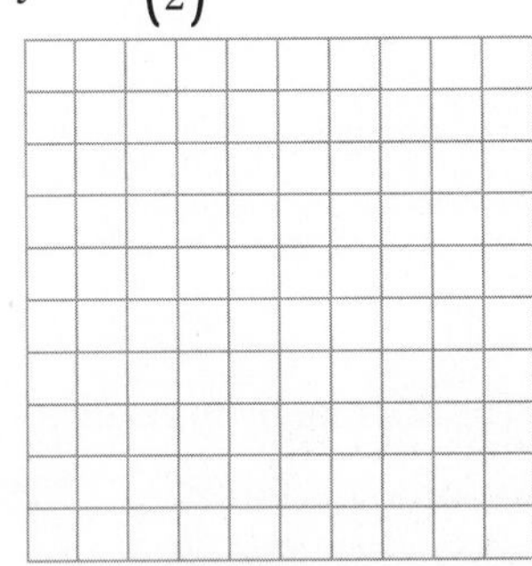

A horizontal shift $y = ab^{(x-h)}$ is the same as the vertical stretch or compression $y = (ab^{-h})b^x$. A vertical shift $y = ab^x + k$ also shifts the horizontal asymptote from $y = 0$ to $y = k$.

## Problem 2 Translating the Parent Function $y = b^x$

**Got It?** How does the graph of each function compare to the graph of the parent function?

**a.** $y = 4^{(x+2)}$

**b.** $y = 5 \cdot 0.25^x + 5$

**Think**

**In part a, how is the graph of $y = 4^{(x+2)}$ different from the graph of $y = 4^x$?**

**Practice** **Graph each function as a transformation of its parent function.**

3. $y = 3(2)^{x-1} + 4$

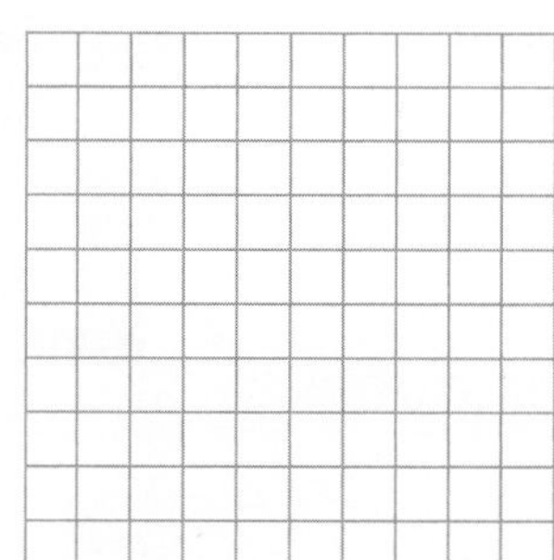

4. $y = -2(3)^{x+1} - 5$

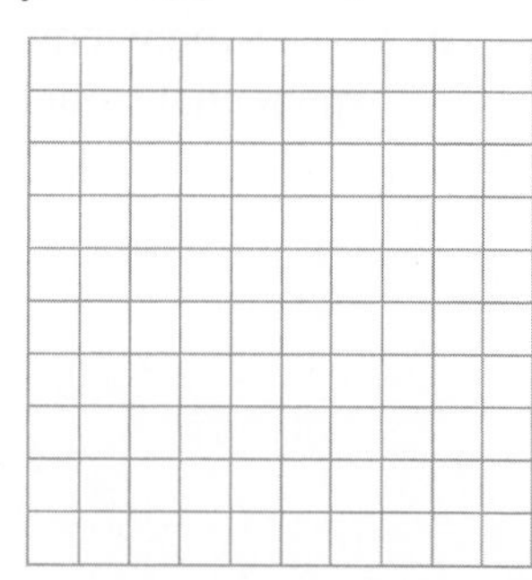

take note

## Concept Summary Families of Exponential Functions

| | |
|---|---|
| Parent function | $y = b^x$ |
| Stretch ($\lvert a \rvert > 1$)<br>Compression (Shrink) ($0 < \lvert a \rvert < 1$)<br>Reflection ($a < 0$) in $x$-axis | $y = ab^x$ |
| Translations (horizontal by $h$; vertical by $k$)<br>All transformations combined | $y = b^{(x-h)} + k$<br>$y = ab^{(x-h)} + k$ |

ONLINE PROBLEMS

## Problem 3 Using an Exponential Model

**Got It?** **a.** Use the model $y = 134.5 \cdot 0.956^x + 68$ from Problem 3. How long does it take for the coffee to reach a temperature of 100 degrees?

**Think**

**Will it take more than 3.1 minutes or less than 3.1 minutes to reach 100 degrees?**

**b. Reasoning** In Problem 3, would the model of the exponential data be useful if you did not translate the data by 68 units? Explain.

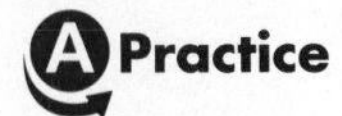

**5. Baking** A cake recipe says to bake the cake until the center is 180°F, then let the cake cool to 120°F.

| Time (min) | Temp (°F) |
|---|---|
| 0 | 180 |
| 5 | 126 |
| 10 | 94 |
| 15 | 80 |
| 20 | 73 |

**a.** Given a room temperature of 70°F, what is an exponential model for this data set?

**b.** How long does it take the cake to cool to the desired temperature?

Sometimes you can rewrite an exponential function to reveal information about the situation it models.

## Problem 4 Rewriting an Exponential Function

**Got It?** The function $V = 110(1.16)^d$ models the value of an antique car, in thousands of dollars, $d$ decades after it sold at an auction for $110,000. What exponential function models the value of the antique car after $t$ years? What is the annual growth rate of the antique car's value?

6. The function $P = 1200(1.4)^d$ models the number of deer in a region after $d$ decades. What exponential function models the number of deer after $t$ years? What is the annual growth rate of the number of deer?

7. The function $V = 250(1.28)^d$ models the value of a rare painting, in thousands of dollars, $d$ decades after it sold at an auction for $250,000. What exponential function models the value of the painting after $t$ years? What is the annual growth rate of the painting's value?

Up to this point you have worked with rational bases. However, exponential functions can have irrational bases as well. One important irrational base is the number $e$. The graph of $y = \left(1 + \frac{1}{x}\right)^x$ has an asymptote at $y = e$ or $y \approx 2.71828$.

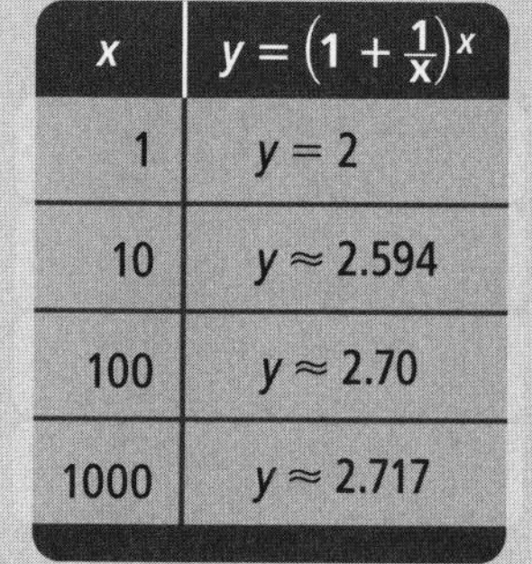

| $x$ | $y = \left(1 + \frac{1}{x}\right)^x$ |
|---|---|
| 1 | $y = 2$ |
| 10 | $y \approx 2.594$ |
| 100 | $y \approx 2.70$ |
| 1000 | $y \approx 2.717$ |

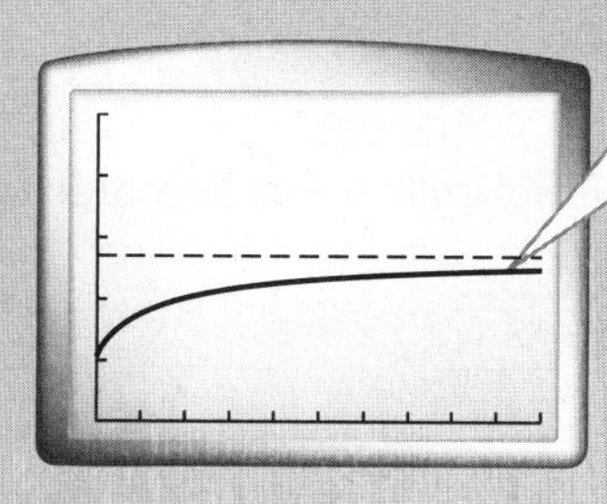


**Natural base exponential functions** are exponential functions with base $e$. These functions are useful for describing continuous growth or decay. Exponential functions with base $e$ have the same properties as other exponential functions.

## Problem 5 Evaluating $e^x$

**Got It?** How can you use a graphing calculator to calculate $e^8$?

**Practice** **Graphing Calculator** Use the graph of $y = e^x$ to evaluate each expression to four decimal places.

**8.** $e^6$

**9.** $e^e$

The formula for continuously compounded interest uses the number $e$.

take note

### Key Concept Continuously Compounded Interest

$$A(t) = P \cdot e^{rt}$$

- amount in account at time $t$: $A(t)$
- interest rate (annual): $r$
- Principal: $P$
- time in years: $t$

## Problem 6 Continuously Compounded Interest

**Got It?** Use the scenario from Problem 6. About how much will be in the account after 4 years of high school?

**Practice** Find the amount in a continuously compounded account for the given conditions.

**10.** principal: \$2000
annual interest rate: 5.1%
time: 3 years

**11.** principal: \$400
annual interest rate: 7.6%
time: 1.5 years

## Lesson Check

### Do you know HOW?

**For each function, identify the transformation from the parent function $y = b^x$.**

**12.** $y = -2 \cdot 3^x$

**13.** $y = \frac{1}{2}(9)^x$

**14.** $y = 7^{(x-5)}$

**15.** $y = 5^x + 3$

## Do you UNDERSTAND?

**16. Vocabulary** Is $y = e^{(x+7)}$ a natural base exponential function?

**17. Reasoning** Is investing $2000 in an account that pays 5% annual interest compounded continuously the same as investing $1000 at 4% and $1000 at 6%, each compounded continuously? Explain.

## More Practice and Problem-Solving Exercises

### B Apply

**18. Think About a Plan** A student wants to save $8000 for college in five years. How much should be put into an account that pays 5.2% annual interest compounded continuously?

- What formula should you use?
- What information do you know?
- What do you need to find?

**19. Investment** How long would it take to double your principal in an account that pays 6.5% annual interest compounded continuously?

**20. Error Analysis** A student says that the graph of $f(x) = \left(\frac{1}{3}\right)^{x+2} + 1$ is a shift of the parent function 2 units up and 1 unit to the left. Describe and correct the student's error.

**21.** Assume that $a$ is positive and $b \geq 1$. Describe the effects of $c > 0$, $c = 0$, and $c < 0$ on the graph of the function $y = ab^{cx}$.

**22. Graphing Calculator** Using a graphing calculator, graph each of the functions below on the same coordinate grid. What do you notice? Explain why the definition of exponential functions has the constraint that $b \neq 1$.

$y = \left(\frac{1}{2}\right)^x$ $\quad y = \left(\frac{8}{10}\right)^x$ $\quad y = \left(\frac{9}{10}\right)^x$ $\quad y = \left(\frac{99}{100}\right)^x$

STEM **23. Botany** The half-life of a radioactive substance is the time it takes for half of the material to decay. Phosphorus-32 is used to study a plant's use of fertilizer. It has a half-life of 14.3 days. Write the exponential decay function for a 50-mg sample. Find the amount of phosphorus-32 remaining after 84 days.

**24. Archaeology** Archaeologists use carbon-14, which has a half-life of 5730 years, to determine the age of artifacts in carbon dating. Write the exponential decay function for a 24-mg sample. How much carbon-14 remains after 30 millennia? (*Hint:* 1 millennium = 1000 years)

**The parent function for each graph below is of the form $y = ab^x$. Write the parent function. Then write a function for the translation indicated.**

**25.**

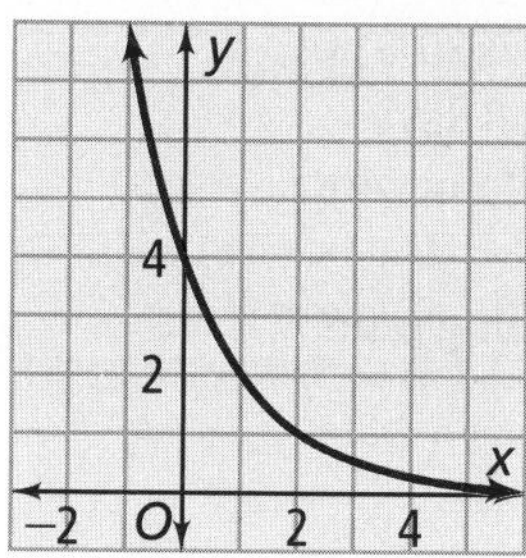


translation: left 4 units, up 3 units

**26.**

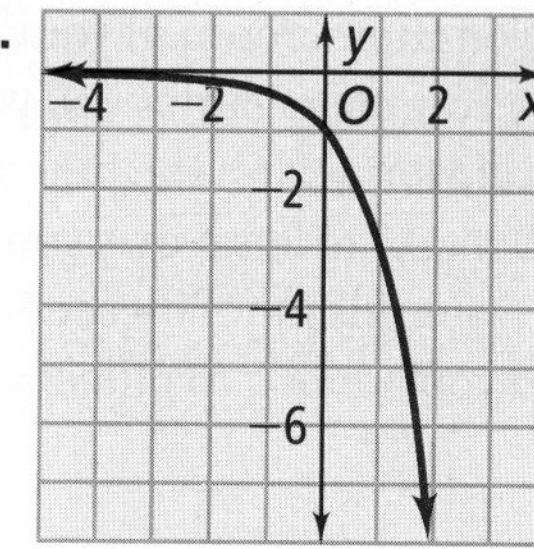


translation: right 8 units, up 2 units

**27.** Two financial institutions offer different deals to new customers. The first bank offers an interest rate of 3% for the first year and 2% for the next two years. The second bank offers an interest rate of 2.49% for three years. You decide to invest the same amount of principal in each bank. To answer the following, assume you make no withdrawal or deposits during the three-year period.

**a.** Write a function that represents the total amount of money in the account in the first bank after three years.

**b.** Write a function that represents the total amount of money in the account in the second bank after three years.

**c.** Write a function that represents the total amount of money in both accounts at the end of three years.

STEM **28. Physics** At a constant temperature, the atmospheric pressure $p$ in pascals is given by the formula $p = 101.3e^{-0.001h}$, where $h$ is the altitude in meters. What is $p$ at an altitude of 500 m?

## Challenge

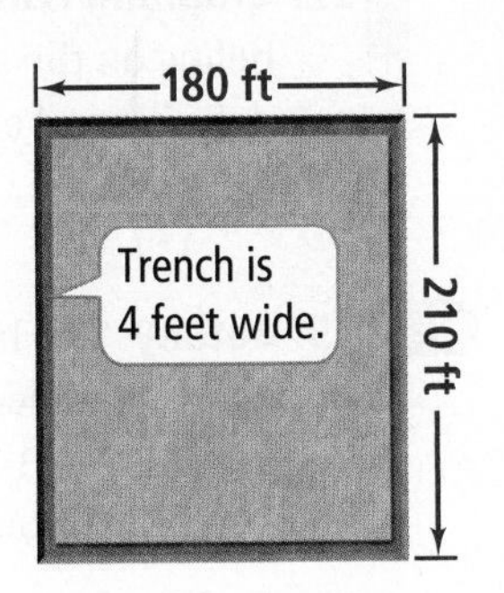


29. **Landscaping** A homeowner is planting hedges and begins to dig a 3-ft-deep trench around the perimeter of his property. After the first weekend, the homeowner recruits a friend to help. After every succeeding weekend, each digger recruits another friend. One person can dig 405 ft$^3$ of dirt per weekend. The figure at the right shows the dimensions of the property and the width of the trench.
    a. **Geometry** Determine the volume of dirt that must be removed for the trench.
    b. Write an exponential function to model the volume of dirt remaining to be shoveled after $x$ weekends. Then use the model to determine how many weekends it will take to complete the trench.

STEM 30. **Psychology** Psychologists use an exponential model of the learning process, $f(t) = c(1 - e^{-kt})$, where $c$ is the total number of tasks to be learned, $k$ is the rate of learning, $t$ is time, and $f(t)$ is the number of tasks learned.
    a. Suppose you move to a new school, and you want to learn the names of 25 classmates in your homeroom. If your learning rate for new tasks is 20% per day, how many complete names will you know after 2 days? After 8 days?
    b. **Graphing Calculator** Graph the function on your graphing calculator. How many days will it take to learn everyone's name? Explain.
    c. **Open-Ended** Does this function seem to describe your own learning rate? If not, how could you adapt it to reflect your learning rate?

# 7-3 Logarithmic Functions as Inverses

F.IF.7.e Graph . . . logarithmic functions, showing intercepts and end behavior . . . Also **A.SSE.3, F.BF.4.a, F.BF.5**

**Objectives** To write and evaluate logarithmic expressions
To graph logarithmic functions

**Solve It!** Write your solution to the Solve It in the space below.

Many even numbers can be written as power functions with base 2. In this lesson you will find ways to express all numbers as powers of a common base.

**Essential Understanding** The exponential function $y = b^x$ is one to one, so its inverse $x = b^y$ is a function. To express "$y$ as a function of $x$" for the inverse, write $y = \log_b x$.

take note

## Key Concept Logarithm

A **logarithm** base $b$ of a positive number $x$ satisfies the following definition.

For $b > 0$, $b \neq 1$, $\log_b x = y$ if and only if $b^y = x$.

You can read $\log_b x$ as "log base $b$ of $x$." In other words, the logarithm $y$ is the exponent to which $b$ must be raised to get $x$.

The exponent $y$ in the expression $b^y$ is the logarithm in the equation $\log_b x = y$. The base $b$ in $b^y$ and the base $b$ in $\log_b x$ are the same. In both, $b \neq 1$ and $b > 0$.

Since $b \neq 1$ and $b > 0$, it follows that $b^y > 0$. Since $b^y = x$, then $x > 0$, so $\log_b x$ is defined only for $x > 0$.

Because $y = b^x$ and $y = \log_b x$ are inverse functions, their compositions map a number $a$ to itself. In other words, $b^{\log_b a} = a$ for $a > 0$ and $\log_b b^a = a$ for all $a$.

You can use the definition of a logarithm to write exponential equations in logarithmic form.

## Problem 1 Writing Exponential Equations in Logarithmic Form

**Got It?** What is the logarithmic form of each equation?

**a.** $36 = 6^2$ **b.** $\frac{8}{27} = \left(\frac{2}{3}\right)^3$ **c.** $1 = 3^0$

**Practice** Write each equation in logarithmic form.

**1.** $\left(\frac{1}{3}\right)^3 = \frac{1}{27}$ **2.** $10^{-2} = 0.01$

You can use the exponential form to help you evaluate logarithms.

## Problem 2 Evaluating a Logarithm

**Got It?** What is the value of each logarithm?

**a.** $\log_5 125$ **b.** $\log_4 32$ **c.** $\log_{64} \frac{1}{32}$

**Plan**

**How can the exponential form help you evaluate logarithms?**

**Practice** Evaluate each logarithm.

**3.** $\log_{49} 7$

**4.** $\log_2 16$

A **common logarithm** is a logarithm with base 10. You can write a common logarithm $\log_{10} x$ simply as $\log x$, without showing the 10.

Many measurements of physical phenomena have such a wide range of values that the reported measurements are logarithms (exponents) of the values, not the values themselves. When you use the logarithm of a quantity instead of the quantity, you are using a **logarithmic scale**. The Richter scale is a logarithmic scale. It gives logarithmic measurements of earthquake magnitude.

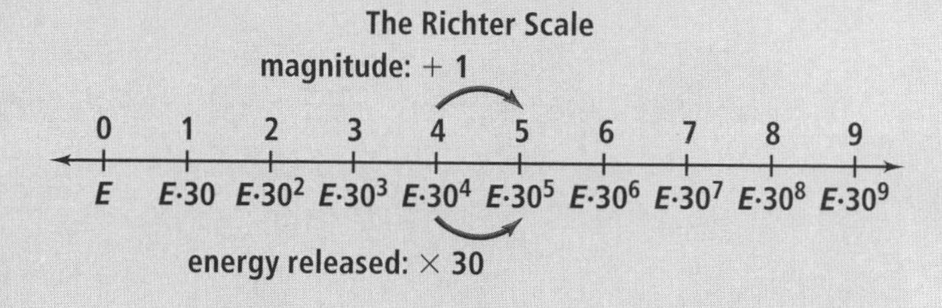


## Problem 3 Using a Logarithmic Scale

**Got It?** In 1995, an earthquake in Mexico registered 8.0 on the Richter scale. In 2001, an earthquake of magnitude 6.8 shook Washington State. How many times more intense was the 1995 earthquake than the 2001 earthquake?

**Seismology** **In 1812, an earthquake of magnitude 7.9 shook New Madrid, Missouri. Compare the intensity level of that earthquake to the intensity level of each earthquake below.**

**5.** magnitude 7.7 in San Francisco, California, in 1906

**6.** magnitude 3.2 in Charlottesville, Virginia, in 2001

A **logarithmic function** is the inverse of an exponential function. The graph shows $y = 10^x$ and its inverse $y = \log x$. Note that $(0, 1)$ and $(1, 10)$ are on the graph of $y = 10^x$, and that $(1, 0)$ and $(10, 1)$ are on the graph of $y = \log x$.

Recall that the graphs of inverse functions are reflections of each other across the line $y = x$. You can graph $y = \log_b x$ as the inverse of $y = b^x$.

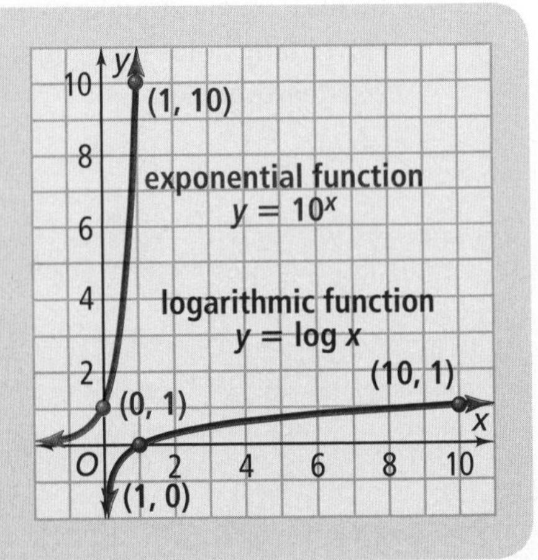

## Problem 4 Graphing a Logarithmic Function

**Think**
**How can the inverse of the function $y = \log_4 x$ help you?**

**Got It?** **a.** What is the graph of $y = \log_4 x$? Describe the domain, range, $y$-intercept, and asymptotes.

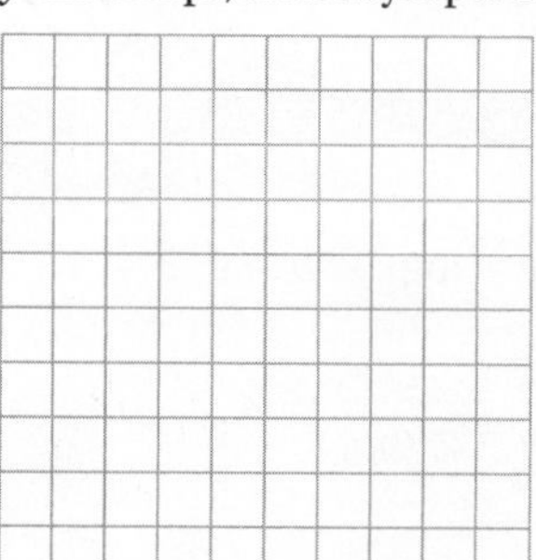

**b. Reasoning** Suppose you use the following table to help you graph $y = \log_2 x$. (Recall that if $y = \log_2 x$, then $2^y = x$.) Complete the table. Explain your answers.

| $x$ | $2^y = x$ | $y$ |
|---|---|---|
| $-1$ | $2^y = -1$ | |
| 0 | $2^y = 0$ | |
| 1 | $2^y = 1$ | |
| 2 | $2^y = 2$ | |

**Practice** **Graph each function on the same set of axes.**

7. $y = \log_2 x$

8. $y = \left(\frac{1}{2}\right)^x$

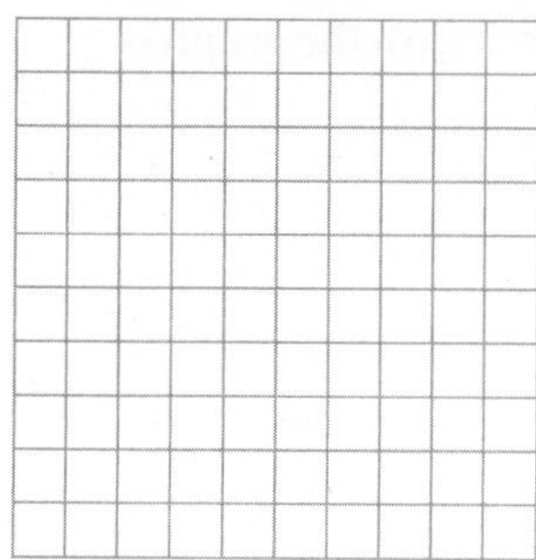

The function $y = \log_b x$ is the parent for a function family. You can graph $y = \log_b(x - h) + k$ by translating the graph of the parent function, $y = \log_b x$, horizontally by $h$ units and vertically by $k$ units. The $a$ in $y = a \log_b x$ indicates a stretch, a compression, and possibly a reflection.

take note

## Concept Summary Families of Logarithmic Functions

| | |
|---|---|
| Parent function: | $y = \log_b x,\ b > 0,\ b \neq 1$ |
| Stretch ($\lvert a \rvert > 1$)<br>Compression (Shrink) ($0 < \lvert a \rvert < 1$)<br>Reflection ($a < 0$) in $x$-axis | $y = a \log_b x$ |
| Translation (horizontal by $h$; vertical by $k$) | $y = \log_b(x - h) + k$ |
| All transformations together | $y = a \log_b(x - h) + k$ |

## Problem 5 Translating $y = \log_b x$

**Got It?** How does the graph of each function compare to the graph of the parent function?

**a.** $y = \log_2(x - 3) + 4$

**b.** $y = 5 \log_2 x$

**A Practice** **Describe how the graph of each function compares with the graph of the parent function, $y = \log_b x$.**

**9.** $y = \log_3(x - 5) + 3$

10. $y = \log_4(x + 2) - 1$

## Lesson Check

### Do you know HOW?

**Write each equation in logarithmic form.**

11. $25 = 5^2$

12. $64 = 4^3$

13. $243 = 3^5$

14. $49 = 7^2$

**In Exercises 15–18, evaluate each logarithm.**

15. $\log_2 8$

16. $\log_9 9$

17. $\log_7 49$

18. $\log_2 \frac{1}{4}$

## Do you UNDERSTAND?

**19. Vocabulary** Determine whether each logarithm is a common logarithm.

a. $\log_2 4$

b. $\log 64$

c. $\log_{10} 100$

d. $\log_5 5$

**20. Reasoning** Explain how you could use an inverse function to graph the logarithmic function $y = \log_6 x$.

**21. Compare and Contrast** Compare the graph of $y = \log_2(x + 4)$ to the graph of $y = \log_2 x$. How are the graphs alike? How are they different?

## More Practice and Problem-Solving Exercises

### B Apply

**22. Think About a Plan** The pH of a substance equals $-\log[H^+]$, where $[H^+]$ is the concentration of hydrogen ions, and it ranges from 0 to 14. A pH level of 7 is neutral. A level greater than 7 is basic, and a level less than 7 is acidic. The table shows the hydrogen ion concentration $[H^+]$ for selected foods. Is each food basic or acidic?

- How can you find the pH value of each food?
- What rule can you use to determine if the food is basic or acidic?

**Approximate $[H^+]$ of Foods**

| Food | $[H^+]$ |
|---|---|
| Apple juice | $3.2 \times 10^{-4}$ |
| Buttermilk | $2.5 \times 10^{-5}$ |
| Cream | $2.5 \times 10^{-7}$ |
| Ketchup | $1.3 \times 10^{-4}$ |
| Shrimp sauce | $7.9 \times 10^{-8}$ |
| Strained peas | $1.0 \times 10^{-6}$ |

STEM **23. Chemistry** Find the concentration of hydrogen ions in seawater, if the pH level of seawater is 8.5.

**Write each equation in exponential form.**

**24.** $\log_2 128 = 7$ **25.** $\log 0.0001 = -4$ **26.** $\log_6 6 = 1$ **27.** $\log_4 1 = 0$

**28.** $\log_7 16{,}807 = 5$ **29.** $\log_2 \frac{1}{2} = -1$ **30.** $\log_3 \frac{1}{9} = -2$ **31.** $\log 10 = 1$

**Find the greatest integer that is less than the value of the logarithm. Use your calculator to check your answers.**

**32.** $\log 5$ **33.** $\log 0.08$ **34.** $\log 17.52$ **35.** $\log(1.3 \times 10^7)$

**36.** Compare the graph at the right to the function $y = \log_5 x$. Describe the domain and range and identify the $y$-intercept of $y = \log_5 x$.

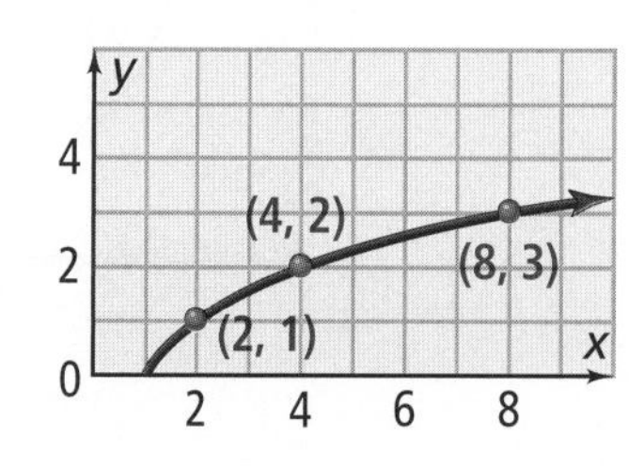


**37.** Write $5 = \log_{2x+1}(a + b)$ in exponential form.

**38. Open-Ended** Write a logarithmic function of the form $y = \log_b x$. Find its inverse function. Graph both functions on one set of axes.

**Find the inverse of each function.**

39. $y = \log_4 x$

40. $y = \log_{0.5} x$

41. $y = \log_{10} x$

42. $y = \log_2 2x$

43. $y = \log(x + 1)$

44. $y = \log 10x$

45. $y = \log_2 4x$

46. $y = \log(x - 6)$

**Graph each logarithmic function.**

47. $y = \log 2x$

48. $y = 2 \log_2 x$

49. $y = \log_4(2x + 3)$

50. $y = \log_3(x + 5)$

**Find the domain and the range of each function.**

51. $y = \log_5 x$

52. $y = 3 \log x$

53. $y = \log_2(x - 3)$

54. $y = 2 \log(x - 2)$

**You can write $5^3 = 125$ in logarithmic form using the fact that $\log_b b^x = x$.**

$\log_5(5^3) = \log_5(125)$ Apply the log base 5 to each side.

$3 = \log_5(125)$ Use $\log_b b^x = x$ to simplify.

**Use this method to write each equation in logarithmic form. Show your work.**

55. $3^4 = 81$

56. $x^4 = y$

57. $6^8 = a + 1$

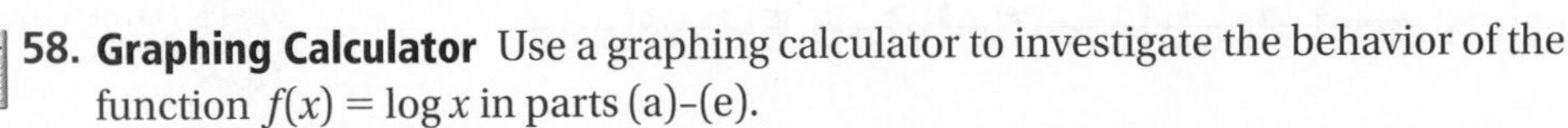

**58. Graphing Calculator** Use a graphing calculator to investigate the behavior of the function $f(x) = \log x$ in parts (a)–(e).

a. Graph the function. Use the graph to estimate the average rate of change of the function between $x = 1$ and $x = 2$, between $x = 2$ and $x = 3$, and between $x = 3$ and $x = 4$. (Adjust the limits of the graphing window if necessary.)

b. Write an expression for the average rate of change of $f(x) = \log x$ from $x$ to $x + 1$.

c. Use a table to find the average rates of change of the function between $x = 10$ and $x = 11$, between $x = 11$ and $x = 12$, and between $x = 12$ and $x = 13$.

d. Find an interval on the positive $x$-axis for which the average rate of change of $f(x)$ is less than 0.005.

e. What value does the average rate of change of the function seem to approach as $x$ increases?

## Challenge

**Find the least integer greater than each number. Do not use a calculator.**

59. $\log_3 38$

60. $\log_{1.5} 2.5$

61. $\log_{\sqrt{7}} \sqrt{50}$

62. $\log_5 \frac{1}{47}$

63. Match each function with the graph of its inverse.

a. $y = \log_3 x$

b. $y = \log_2 4x$

c. $y = \log_{\frac{1}{2}} x$

I.

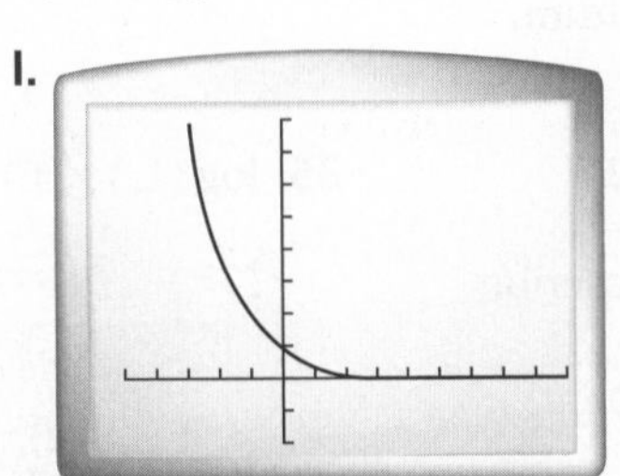

II.

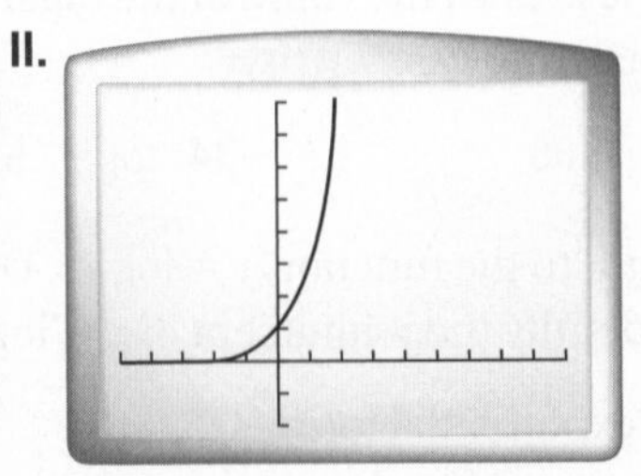

II.

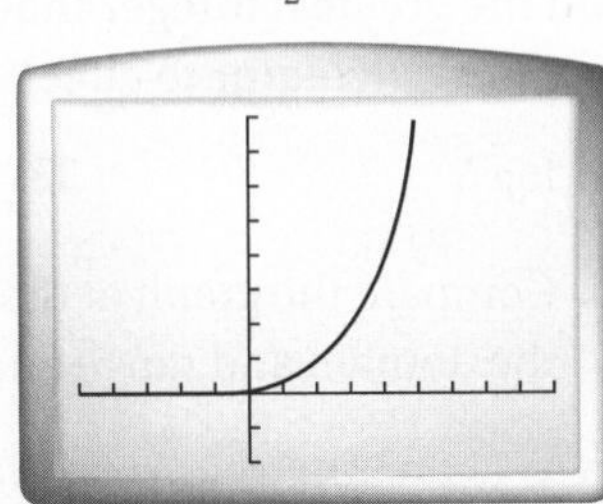

# 7-4 Properties of Logarithms

**A.SSE.3** Choose and produce an equivalent form of an expression to reveal and explain properties of the quantity . . .
Also **A.SSE.2, F.IF.8**

**Objective** To use the properties of logarithms

**Solve It!** Write your solution to the Solve It in the space below.

You can derive the properties of logarithms from the properties of exponents.

**Essential Understanding** Logarithms and exponents have corresponding properties.

**Here's Why It Works** You can use a product property of exponents to derive a product property of logarithms.

Let $x = \log_b m$ and $y = \log_b n$.

| | |
|---|---|
| $m = b^x$ and $n = b^y$ | Definition of logarithm |
| $mn = b^x \cdot b^y$ | Write *mn* as a product of powers. |
| $mn = b^{x+y}$ | Product Property of Exponents |
| $\log_b mn = x + y$ | Definition of logarithm |
| $\log_b mn = \log_b m + \log_b n$ | Substitute for *x* and *y*. |

take note

## Properties Properties of Logarithms

For any positive numbers $m$, $n$, and $b$, where $b \neq 1$, the following properties apply.

| | |
|---|---|
| **Product Property** | $\log_b mn = \log_b m + \log_b n$ |
| **Quotient Property** | $\log_b \frac{m}{n} = \log_b m - \log_b n$ |
| **Power Property** | $\log_b m^n = n \log_b m$ |

## Problem 1 Simplifying Logarithms

**Got It?** What is each expression written as a single logarithm?

**a.** $\log_4 5x + \log_4 3x$

**b.** $2 \log_4 6 - \log_4 9$

**Think**

**In part (a), what property of logarithms can be used to simplify the expression?**

**A Practice** Write each expression as a single logarithm.

**1.** $\log_2 9 - \log_2 3$

**2.** $\log_7 x + \log_7 y - \log_7 z$

You can expand a single logarithm to involve the sum or difference of two or more logarithms.

## Problem 2 Expanding Logarithms

**Got It?** What is each logarithm expanded?

**a.** $\log_3 \frac{250}{37}$

**b.** $\log_3 9x^5$

**Practice** Expand each logarithm.

**3.** $\log_3 7(2x-3)^2$

**4.** $\log_8 8\sqrt{3a^5}$

You have seen logarithms with many bases. The **log** key on a calculator finds $\log_{10}$ of a number. To evaluate a logarithm with any base, use the **Change of Base Formula**.

take note

### Property Change of Base Formula

For any positive numbers $m$, $b$, and $c$, with $b \neq 1$ and $c \neq 1$,

$$\log_b m = \frac{\log_c m}{\log_c b}$$

**Here's Why It Works**

$$\log_b m = \frac{(\log_b m)(\log_c b)}{\log_c b}$$ Multiply $\log_b m$ by $\frac{\log_c b}{\log_c b} = 1$.

$$= \frac{\log_c (b^{\log_b m})}{\log_c b}$$ Power Property of Logarithms

$$= \frac{\log_c m}{\log_c b}$$ $b^{\log_b m} = m$

## Problem 3 Using the Change of Base Formula

**Got It?** Use the Change of Base Formula. What is the value of each expression?

**a.** $\log_8 32$

**b.** $\log_4 18$

**Plan**

**In part (a), what common base has powers that equal 8 and 32?**

**Practice** Use the Change of Base Formula to evaluate each expression.

**5.** $\log_{12} 20$

**6.** $\log_3 33$

## Problem 4 Using a Logarithmic Scale

**Got It?** STEM **Reasoning** The pH of a substance equals $-\log[H^+]$, where $[H^+]$ is the concentration of hydrogen ions. Suppose the hydrogen ion concentration for Substance A is twice that for Substance B. Which substance has the greater pH level? What is the greater pH level minus the lesser pH level? Explain.

**Practice** STEM **7. Science** The concentration of hydrogen ions in household dish detergent is $10^{-12}$. What is the pH level of household dish detergent?

# Lesson Check

## Do you know HOW?

**Write each expression as a single logarithm.**

**8.** $\log_4 2 + \log_4 8$

**9.** $\log_6 24 - \log_6 4$

**Expand each logarithm.**

**10.** $\log_3 \frac{x}{y}$

**11.** $\log m^2n^5$

**12.** $\log_2 \sqrt{x}$

## Do you UNDERSTAND?

**13. Vocabulary** State which property or properties need to be used to write each expression as a single logarithm.

**a.** $\log_4 5 + \log_4 5$

**b.** $\log_5 4 - \log_5 6$

**14. Reasoning** If $\log x = 5$, what is the value of $\frac{1}{x}$?

**15. Open-Ended** Write log 150 as a sum or difference of two logarithms. Simplify if possible.

## More Practice and Problem-Solving Exercises

**Use the properties of logarithms to evaluate each expression.**

**16.** $\log_2 4 - \log_2 16$

**17.** $\log_2 96 - \log_2 3$

**18.** $\log_3 27 - 2\log_3 3$

**19.** $\log_6 12 + \log_6 3$

**20.** $\log_4 48 - \frac{1}{2}\log_4 9$

**21.** $\frac{1}{2}\log_5 15 - \log_5 \sqrt{75}$

**22. Think About a Plan** The loudness in decibels (dB) of a sound is defined as $10 \log \frac{I}{I_0}$, where $I$ is the intensity of the sound in watts per square meter ($W/m^2$). $I_0$, the intensity of a barely audible sound, is equal to $10^{-12}$ $W/m^2$. Town regulations require the loudness of construction work not to exceed 100 dB. Suppose a construction team is blasting rock for a roadway. One explosion has an intensity of $1.65 \times 10^{-2}$ $W/m^2$. Is this explosion in violation of town regulations?

- Which physical value do you need to calculate to answer the question?
- What values should you use for $I$ and $I_0$?

STEM **23. Construction** The foreman of a construction team puts up a sound barrier that reduces the intensity of the noise by 50%. By how many decibels is the noise reduced? Use the formula $L = 10 \log \frac{I}{I_0}$ to measure loudness. (*Hint:* Find the difference between the expression for loudness for intensity $I$ and the expression for loudness for intensity $0.5I$.)

**24. Error Analysis** Explain why the expansion at the right of $\log_4 \sqrt{\frac{t}{s}}$ is incorrect. Then do the expansion correctly.

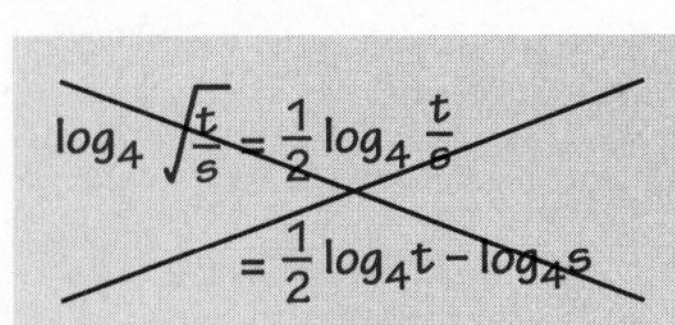

**25. Reasoning** Can you expand $\log_3(2x+1)$? Explain.

**26. Writing** Explain why $\log(5 \cdot 2) \neq \log 5 \cdot \log 2$.

**Determine if each statment is *true* or *false*. Justify your answer.**

**27.** $\log_2 4 + \log_2 8 = 5$

**28.** $\log_3 \frac{3}{2} = \frac{1}{2}\log_3 3$

**29.** $\log(x-2) = \frac{\log x}{\log 2}$

**30.** $\frac{\log_b x}{\log_b y} = \log_b \frac{x}{y}$

**31.** $(\log x)^2 = \log x^2$

**32.** $\log_4 7 - \log_4 3 = \log_4 4$

**Write each logarithmic expression as a single logarithm.**

**33.** $\frac{1}{4}\log_3 2 + \frac{1}{4}\log_3 x$

**34.** $\frac{1}{2}(\log_x 4 + \log_x y) - 3\log_x z$

**35.** $x\log_4 m + \frac{1}{y}\log_4 n - \log_4 p$

**36.** $\left(\frac{2\log_b x}{3} + \frac{3\log_b y}{4}\right) - 5\log_b z$

**Expand each logarithm.**

**37.** $\log\sqrt{\frac{2x}{y}}$

**38.** $\log\frac{s\sqrt{7}}{t^2}$

**39.** $\log\left(\frac{2\sqrt{x}}{5}\right)^3$

**40.** $\log\frac{m^3}{n^4p^{-2}}$

**41.** $\log 4\sqrt{\frac{4r}{s^2}}$

**42.** $\log_b\frac{\sqrt{x}\sqrt[3]{y^2}}{\sqrt[5]{z^2}}$

**43.** $\log_4\frac{\sqrt{x^5y^7}}{zw^4}$

**44.** $\log\frac{\sqrt{x^2-4}}{(x+3)^2}$

**Write each logarithm as the quotient of two common logarithms. Do not simplify the quotient.**

**45.** $\log_7 2$

**46.** $\log_3 8$

**47.** $\log_5 140$

**48.** $\log_9 3.3$

**49.** $\log_4 3x$

STEM **Astronomy** **The apparent brightness of stars is measured on a logarithmic scale called magnitude, in which lower numbers mean brighter stars. The relationship between the ratio of apparent brightness of two objects and the difference in their magnitudes is given by the formula $m_2 - m_1 = -2.5\log\frac{b_2}{b_1}$, where $m$ is the magnitude and $b$ is the apparent brightness.**

**50.** How many times brighter is a magnitude 1.0 star than a magnitude 2.0 star?

**51.** The star Rigel has a magnitude of 0.12. How many times brighter is Capella than Rigel?

Capella
$m = 0.1$

## Challenge

**Expand each logarithm.**

**52.** $\log\sqrt{\frac{x\sqrt{2}}{y^2}}$

**53.** $\log_3[(xy^{\frac{1}{3}}) + z^2]^3$

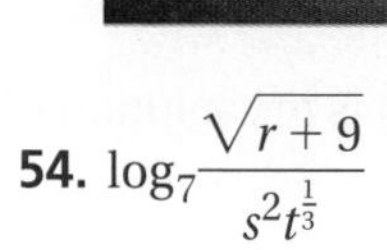

**54.** $\log_7\frac{\sqrt{r+9}}{s^2t^{\frac{1}{3}}}$

**Simplify each expression.**

**55.** $\log_3(x+1) - \log_3(3x^2 - 3x - 6) + \log_3(x-2)$

**56.** $\log(a^2 - 10a + 25) + \frac{1}{2}\log\frac{1}{(a-5)^3} - \log(\sqrt{a} - 5)$

# Exponential and Logarithmic Equations

**F.LE.4** For exponential models, express as a logarithm the solution to $ab^{ct} = d$ where $a$, $c$, and $d$ are numbers and the base $b$ is 2, 10, or $e$; evaluate . . . using technology. Also **A.SSE.3, F.IF.7, F.BF.5**

**Objective** To solve exponential and logarithmic equations

**Solve It!** Write your solution to the Solve It in the space below.

Any equation that contains the form $b^{cx}$, such as $a = b^{cx}$, where the exponent includes a variable, is an **exponential equation**.

**Essential Understanding** You can use logarithms to solve exponential equations. You can use exponents to solve logarithmic equations.

## Problem 1 Solving an Exponential Equation—Common Base

**Got It?** What is the solution of $27^{3x} = 81$?

**Plan**
What common base is appropriate?

 Solve each equation.

1. $3^{-2x+2} = 81$

2. $2^{3x} = 4^{x+1}$

When bases are not the same, you can solve an exponential equation by taking the logarithm of each side of the equation. If $m$ and $n$ are positive and $m = n$, then $\log m = \log n$.

## Problem 2 Solving an Exponential Equation—Different Bases

**Think**

**What property of logarithms will help isolate *x*?**

**Got It?** a. What is the solution of $5^{2x} = 130$?

b. **Reasoning** Why can't you use the same method you used in Problem 1 to solve Problem 2?

**Practice** **Solve each equation. Round to the nearest ten thousandth. Check your answers.**

**3.** $5 - 3^x = -40$

**4.** $12^{y-2} = 20$

## Problem 3 Solving an Exponential Equation With a Graph or Table

**Got It?** What is the solution of each exponential equation? Check your answer.

**a.** $7^{4x} = 800$

**b.** $5.2^{3x} = 400$

**5. Graphing Calculator** Solve the equation $5^{3x} = 500$ by graphing. Round to the nearest ten thousandth.

**6.** Use a table to solve the equation $3^{x-1} = 72$. Round to the nearest hundredth.

## Problem 4 Modeling With an Exponential Equation

**Got It?** STEM **Resource Management** Wood is a sustainable, renewable, natural resource when you manage forests properly. Your lumber company has 1,200,000 trees. You plan to harvest 5% of the trees each year. How many years will it take to harvest half of the trees?

7. The equation $y = 6.72(1.014)^x$ models the world population $y$, in billions of people, $x$ years after the year 2000. Find the year in which the world population is about 8 billion.

A **logarithmic equation** is an equation that includes one or more logarithms involving a variable.

## Problem 5 Solving a Logarithmic Equation

**Got It?** What is the solution of $\log(3 - 2x) = -1$?

**Practice** **Solve each equation. Check your answers.**

8. $2\log(x + 1) = 5$

9. $\log(5 - 2x) = 0$

## Problem 6 Using Logarithmic Properties to Solve an Equation

**Got It?** What is the solution of $\log 6 - \log 3x = -2$?

**Practice** Solve each equation.

**10.** $2 \log x + \log 4 = 2$

**11.** $\log (7x + 1) = \log (x - 2) + 1$

## Lesson Check

### Do you know HOW?

Solve each equation.

**12.** $3^x = 9$

**13.** $2^{y+1} = 25$

**14.** $\log 4x = 2$

**15.** $\log x - \log 2 = 3$

## Do you UNDERSTAND?

**16. Error Analysis** Describe and correct the error made in solving the equation.

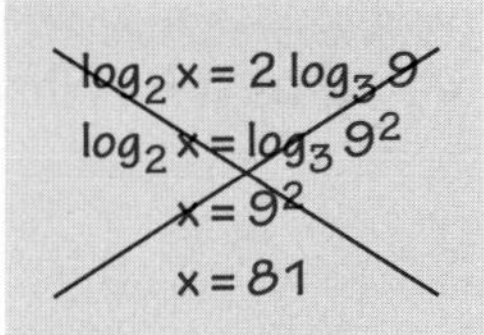


**17. Reasoning** Is it possible for an exponential equation to have no solutions? If so, give an example. If not, explain why.

## More Practice and Problem-Solving Exercises

### B Apply

**18. Think About a Plan** An earthquake of magnitude 9.1 occurred in 2004 in the Indian Ocean near Indonesia. It was about 74,900 times as strong as the greatest earthquake ever to hit Texas. Find the magnitude of the Texas earthquake. (Remember that an increase of 1.0 on the Richter scale means an earthquake is 30 times stronger.)

- Can you write an exponential or logarithmic equation?
- How does the solution of your equation help you find the magnitude?

**19.** Consider the equation $2^{\frac{x}{3}} = 80$.

**a.** Solve the equation by taking the logarithm base 10 of each side.

**b.** Solve the equation by taking the logarithm base 2 of each side.

**c. Writing** Compare your result in parts (a) and (b). What are the advantages of each method? Explain.

STEM **20. Seismology** An earthquake of magnitude 7.7 occurred in 2001 in Gujarat, India. It was about 4900 times as strong as the greatest earthquake ever to hit Pennsylvania. What is the magnitude of the Pennsylvania earthquake? (*Hint*: Refer to the Richter scale on page 527.)

**21.** As a town gets smaller, the population of its high school decreases by 6% each year. The senior class has 160 students now. In how many years will it have about 100 students? Write an equation. Then solve the equation without graphing.

**Mental Math** Solve each equation.

**22.** $2^x = \frac{1}{2}$ **23.** $3^x = 27$ **24.** $\log_9 3 = x$ **25.** $\log_4 64 = x$

**26.** $\log_8 2 = x$ **27.** $10^x = \frac{1}{100}$ **28.** $\log_7 343 = x$ **29.** $25^x = \frac{1}{5}$

**30. Demography** The table below lists the states with the highest and with the lowest population growth rates. Determine in how many years each event can occur. Use the model $P = P_0(1 + r)^x$, where $P_0$ is population from the table as of July 2007, $x$ is the number of years after July 2007, $P$ is the projected population, and $r$ is the growth rate.

a. Population of Idaho exceeds 2 million.
b. Population of Michigan decreases by 1 million.
c. Population of Nevada doubles.

| State | Growth rate (%) | Population (in thousands) | State | Growth rate (%) | Population (in thousands) |
|---|---|---|---|---|---|
| 1. Nevada | 2.93 | 2,565 | 46. New York | 0.08 | 19,298 |
| 2. Arizona | 2.81 | 6,339 | 47. Vermont | 0.08 | 621 |
| 3. Utah | 2.55 | 2,645 | 48. Ohio | 0.03 | 11,467 |
| 4. Idaho | 2.43 | 1,499 | 49. Michigan | −0.30 | 10,072 |
| 5. Georgia | 2.17 | 9,545 | 50. Rhode Island | −0.36 | 1,058 |

SOURCE: U.S. Census Bureau

**31. Open-Ended** Write and solve a logarithmic equation.

**32. Reasoning** The graphs of $y = 2^{3x}$ and $y = 3^{x+1}$ intersect at approximately (1.1201, 10.2692). What is the solution of $2^{3x} = 3^{x+1}$?

**33. Reasoning** If $\log 12^{0.5x} = \log 143.6$, then $12^{0.5x} =$ ___?___.

**STEM Acoustics In Exercises 34–35, the loudness measured in decibels (dB) is defined by loudness $= 10 \log \frac{I}{I_0}$, where $I$ is the intensity and $I_0 = 10^{-12}\,\text{W/m}^2$.**

**34.** The human threshold for pain is 120 dB. Instant perforation of the eardrum occurs at 160 dB.

a. Find the intensity of each sound.
b. How many times as intense is the noise that will perforate an eardrum as the noise that causes pain?

**35.** The noise level inside a convertible driving along the freeway with its top up is 70 dB. With the top down, the noise level is 95 dB.

a. Find the intensity of the sound with the top up and with the top down.
b. By what percent does leaving the top up reduce the intensity of the sound?

**Solve each equation of the form $f(x) = g(x)$ by graphing $y = f(x)$ and $y = g(x)$ and finding the point(s) of intersection.**

**36.** $\frac{2^x}{5} = 5 \log x$ **37.** $-\frac{x^2}{5} + 6 = 3^x$

Solve each equation. If necessary, round to the nearest ten thousandth.

**38.** $8^x = 444$

**39.** $\frac{1}{2}\log x + \log 4 = 2$

**40.** $4\log_3 2 - 2\log_3 x = 1$

**41.** $\log x^2 = 2$

**42.** $9^{2x} = 42$

**43.** $\log_8(2x - 1) = \frac{1}{3}$

**44.** $\log(5x - 4) = 3$

**45.** $12^{4-x} = 20$

**46.** $5^{3x} = 125$

**47.** $\log 4 + 2\log x = 6$

**48.** $4^{3x} = 77.2$

**49.** $\log_7 3x = 3$

Use the properties of exponential and logarithmic functions to solve each system. Check your answers.

**50.** $\begin{cases} y = 2^{x+4} \\ y - 4^{x-1} = 0 \end{cases}$

**51.** $\begin{cases} 2^{x+y} = 16 \\ 4^{x-y} = 1 \end{cases}$

**52.** $\begin{cases} \log(2x - y) = 1 \\ \log(x + y) = 3\log 2 \end{cases}$

## Challenge

Solve each equation.

**53.** $\log_7(2x - 3)^2 = 2$

**54.** $\log_2(x^2 + 2x) = 3$

**55.** $\frac{3}{2}\log_2 4 - \frac{1}{2}\log_2 x = 3$

**56. Meteorology** In the formula $P = P_0\left(\frac{1}{2}\right)^{\frac{h}{4795}}$, $P$ is the atmospheric pressure in millimeters of mercury at elevation $h$ meters above sea level. $P_0$ is the atmospheric pressure at sea level. If $P_0$ equals 760 mm, at what elevation is the pressure 42 mm?

STEM **57. Music** The pitch, or frequency, of a piano note is related to its position on the keyboard by the function $F(n) = 440 \cdot 2^{\frac{n}{12}}$, where $F$ is the frequency of the sound waves in cycles per second and $n$ is the number of piano keys above or below Concert A, as shown. If $n = 0$ at Concert A, which of the instruments shown in the diagram can sound notes at the given frequency?

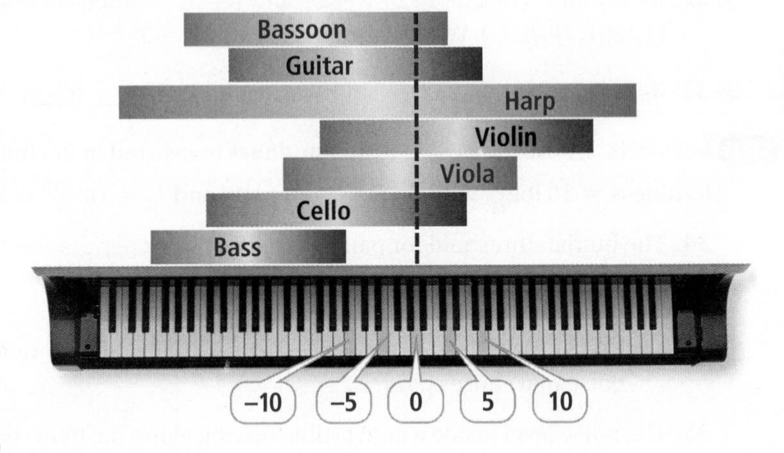


**a.** 590

**b.** 120

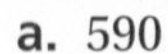

**c.** 1440

**d.** 2093

TECHNOLOGY LAB

Use With Lesson 7-5

# Using Logarithms for Exponential Models

**F.IF.8** Write a function defined by an expression in . . . equivalent forms to reveal and explain different properties of the function. Also **F.IF.7.e, S.ID.6.a**

You can transform an exponential function into a linear function by taking the logarithm of each side. Since linear models are easy to recognize, you can then determine whether an exponential function is a good model for a set of values.

| | |
|---|---|
| $y = ab^x$ | Write the general form of an exponential function. |
| $\log y = \log ab^x$ | Take the logarithm of each side. |
| $\log y = \log a + x(\log b)$ | Use the Product Property and the Power Property. |

If $\log b$ and $\log a$ are constants, then $\log y = (\log b)x + \log a$ is a linear equation in slope-intercept form when you plot the points as $(x, \log y)$.

## Activity

**Determine whether an exponential function is a good model for the values in the table.**

| $x$ | 0 | 2.1 | 3.8 | 5.5 | 8.3 | 9.8 |
|---|---|---|---|---|---|---|
| $y$ | 0.5 | 2.1 | 7 | 22.6 | 157.6 | 445.7 |

**Step 1** Enter the values into **stat** lists $L_1$ and $L_2$. To enter the values of $\log y$, place the cursor in the heading of $L_3$ and press **log** $L_2$ **enter**.

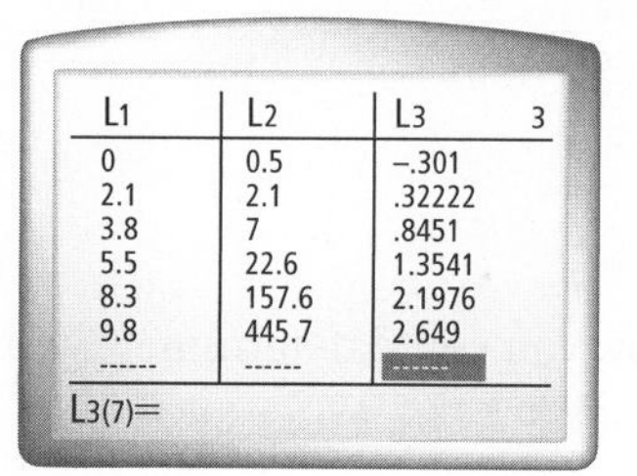


**Step 2** To graph $\log y$, access the **stat plot** feature and press **1**. Then enter $L_3$ next to **YLIST**. Then press **zoom** **9**.

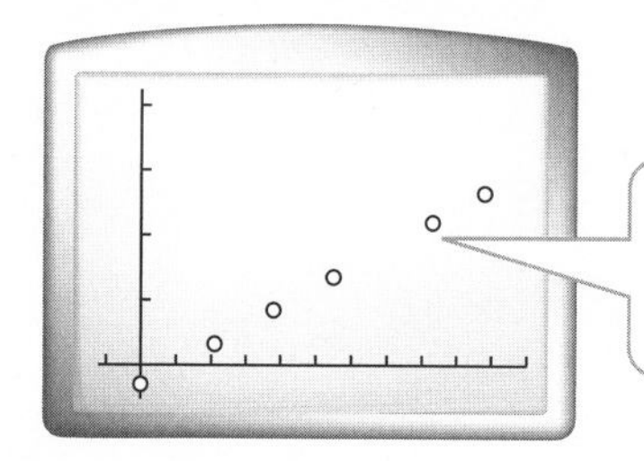

The points $(x, \log y)$ lie on a line, so an exponential model is appropriate.

**Step 3** Press **stat** ▷ **0** **enter** to find the exponential function $y = 0.5(2)^x$.

## Exercises

**For each set of values, determine whether an exponential function is a good model. If so, find the exponential function.**

1.

| $x$ | 1.5 | 3.2 | 4.9 | 7.8 | 8.7 |
|---|---|---|---|---|---|
| $y$ | 1.5 | 3.2 | 4.9 | 7.8 | 8.7 |

2.

| $x$ | −0.8 | 0.1 | 1 | 2.5 | 3.9 |
|---|---|---|---|---|---|
| $y$ | 34.8 | 18.7 | 10.1 | 3.5 | 1.3 |

3. The table at the right show the number of degrees Fahrenheit $d$ over room temperature of a cup of tea $t$ minutes after being brewed. Verify that the data are modeled by an exponential function. Then find an exponential function that models the data.

| $t$ | $d$ |
|---|---|
| 1 | 97.2 |
| 5 | 55.9 |
| 10 | 28.8 |
| 15 | 14.7 |
| 20 | 7.6 |
| 25 | 3.9 |

4. **Writing** Explain how you could determine whether a logarithmic function was a good model for a set of data.

# 7-6 Natural Logarithms

**F.LE.4** For exponential models, express as a logarithm the solution to $ab^{ct} = d$ where $a$, $c$, and $d$ are numbers and the base $b$ is 2, 10, or $e$ . . . Also **A.SSE.3**

**Objectives** To evaluate and simplify natural logarithmic expressions
To solve equations using natural logarithms

**Solve It!** Write your solution to the Solve It in the space below.

The function $y = e^x$ has an inverse, the **natural logarithmic function**, $y = \log_e x$, or $y = \ln x$.

**Essential Understanding** The functions $y = e^x$ and $y = \ln x$ are inverse functions. Just as before, this means that if $a = e^b$, then $b = \ln a$, and vice versa.

take note

## Key Concept Natural Logarithmic Function

If $y = e^x$, then $x = \log_e y = \ln y$. The natural logarithmic function is the inverse of $x = \ln y$, so you can write it as $y = \ln x$.

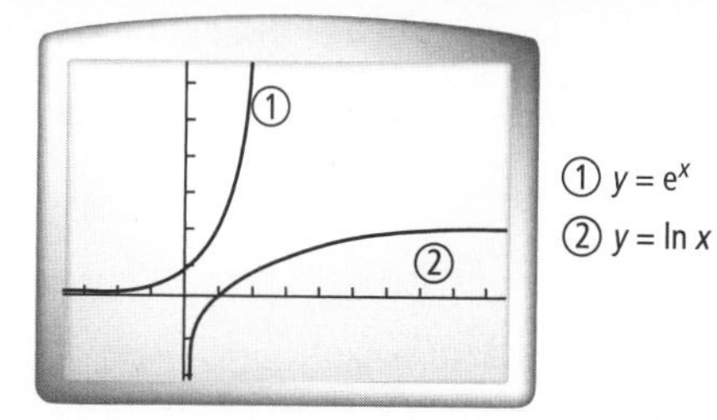

## Problem 1 Simplifying a Natural Logarithmic Expression

**Plan**

**Which property of logarithms should you use first?**

**Got It?** What is each expression written as a single natural logarithm?

**a.** $\ln 7 + 2 \ln 5$

**b.** $3 \ln x - 2 \ln 2x$

**c.** $3 \ln x + 2 \ln y + \ln 5$

**A Practice** **Write each expression as a single natural logarithm.**

**1.** $4 \ln 8 + \ln 10$

**2.** $2 \ln 8 - 3 \ln 4$

You can use the inverse relationship between the functions $y = \ln x$ and $y = e^x$ to solve certain logarithmic and exponential equations.

## Problem 2 Solving a Natural Logarithmic Equation

**Plan**

**How can the exponential form help you solve this equation?**

**Got It?** What are the solutions of each equation? Check your answers.

**a.** $\ln x = 2$

**b.** $\ln (3x + 5)^2 = 4$

**c.** $\ln 2x + \ln 3 = 2$

**Practice** Solve each equation. Check your answers.

**3.** $2 \ln 2x^2 = 1$

**4.** $\ln (2m + 3) = 8$

## Problem 3 Solving an Exponential Equation

**Got It?** What is the solution of each equation? Check your answers.

**a.** $e^{x-2} = 12$

**b.** $2e^{-x} = 20$

**c.** $e^{3x} + 5 = 15$

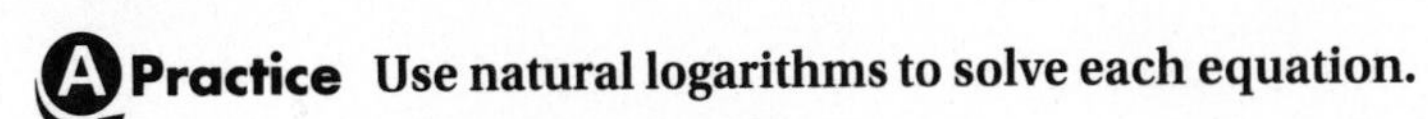

**Practice** **Use natural logarithms to solve each equation.**

**5.** $e^{x+1} = 30$

**6.** $7 - 2e^{\frac{x}{2}} = 1$

Natural logarithms are useful because they help express many relationships in the physical world.

## Problem 4 Using Natural Logarithms

**Got It?** STEM **Space** Use the formula $v = -0.0098t + c \ln R$, where $v$ is the velocity of the rocket, $t$ is the firing time, $c$ is the velocity of the exhaust, and $R$ is the ratio of the mass of the rocket filled with fuel to the mass of the rocket without fuel. See Problem 4.

**a.** A booster rocket for a spacecraft has a mass ratio of about 15, an exhaust velocity of 2.1 km/s, and a firing time of 30 s. Can the spacecraft achieve a stable orbit 300 km above Earth?

**b. Reasoning** Suppose a rocket, as designed, cannot provide enough velocity to achieve a stable orbit. Could alterations to the rocket make a stable orbit achievable? Explain.

**Space** For Exercises 7 and 8, use $v = -0.0098t + c \ln R$, where $v$ is the velocity of the rocket, $t$ is the firing time, $c$ is the velocity of the exhaust, and $R$ is the ratio of the mass of the rocket filled with fuel to the mass of the rocket without fuel. See Problem 4.

**7.** Find the velocity of a spacecraft whose booster rocket has a mass ratio of 20, an exhaust velocity of 2.7 km/s, and a firing time of 30 s. Can the spacecraft achieve a stable orbit 300 km above Earth?

**8.** A rocket has a mass ratio of 24 and an exhaust velocity of 2.5 km/s. Determine the minimum firing time for a stable orbit 300 km above Earth.

## Lesson Check

### Do you know HOW?

**Write each expression as a single natural logarithm.**

**9.** $4 \ln 3$

**10.** $\ln 18 - \ln 10$

**11.** $\ln 3 + \ln 4$

**12.** $-2 \ln 2$

**Solve each equation.**

**13.** $\ln 5x = 4$

**14.** $\ln (x - 7) = 2$

**15.** $2 \ln x = 4$

**16.** $\ln (2 - x) = 1$

## Do you UNDERSTAND?

**17. Error Analysis** Describe the error made in solving the equation. Then find the correct solution.

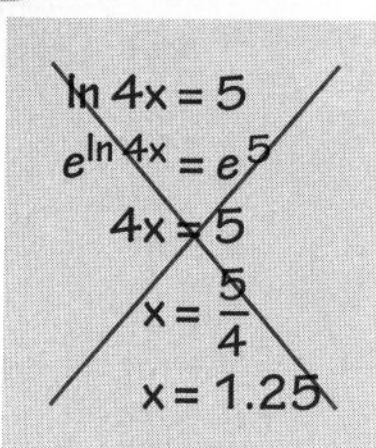

**18. Reasoning** Can $\ln 5 + \log_2 10$ be written as a single logarithm? Explain your reasoning.

## More Practice and Problem-Solving Exercises

### B Apply

**19. Think About a Plan** By measuring the amount of carbon-14 in an object, a paleontologist can determine its approximate age. The amount of carbon-14 in an object is given by $y = ae^{-0.00012t}$, where $a$ is the amount of carbon-14 originally in the object, and $t$ is the age of the object in years. In 2003, a bone believed to be from a dire wolf was found at the La Brea Tar Pits. The bone contains 14% of its original carbon-14. How old is the bone?

- What numbers should you substitute for $y$ and $t$?
- What properties of logarithms and exponents can you use to solve the equation?

STEM **20. Archaeology** A fossil bone contains 25% of its original carbon-14. What is the approximate age of the bone?

**Simplify each expression.**

**21.** $\ln 1$ **22.** $\frac{\ln e}{4}$ **23.** $\frac{\ln e^2}{2}$ **24.** $\ln e^{83}$ **25.** $\ln e$

**26.** $\ln e^2$ **27.** $\ln e^{10}$ **28.** $10 \ln e$ **29.** $\ln e^3$ **30.** $\frac{\ln e^4}{8}$

**31. Error Analysis** A student has broken the natural logarithm key on his calculator, so he decides to use the Change of Base Formula to find ln 100. Explain his error and find the correct answer.

$\ln 100 = \frac{\log 100}{\log e} = \frac{\log 10^2}{\log e} = \frac{2\log 10}{\log e} = \frac{2(1)}{1} = 2$

STEM **32. Satellite** The battery power available to run a satellite is given by the formula $P = 50e^{-\frac{t}{250}}$, where $P$ is power in watts and $t$ is time in days. For how many days can the satellite run if it requires 15 watts of power?

**Determine whether each statement is *always, sometimes,* or *never* true.**

**33.** $\ln e^x \geq 1$ **34.** $\ln e^x = \ln e^x + 1$ **35.** $\ln t = \log_e t$

STEM **36. Space** Use the formula for maximum velocity $v = -0.0098t + c \ln R$. Find the mass ratio of a rocket with an exhaust velocity of 3.1 km/s, a firing time of 50 s, and a maximum shuttle velocity of 6.9 km/s.

**STEM Biology** **The formula $H = \frac{1}{r}(\ln P - \ln A)$ models the number of hours it takes a bacteria culture to decline, where $H$ is the number of hours, $r$ is the rate of decline, $P$ is the initial bacteria population, and $A$ is the reduced bacteria population.**

**37.** A scientist determines that an antibiotic reduces a population of 20,000 bacteria to 5000 in 24 hours. Find the rate of decline caused by the antibiotic.

**38.** A laboratory assistant tests an antibiotic that causes a rate of decline of 0.14. How long should it take for a population of 8000 bacteria to shrink to 500?

## Challenge

**Solve each equation.**

**39.** $\frac{1}{3}\ln x + \ln 2 - \ln 3 = 3$

**40.** $\ln(x + 2) - \ln 4 = 3$

**41.** $2e^{x-2} = e^x + 7$

**42. Error Analysis** Consider the solution to the equation $\ln(x - 3)^2 = 4$ at the right. In Problem 2 you saw that there are two solutions to this equation, $3 + e^2$ and $3 - e^2$. Why do you get only one solution using this method?

$\ln(x - 3)^2 = 4$
$2\ln(x - 3) = 4$
$\ln(x - 3) = 2$
$e^{\ln(x - 3)} = e^2$
$x - 3 = e^2$
$x = e^2 + 3$

**STEM 43. Technology** In 2008, there were about 1.5 billion Internet users. That number is projected to grow to 3.5 billion in 2015.

**a.** Let $t$ represent the time, in years, since 2008. Write a function of the form $y = ae^{ct}$ that models the expected growth in the population of Internet users.

**b.** In what year will there be 2 billion Internet users?

**c.** In what year will there be 5 billion Internet users?

**d.** Solve your equation for $t$.

**e. Writing** Explain how you can use your equation from part (d) to verify your answers to parts (b) and (c).

**STEM 44. Physics** The function $T(t) = T_r + (T_i - T_r)e^{kt}$ models Newton's Law of Cooling. $T(t)$ is the temperature of a heated substance $t$ minutes after it has been removed from a heat (or cooling) source. $T_i$ is the substance's initial temperature, $k$ is a constant for that substance, and $T_r$ is room temperature.

**a.** The initial surface temperature of a beef roast is 236°F, and room temperature is 72°F. If $k = -0.041$, how long will it take for this roast to cool to 100°F?

**b. Graphing Calculator** Write and graph an equation that you can use to check your answer to part (a). Use your graph to complete the table below.

| Temperature (°F) | 225 | 200 | 175 | 150 | 125 | 100 | 75 |
|---|---|---|---|---|---|---|---|
| Minutes Later | ■ | ■ | ■ | ■ | ■ | ■ | ■ |

LESSON LAB

Use With Lesson 7-6

# Exponential and Logarithmic Inequalities

**A.CED.1** Create equations and inequalities in one variable and use them to solve problems . . . Also **A.REI.11**

You can use the graphing and table capabilities of your calculator to solve problems involving exponential and logarithmic inequalities.

## Example 1

**Solve $2(3)^{x+4} > 10$ using a graph.**

**Step 1**

Define $\mathbf{Y_1}$ and $\mathbf{Y_2}$.

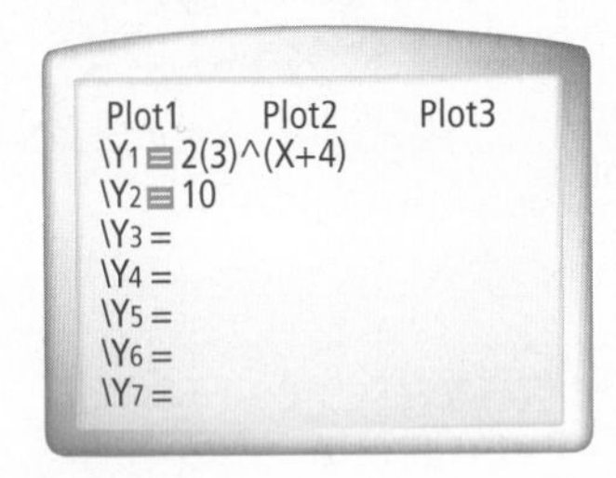


**Step 2**

Make a graph and find the point of intersection.

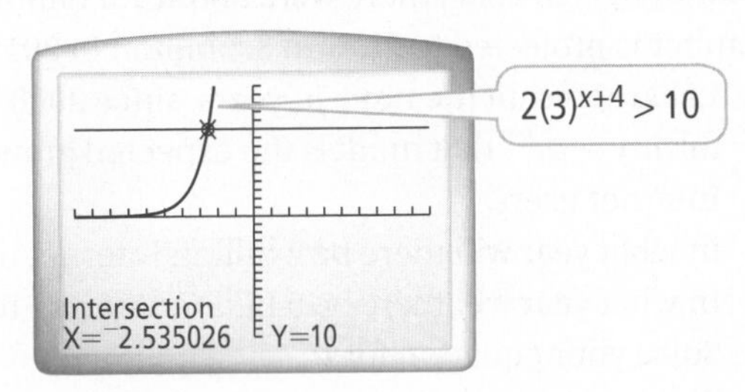


**Step 3**

Identify the $x$-values that make the inequality true.

The solution is $x > -2.535$.

## Exercises

**Solve each inequality using a graph.**

**1.** $4(3)^{x+1} > 6$

**2.** $\log x + 3\log(x-1) < 4$

**3.** $3(2)^{x+2} \geq 5$

**4.** $x + 1 < 12\log x$

**5.** $2(3)^{x-4} > 7$

**6.** $\log x + 2\log(x-1) < 1$

**7.** $4(2)^{x-1} \leq 5$

**8.** $2 \log x + 4 \log(x + 3) > 3$

**9.** $5(4)^{x-1} < 2$

STEM **10. Bacteria Growth** Scientists are growing bacteria in a laboratory. They start with a known population of bacteria and measure how long it takes the population to double.

**Bacteria Population**

| Sample | Initial Population | Doubling Time (in hours) |
| --- | --- | --- |
| Sample A | 200,000 | 1 |
| Sample B | 50,000 | 0.5 |

**a.** Write an exponential function that models the population in Sample A as a function of time in hours.

**b.** Write an exponential function that models the population in Sample B as a function of time in hours.

**c.** Write an inequality that models the population in Sample B overtaking the population in Sample A.

**d.** Use a graphing calculator to solve the inequality in part (c).

**11. Writing** Describe the solution sets to the inequality $x + c < \log x$ as $c$ varies over the real numbers.

## Example 2

**Solve $\log x + 2\log(x + 1) < 2$ using a table.**

### Step 1

Define $\mathbf{Y_1}$ and $\mathbf{Y_2}$.

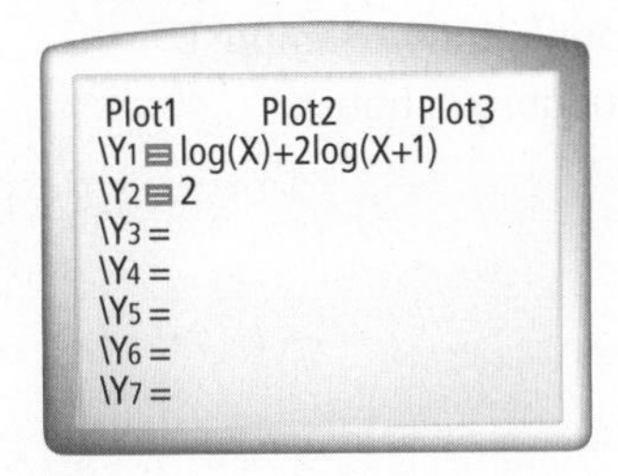


### Step 2

Make a table and examine the values.

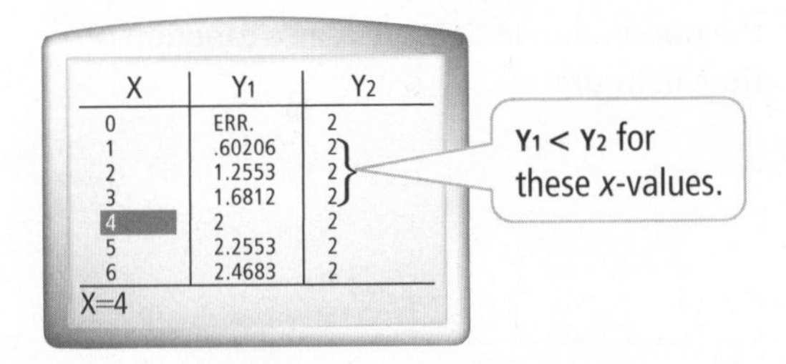

| X | Y1 | Y2 |
|---|---|---|
| 0 | ERR. | 2 |
| 1 | .60206 | 2 |
| 2 | 1.2553 | 2 |
| 3 | 1.6812 | 2 |
| 4 | 2 | 2 |
| 5 | 2.2553 | 2 |
| 6 | 2.4683 | 2 |

X=4



### Step 3

Identify the $x$-values that make the inequality true.

The solution is $0 < x < 4$.

## Exercises

**Solve each inequality using a table. (*Hint:* For more accurate results, set $\delta$Tbl = 0.001.)**

**12.** $\log x + \log(x + 1) < 3$

**13.** $3(2)^{x+1} > 5$

**14.** $\log x + 5\log(x - 1) \geq 3$

**15.** $5(3)^x \leq 2$

**16.** $3 \log x + \log(x + 2) > 1$

**17.** $2(4)^{x+3} \leq 8$

**Barometric Pressure** **Average barometric pressure varies with the altitude of a location. The greater the altitude is, the lower the pressure. The altitude $A$ is measured in feet above sea level. The barometric pressure $P$ is measured in inches of mercury (in. Hg). The altitude can be modeled by the function $A(P) = 90{,}000 - 26{,}500 \ln P$.**

**18.** What is a reasonable domain of the function? What is the range of the function?

**19. Graphing Calculator** Use a graphing calculator to make a table of function values. Use **TblStart** $= 30$ and $\Delta$**Tbl** $= -1$.

**20.** Write an equation to find what average pressure the model predicts at sea level, or $A = 0$. Use your table to solve the equation.

**21.** Kilimanjaro is a mountain in Tanzania that formed from three extinct volcanoes. The base of the mountain is at 3000 ft above sea level. The peak is at 19,340 ft above sea level. On Kilimanjaro, $3000 \leq A(P) \leq 19{,}340$ is true for the altitude. Write an inequality from which you can find minimum and maximum values of normal barometric pressure on Kilimanjaro. Use a table and solve the inequality for $P$.

**22.** Denver, Colorado, is nicknamed the "Mile-High City" because its elevation is about 1 mile, or 5280 ft, above sea level. The lowest point in Phoenix, Arizona, is 1117 ft above sea level. Write an inequality that describes the range of $A(P)$ as you drive from Phoenix to Denver. Then solve the inequality for $P$. (Assume that you never go lower than 1117 ft and you never go higher than 5280 ft.)

# Chapter Review

## 7-1 Exploring Exponential Models

### Quick Review

The general form of an **exponential function** is $y = ab^x$, where $x$ is a real number, $a \neq 0$, $b > 0$, and $b \neq 1$. When $b > 1$, the function models **exponential growth**, and $b$ is the **growth factor**. When $0 < b < 1$, the function models **exponential decay**, and $b$ is the **decay factor**. The $y$-intercept is $(0, a)$.

### Example

Determine whether $y = 2(1.4)^x$ is an example of exponential growth or decay. Then find the $y$-intercept.

Since $b = 1.4 > 1$, the function represents exponential growth.

Since $a = 2$, the $y$-intercept is $(0, 2)$.

### Exercises

**Determine whether each function is an example of exponential growth or decay. Then find the $y$-intercept.**

**1.** $y = 5^x$

**2.** $y = 2(4)^x$

**3.** $y = 0.2(3.8)^x$

**4.** $y = 3(0.25)^x$

**5.** $y = \frac{25}{7}\left(\frac{7}{5}\right)^x$

**6.** $y = 0.0015(10)^x$

**7.** $y = 2.25\left(\frac{1}{3}\right)^x$

**8.** $y = 0.5\left(\frac{1}{4}\right)^x$

**Write a function for each situation. Then find the value of each function after five years. Round to the nearest dollar.**

**9.** A $12,500 car depreciates 9% each year.

**10.** A baseball card bought for $50 increases 3% in value each year.

## 7-2 Properties of Exponential Functions

### Quick Review

Exponential functions can be translated, stretched, compressed, and reflected.

The graph of $y = ab^{x-h} + k$ is the graph of the parent function $y = b^x$ stretched or compressed by a factor $|a|$, reflected across the $x$-axis if $a < 0$, and translated $h$ units horizontally and $k$ units vertically.

The **continuously compounded interest** formula is $A = Pe^{rt}$, where $P$ is the principal, $r$ is the annual interest rate, and $t$ is time in years.

### Example

How does the graph of $y = -3^x + 1$ compare to the graph of the parent function?

The parent function is $y = 3^x$.

Since $a = -1$, the graph is reflected across the $x$-axis.

Since $k = 1$, it is translated up 1 unit.

### Exercises

**How does the graph of each function compare to the graph of the parent function?**

**11.** $y = 5(2)^{x+1} + 3$

**12.** $y = -2\left(\frac{1}{3}\right)^{x-2}$

**Find the amount in a continuously compounded account for the given conditions.**

**13.** principal: $1000
annual interest rate: 4.8%
time: 2 years

**14.** principal: $250
annual interest rate: 6.2%
time: 2.5 years

**Evaluate each expression to four decimal places.**

**15.** $e^{-3}$

**16.** $e^{-1}$

**17.** $e^5$

**18.** $e^{-\frac{1}{2}}$

# 7-3 Logarithmic Functions as Inverses

## Quick Review

If $x = b^y$, then $\log_b x = y$. The **logarithmic function** is the inverse of the exponential function, so the graphs of the functions are reflections of one another across the line $y = x$. Logarithmic functions can be translated, stretched, compressed, and reflected, as represented by $y = a\log_b(x - h) + k$, similarly to exponential functions.

When $b = 10$, the logarithm is called a **common logarithm**, which you can write as $\log x$.

## Example

Write $5^{-2} = 0.04$ in logarithmic form.

If $y = b^x$, then $\log_b y = x$.

$y = 0.04$, $b = 5$, and $x = -2$.

So $\log_5 0.04 = -2$.

## Exercises

**Write each equation in logarithmic form.**

**19.** $6^2 = 36$ **20.** $2^{-3} = 0.125$

**21.** $3^3 = 27$ **22.** $10^{-3} = 0.001$

**Evaluate each logarithm.**

**23.** $\log_2 64$ **24.** $\log_3 \frac{1}{9}$

**25.** $\log 0.00001$ **26.** $\log_2 1$

**Graph each logarithmic function.**

**27.** $y = \log_3 x$ **28.** $y = \log x + 2$

**29.** $y = 3\log_2(x)$ **30.** $y = \log_5(x + 1)$

**How does the graph of each function compare to the graph of the parent function?**

**31.** $y = 3\log_4(x + 1)$ **32.** $y = -\ln x + 2$

# 7-4 Properties of Logarithms

## Quick Review

For any positive numbers $m$, $n$, and $b$ where $b \neq 1$, each of the following statements is true. Each can be used to rewrite a logarithmic expression.

- $\log_b mn = \log_b m + \log_b n$, by the Product Property
- $\log_b \frac{m}{n} = \log_b m - \log_b n$, by the Quotient Property
- $\log_b m^n = n\log_b m$, by the Power Property

## Example

Write $2\log_2 y + \log_2 x$ as a single logarithm. Identify any properties used.

$2\log_2 y + \log_2 x$

$= \log_2 y^2 + \log_2 x$ Power Property

$= \log_2 xy^2$ Product Property

## Exercises

**Write each expression as a single logarithm. Identify any properties used.**

**33.** $\log 8 + \log 3$ **34.** $\log_2 5 - \log_2 3$

**35.** $4\log_3 x + \log_3 7$ **36.** $\log x - \log y$

**37.** $\log 5 - 2\log x$ **38.** $3\log_4 x + 2\log_4 x$

**Expand each logarithm. State the properties of logarithms used.**

**39.** $\log_4 x^2y^3$ **40.** $\log 4s^4t$

**41.** $\log_3 \frac{2}{x}$ **42.** $\log(x + 3)^2$

**43.** $\log_2(2y - 4)^3$ **44.** $\log \frac{z^2}{5}$

**Use the Change of Base Formula to evaluate each expression.**

**45.** $\log_2 7$ **46.** $\log_3 10$

## 7-5 Exponential and Logarithmic Equations

### Quick Review

An equation in the form $b^{cx} = a$, where the exponent includes a variable, is called an **exponential equation**. You can solve exponential equations by taking the logarithm of each side of the equation. An equation that includes one or more logarithms involving a variable is called a **logarithmic equation**.

### Example

Solve and round to the nearest ten thousandth.

$6^{2x} = 75$

| | |
|---|---|
| $\log 6^{2x} = \log 75$ | Take the logarithm of both sides. |
| $2x \log 6 = \log 75$ | Power Property of logarithms |
| $x = \frac{\log 75}{2 \log 6}$ | Divide both sides by 2 log 6. |
| $x \approx 1.2048$ | Evaluate using a calculator. |

### Exercises

**Solve each equation. Round to the nearest ten thousandth.**

**47.** $25^{2x} = 125$

**48.** $3^x = 36$

**49.** $7^{x-3} = 25$

**50.** $5^x + 3 = 12$

**51.** $\log 3x = 1$

**52.** $\log_2 4x = 5$

**53.** $\log x = \log 2x^2 - 2$

**54.** $2 \log_3 x = 54$

**Solve by graphing. Round to the nearest ten thousandth.**

**55.** $5^{2x} = 20$

**56.** $3^{7x} = 160$

**57.** $6^{3x+1} = 215$

**58.** $0.5^x = 0.12$

**59.** A culture of 10 bacteria is started, and the number of bacteria will double every hour. In about how many hours will there be 3,000,000 bacteria?

## 7-6 Natural Logarithms

### Quick Review

The inverse of $y = e^x$ is the **natural logarithmic function** $y = \log_e x = \ln x$. You solve natural logarithmic equations in the same way as common logarithmic equations.

### Example

Use natural logarithms to solve $\ln x - \ln 2 = 3$.

$\ln x - \ln 2 = 3$

| | |
|---|---|
| $\ln \frac{x}{2} = 3$ | Quotient Property |
| $\frac{x}{2} = e^3$ | Rewrite in exponential form. |
| $\frac{x}{2} \approx 20.0855$ | Use a calculator to find $e^3$. |
| $x \approx 40.171$ | Simplify |

### Exercises

**Solve each equation. Check your answers.**

**60.** $e^{3x} = 12$

**61.** $\ln x + \ln (x + 1) = 2$

**62.** $2 \ln x + 3 \ln 2 = 5$

**63.** $\ln 4 - \ln x = 2$

**64.** $4\, e^{(x-1)} = 64$

**65.** $3 \ln x + \ln 5 = 7$

**66.** An initial investment of $350 is worth $429.20 after six years of continuous compounding. Find the annual interest rate.

# Pull It All Together

## Apparent Magnitudes of Stars

Astronomers refer to the brightness of a star as its *apparent magnitude*. Apparent magnitude is measured on a decreasing scale in that brighter stars have lower apparent magnitudes. For example, Polaris (the North Star) is one of the brighter stars in the night sky and has an apparent magnitude of 1.97, while stars that can barely be seen with the unaided eye have apparent magnitudes of about 6.5. The sun has an apparent magnitude of $-26.74$.

Apparent magnitude does not indicate how brightly a star burns. Many stars burn brighter than our sun, but they appear faint and dim because of their great distance from us.

In the scale for apparent magnitude, a decrease of 1 unit corresponds to an increase in brightness by a factor of $\sqrt[5]{100}$. For example, a star of magnitude 3 and a star of magnitude 1 are separated by 2 units on the apparent magnitude scale, so the star of magnitude 1 is $\left(\sqrt[5]{100}\right)^2 \approx 6.3$ times as bright.

### Task Description

**Sirius, the brightest star in the night sky, is about 24 times as bright as Polaris. What is the apparent magnitude of Sirius?**

# Get Ready!

## Analyzing Graphs of Rational Functions

**Find the vertical asymptotes and holes for the graph of each rational function.**

**1.** $y = \frac{2}{x - 3}$

**2.** $y = \frac{x + 2}{(2x + 1)(x - 4)}$

## Solving Quadratic Equations

**Solve each equation.**

**3.** $4x^2 = 25$

**4.** $x^2 - 23 = 0$

**5.** $3x^2 = 80$

**6.** $8x^2 - 44 = 0$

**7.** $0.5x^2 = 15$

**8.** $6x^2 - 13 = 11$

## Finding the Inverse of a Function

**For each function $f$, find $f^{-1}$ and the domain and range of $f$ and $f^{-1}$. Determine whether $f^{-1}$ is a function.**

**9.** $f(x) = 5x + 2$

**10.** $f(x) = \sqrt{3x - 4}$

**11.** $f(x) = \frac{10}{x - 1}$

## Solving Exponential and Logarithmic Equations

**Solve each equation.**

**12.** $4^x = \frac{1}{8}$

**13.** $\log 5x + 1 = -1$

**14.** $7^{3x} = 500$

**15.** $\log 3x + \log x = 9$

**16.** $\log(4x + 3) - \log x = 5$

**17.** $3^x = 243$

## Looking Ahead Vocabulary

VOCABULARY

**18.** If you were to graph the average monthly rainfall for your community for the past 5 years, you would very likely graph a *periodic function*. Why do you think it is called a periodic function?

**19.** Graph the month-by-month attendance at one of these larger National Parks—The Everglades, Grand Canyon, Yellowstone, or Yosemite—for several years. The pattern that results may resemble a *sine curve*. Describe the features of this curve.

# Trigonometric Functions

## Big Ideas

**1 Modeling**
**Essential Question:** How can you model periodic behavior?

**2 Function**
**Essential Question:** If you know the value of sin $\theta$, how can you find cos $\theta$, tan $\theta$, csc $\theta$, sec $\theta$, and cot $\theta$?

**3 Equivalence**
**Essential Question:** How do you verify that an equation involving the variable *x* is an identity?

## © Domains

- Trigonometric Functions
- Interpreting Functions

Log in to **pearsonsuccessnet.com** and click on Interactive Digital Path to access the Solve Its and animated Problems.

## Chapter Preview

**8-1** **Exploring Periodic Data**
**8-2** **Angles and the Unit Circle**
**8-3** **Radian Measure**
**8-4** **The Sine Function**
**8-5** **The Cosine Function**
**8-6** **The Tangent Function**
**8-7** **Translating Sine and Cosine Functions**
**8-8** **Reciprocal Trigonometric Functions**
**8-9** **Trigonometric Identities**
**8-10** **Area and the Law of Sines**
**8-11** **The Law of Cosines**

## Vocabulary

**English/Spanish Vocabulary Audio Online:**

| English | Spanish |
|---|---|
| amplitude, *p. 576* | amplitud |
| central angle, *p. 589* | ángulo central |
| cosine, *p. 584* | coseno |
| cycle, *p. 573* | ciclo |
| midline, *p. 576* | línea media |
| period, *p. 573* | período |
| periodic function, *p. 573* | función periódica |
| phase shift, *p. 628* | cambio de fase |
| radian, *p. 589* | radian |
| sine, *p. 584* | seno |
| tangent, *p. 619* | tangente |
| trigonometric identity, *p. 651* | identidad trigonométrica |
| unit circle, *p. 584* | círculo unitario |

# 8-1 Exploring Periodic Data

**F.IF.4** For a function that models a relationship between two quantities, interpret key features of graphs . . . and sketch graphs . . .

**Objectives** To identify cycles and periods of periodic functions
To find the amplitude of periodic functions

**Solve It!** Write your solution to the Solve It in the space below.

A **periodic function** is a function that repeats a pattern of $y$-values (outputs) at regular intervals. One complete pattern is a **cycle**. A cycle may begin at any point on the graph of the function. The **period** of a function is the horizontal length—the distance along the $x$-axis—of one cycle. The $x$-value in a periodic function often represents time.

**Essential Understanding** Periodic behavior is behavior that repeats over intervals of constant length.

## Problem 1 Identifying Cycles and Periods

**Got It?** Analyze each periodic function. Identify the cycle in two different ways. What is the period of the function?

a. 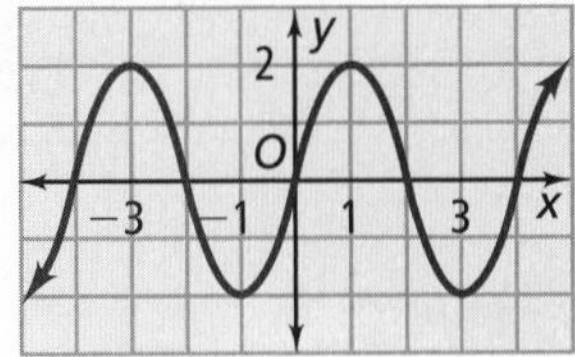

b. 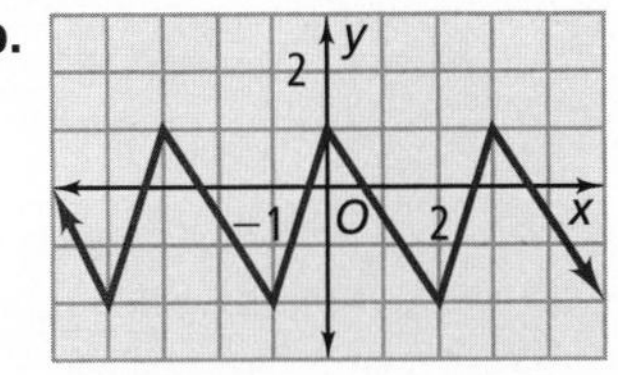


**Practice** **Identify one cycle in two different ways. Then determine the period of the function.**

1. 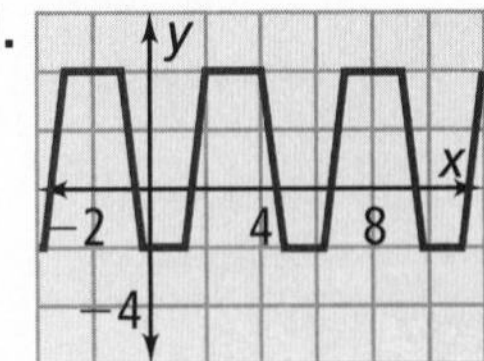


2. 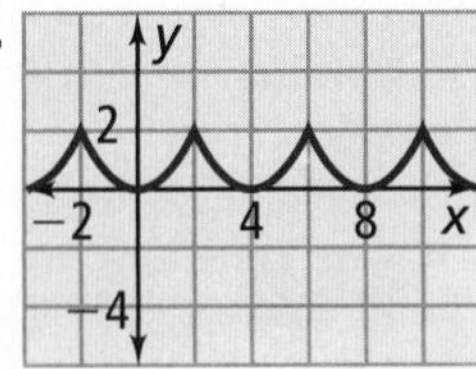

You can analyze the graph of a function to determine if the function is periodic.

## Problem 2 Identifying Periodic Functions

**Think**

**Do the $y$-values of the function repeat?**

**Got It?** Is the function periodic? If it is, what is its period?

**a.**

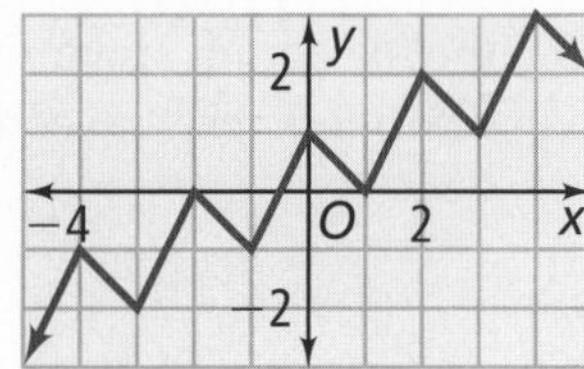


**b.**

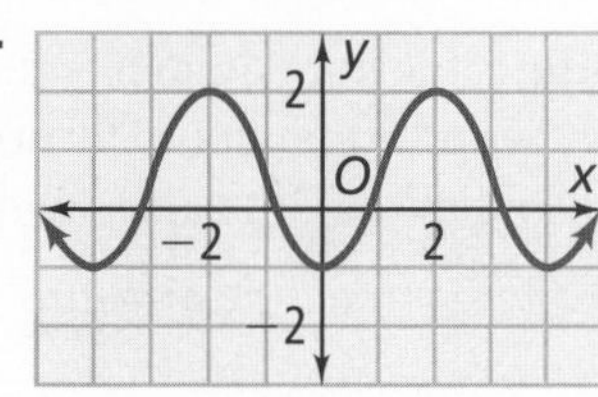


**c. Reasoning** If the period of a function is 4 seconds, how many cycles does it have in a minute? What is the period of a function that has 180 cycles per minute (for example, a point on a spinning wheel)? Of a function that has 440 cycles per second (for example, a point on the end of a tuning fork)?

**Practice** **Determine whether each function *is* or *is not* periodic. If it is, find the period.**

**3.**

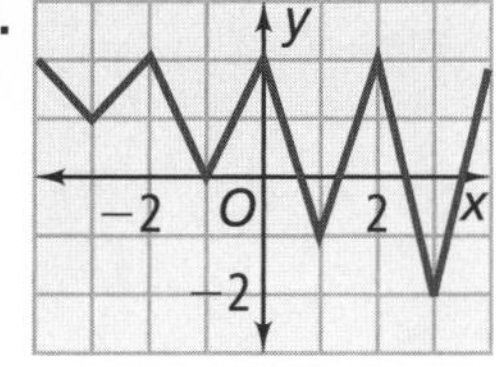


**4.**

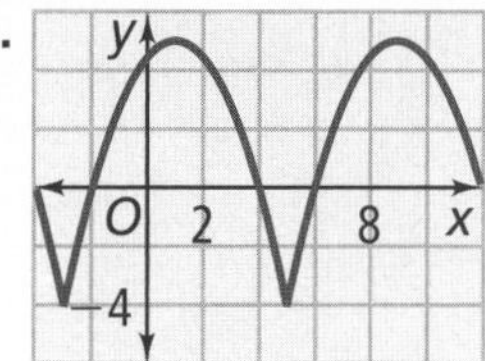

The *amplitude* of a periodic function measures the amount of variation in the function values.

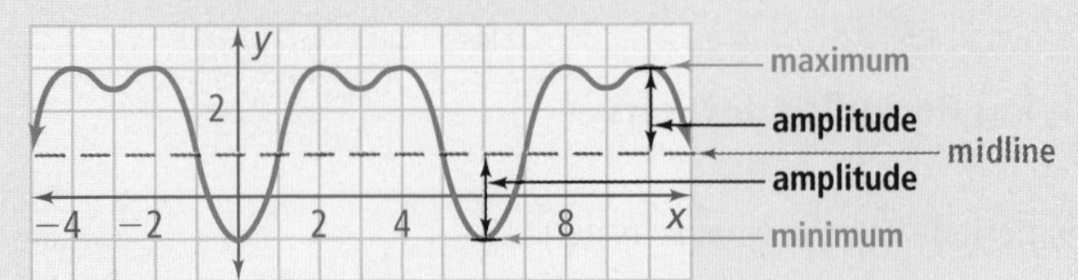


The **midline** is the horizontal line midway between the maximum and minimum values of a periodic function. The **amplitude** is half the difference between the maximum and minimum values of the function.

$$\text{amplitude} = \frac{1}{2}(\text{maximum value} - \text{minimum value})$$

## Problem 3 Finding Amplitude and Midline of a Periodic Function

**Got It?** What is the amplitude of each periodic function? What is the equation of the midline?

**a.**

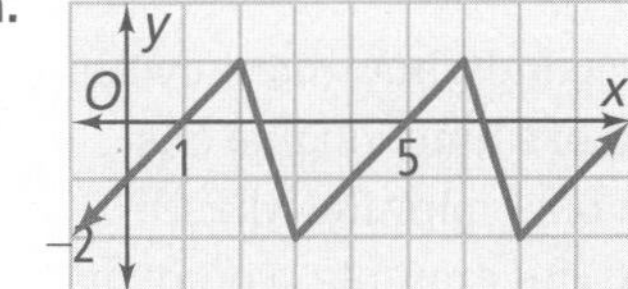


**b.**

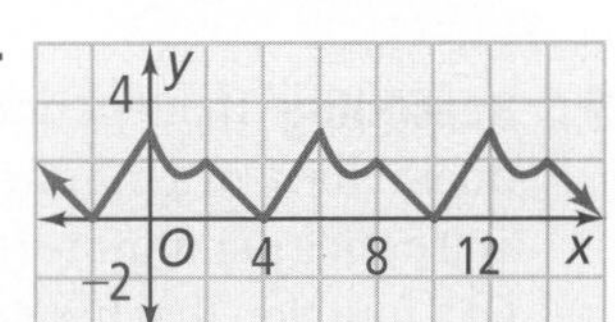


**Practice** Find the amplitude of each periodic function, and midline.

**5.**

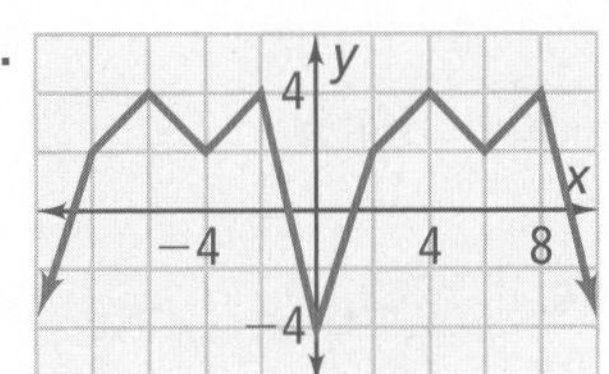


**6.**

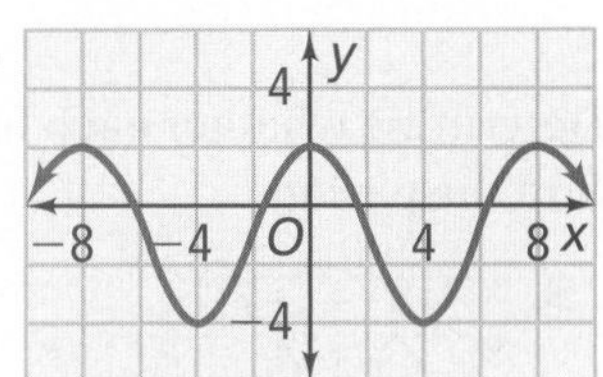


You can model some data with periodic functions. The rotation of a Ferris wheel, the beating of a heart, and the movement of sound waves are all examples of real-world events that generate periodic data.

## Problem 4 Using a Periodic Function to Solve a Problem

**Got It?** What are the period, the amplitude, and the equation of the midline of the green graph in the digital wave display in Problem 4?

**Plan**

**How does identifying the cycle help you?**

**Practice** **Find the amplitude of the periodic function, and midline.**

**7.**

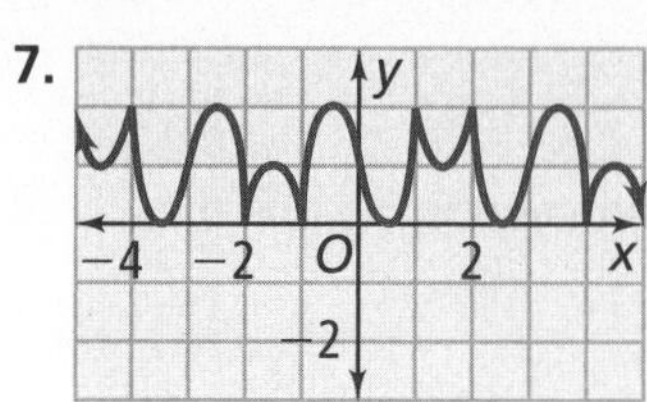

## Lesson Check

### Do you know HOW?

**Determine if the function *is* or *is not* periodic. If it is, find the period.**

**8.**

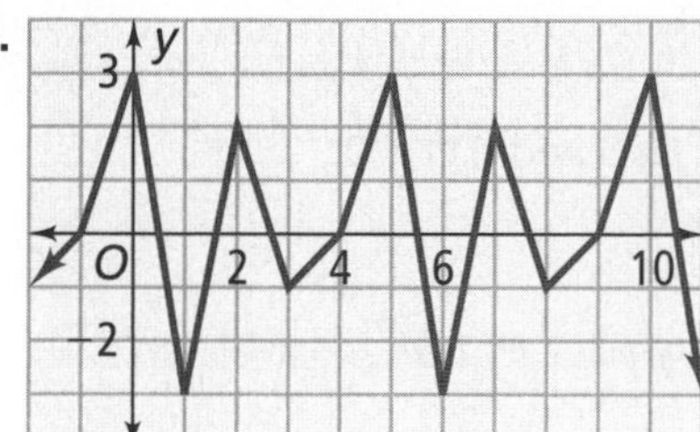


**9.**

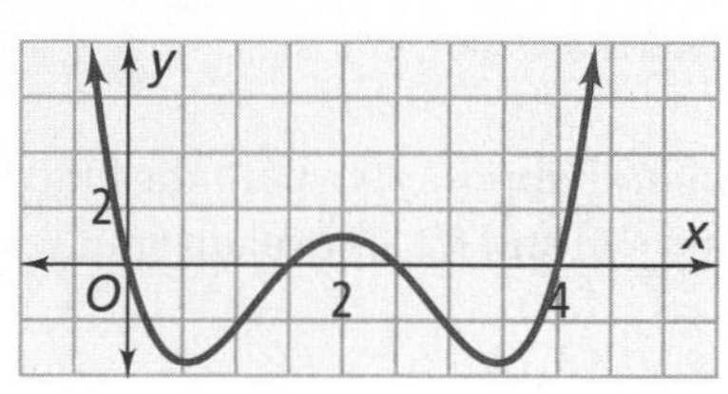

## Do you UNDERSTAND?

**10. Writing** A sound wave can be graphed as a periodic function. Name two more real-world examples of periodic functions.

**11. Error Analysis** A student looked at the following function and wrote that the amplitude was 2. Describe and correct the student's error.

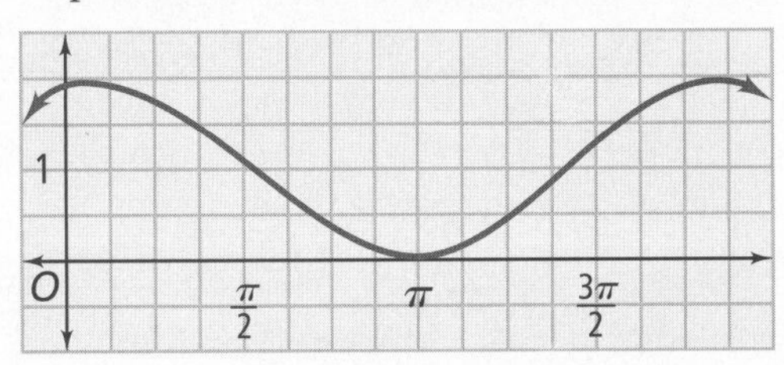


**12. Reasoning** Suppose $f$ is a periodic function. The period of $f$ is 5 and $f(1) = 2$. What are $f(6)$ and $f(11)$? Explain your reasoning.

**13.** A wave has a maximum of 6. If its midline is at $y = 1$, what is its minimum?

## More Practice and Problem-Solving Exercises

**Sketch the graph of a sound wave with the given period, amplitude, and midline.**

**14.** period 0.02, amplitude 4, midline 6

**15.** period 0.005, amplitude 9, midline $-5$

**16.** Complete each statement with $x$ or $y$.

- **a.** You use ■-values to compute the amplitude of a function.
- **b.** You use ■-values to compute the period of a function.

**17.** Which of the following could be represented by a periodic function? Explain.

- **a.** the average monthly temperature in your community, recorded every month for three years
- **b.** the population in your community, recorded every year for the last 50 years
- **c.** the number of cars per hour that pass through an intersection near where you live, recorded for two consecutive work days

**18. Writing** What do all periodic functions have in common?

**19. Think About a Plan** A person's pulse rate is the number of times his or her heart beats in one minute. Each cycle in the graph represents one heartbeat. What is the pulse rate?

- Will you compute the period or the amplitude, or both?
- Does the graph provide information you do NOT need?

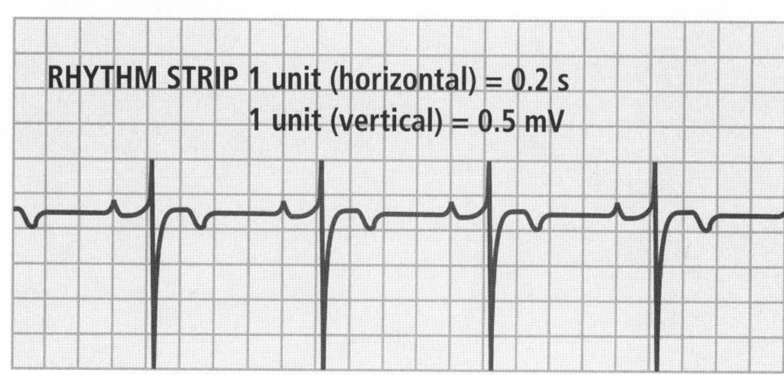


**20. Health** An electrocardiogram (EKG or ECG) measures the electrical activity of a person's heart in millivolts over time. Refer to the graph in the previous exercise.

- **a.** What is the period of the EKG shown above?
- **b.** What is the amplitude of the EKG?

**21. Open-Ended** Sketch a graph of a periodic function that has a period of 3 and an amplitude of 2.

**Find the maximum, minimum, and period of each periodic function. Then copy the graph and sketch two more cycles.**

**22.**

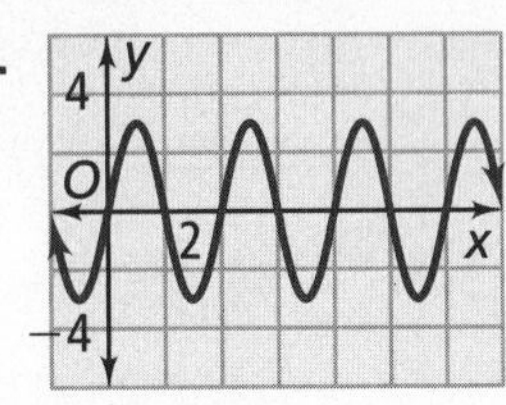


**23.**

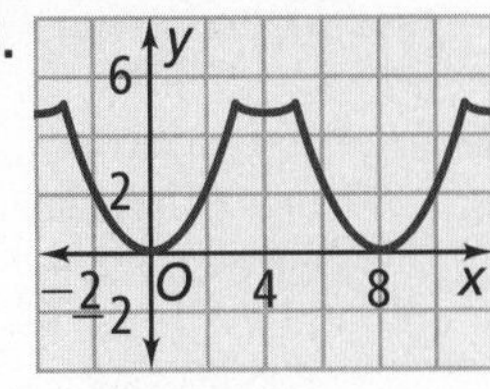


**24.**

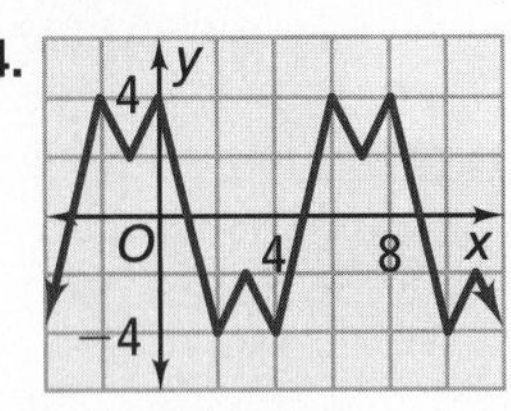


**Language Arts Functions that repeat over time are common in everyday life. The English language has many words that stand for common periods of time. State the period of time from which each term derives.**

**25.** annual **26.** biweekly **27.** quarterly **28.** hourly **29.** circadian

## Challenge

**30.** Suppose $g$ is a periodic function. The period of $g$ is 24, $g(3) = 67$, and $g(8) = 70$. Find each function value.

**a.** $g(27)$ **b.** $g(80)$ **c.** $g(-16)$ **d.** $g(51)$

**31. Calendar** A day is a basic measure of time. A solar year is about 365.2422 days. We try to keep our calendar in step with the solar year.

**a.** If every calendar year had 365 days, by how many days would the calendar year and the solar year differ after 100 years?

**b.** If every fourth year had an extra "leap" day added, by how many days would the two systems differ after 100 years?

**c.** If every hundred years the "leap" day were omitted, by how many days would the two systems differ after 100 years?

**d. Reasoning** Why is it important for the difference between the calendar year and the solar year to be zero?

# Angles and the Unit Circle

Prepares for **F.TF.2** Explain how the unit circle . . . enables the extension of trigonometric functions to all real numbers, interpreted as radian measures of angles traversed counterclockwise around the unit circle. Also prepares for **F.TF.1**

**Objectives** To work with angles in standard position
To find coordinates of points on the unit circle

**Solve It!** Write your solution to the Solve It in the space below.

An angle in the coordinate plane is in **standard position** when the vertex is at the origin and one ray is on the positive $x$-axis. The ray on the $x$-axis is the **initial side** of the angle. The other ray is the **terminal side** of the angle.

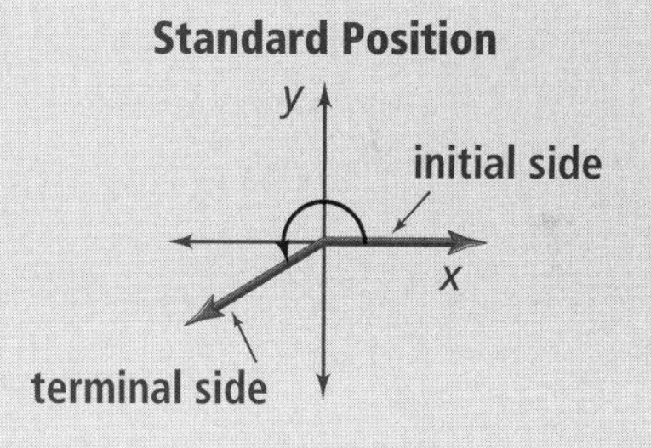


The measure of an angle in standard position is the amount of rotation from the initial side to the terminal side.

**Essential Understanding** The measure of an angle in standard position is the input for two important functions. The outputs are the coordinates (called *cosine* and *sine*) of the point on the terminal side of the angle that is 1 unit from the origin.

The measure of an angle is positive when the rotation from the initial side to the terminal side is in the counterclockwise direction. The measure is negative when the rotation is clockwise.

y
+120°
Counterclockwise
x

y
Clockwise
x
−120°

## Problem 1 Measuring Angles in Standard Position

**Got It?** What is the measure of the angle shown?

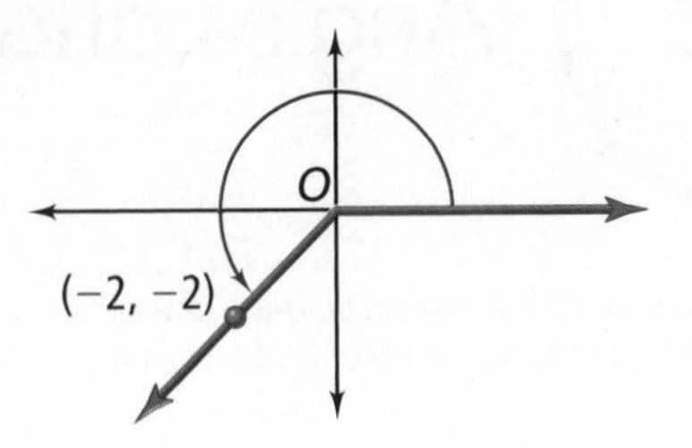

**Practice** Find the measure of each angle in standard position.

**1.**

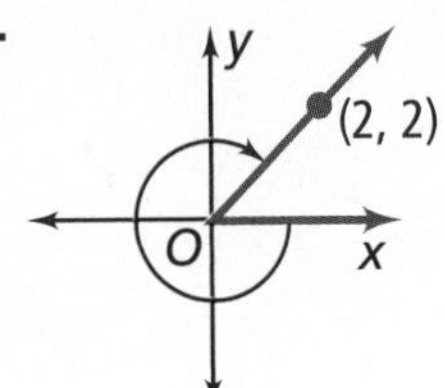


**2.**

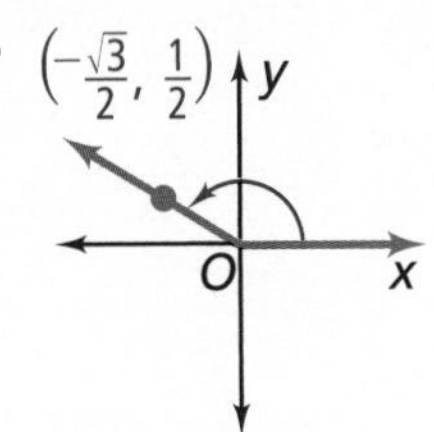


## Problem 2 Sketching Angles in Standard Position

**Got It?** What is a sketch of each angle in standard position?

**a.** 85° **b.** −320° **c.** 180°

**Practice** **Sketch each angle in standard position.**

**3.** $-130°$

**4.** $95°$

Two angles in standard position are **coterminal angles** if they have the same terminal side.

Angles in standard position that have measures $135°$ and $-225°$ are coterminal.

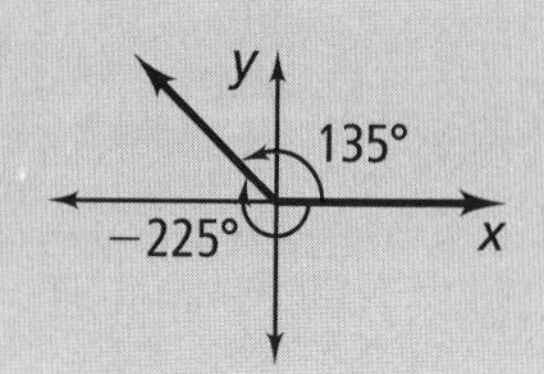


## Problem 3 Identifying Coterminal Angles

**Got It?** Which angles in standard position are coterminal?

**A.** $-315°$ **B.** $45°$ **C.** $315°$ **D.** $405°$

**Practice** **Find the measure of an angle between 0° and 360° coterminal with each given angle.**

**5.** $500°$

**6.** $-180°$

In a 360° angle, a point 1 unit from the origin on the terminal ray makes one full rotation about the origin. The resulting circle is a unit circle. The **unit circle** has a radius of 1 unit and its center at the origin of the coordinate plane. Any right triangle formed by the radius of the unit circle has a hypotenuse of 1. Points on the unit circle are related to periodic functions.

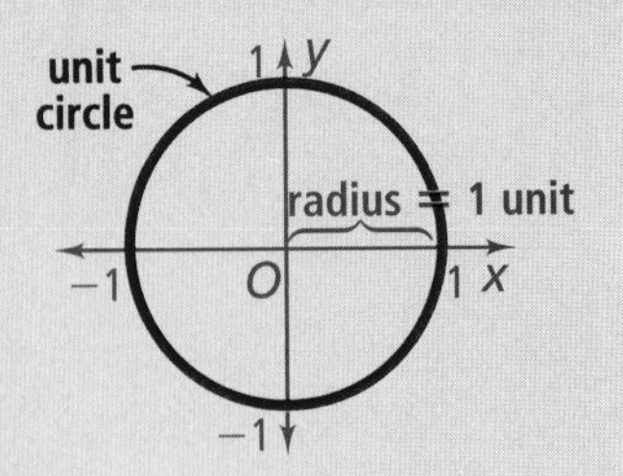


You can use the symbol $\theta$ for the measure of an angle in standard position.

take note

## Key Concepts Cosine and Sine of an Angle

Suppose an angle in standard position has measure $\theta$.

The **cosine of $\theta$** ($\cos\theta$) is the $x$-coordinate of the point at which the terminal side of the angle intersects the unit circle. The **sine of $\theta$** ($\sin\theta$) is the $y$-coordinate.

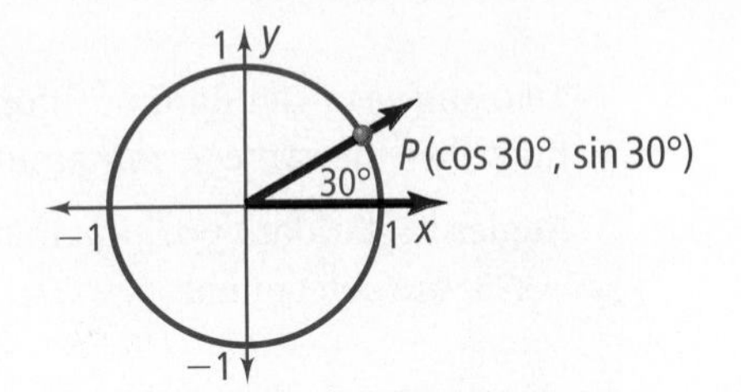


## Problem 4 Finding Cosines and Sines of Angles

**Think**

**How can you use coterminal angles to find these values?**

**Got It?** a. What are $\cos\theta$ and $\sin\theta$ for $\theta = -90°$, $\theta = 360°$, and $\theta = 540°$?

b. In a triangle, sine and cosine are ratios between side lengths. What ratios produce the values in (a)?

**Practice** Find the cosine and sine of each angle.

7. $-270°$

8. $720°$

You can find the exact value of sine and cosine for angles that are multiples of 30° or 45°.

## Problem 5 Finding Exact Values of Cosine and Sine

**Got It?** What are the cosine and sine of the angle?

a. $\theta = -45°$

b. $\theta = 150°$

**Plan**

How can a sketch of the angle on the unit circle be helpful?

**c. Reasoning** For an angle $\theta$, can $\cos \theta$ equal $\sin \theta$? Explain.

**A Practice** Find the exact values of the cosine and sine of each angle. Then find the decimal values. Round your answers to the nearest hundredth.

**9.** $-240^\circ$

**10.** $315^\circ$

## Lesson Check

### Do you know HOW?

Find the measure of each angle in standard position.

**11.**

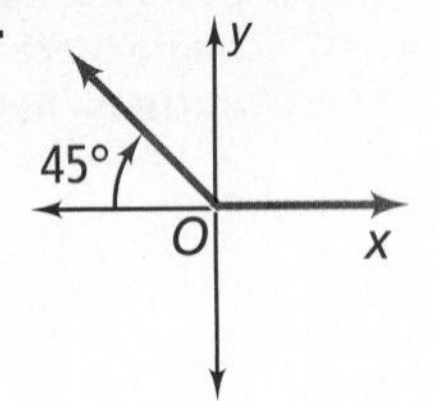


**12.**

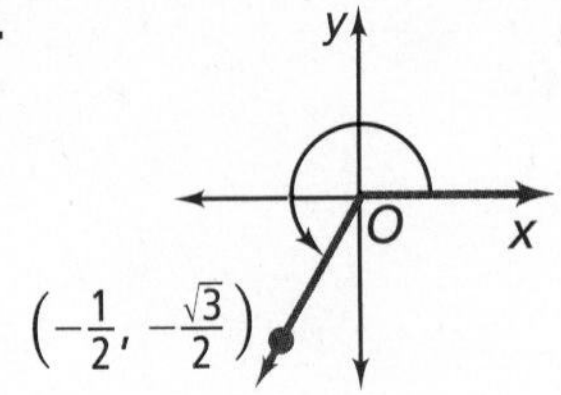


Sketch each angle in standard position. Then find the measure of a coterminal angle.

**13.** $28^\circ$

**14.** $325^\circ$

## Do you UNDERSTAND?

15. **Open-Ended** Find a positive and a negative coterminal angle for an angle that measures 1485°.

16. **Error Analysis** On a test a student wrote that the measure of an angle coterminal to a 50° angle is 310°. Describe and correct the student's error.

## More Practice and Problem-Solving Exercises

### B Apply

**Graphing Calculator** **For each angle $\theta$, find the values of $\cos\theta$ and $\sin\theta$. Round your answers to the nearest hundredth.**

**17.** $-95°$ **18.** $-10°$ **19.** 154° **20.** 90° **21.** 210°

22. **Think About a Plan** On an analog clock, the minute hand has moved 128° from the hour. What number will it pass next?
    - How can a drawing help you understand the problem?
    - How can you find the number of degrees between every two consecutive numbers?

**Open-Ended** **Find a positive and a negative coterminal angle for the given angle.**

**23.** 45° **24.** 10° **25.** $-675°$ **26.** 400° **27.** 213°

**Determine the quadrant or axis where the terminal side of each angle lies.**

**28.** 150°  **29.** 210°  **30.** 540°  **31.** −60°  **32.** 0°

**33. Time** The time is 2:46 P.M. What is the measure of the angle that the minute hand swept through since 2:00 P.M.?

**34. a.** Copy and complete the chart at the right.

**b.** Suppose you know that cos $\theta$ is negative and sin $\theta$ is positive. In which quadrant does the terminal side of the angle lie?

**c. Writing** Summarize how the quadrant in which the terminal side of an angle lies affects the sign of the sine and cosine of that angle.

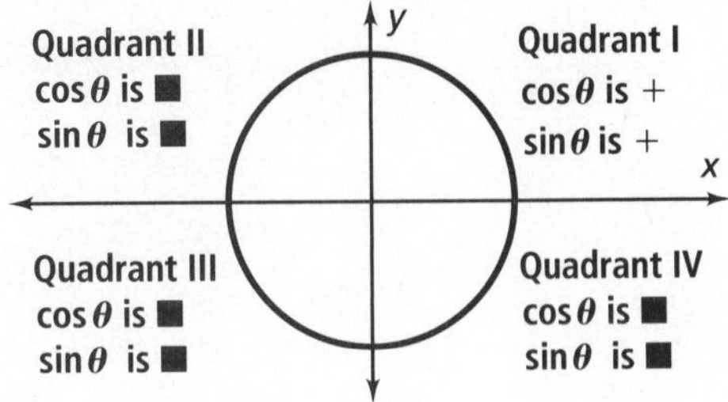


**35. a. Graphing Calculator** Use a calculator to find the value of each expression: cos 40°, cos 400°, and cos (−320°).

**b. Reasoning** What do you notice about the values you found in part (a)? Explain.

## Challenge

**Sketch each angle in standard position. Use the unit circle and a right triangle to find exact values of the cosine and the sine of the angle.**

**36.** −300°  **37.** 120°  **38.** 225°  **39.** −780°  **40.** 1020°

**41. Open-Ended** Find the measures of four angles in standard position that have a sine of 0.5. (*Hint:* Use the unit circle and right triangles.)

**42. Reasoning** Suppose $\theta$ is an angle in standard position and $\cos\theta = -\frac{1}{2}$ and $\sin\theta = -\frac{\sqrt{3}}{2}$. Can the value of $\theta$ be 60°? Can it be −120°? Draw a diagram and justify your reasoning.

# 8-3 Radian Measure

**F.TF.1** Understand radian measure . . . as the length of the arc on the unit circle subtended by the angle. Also prepares for **F.TF.2**

**Objectives** To use radian measure for angles
To find the length of an arc of a circle

**Solve It!** Write your solution to the Solve It in the space below.

A **central angle** of a circle is an angle with a vertex at the center of a circle. An **intercepted arc** is the portion of the circle with endpoints on the sides of the central angle and remaining points within the interior of the angle.

A **radian** is the measure of a central angle that intercepts an arc with length equal to the radius of the circle. Radians, like degrees, measure the amount of rotation from the initial side to the terminal side of an angle. An equivalent definition of the radian measure of a central angle is the length of the arc the angle intercepts on the unit circle.

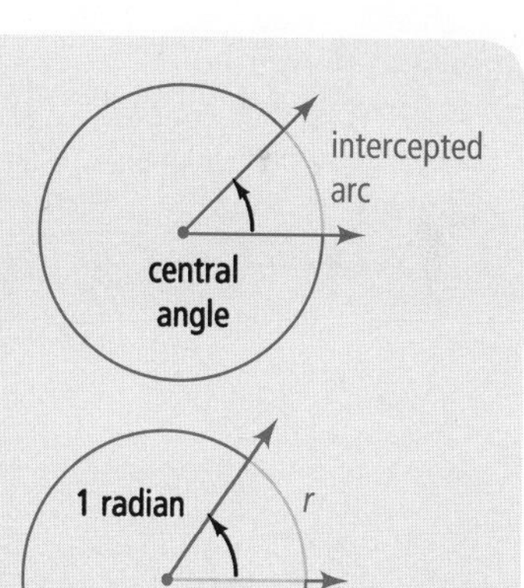


**Essential Understanding** An angle with a full circle rotation measures $2\pi$ radians. An angle with a semicircle rotation measures $\pi$ radians.

take note

## Key Concepts Proportion Relating Radians and Degrees

You can use the proportion $\frac{d^\circ}{180^\circ} = \frac{r \text{ radians}}{\pi \text{ radians}}$ to convert between radians and degrees.

**Here's Why It Works** Because the circumference of a circle is $2\pi r$, there are $2\pi$ radians in any circle. Since $2\pi$ radians $= 360°$, it follows that $\pi$ radians $= 180°$. This equality leads to the following *conversion factors* for converting between radian measure and degree measure.

take note

### Key Concepts Converting Between Radians and Degrees

To convert degrees to radians, multiply by $\frac{\pi \text{ radians}}{180°}$.

To convert radians to degrees, multiply by $\frac{180°}{\pi \text{ radians}}$.

You can use the conversion factors and dimensional analysis to convert between angle measurement systems.

ONLINE PROBLEMS

## Problem 1 Using Dimensional Analysis

**Think**

**How do you know which conversion factor to use?**

**Got It?** What is the degree measure of each angle expressed in radians? What is the radian measure of each angle expressed in degrees? (Express radian measures in terms of $\pi$.)

**a.** $\frac{\pi}{2}$ radians

**b.** $225°$

**c.** 2 radians

**d.** $150°$

**Practice** 1. Write $-60^\circ$ in radians. Express your answer in terms of $\pi$.

2. Write $\frac{11\pi}{10}$ radians in degrees. Round your answer to the nearest degree.

## Problem 2 Finding Cosine and Sine of a Radian Measure

**Got It?** What are the exact values of $\cos\left(\frac{7\pi}{6}\text{ radians}\right)$ and $\sin\left(\frac{7\pi}{6}\text{ radians}\right)$?

**Think**

**How can a sketch of the angle on the unit circle be helpful?**

**Practice** **The measure $\theta$ of an angle in standard position is given. Find the exact values of $\cos\theta$ and $\sin\theta$ for each angle measure.**

3. $-\frac{\pi}{4}$ radians

4. $\frac{2\pi}{3}$ radians

If you know the radius and the measure in radians of a central angle, you can find the length of the intercepted arc.

take note

## Key Concept Length of an Intercepted Arc

For a circle of radius $r$ and a central angle of measure $\theta$ (in radians), the length $s$ of the intercepted arc is $s = r\theta$.

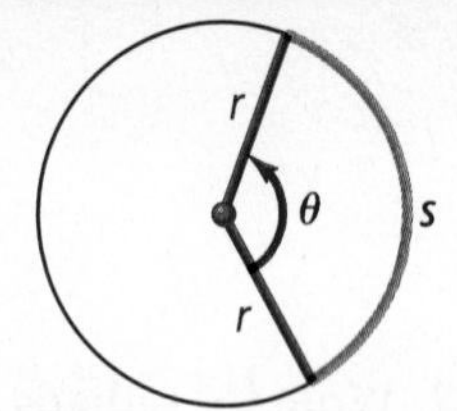


**Here's Why It Works** The length of the intercepted arc is the same fraction of the circumference of the circle as the central angle is of $2\pi$. So $\frac{\theta}{2\pi} = \frac{s}{C}$. Since $C = 2\pi r$, then $\frac{\theta}{2\pi} = \frac{s}{2\pi r}$. This simplifies to $\theta = \frac{s}{r}$. Multiplying by $r$ results in $s = r\theta$.

ONLINE PROBLEMS

## Problem 3 Finding the Length of an Arc

**Got It?** **a.** What is length $b$ in the circle at the right to the nearest tenth?

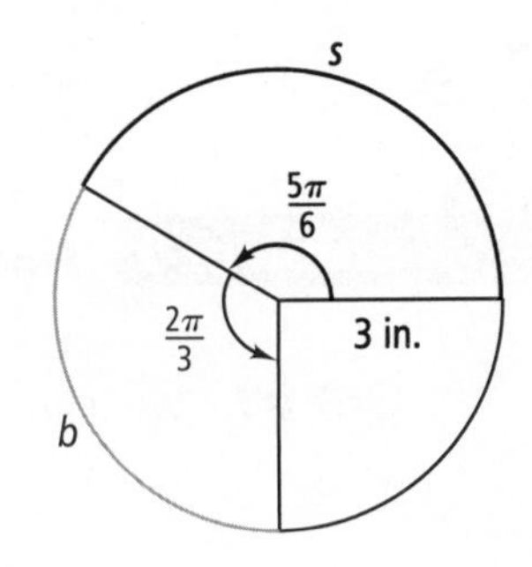


**b. Reasoning** If the radius of the circle doubled, how would the arc length change?

5. Use the circle to find the length of the indicated arc. Round your answer to the nearest tenth.

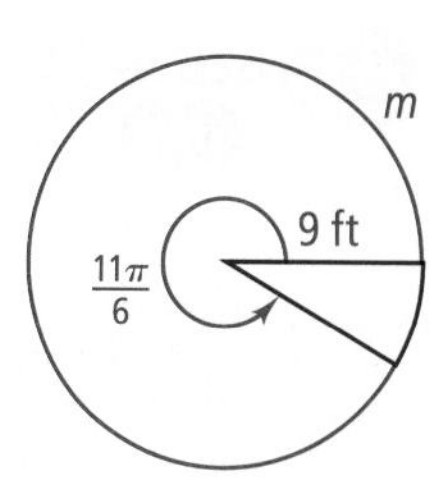


6. Find the length of the arc. Round your answer to the nearest foot.

## Problem 4 Using Radian Measure to Solve a Problem

**Got It?** STEM Suppose a satellite orbits 3600 km above Earth's surface and completed an orbit every 4 h. How far would the satellite have travelled in 1 h?

7. **Space** A geostationary satellite is positioned 35,800 km above Earth's surface. It takes 24 h to complete one orbit. The radius of Earth is about 6400 km.

a. What distance does the satellite travel in 1 h? 3 h? 2.5 h? 25 h?

b. **Reasoning** After how many hours has the satellite traveled 200,000 km?

## Lesson Check

### Do you know HOW?

8. Find the radian measure of an angle of 300°.

9. Find the degree measure of an angle of $\frac{3\pi}{4}$ radians.

**10.** Find the length $a$.

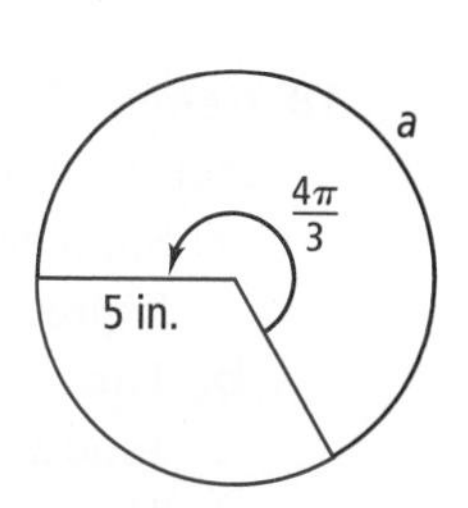


## Do you UNDERSTAND?

**11. Vocabulary** The radius of a circle is 9 cm. A central angle intercepts an arc that is 9 cm. What is the measure of the central angle in radians?

**12. Reasoning** A certain baker believes that a perfect slice of pie has a central angle of 1 radian. How many "perfect" slices can he get out of one pie?

## More Practice and Problem-Solving Exercises

### B Apply

**13. Think About a Plan** Suppose a windshield wiper arm has a length of 22 in. and rotates through an angle of 110°. What distance does the tip of the wiper travel as it moves once across the windshield?

- Which formula can help you answer this question?
- Do you need to convert between degrees and radians?

**Determine the quadrant or axis where the terminal side of each angle lies.**

**14.** $\frac{4\pi}{3}$ radians **15.** $-\frac{5\pi}{4}$ radians **16.** $-\pi$ radians **17.** $\frac{6\pi}{5}$ radians

**18. Geography** The 24 lines of longitude that approximate the 24 standard time zones are equally spaced around the equator.

a. Suppose you use 24 central angles to divide a circle into 24 equal arcs. Express the measure of each angle in degrees and in radians.

b. The radius of the equator is about 3960 mi. About how wide is each time zone at the equator?

c. The radius of the Arctic Circle is about 1580 mi. About how wide is each time zone at the Arctic Circle?

**Draw an angle in standard position with each given measure. Then find the values of the cosine and sine of the angle.**

**19.** $\frac{7\pi}{4}$ radians **20.** $-\frac{2\pi}{3}$ radians **21.** $\frac{5\pi}{2}$ radians **22.** $\frac{7\pi}{6}$ radians

**23. Writing** Two angles are measured in radians. Explain how to tell whether the angles are coterminal without rewriting their measures in degrees.

**24. Open-Ended** Draw an angle in standard position. Draw a circle with its center at the vertex of the angle. Find the measure of the angle in radians and degrees.

**25. Transportation** Suppose the radius of a bicycle wheel is 13 in. (measured to the outside of the tire). Find the number of radians through which a point on the tire turns when the bicycle has moved forward a distance of 12 ft.

**26. Error Analysis** A student wanted to rewrite $\frac{9\pi}{4}$ radians in degrees. The screen shows her calculation. What error did the student make?

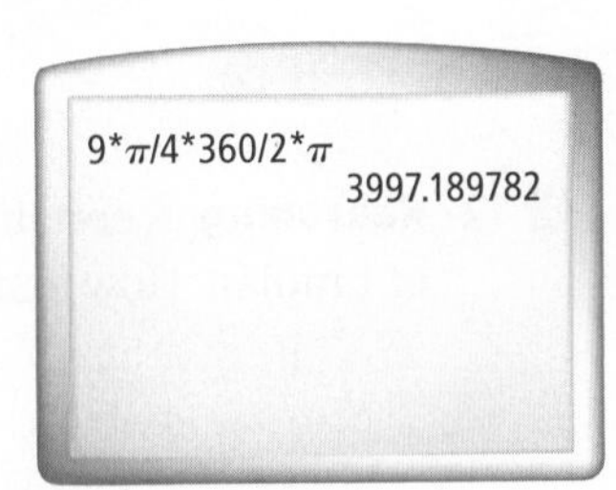


**27. Music** A CD with diameter 12 cm spins in a CD player. Calculate how much farther a point on the outside edge of the CD travels in one revolution than a point 1 cm closer to the center of the CD.

**28. Geography** Assume that Earth is a sphere with radius 3960 miles. A town is at latitude 32° N. Find the distance in miles from the town to the North Pole. (*Hint*: Latitude is measured north and south from the equator.)

## Challenge

**The given angle $\theta$ is in standard position. Find the radian measure of the angle that results after the given number of revolutions from the terminal side of $\theta$.**

**29.** $\theta = \frac{\pi}{2}$; 1 clockwise revolution **30.** $\theta = -\frac{2\pi}{3}$; 1 counterclockwise revolution

**31. Reasoning** Use the proportion $\frac{\text{measure of central angle}}{\text{length of intercepted arc}} = \frac{\text{measure of one completed rotation}}{\text{circumference}}$ to derive the formula $s = r\theta$. Use $\theta$ for the central angle measure and $s$ for the arc length. Measure the rotation in radians.

# 8-4 The Sine Function

**F.TF.2** Explain how the unit circle . . . enables the extension of trigonometric functions to all real numbers . . .
Also **F.IF.7, F.IF.7.e, F.TF.5**

**Objectives** To identify properties of the sine function
To graph sine curves

**Solve It!** Write your solution to the Solve It in the space below.

The **sine function**, $y = \sin \theta$, matches the measure $\theta$ of an angle in standard position with the $y$-coordinate of a point on the unit circle. This point is where the terminal side of the angle intersects the unit circle.

You can graph the sine function in radians or degrees. In this book, you should use radians unless degrees are specified. For each and every point along the unit circle, the radian measure of the arc has a corresponding sine value. In the graphs below, the points for 1, 2, and 3 radians are marked on the unit circle. The vertical bars represent the sine values of the points on the circle translated onto the sine graph.

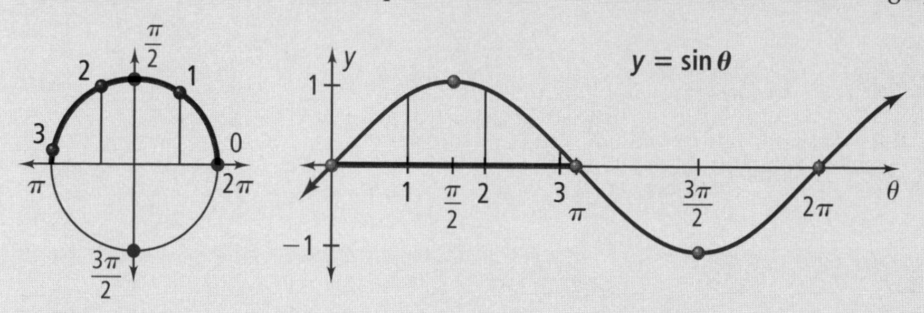


**Essential Understanding** As the terminal side of an angle rotates about the origin (beginning at 0), its sine value on the unit circle increases from 0 to 1, decreases from 1 to −1, and then increases back to 0.

## Problem 1 Estimating Sine Values Graphically

**Got It?** What is a reasonable estimate for each value from the graph? Check your estimate with a calculator.

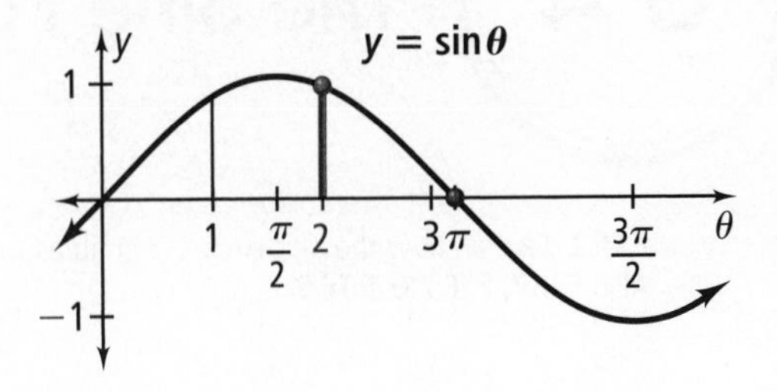


**a.** sin 3

**b.** $\sin \frac{3\pi}{2}$

**A Practice** **Use the graph at the right to find the value of $y = \sin \theta$ for each value of $\theta$.**

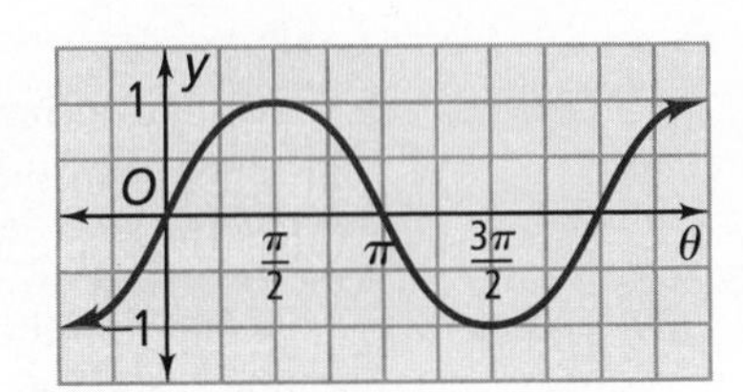


**1.** 5 radians

**2.** $\frac{7\pi}{4}$ radians

The graph of a sine function is called a **sine curve**. By varying the period (horizontal length of one cycle), you get different sine curves.

## Problem 2 Finding the Period of a Sine Curve

**Got It?** How many cycles occur in the graph? What is the period of the sine curve?

**a.** 

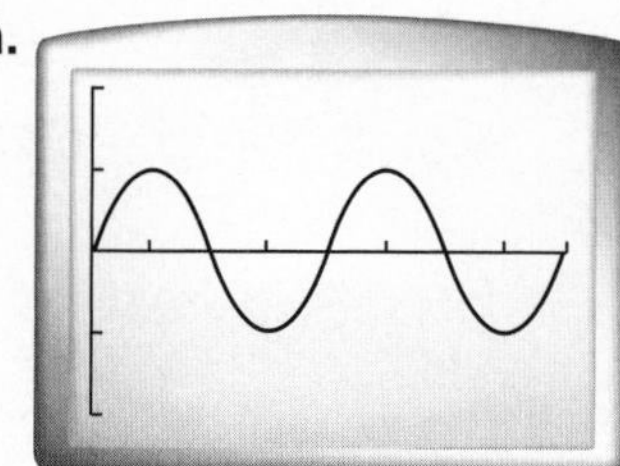

Xmin = 0
Xmax = $4\pi$
Xscl = $\pi/2$
Ymin = −2
Ymax = 2
Yscl = 1

**b.**

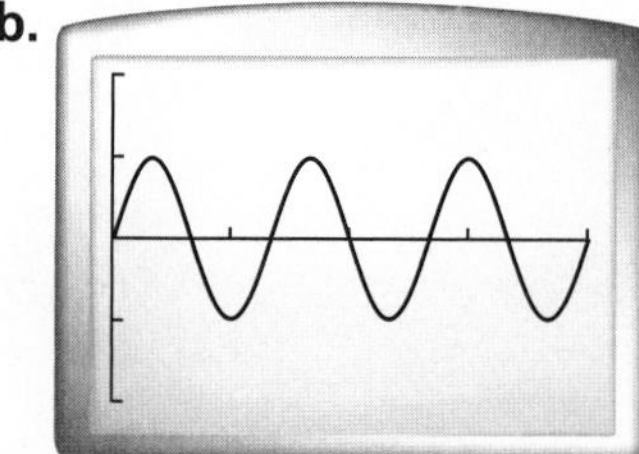

Xmin = 0
Xmax = $4\pi$
Xscl = $\pi/2$
Ymin = −2
Ymax = 2
Yscl = 1

**Practice** **Determine the number of cycles each sine function has in the interval from 0 to $2\pi$. Find the period of each function.**

**3.**

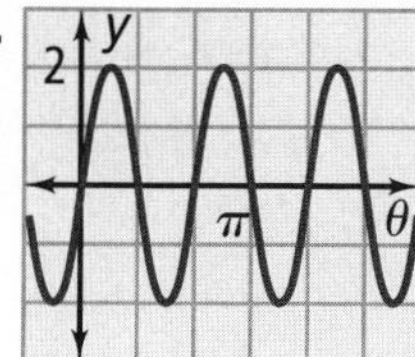


**4.**

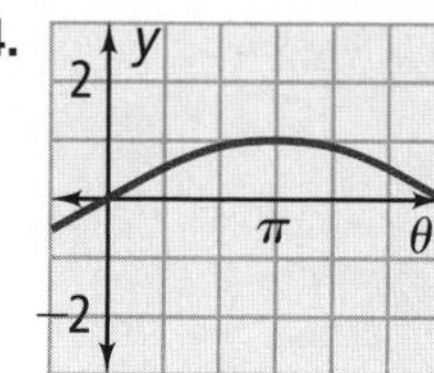

You can also vary the amplitude of a sine curve.

## Problem 3 Finding the Amplitude of a Sine Curve

**Think**

**Is the value of *a* always equal to the amplitude of the sine curve?**

**Got It?** The equation of the graph is of the form $y = a \sin x$. What is the amplitude of the sine curve? What is the value of $a$?

**a.**

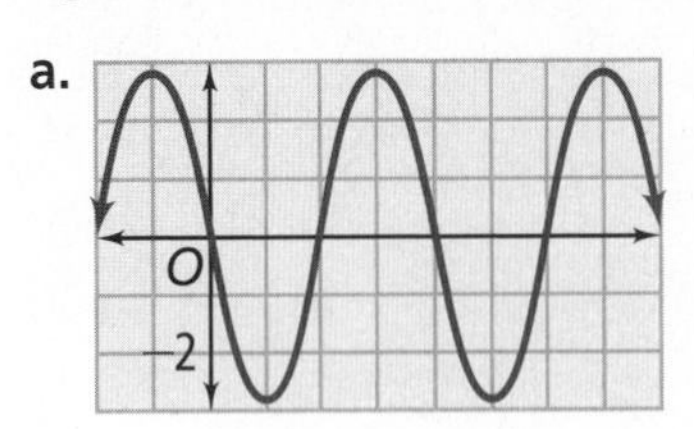


**b.**

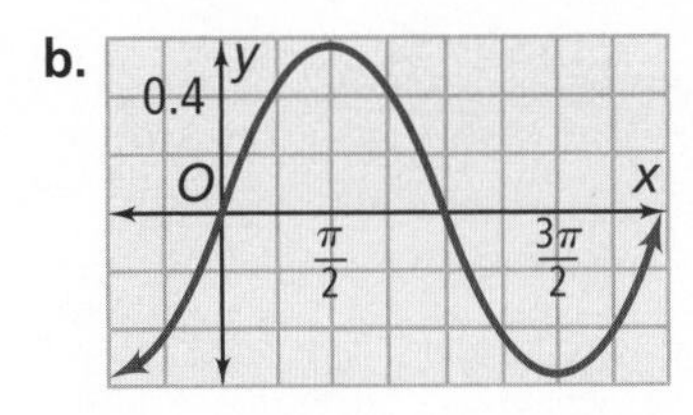


**A Practice** **5.** Determine the number of cycles the sine function has in the interval from 0 to $2\pi$. Find the amplitude and period of the function.

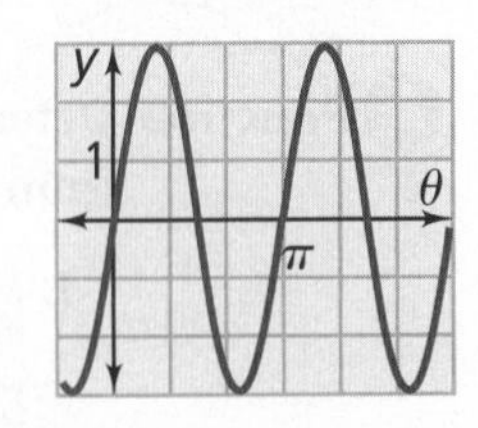

The summary box below lists the properties of sine functions.

take note

## Concept Summary Properties of Sine Functions

Suppose $y = a \sin b\theta$, with $a \neq 0$, $b > 0$, and $\theta$ in radians.

- $|a|$ is the amplitude of the function.
- $b$ is the number of cycles in the interval from 0 to $2\pi$.
- $\frac{2\pi}{b}$ is the period of the function.

You can use five points equally spaced through one cycle to sketch a sine curve. For $a > 0$, this five-point pattern is *zero-max-zero-min-zero*.

## Problem 4 Sketching a Graph

**Got It?** What is the graph of one cycle of a sine curve with amplitude 3, period $4\pi$, and $a > 0$? Use the form $y = a \sin b\theta$. What is an equation with $a > 0$ for the sine curve?

**How is the period of the function related to the value of *b* in the equation?**

**A Practice** **Sketch one cycle of each sine curve. Assume $a > 0$. Write an equation for each graph.**

**6.** amplitude $\frac{1}{3}$, period $\pi$

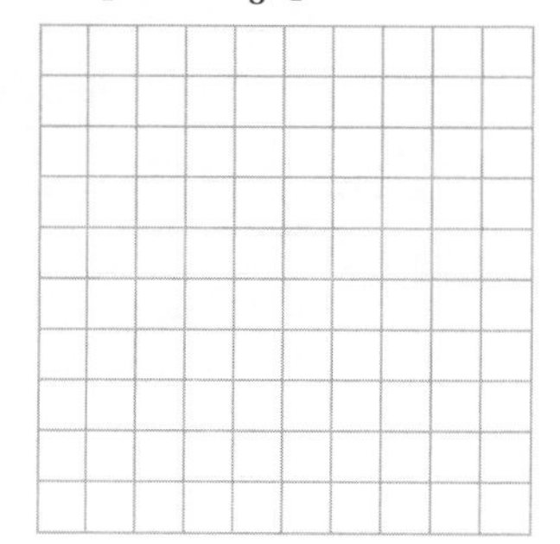

**7.** amplitude 3, period $2\pi$

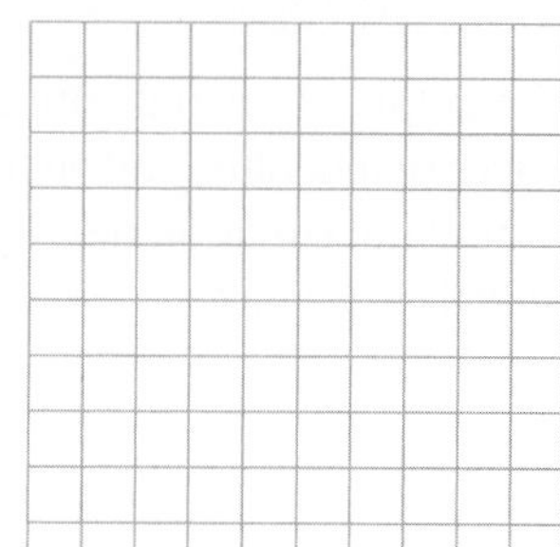

## Problem 5 Graphing From a Function Rule

**Got It?** What is the graph of one cycle of each sine function?

**a.** $y = 1.5 \sin 2\theta$

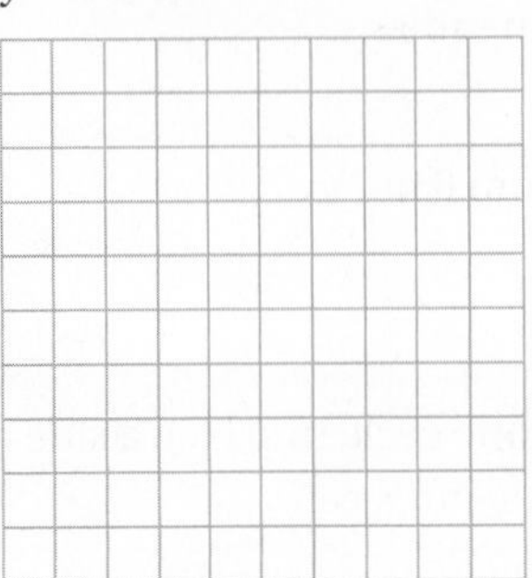

**b.** $y = 3 \sin \frac{\pi}{2}\theta$

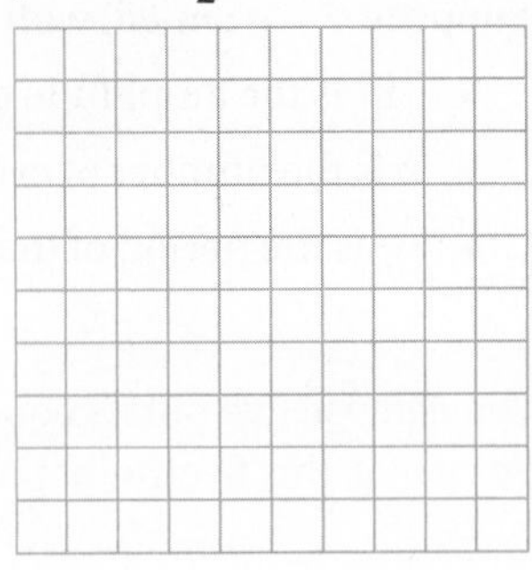

**A Practice** Sketch one cycle of the graph of each sine function.

**8.** $y = -\sin \frac{\pi}{2}\theta$

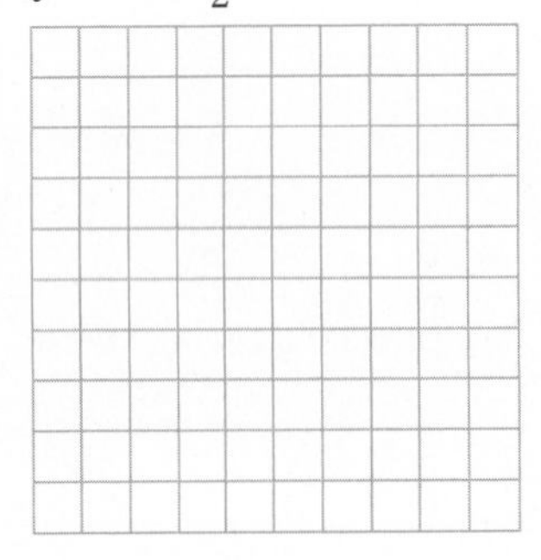

**9.** $y = 4 \sin \frac{1}{2}\theta$

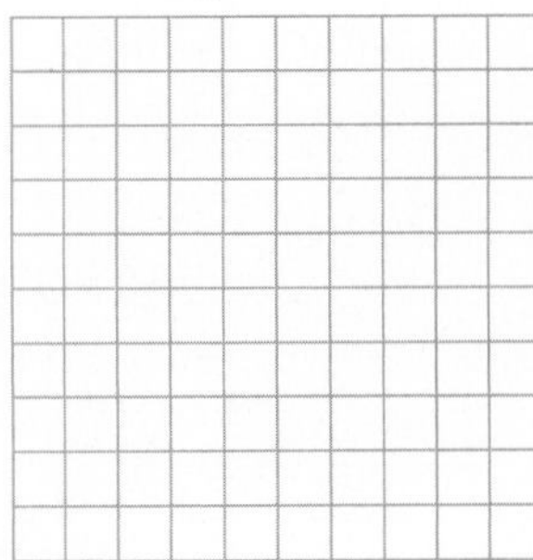

## Problem 6 Using the Sine Function to Model Light Waves

**Got It?** The graphs at the right model waves of red, blue, and yellow light. What equation best models red light?

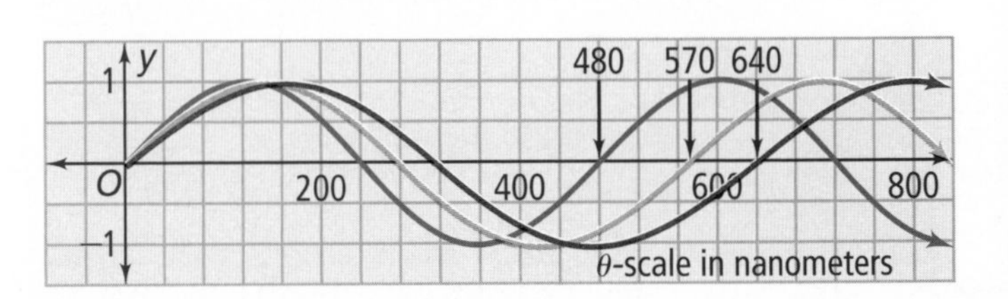

**Practice** **Find the period of each sine curve. Then write an equation for each sine function.**

**10.**

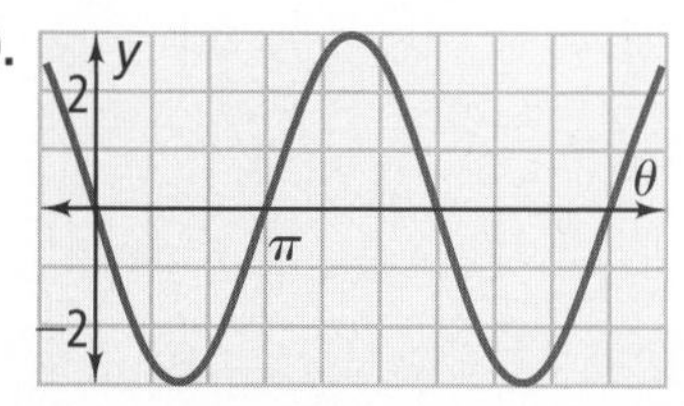


**11.**

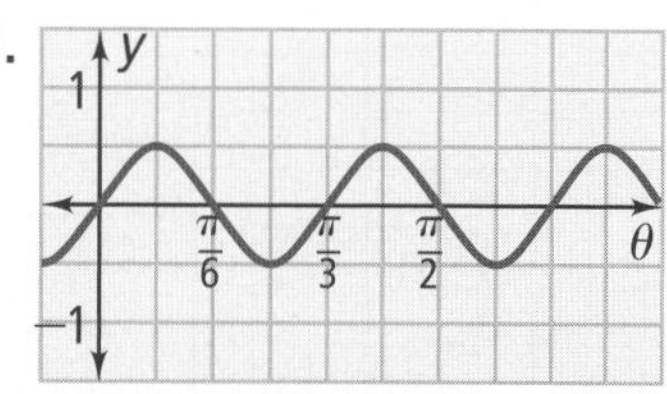


## Lesson Check

### Do you know HOW?

**12. a.** How many cycles does this graph of a sine function have in the interval from 0 to $2\pi$?

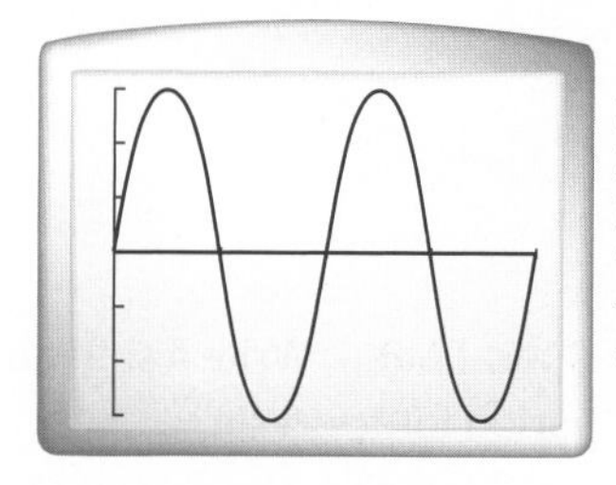


**b.** What are the amplitude and period?

**c.** Write an equation for the function.

**13.** Sketch one cycle of the sine curve that has amplitude 2 and period $\frac{\pi}{3}$.

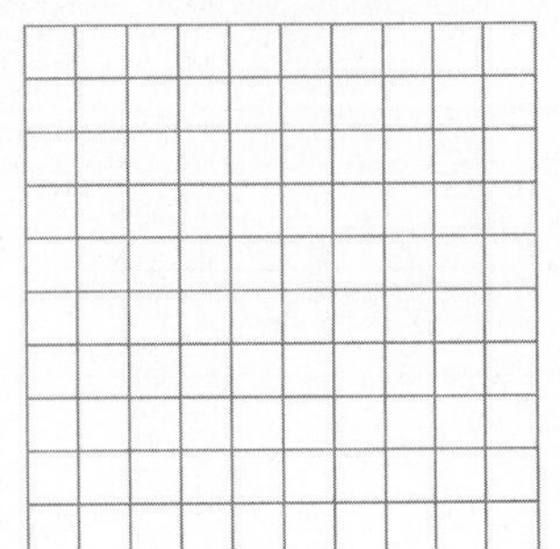

## Do you UNDERSTAND?

**14. Vocabulary** What is the difference between one cycle and the period of a sine curve?

**15. Open-Ended** Write a sine function that has a period greater than the period for $y = 5 \sin \frac{\theta}{2}$.

**16. Error Analysis** A student drew this graph for the function $y = -3 \sin \pi\theta$. Describe and correct the student's errors.

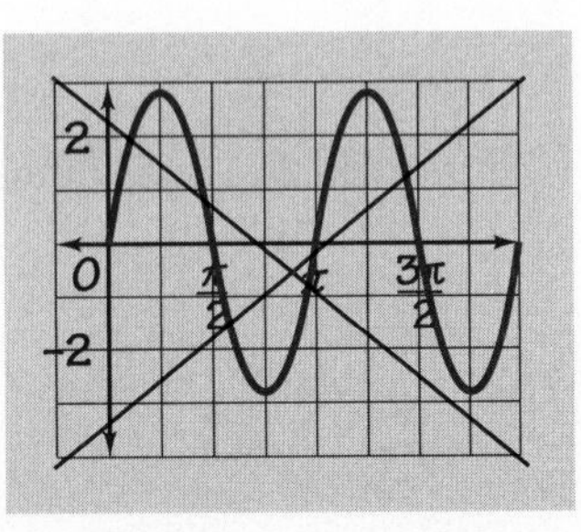

## More Practice and Problem-Solving Exercises

### B Apply

**Determine the number of cycles each sine function has in the interval from 0 to $2\pi$. Find the amplitude and period of each function.**

**17.** $y = \sin\theta$ **18.** $y = \sin 5\theta$ **19.** $y = \sin \pi\theta$

**20.** $y = 3\sin\theta$ **21.** $y = -5\sin\theta$ **22.** $y = -5\sin 2\pi\theta$

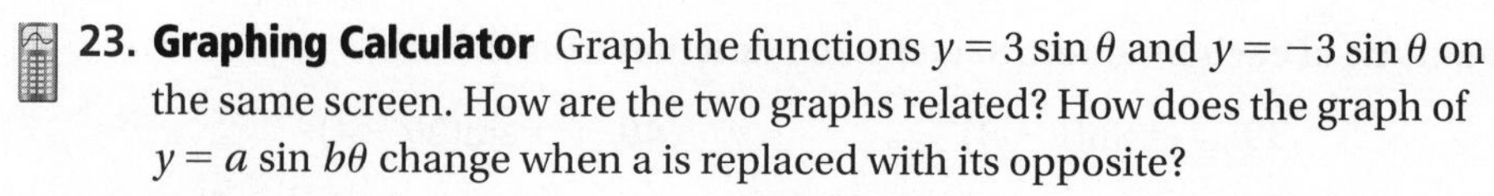

**23. Graphing Calculator** Graph the functions $y = 3\sin\theta$ and $y = -3\sin\theta$ on the same screen. How are the two graphs related? How does the graph of $y = a\sin b\theta$ change when a is replaced with its opposite?

**24.** Use the formula Period $= \frac{2\pi}{b}$ to find the period of each sine function.

**a.** $y = 1.5\sin 2\theta$ **b.** $y = 3\sin\frac{\pi}{2}\theta$

**25. Think About a Plan** The sound wave for the note A above middle C can be modeled by the function $y = 0.001\sin 880\pi\theta$. Sketch a graph of the sine curve.

- What is the period of the function?
- What is the amplitude of the function?
- How many cycles of the graph are between 0 and $2\pi$?

**Find the period and amplitude of each sine function. Then sketch each function from 0 to $2\pi$.**

**26.** $y = -3.5\sin 5\theta$ **27.** $y = \frac{5}{2}\sin 2\theta$ **28.** $y = -2\sin 2\pi\theta$

**29.** $y = 0.4\sin 3\theta$ **30.** $y = 0.5\sin\frac{\pi}{3}\theta$ **31.** $y = -1.2\sin\frac{5\pi}{6}\theta$

**32. Open-Ended** Write the equations of three sine functions with the same amplitude that have periods of 2, 3, and 4. Then sketch all three graphs.

**33. Music** The sound wave for a certain tuning fork can be modeled by the function $y = 0.001\sin 1320\pi\theta$. Sketch a graph of the sine curve.

**34. a.** What is the average rate of change of $f(x) = \sin x$ from $x = 0$ to $x = \pi$?

**b.** Find two other intervals over which the average rate of change of the sine function is 0.

**c. Reasoning** Explain why for any periodic function, you can find an infinite number of intervals over which the average rate of change is 0.

## Challenge

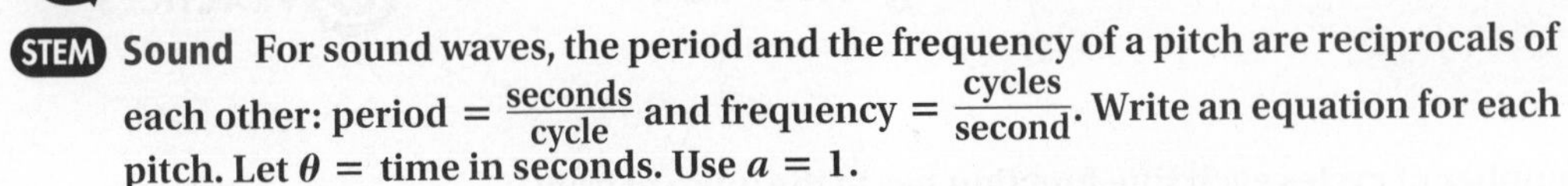

STEM **Sound** **For sound waves, the period and the frequency of a pitch are reciprocals of each other: period $= \frac{\text{seconds}}{\text{cycle}}$ and frequency $= \frac{\text{cycles}}{\text{second}}$. Write an equation for each pitch. Let $\theta =$ time in seconds. Use $a = 1$.**

**35.** the lowest pitch easily heard by humans: 30 cycles per second

**36.** the lowest pitch heard by elephants: 15 cycles per second

**37.** the highest pitch heard by bats: 120,000 cycles per second

**Find the period and amplitude of each function. Sketch each function from 0 to $2\pi$.**

**38.** $y = \sin(\theta + 2)$

**39.** $y = \sin(\theta - 3)$

**40.** $y = \sin(2\theta + 4)$

 **41. Astronomy** In Houston, Texas, at the spring equinox (March 21), there are 12 hours and 9 minutes of sunlight. The longest and shortest day of the year vary from the equinox by 1 h 55 min. The amount of sunlight during the year can be modeled by a sine function.

**a.** Define the independent and dependent variables for a function that models the variation in hours of sunlight in Houston.

**b.** What are the amplitude and period of the function measured in days?

**c.** Write a function that relates the number of days away from the spring equinox to the variation in hours of sunlight in Houston.

**d. Estimation** Use your function from part (c). In Houston, about how much less sunlight does February 14 have than March 21?

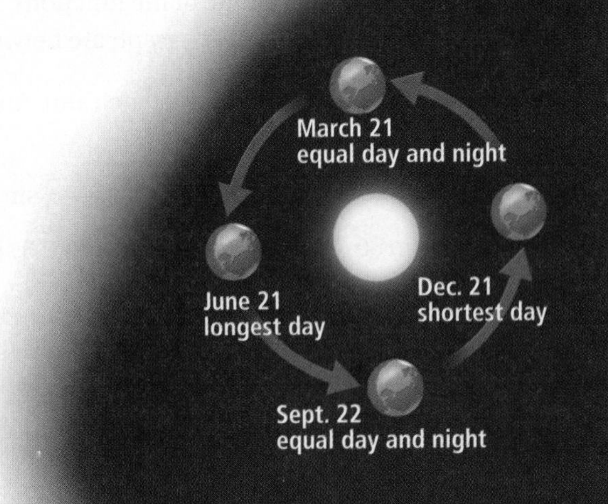

TECHNOLOGY LAB

Use With Lesson 8-4

# Graphing Trigonometric Functions

**F.IF.7** Graph functions expressed symbolically and show key features of the graph, . . .

## Activity 1

Compare the graphs of $y = \cos x$ from $-360°$ to $360°$ and from $-2\pi$ to $2\pi$ radians.

**Step 1** Press mode to set the mode to degrees. Adjust the window values. Graph the function.

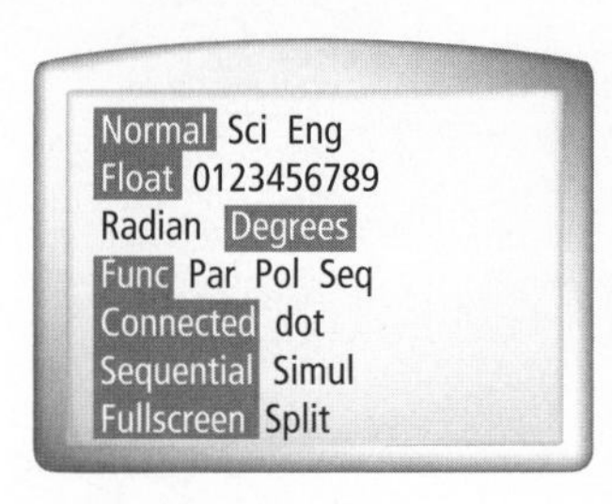


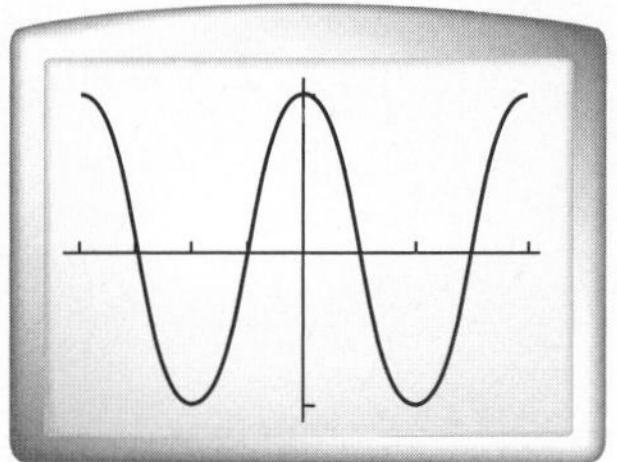

Xmin = −360
Xmax = 360
Xscl = 90
Ymin = −1.2
Ymax = 1.2
Yscl = 1

**Step 2** Change the mode to radians. Graph the function.

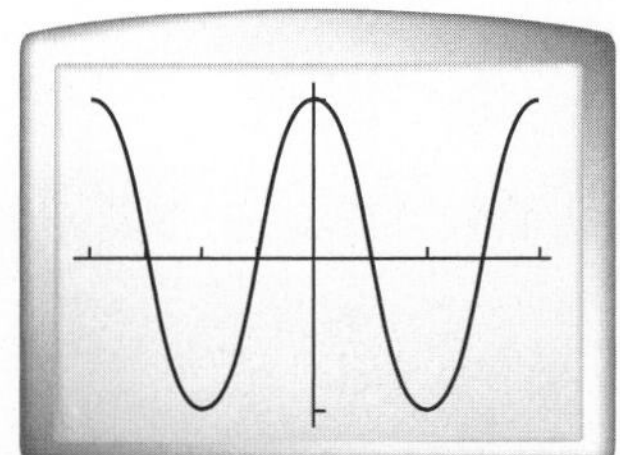

Xmin = $-2\pi$
Xmax = $2\pi$
Xscl = $\pi/2$
Ymin = −1.2
Ymax = 1.2
Yscl = 1

The graphs appear to be identical. The function has a period of 360°, or $2\pi$ radians.

## Activity 2

Graph the function $y = \sin x$. Find sin 30° and sin 150°.

**Step 1** Set the mode to degrees and adjust the window values as shown.

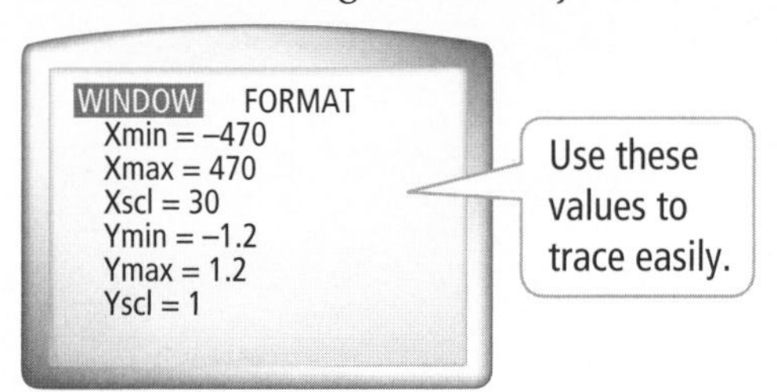

**Step 2** Graph the function. Use the trace key to find the *y*-values when $x = 30$ and $x = 150$.

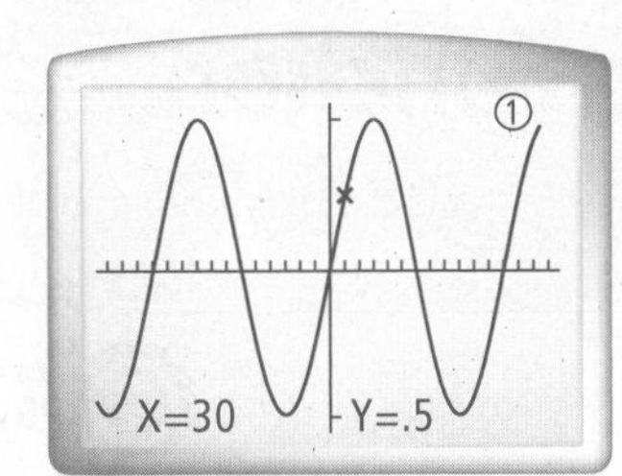

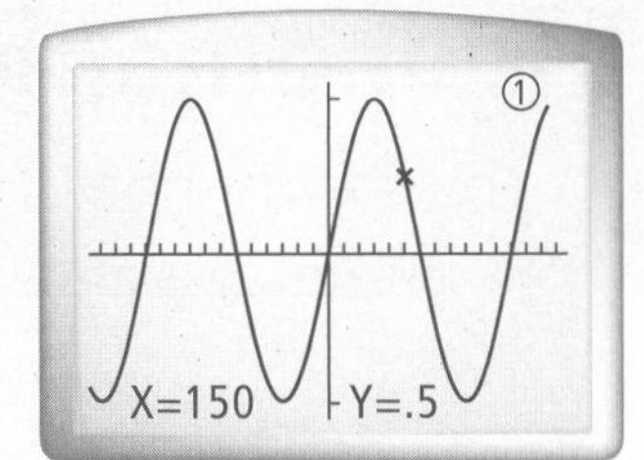


## Exercises

**Use appropriate window values to identify the period of each function in radians and in degrees. Then evaluate each function at 90°.**

**1.** $y = \cos x$

**2.** $y = \sin x$

**3.** $y = \sin 3x$

**4.** $y = -3 \sin x$

**5.** $y = \cos(x + 30)$

**Writing** Graph the two functions in the same window. Compare the graphs. How are they similar? How are they different?

**6.** $y = \sin x, y = \cos x$

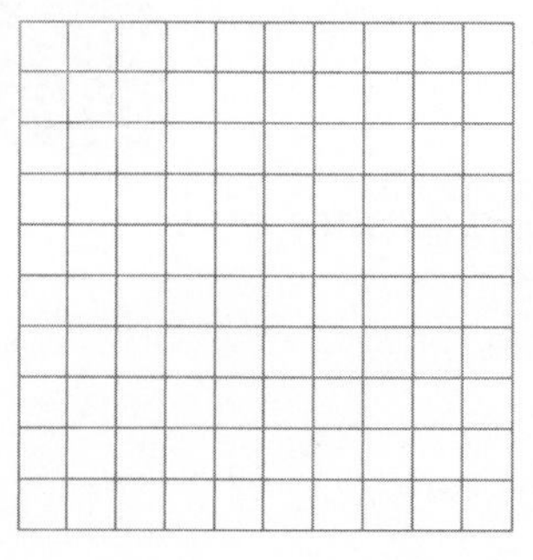

**7.** $y = \sin x, y = \cos\left(x - \frac{\pi}{2}\right)$

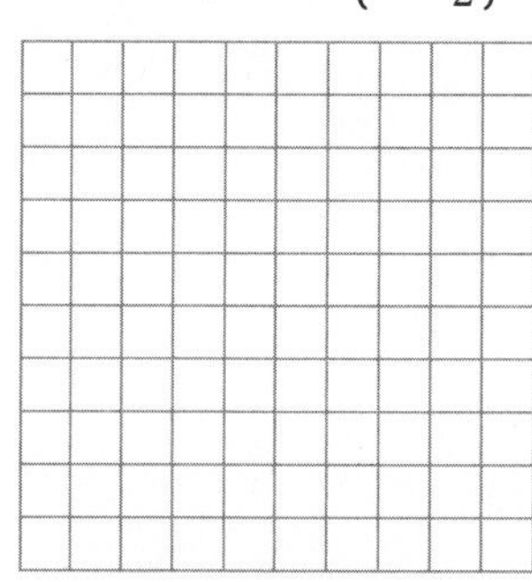

**8.** $y = \sin x, y = \cos\left(x + \frac{\pi}{2}\right)$

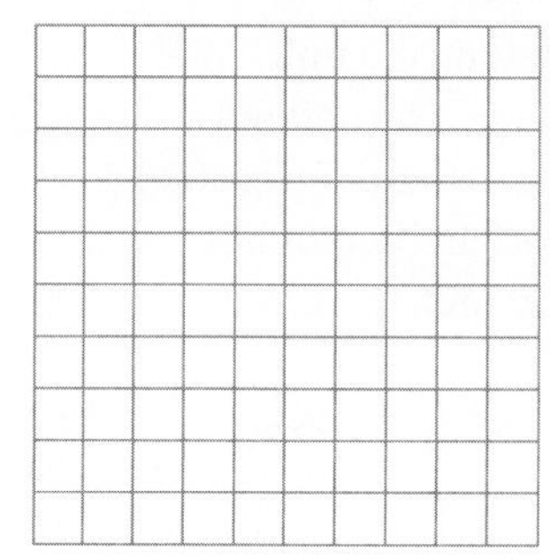

# 8-5 The Cosine Function

**F.IF.7.e** Graph . . . trigonometric functions, showing period, midline, and amplitude. Also **F.IF.7, F.TF.2, F.TF.5**

**Objectives** To graph and write cosine functions
To solve trigonometric equations

**Solve It!** Write your solution to the Solve It in the space below.

The **cosine function**, $y = \cos\theta$, matches $\theta$ with the $x$-coordinate of the point on the unit circle where the terminal side of angle $\theta$ intersects the unit circle. The symmetry of the set of points $(x, y) = (\cos\theta, \sin\theta)$ on the unit circle guarantees that the graphs of sine and cosine are congruent translations of each other.

**Essential Understanding** For each and every point along the unit circle the radian measure of the arc has a corresponding cosine value. The colored bars represent the cosine values of the points on the circle translated onto the cosine graph. So as the terminal side of an angle rotates about the origin (beginning at 0°), its cosine value on the unit circle decreases from 1 to −1, and then increases back to 1.

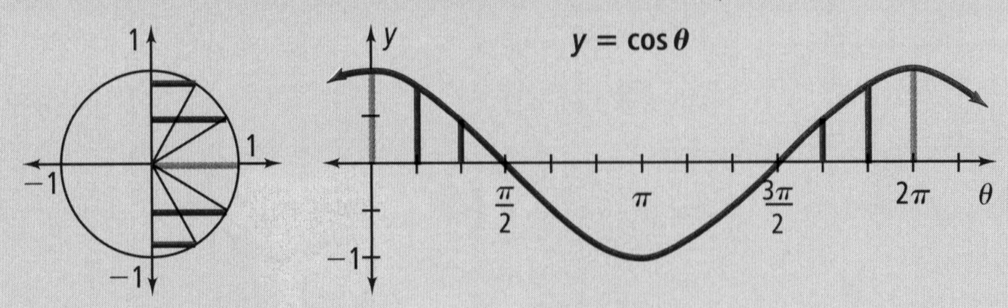

## Problem 1 Interpreting a Graph

**Got It?** Use the graph. What are the domain, period, range, and amplitude of the sine function? Where do the maximum and minimum values occur? Where do the zeros occur?

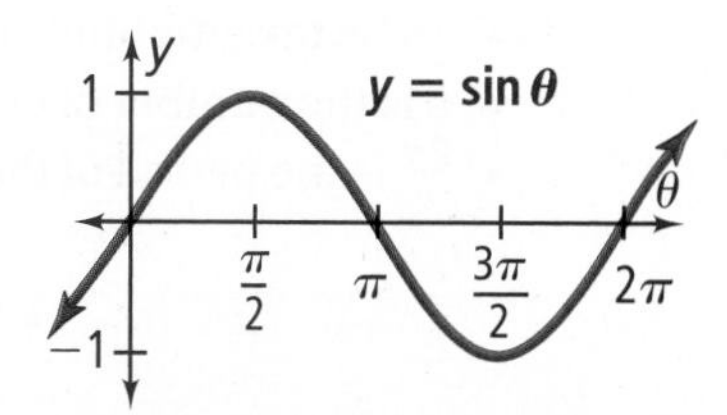


**Practice** **Find the period and amplitude of each cosine function. Determine the values of $x$ for $0 \leq x \leq 2\pi$ where the maximum value(s), minimum value(s), and zeros occur.**

**1.**

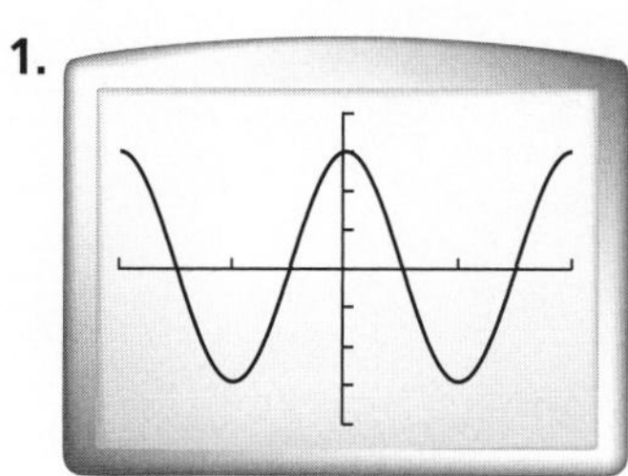

Xmin = $-2\pi$
Xmax = $2\pi$
Xscl = $\pi$
Ymin = $-4$
Ymax = 4
Yscl = 1

**2.**

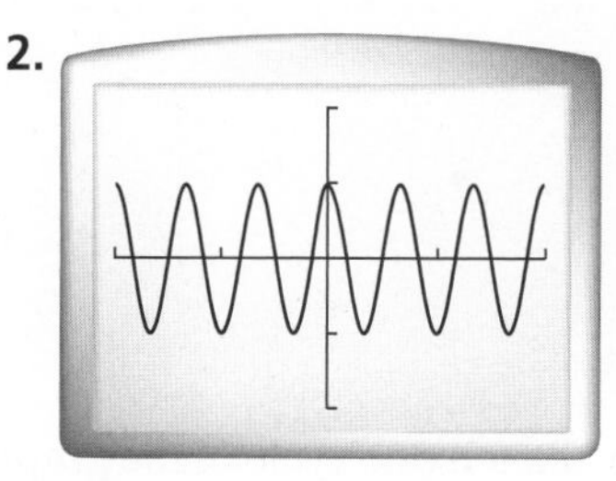

Xmin = $-2\pi$
Xmax = $2\pi$
Xscl = $\pi$
Ymin = $-2$
Ymax = 2
Yscl = 1

take note

## Concept Summary Properties of Cosine Functions

Suppose $y = a \cos b\theta$, with $a \neq 0$, $b > 0$, and $\theta$ in radians.

- $|a|$ is the amplitude of the function.
- $b$ is the number of cycles in the interval from 0 to $2\pi$.
- $\frac{2\pi}{b}$ is the period of the function.

To graph a cosine function, locate five points equally spaced through one cycle. For $a > 0$, this five-point pattern is *max-zero-min-zero-max*.

## Problem 2 Sketching the Graph of a Cosine Function

**Plan**

**What should you find to graph the function?**

**Got It?** Sketch one cycle of $y = 2 \cos \frac{\theta}{3}$.

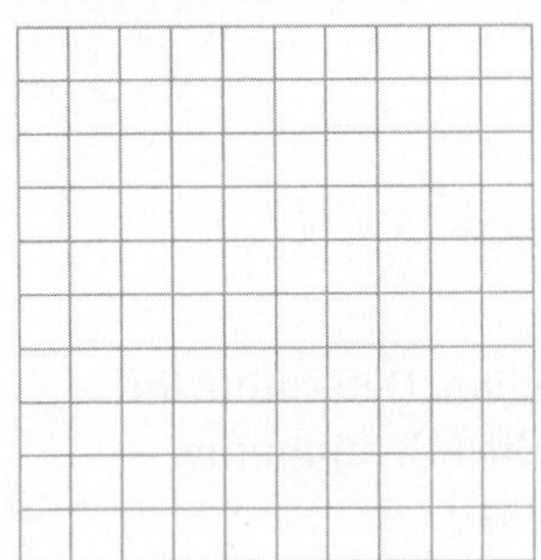

**Practice** Sketch one cycle of the graph of each cosine function.

**3.** $y = \cos 2\theta$

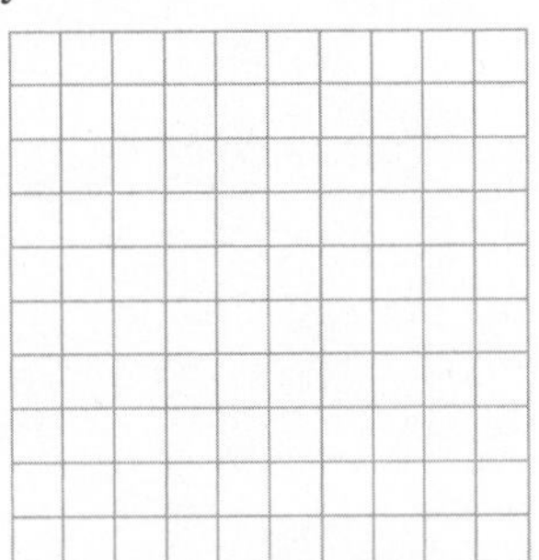

**4.** $y = -\cos \pi\theta$

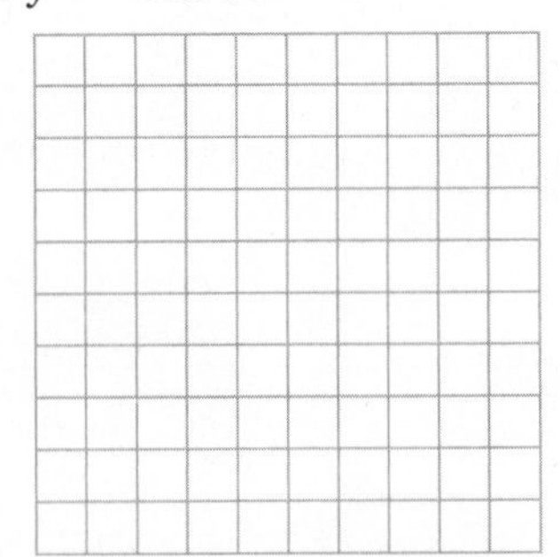

## Problem 3 Modeling with a Cosine Function

**Got It?** STEM

**a.** Suppose that the water level varies 70 inches between low tide at 8:40 A.M. and high tide at 2:55 P.M. What is a cosine function that models the variation in inches above and below the average water level as a function of the number of hours since 8:40 A.M.?

**b.** At what point in the cycle does the function cross the midline? What does the midline represent?

**5.** Write a cosine function with amplitude $\pi$ and period 2. Assume that $a > 0$.

6. Write an equation of a cosine function for the graph shown.

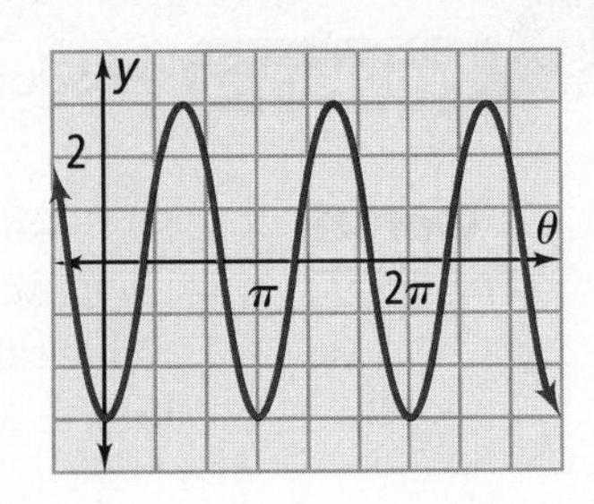


You can solve an equation by graphing to find an exact location along a sine or cosine curve.

## Problem 4 Solving a Cosine Equation

**Got It?** What are all solutions to each equation in the interval from 0 to $2\pi$?

**a.** $3 \cos 2t = -2$

**b.** $-2 \cos \theta = 1.2$

**Plan**

**How can two equations help you find the solutions?**

**c. Reasoning** In the interval from 0 to $2\pi$, when is $-2 \cos \theta$ less than 1.2? Greater than 1.2?

**Practice** Solve each equation in the interval from 0 to $2\pi$. Round your answer to the nearest hundredth.

**7.** $-2\cos \pi\theta = 0.3$

**8.** $8\cos \frac{\pi}{3}t = 5$

## Lesson Check

### Do you know HOW?

**Sketch the graph of each function in the interval from 0 to $2\pi$.**

**9.** $y = \cos \frac{1}{2}\theta$

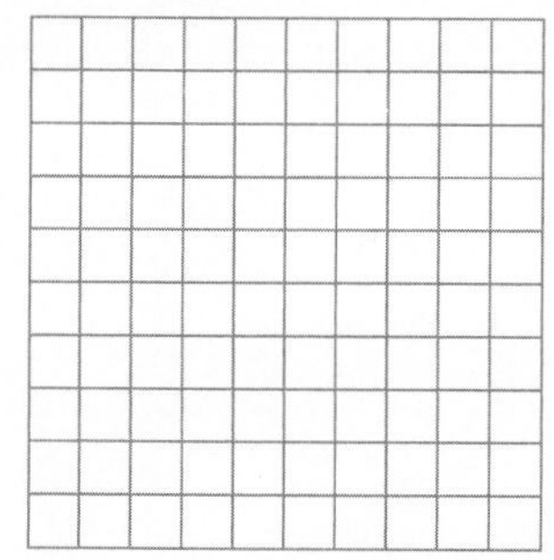

**10.** $y = 2\cos \frac{\pi}{3}\theta$

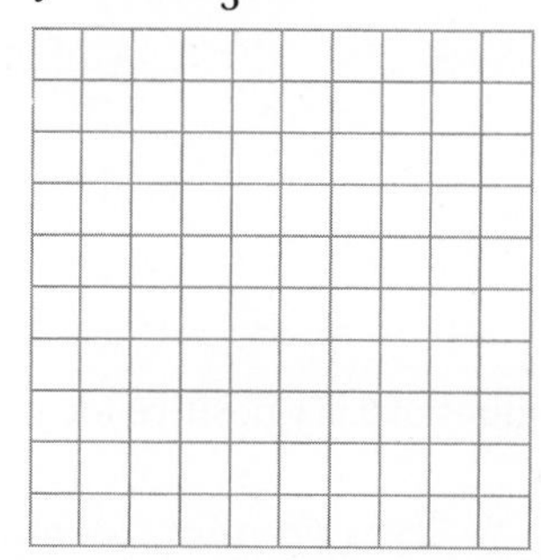

**Write a cosine function for each description. Assume that $a > 0$.**

**11.** amplitude 3, period $2\pi$

**12.** amplitude 1.5, period $\pi$

## Do you UNDERSTAND?

13. **Open-Ended** Write a cosine function with amplitude 5 and between 2 and 3 cycles from 0 to $2\pi$.

14. Assume $\theta$ is in the interval from 0 to $2\pi$.

**a.** For what values of $\theta$ is $y$ positive for $y = \cos\theta$?

**b.** For what values of $\theta$ is $y$ positive for $y = -\sin\theta$?

**c.** **Reasoning** What sine function has the same graph as $y = -3\cos\frac{2\pi}{3}\theta$?

## More Practice and Problem-Solving Exercises

### B Apply

**Identify the period, range, and amplitude of each function.**

**15.** $y = 3\cos\theta$

**16.** $y = -\cos 2t$

**17.** $y = 2\cos\frac{1}{2}t$

**18.** $y = \frac{1}{3}\cos\frac{\theta}{2}$

**19.** $y = 3\cos\left(-\frac{\theta}{3}\right)$

**20.** $y = -\frac{1}{2}\cos 3\theta$

**21.** $y = 16\cos\frac{3\pi}{2}t$

**22.** $y = 0.7\cos\pi t$

**23. Think About a Plan** In Buenos Aires, Argentina, the average monthly temperature is highest in January and lowest in July, ranging from 83°F to 57°F. Write a cosine function that models the change in temperature according to the month of the year.

- How can you find the amplitude?
- What part of the problem describes the length of the cycle?

**24. Writing** Explain how you can apply what you know about solving cosine equations to solving sine equations. Use $-1 = 6\sin 2t$ as an example.

**Solve each equation in the interval from 0 to $2\pi$. Round your answers to the nearest hundredth.**

**25.** $\sin\theta = 0.6$

**26.** $-3\sin 2\theta = 1.5$

**27.** $\sin\pi\theta = 1$

**Compare the amplitude and period of the cosine functions $f(x)$ and $g(x)$.**

**28.** $f(x) = -\cos 4x$

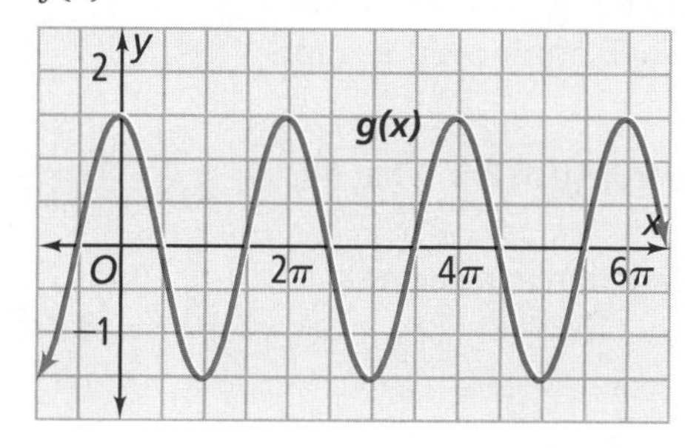


**29.** $f(x) = 2\cos 2x$

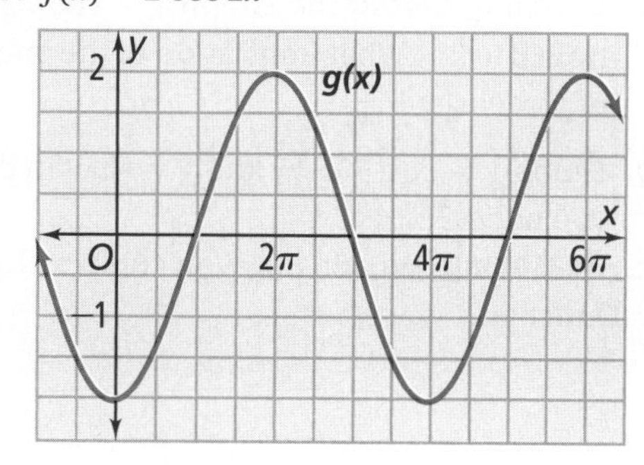


**30. a.** Solve $-2\sin\theta = 1.2$ in the interval from 0 to $2\pi$.

**b.** Solve $-2\sin\theta = 1.2$ in the interval $2\pi \leq \theta \leq 4\pi$. How are these solutions related to the solutions in part (a)?

**31. a.** Graph the equation $y = -30\cos\left(\frac{6\pi}{37}t\right)$ from Problem 3.

**b.** The independent variable $\theta$ represents time (in hours). Find four times at which the water level is the highest.

**c.** For how many hours during each cycle is the water level above the line $y = 0$? Below $y = 0$?

STEM **32. Tides** The table at the right shows the times for high tide and low tide of one day. The markings on the side of a local pier showed a high tide of 7 ft and a low tide of 4 ft on the previous day.

**a.** What is the average depth of water at the pier? What is the amplitude of the variation from the average depth?

**b.** How long is one cycle of the tide?

**c.** Write a cosine function that models the relationship between the depth of water and the time of day. Use $y = 0$ to represent the average depth of water. Use $t = 0$ to represent the time 4:03 A.M.

**d. Reasoning** Suppose your boat needs at least 5 ft of water to approach or leave the pier. Between what times could you come and go?

| Tide Table | |
|---|---|
| High tide | 4:03 A.M. |
| Low tide | 10:14 A.M. |
| High tide | 4:25 P.M. |
| Low tide | 10:36 P.M. |

## Challenge

**33.** Graph one cycle of $y = \cos\theta$, one cycle of $y = -\cos\theta$, and one cycle of $y = \cos(-\theta)$ on the same set of axes. Use the unit circle to explain any relationships you see among these graphs.

STEM **34. Biology** A helix is a three-dimensional spiral. The coiled strands of DNA and the edges of twisted crepe paper are examples of helixes. In the diagram, the $y$-coordinate of each edge illustrates a cosine function. Write an equation for the $y$-coordinate of one edge.

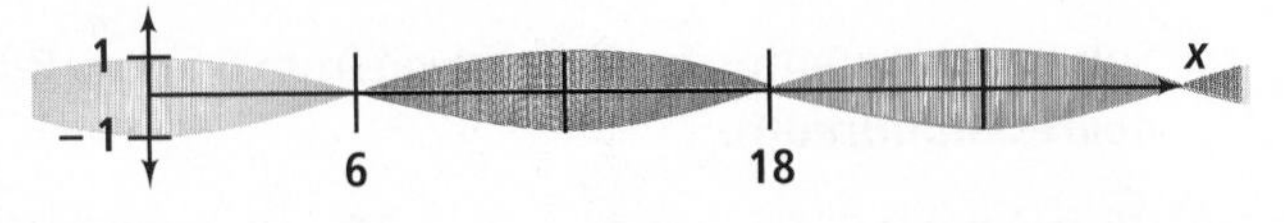


**35. a. Graphing Calculator** Graph $y = \cos\theta$ and $y = \cos\left(\theta - \frac{\pi}{2}\right)$ in the interval from 0 to $2\pi$. What translation of the graph of $y = \cos\theta$ produces the graph of $y = \cos\left(\theta - \frac{\pi}{2}\right)$?

**b.** Graph $y = \cos\left(\theta - \frac{\pi}{2}\right)$ and $y = \sin\theta$ in the interval from 0 to $2\pi$. What do you notice?

**c. Reasoning** Explain how you could rewrite a sine function as a cosine function.

# The Tangent Function

**F.IF.7.e** Graph . . . trigonometric functions, showing period, midline, and amplitude. Also **F.IF.7, F.TF.2, F.TF.5**

**Objective** To graph the tangent function

**Solve It!** Write your solution to the Solve It in the space below.

The tangent function is closely associated with the sine and cosine functions, but it differs from them in three dramatic ways.

**Essential Understanding** The tangent function has infinitely many points of discontinuity, with a vertical asymptote at each point. Its range is all real numbers. Its period is $\pi$, half that of both the sine and cosine functions. Its domain is all real numbers except odd multiples of $\frac{\pi}{2}$.

take note

## Key Concept Tangent of an Angle

Suppose the terminal side of an angle $\theta$ in standard position intersects the unit circle at the point $(x, y)$. Then the ratio $\frac{y}{x}$ is the **tangent of $\theta$**, denoted $\tan \theta$.

In this diagram, $x = \cos \theta$, $y = \sin \theta$, and $\frac{y}{x} = \tan \theta$.

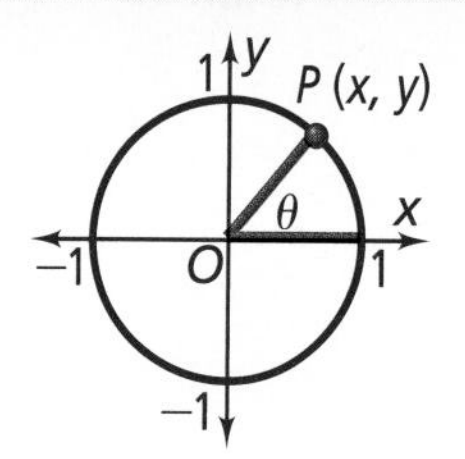

## Problem 1 Finding Tangents Geometrically

**Got It?** What is the value of each expression? Do not use a calculator.

**Think**
**Will a graph help?**

**a.** $\tan \frac{\pi}{2}$

**b.** $\tan \frac{2\pi}{3}$

**c.** $\tan\left(-\frac{\pi}{4}\right)$

**Practice** Find each value without using a calculator.

**1.** $\tan 2\pi$

**2.** $\tan\left(-\frac{3\pi}{4}\right)$

There is another way to geometrically define $\tan\theta$.

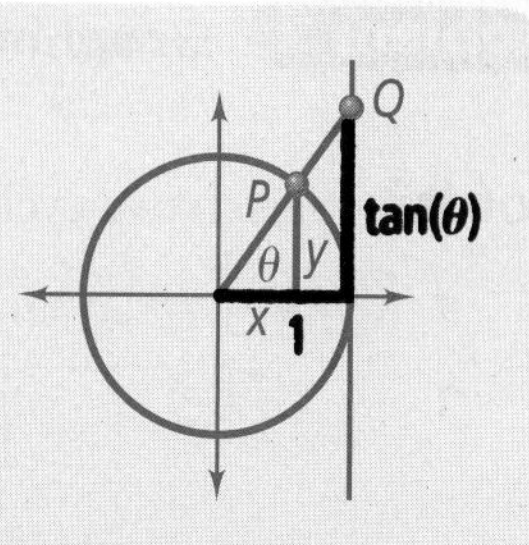


The diagram shows the unit circle and the vertical line $x = 1$. The angle $\theta$ in standard position determines a point $P(x, y)$.

By similar triangles, the length of the vertical red segment divided by the length of the horizontal red segment is equal to $\frac{y}{x}$. The horizontal red segment has length 1 since it is a radius of the unit circle, so the length of the vertical red segment is $\frac{y}{x}$, or $\tan\theta$, which is also the $y$-coordinate of $Q$.

If $\theta$ is an angle in standard position and *not* an odd multiple of $\frac{\pi}{2}$, then the line containing the terminal side of $\theta$ intersects the line $x = 1$ at a point $Q$ with $y$-coordinate $\tan\theta$.

The graph at the right shows one cycle of the **tangent function**, $y = \tan\theta$, for $-\frac{\pi}{2} < \theta < \frac{\pi}{2}$. The pattern repeats periodically with period $\pi$. At $\theta = \pm\frac{\pi}{2}$, the line through $P$ fails to intersect the line $x = 1$, so $\tan\theta$ is undefined.

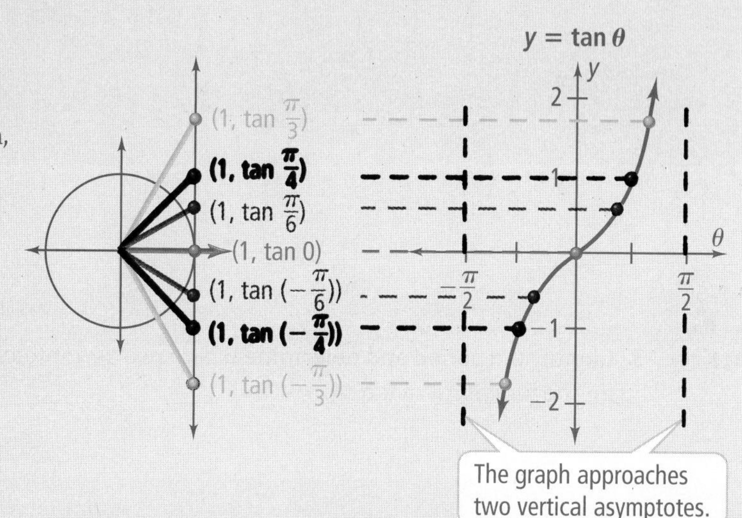


take note

## Concept Summary Properties of Tangent Functions

Suppose $y = a\tan b\theta$, with $a \neq 0$, $b > 0$, and $\theta$ in radians.

- $\frac{\pi}{b}$ is the period of the function.
- One cycle occurs in the interval from $-\frac{\pi}{2b}$ to $\frac{\pi}{2b}$.
- There are vertical asymptotes at each end of the cycle.

You can use asymptotes and three points to sketch one cycle of a tangent curve. As with sine and cosine, the five elements are equally spaced through one cycle. Use the pattern *asymptote-*$(-a)$*-zero-*$(a)$*-asymptote*. In the graph at the right, $a = b = 1$.

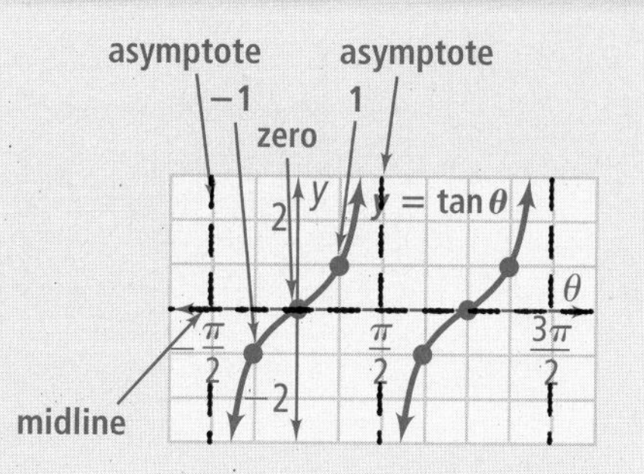


The next example shows how to use the period, asymptotes, and points to graph a tangent function.

## Problem 2 Graphing a Tangent Function

**Think**
**What is the period of each tangent curve?**

**Got It?** Sketch two cycles of the graph of each tangent curve.

**a.** $y = \tan 3\theta, 0 \leq \theta \leq \frac{2\pi}{3}$

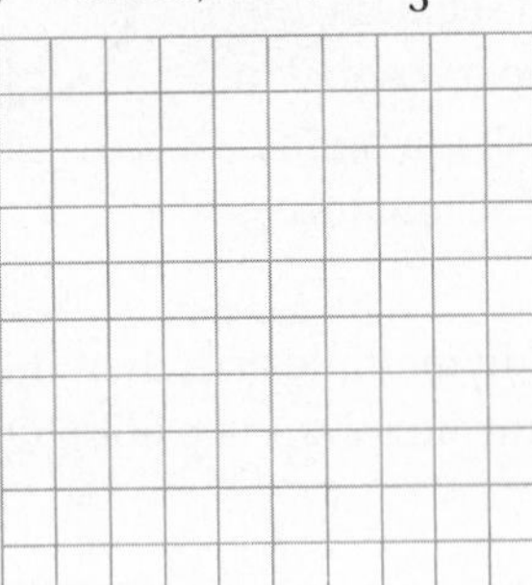

**b.** $y = \tan \frac{\pi}{2}\theta, 0 \leq \theta \leq 4$

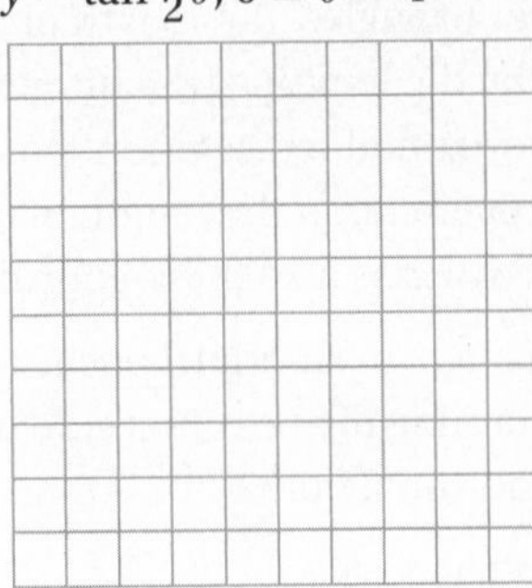

**Practice** **3.** Identify the period and determine where two asymptotes occur for the function $y = \tan 4\theta$.

**4.** Sketch the graph of $y = \tan(-\theta)$ in the interval from 0 to $2\pi$.

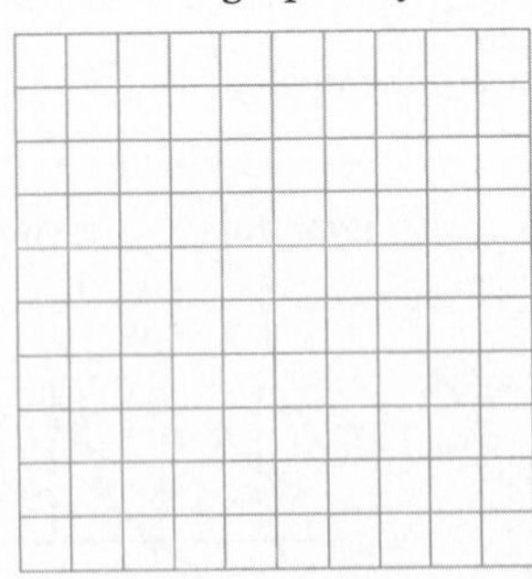

## Problem 3 Using the Tangent Function to Solve Problems

**Got It?** **STEM**

**a.** The function $y = 100 \tan \theta$ models the height of the triangle, where $\theta$ is the angle indicated (from Problem 3). What is the height of the triangle when $\theta = 25°$?

**b. Reasoning** The architect wants the triangle to be at least one story tall. The average height of a story is 14 ft. What must $\theta$ be for the height of the triangle to be at least 14 ft?

**Practice** **Graphing Calculator** Graph each function on the interval $0 \le x \le 2\pi$ and $-200 \le y \le 200$. Evaluate each function at $x = \frac{\pi}{4}, \frac{\pi}{2}$, and $\frac{3\pi}{4}$.

**5.** $y = 50 \tan x$

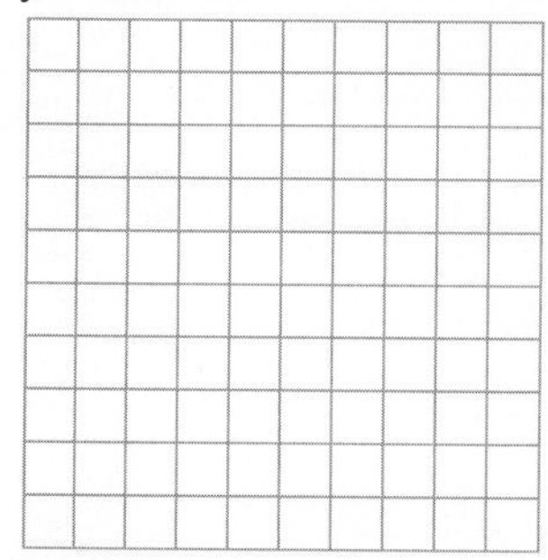

**6.** $y = -100 \tan x$

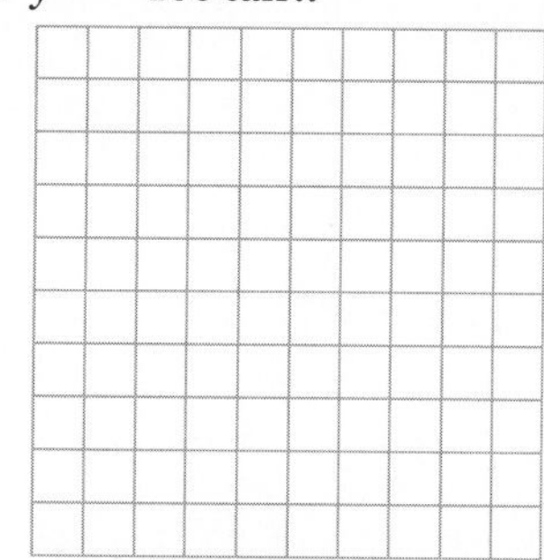

## Lesson Check

### Do you know HOW?

**Find each value without using a calculator.**

**7.** $\tan \frac{\pi}{4}$

**8.** $\tan \frac{7\pi}{6}$

**9.** $\tan \left(-\frac{\pi}{4}\right)$

**10.** $\tan \left(-\frac{3\pi}{3}\right)$

### Do you UNDERSTAND?

**11. Vocabulary** Successive asymptotes of a tangent curve are $x = \frac{\pi}{3}$ and $x = -\frac{\pi}{3}$. What is the period?

**12. Error Analysis** A quiz contained a question asking students to solve the equation $8 = -2 \tan 3\theta$ to the nearest hundredth of a radian. One student did not receive full credit for writing $\theta = -1.33$. Describe and correct the student's error.

**13. Writing** Explain how you can write a tangent function that has the same period as $y = \sin 4\theta$.

## More Practice and Problem-Solving Exercises

### B Apply

**Identify the period for each tangent function. Then graph each function in the interval from $-2\pi$ to $2\pi$.**

**14.** $y = \tan \frac{\pi}{6}\theta$

**15.** $y = \tan 2.5\theta$

**16.** $y = \tan\left(-\frac{3}{2\pi}\theta\right)$

**Graphing Calculator Solve each equation in the interval from 0 to $2\pi$. Round your answers to the nearest hundredth.**

**17.** $\tan \theta = 2$

**18.** $\tan \theta = -2$

**19.** $6 \tan 2\theta = 1$

**20.** **a. Open-Ended** Write a tangent function.
**b.** Graph the function on the interval $-2\pi$ to $2\pi$.
**c.** Identify the period and the asymptotes of the function.

**21. Think About a Plan** A quilter is making hexagonal placemats by sewing together six quilted isosceles triangles. Each triangle has a base length of 10 in. The function $y = 5 \tan \theta$ models the height of the triangular quilts, where $\theta$ is the measure of one of the base angles. Graph the function. What is the area of the placemat if the triangles are equilateral?

- How can a graph of the function help you find the height of each triangle?
- How can you find the area of each triangle?
- What will be the last step in your solution?

**22. Ceramics** An artist is making triangular ceramic tiles for a triangular patio. The patio will be an equilateral triangle with base 18 ft and height 15.6 ft.

**a.** Find the area of the patio in square feet.

**b.** The artist uses tiles that are isosceles triangles with base 6 in. The function $y = 3 \tan \theta$ models the height of the triangular tiles, where $\theta$ is the measure of one of the base angles. Graph the function. Find the height of the tile when $\theta = 30°$ and when $\theta = 60°$.

**c.** Find the area of one tile in square inches when $\theta = 30°$ and when $\theta = 60°$.

**d.** Find the number of tiles the patio will require if $\theta = 30°$ and if $\theta = 60°$.

**Use the function $y = 200 \tan x$ on the interval $0° \leq x \leq 141°$. Complete each ordered pair. Round your answers to the nearest whole number.**

**23.** (45°, ___) **24.** (___°, 0) **25.** (___°, −200) **26.** (141°, ___) **27.** (___°, 550)

**Write an equation of a tangent function for each graph.**

**28.**

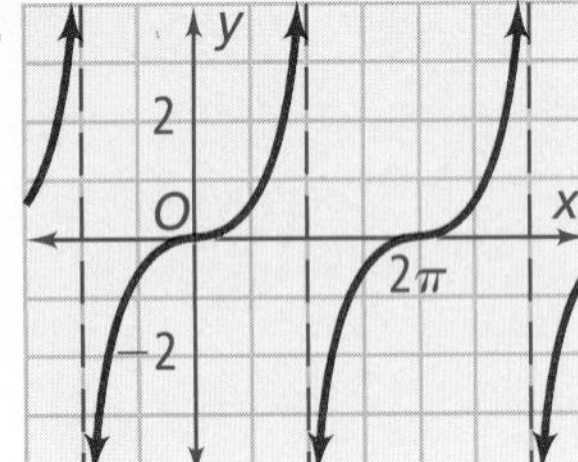


**29.**

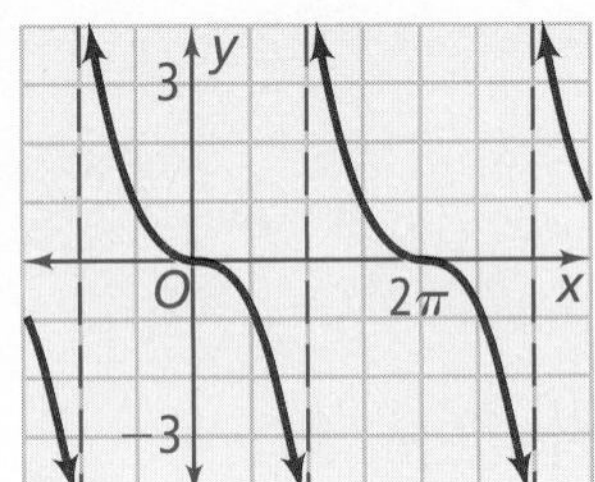


**30.**

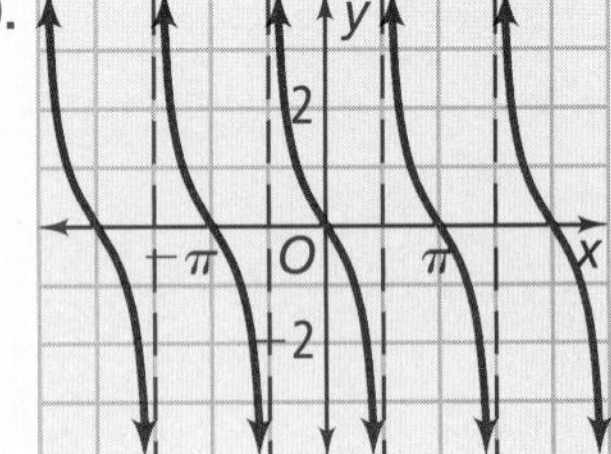


**31. Construction** An architect is designing a hexagonal gazebo. The floor is a hexagon made up of six isosceles triangles. The function $y = 4 \tan \theta$ models the height of one triangle, where $\theta$ is the measure of one of the base angles and the base of the triangle is 8 ft long.

**a.** Graph the function. Find the height of one triangle when $\theta = 60°$.

**b.** Find the area of one triangle in square feet when $\theta = 60°$.

**c.** Find the area of the gazebo floor in square feet when the triangles forming the hexagon are equilateral.

**32.** **a.** The graph of $y = \frac{1 - \cos x}{\sin x}$ suggests a tangent curve of the form $y = a \tan bx$. Graph the function using the window $[-3\pi, 3\pi]$ by $[-4, 4]$.

**b.** What is the period of the curve? What is the value of $a$?

**c.** Find the $x$-coordinate halfway between a removable discontinuity and the asymptote to its right. Find the corresponding $y$-coordinate.

**d.** Find an equivalent function of the form $y = a \tan bx$.

## Challenge

**33. Geometry** Use the drawing at the right and similar triangles. Justify the statement that $\tan \theta = \frac{\sin \theta}{\cos \theta}$.

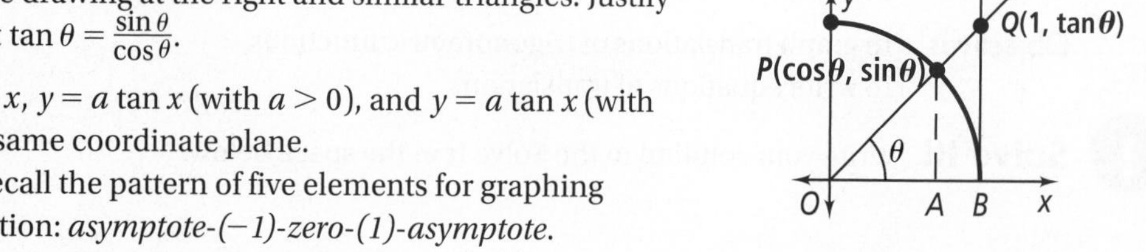


**34.** **a.** Graph $y = \tan x$, $y = a \tan x$ (with $a > 0$), and $y = a \tan x$ (with $a < 0$) on the same coordinate plane.

**b. Reasoning** Recall the pattern of five elements for graphing a tangent function: *asymptote-(−1)-zero-(1)-asymptote.* How does the value of $a$ affect this pattern?

**35. Writing** How many solutions does the equation $x = \tan x$ have for $0 \leq x \leq 2\pi$? Explain.

# 8-7 Translating Sine and Cosine Functions

F.TF.5 Choose trigonometric functions to model periodic phenomena . . . Also F.IF.7, F.IF.7.e, F.BF.3

**Objectives** To graph translations of trigonometric functions
To write equations of translations

**Solve It!** Write your solution to the Solve It in the space below.

Recall that for any function $f$, you can graph $f(x - h)$ by translating the graph of $f$ by $h$ units horizontally. You can graph $f(x) + k$ by translating the graph of $f$ by $k$ units vertically.

**Essential Understanding** You can translate periodic functions in the same way that you translate other functions.

Each horizontal translation of certain periodic functions is a **phase shift**.

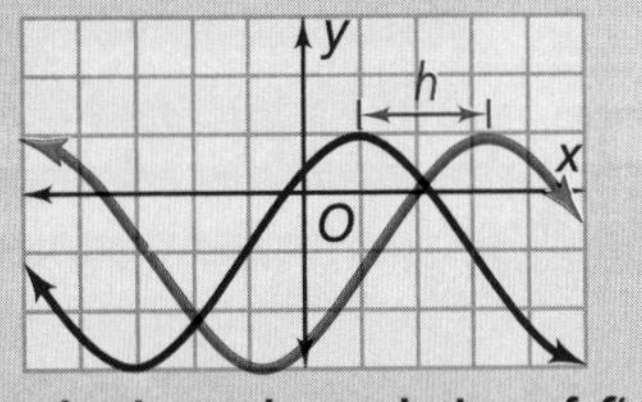


$g(x)$: **horizontal translation of $f(x)$**
$g(x) = f(x - h)$

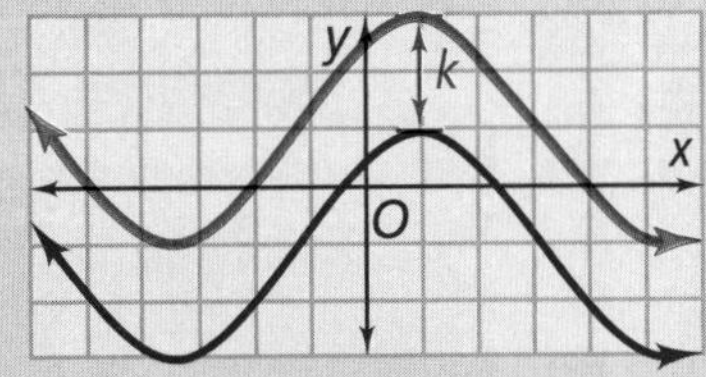


$h(x)$: **vertical translation of $f(x)$**
$h(x) = f(x) + k$

When $g(x) = f(x - h)$, the value of $h$ is the amount of the shift. If $h > 0$, the shift is to the right. If $h < 0$, the shift is to the left. When $h(x) = f(x) + k$, the value of $k$ is the amount of the midline shift. If $k > 0$, the midline shifts up. If $k < 0$, the midline shifts down.

## Problem 1 Identifying Phase Shifts

**Got It?** What is the value of $h$ in each translation? Describe each phase shift (using a phrase such as 3 *units to the left*).

**a.** $g(t) = f(t - 5)$

**b.** $y = \sin(x + 3)$

**Think**
How can you rewrite the equation to help find the value of $h$?

**Practice** **Determine the value of $h$ in each translation. Describe each phase shift (using a phrase like 3 *units to the left*).**

**1.** $f(x) = g(x - 3)$

**2.** $y = \sin(x + \pi)$

You can analyze a translation to determine how it relates to the parent function.

## Problem 2 Graphing Translations

**Got It?** Use the graph of $y = \sin x$ from Problem 2. What is the graph of each translation in the interval $0 \le x \le 2\pi$?

**a.** $y = \sin x - 2$

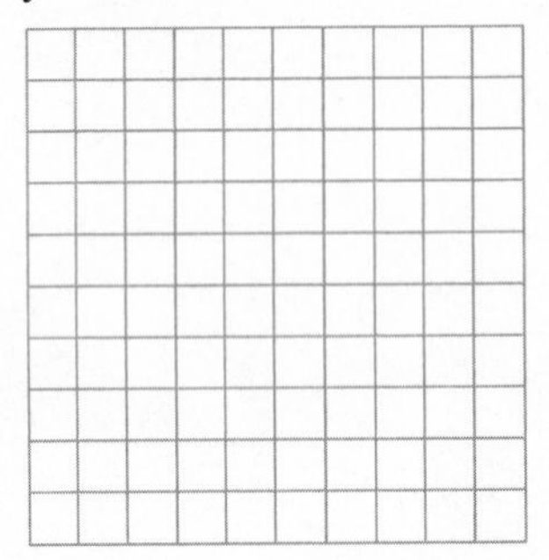

**b.** $y = \sin(x - 2)$

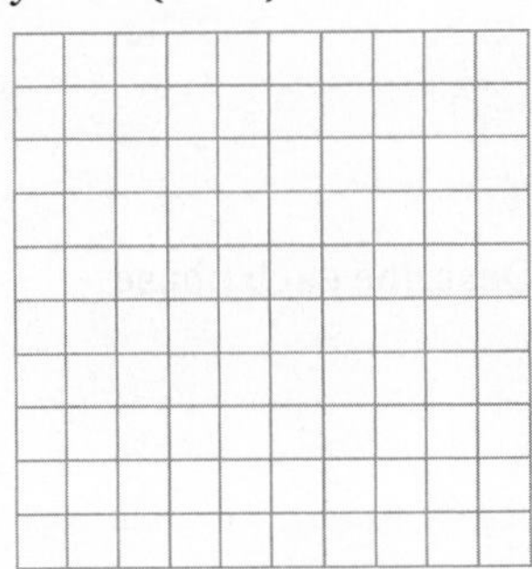

**c.** Which translation is a phase shift?

**d.** Which translation gives the graph a new midline?

**Practice** 3. Use the function $f(x)$ at the right. Graph the translation.

$g(x) = f(x + 2)$

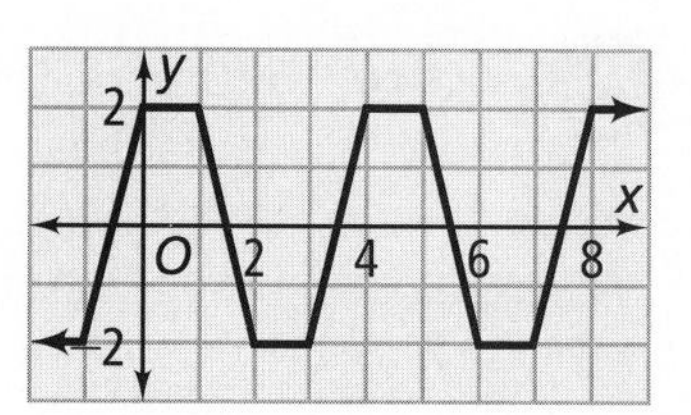


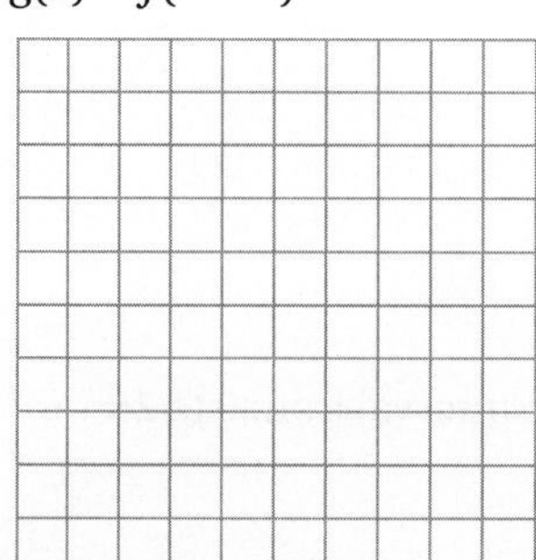

4. Graph the translation of $y = \cos x$ in the interval from 0 to $2\pi$.

$y = \cos(x - \pi)$

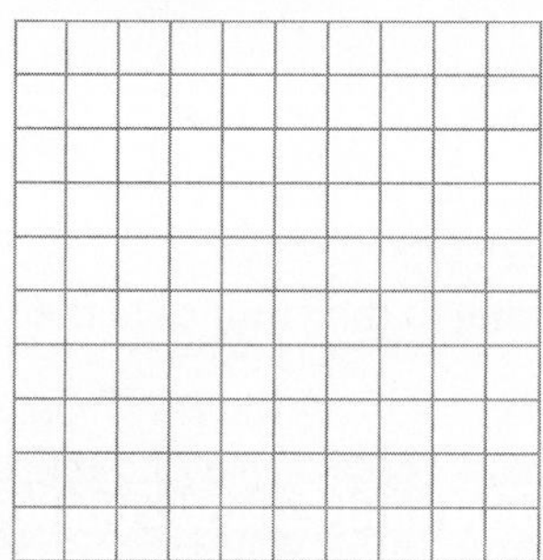

You can translate both vertically and horizontally to produce combined translations.

## Problem 3 Graphing a Combined Translation

**Got It?** Use the graph at the right of the parent function $y = \cos x$. What is the graph of each translation in the interval $0 \leq x \leq 2\pi$?

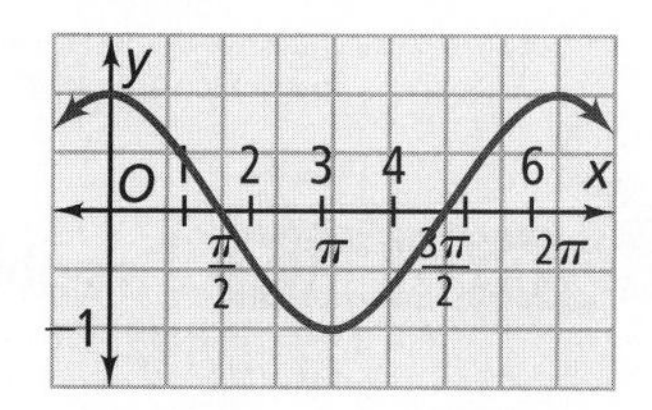


a. $y = \cos(x - 2) + 5$

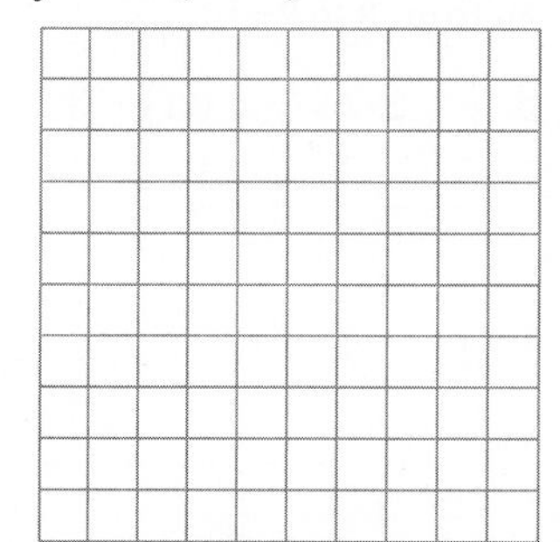

b. $y = \cos(x + 1) + 3$

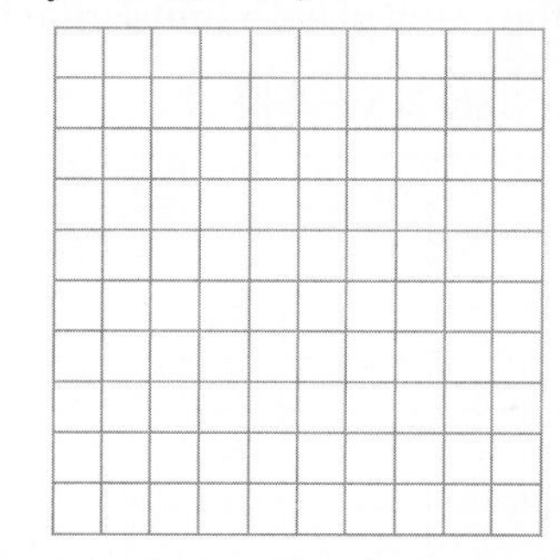

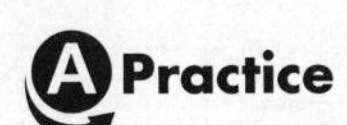

**Practice** 5. Describe any phase shift and vertical shift in the graph of $y = \sin(x - 3) + 2$.

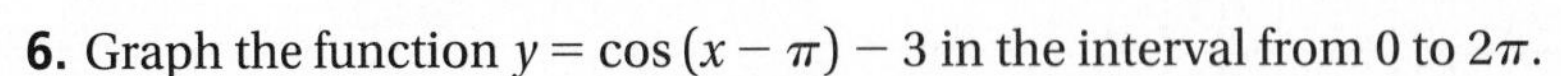

6. Graph the function $y = \cos(x - \pi) - 3$ in the interval from 0 to $2\pi$.

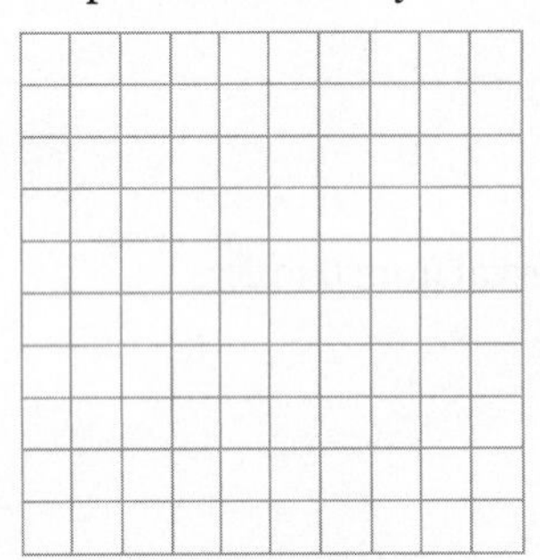

The translations graphed in Problems 2 and 3 belong to the families of the sine and cosine functions.

take note

## Concept Summary Families of Sine and Cosine Functions

| Parent Function | Transformed Function |
|---|---|
| $y = \sin x$ | $y = a \sin b(x - h) + k$ |
| $y = \cos x$ | $y = a \cos b(x - h) + k$ |

- $|a|$ = amplitude (vertical stretch or shrink)
- $\frac{2\pi}{b}$ = period (when $x$ is in radians and $b > 0$)
- $h$ = phase shift, or horizontal shift
- $k$ = vertical shift ($y = k$ is the midline)

## Problem 4 Graphing a Translation of $y = \sin 2x$

**Got It?** What is the graph of each translation in the interval from 0 to $2\pi$?

a. $y = -3 \sin 2\left(x - \frac{\pi}{3}\right) - \frac{3}{2}$

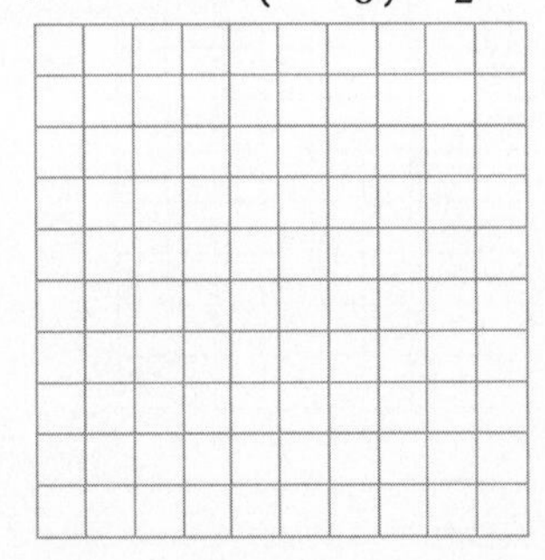

b. $y = 2 \cos \frac{\pi}{2}(x + 1) - 3$

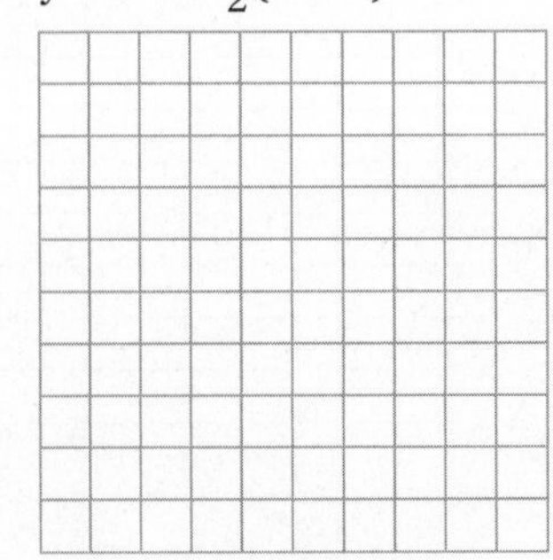

**Practice** Graph each function in the interval from 0 to $2\pi$.

**7.** $y = \cos 2\left(x + \frac{\pi}{2}\right) - 2$

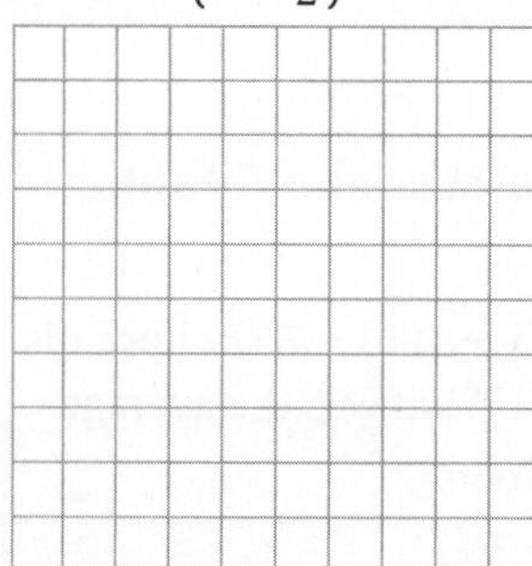

**8.** $y = 3 \sin \frac{\pi}{2}(x - 2)$

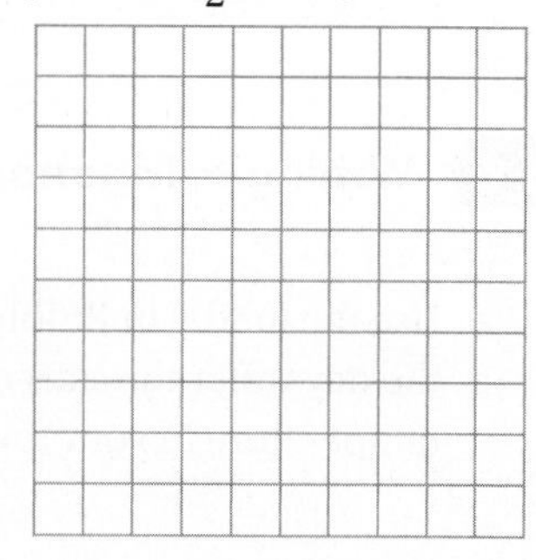

You can write an equation to describe a translation.

## Problem 5 Writing Translations

**Got It?** What is an equation that models each translation?

**a.** $y = \cos x$, $\frac{\pi}{2}$ units up

**b.** $y = 2 \sin x$, $\frac{\pi}{4}$ units to the right

**Think**

**What are *a*, *b*, *h*, and *k* in $y = a \sin b(x - h) + k$?**

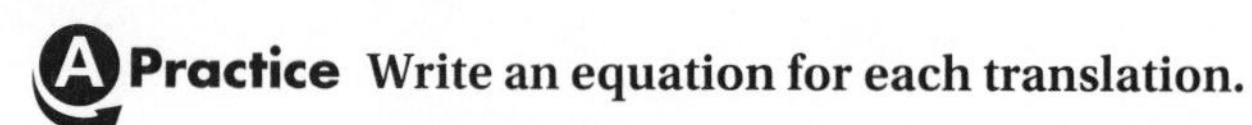

**Practice** Write an equation for each translation.

**9.** $y = \sin x$, 3 units up

**10.** $y = \cos x$, 1.5 units to the right

You can write a trigonometric function to model a situation.

## Problem 6 Writing a Trigonometric Function to Model a Situation

**Got It?** STEM

**a.** Use the model in Problem 6 ($y = 22\cos\frac{2\pi}{365}(x - 198) + 55$, where $x$ is the days after the start of the calendar year). What was the average temperature in your town 150 days into the year?

**b.** What value does the midline of this model represent?

**c. Reasoning** Can you use this model to predict temperatures for next year? Explain your answer.

**11. Temperature** The table below shows water temperatures at a buoy in the Gulf of Mexico on several days of the year.

STEM

| Day of Year | 16 | 47 | 75 | 106 | 136 | 167 | 198 | 228 | 258 | 289 | 319 | 350 |
|---|---|---|---|---|---|---|---|---|---|---|---|---|
| Temperature (°F) | 71 | 69 | 70 | 73 | 77 | 82 | 85 | 86 | 84 | 82 | 78 | 74 |

**a.** Plot the data.

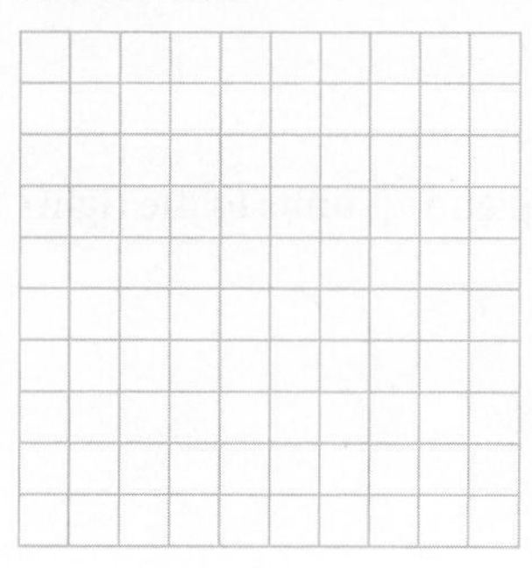

**b.** Write a cosine model for the data.

## Lesson Check

### Do you know HOW?

**12.** Graph $y = \sin\left(x + \frac{\pi}{4}\right)$ in the interval from 0 to $2\pi$.

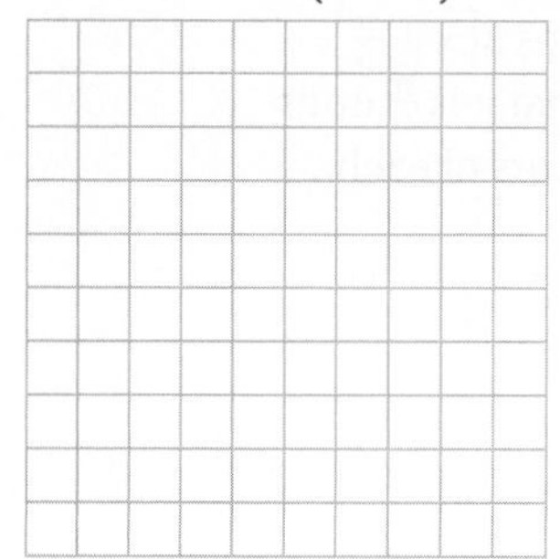

**13.** Describe any phase shift or vertical shift in the graph of $y = 4\cos(x - 2) + 9$.

**14.** What is an equation that shifts $y = \cos x$, 3 units up and $\frac{2\pi}{3}$ units to the right?

## Do you UNDERSTAND?

**15. Vocabulary** Write a sine function that has amplitude 4, period $3\pi$, phase shift $\pi$, and vertical shift $-5$.

**16. Error Analysis** Two students disagree on the translation for $y = \cos 3\left(x + \frac{\pi}{6}\right)$. Amberly says that it is $\frac{\pi}{2}$ units to the left of $y = \cos 3x$. Scott says that it is $\frac{\pi}{6}$ units to the left of $y = \cos 3x$. Is either student correct? Describe any errors of each student.

## More Practice and Problem-Solving Exercises

### B Apply

**Write an equation for each translation.**

**17.** $y = \cos x$, 3 units to the left and $\pi$ units up

**18.** $y = \sin x$, $\frac{\pi}{2}$ units to the right and 3.5 units up

**19. Think About a Plan** The function $y = 1.5 \sin \frac{\pi}{6}(x - 6) + 2$ represents the average monthly rainfall for a town in central Florida, where $x$ represents the number of the month (January = 1, February = 2, and so on). Rewrite the function using a cosine model.

- How does the graph of $y = \sin x$ translate to the graph of $y = \cos x$?
- What parts of the sine function will stay the same? What must change?

**Write a cosine function for each graph. Then write a sine function for each graph.**

**20.**

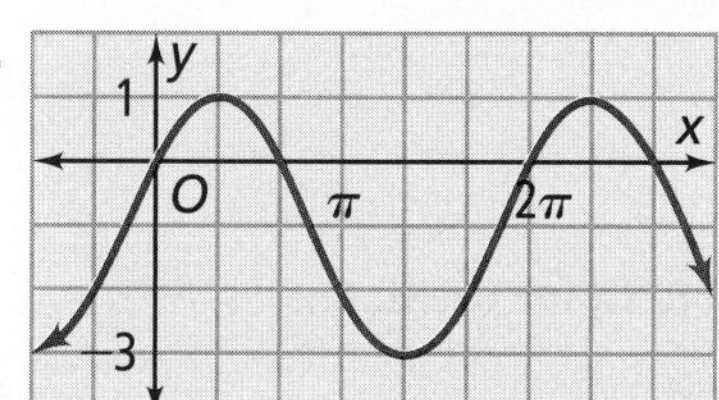


**21.**

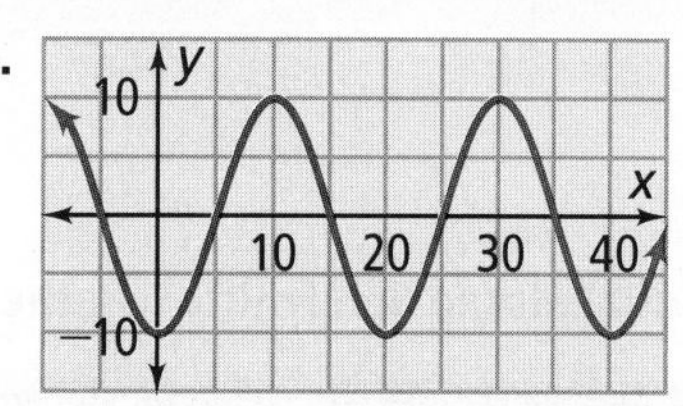


**22.** The graphs of $y = \sin x$ and $y = \cos x$ are shown at the right.

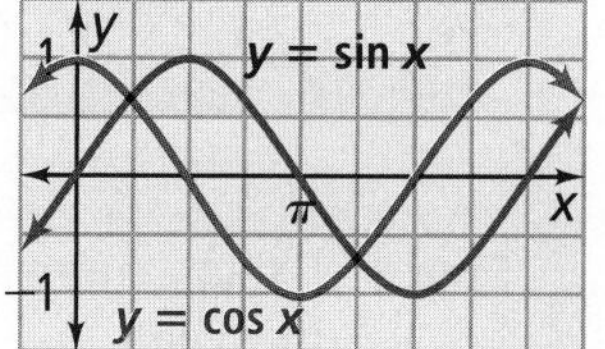


**a.** What phase shift will translate the cosine graph onto the sine graph? Write your answer as an equation in the form $\sin x = \cos(x - h)$.

**b.** What phase shift will translate the sine graph onto the cosine graph? Write your answer as an equation in the form $\cos x = \sin(x - h)$.

**23. a. Open-Ended** Draw a periodic function. Find its amplitude and period. Then sketch a translation of your function 3 units down and 4 units to the left.

**b. Reasoning** Suppose your original function is $f(x)$. Describe your translation using the form $g(x) = f(x - h) + k$.

**24. a.** Write $y = 3 \sin(2x - 4) + 1$ in the form $y = a \sin b(x - h) + k$. (*Hint:* Factor where possible.)

**b.** Find the amplitude, midline, and period. Describe any translations.

### C Challenge

**Use a graphing calculator to graph each function in the interval from 0 to $2\pi$. Then sketch each graph.**

**25.** $y = \sin x + x$

**26.** $y = \sin x + 2x$

**27.** $y = \cos x - 2x$

**28.** $y = \cos x + x$

**29.** $y = \sin(x + \cos x)$

**30.** $y = \sin(x + 2\cos x)$

TECHNOLOGY LAB

Use With Lesson 8-7

# Plotting and Analyzing Residuals

**S.ID.6.b** Informally assess the fit of a function by . . . analyzing residuals.

Recall that you can use a *residual plot* to determine whether a particular function is a good fit for a set of data points. A *residual* is the difference between the $y$-value of a data point and $\hat{y}$, the corresponding $y$-value of a model for the data set. You can plot each of the points $(x, y - \hat{y})$ on a coordinate plane, and analyze the resulting residual plot to assess whether the function is a good fit for the data. For a good fit, the points in the plot have no apparent pattern.

## Activity

**Analyze the residual plot to determine whether the model is a good fit for the data.**

| $x$ | 0.4 | 1.3 | 2.3 | 4.1 | 5.9 | 7.3 | 8.7 | 10.5 | 11.1 | 13 | 13.6 | 15.4 | 17.7 |
|---|---|---|---|---|---|---|---|---|---|---|---|---|---|
| $y$ | 0.7 | 2.5 | 3.6 | 3.5 | 0.7 | −2 | −3.7 | −3.4 | −2.7 | 0.83 | 2 | 4 | 2.2 |

**Step 1** Using a graphing calculator, create a scatter plot of the data.

The data appear to be best modeled by a sine function.

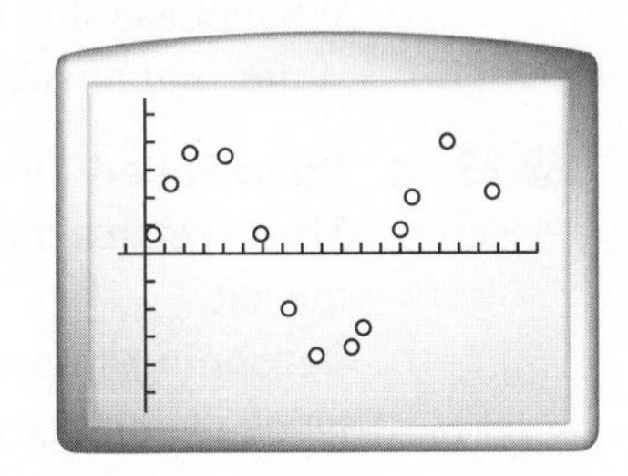

**Step 2** Perform a regression.

Press **stat**. Select **CALC** and **SinReg** to find the model. The residuals are stored in the **RESID** list variable.

**Step 3** Plot the residuals.

Press **stat plot** 1. Turn on Plot 1 using the list variable used for the $x$-values of the data set for the Xlist. Place the cursor to select the Ylist. Press **LIST** (2nd **STAT**) and select **RESID**. Press **zoom** 9 to graph.

There is no apparent pattern in the residual plot. When there is no apparent patter in the residual plot, the model is a good fit for the data.

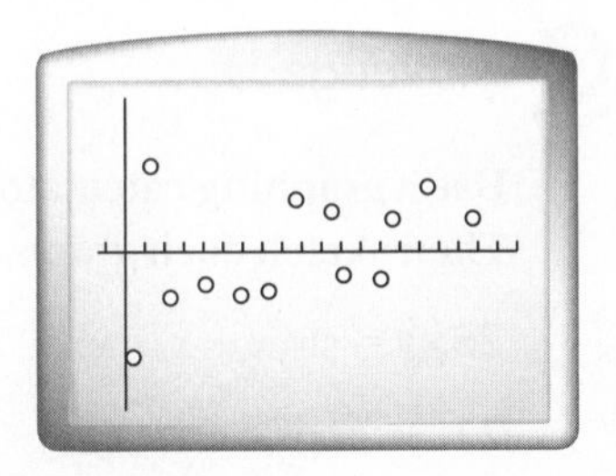

## Exercises

**In Exercises 1 and 2, use the SinReg function on a graphing calculator to find a sine function that models the data. Then make a residual plot. Does the sine function model the data well? Carefully sketch the residual plot and explain your reasoning.**

1.

| $x$ | 0 | 0.3 | 1 | 2.3 | 2.9 | 3.6 | 4.6 | 5.6 | 6.4 | 7.2 |
|---|---|---|---|---|---|---|---|---|---|---|
| $y$ | 0 | 1.9 | 3.3 | 2.2 | 0.6 | −0.9 | −1.8 | −1.1 | 0.2 | 1.2 |

| $x$ | 8.3 | 9.2 | 10.2 | 11 | 12 | 12.8 | 13.7 | 14.8 | 15.6 | 16.4 |
|---|---|---|---|---|---|---|---|---|---|---|
| $y$ | 1.2 | 0.2 | −0.8 | −1.2 | −0.7 | 0.2 | 0.9 | 0.9 | 0.2 | −0.6 |

2.

| $x$ | 0.2 | 0.5 | 1.3 | 2.6 | 3.6 | 4.3 | 5.5 | 5.9 | 7.8 | 8.6 | 9.6 | 10.2 |
|---|---|---|---|---|---|---|---|---|---|---|---|---|
| $y$ | 0.1 | 2.9 | 4.6 | 3.4 | −1.5 | −4.2 | −4.1 | −1.2 | 5.2 | 3 | 0.1 | −4.2 |

**3.** Find linear, quadratic, cubic, and exponential functions that model the data below using the **LinReg**, **QuadReg**, **CubicReg**, and **ExpReg** functions on a graphing calculator. Determine which functions model the data well by analyzing the residual plots for each function.

| $x$ | −1.2 | −0.3 | 0.8 | 1.5 | 2.5 | 3.2 | 4.1 | 4.9 | 5.4 | 6.3 |
|---|---|---|---|---|---|---|---|---|---|---|
| $y$ | 0.43 | 0.61 | 0.81 | 1.74 | 2.3 | 2.83 | 5.66 | 9.19 | 12.13 | 17.15 |

# Reciprocal Trigonometric Functions

**F.IF.7.e** Graph . . . trigonometric functions, showing period, midline, and amplitude. Also **F.IF.7, F.TF.2, F.TF.5**

**Objectives** To evaluate reciprocal trigonometric functions
To graph reciprocal trigonometric functions

**Solve It!** Write your solution to the Solve It in the space below.

To solve an equation $ax = b$, you multiply each side by the reciprocal of $a$. If $a$ is a trigonometric expression, you need to use its reciprocal.

**Essential Understanding** Cosine, sine, and tangent have reciprocals. Cosine and *secant* are reciprocals, as are sine and *cosecant*. Tangent and *cotangent* are also reciprocals.

take note

## Key Concept Cosecant, Secant, and Cotangent Functions

The **cosecant** (csc), **secant** (sec), and **cotangent** (cot) functions are defined using reciprocals. Their domains do not include the real numbers $\theta$ that make the denominator zero.

$$\csc\theta = \frac{1}{\sin\theta} \qquad \sec\theta = \frac{1}{\cos\theta} \qquad \cot\theta = \frac{1}{\tan\theta}$$

($\cot\theta = 0$ at odd multiples of $\frac{\pi}{2}$, where $\tan\theta$ is undefined.)

You can use the unit circle to evaluate the reciprocal trigonometric functions directly. Suppose the terminal side of an angle $\theta$ in standard position intersects the unit circle at the point $(x, y)$.

Then $\csc\theta = \frac{1}{y}$, $\sec\theta = \frac{1}{x}$, $\cot\theta = \frac{x}{y}$.

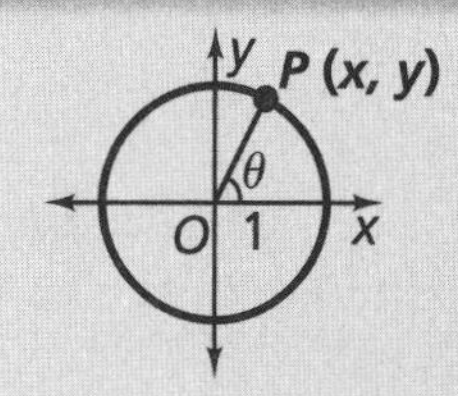

You can use what you know about the unit circle to find exact values for reciprocal trigonometric functions.

## Problem 1 Finding Values Geometrically

**Got It?** What is the exact value of each expression? Do not use a calculator.

**a.** $\csc \frac{\pi}{3}$  **b.** $\cot\left(-\frac{5\pi}{4}\right)$  **c.** $\sec 3\pi$

**d. Reasoning** Use the unit circle at the right to find $\cot n$, $\csc n$, and $\sec n$. Explain how you found your answers.

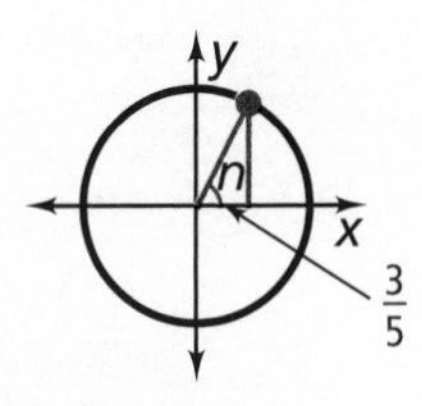


**Practice Find each value without using a calculator. If the expression is undefined, write *undefined*.**

**1.** $\csc \frac{7\pi}{6}$  **2.** $\cot(-\pi)$

Use the reciprocal relationships to evaluate secant, cosecant, or cotangent on a calculator, since most calculators do not have these functions as menu options.

## Problem 2 Finding Values with a Calculator

**Think**

**In part (a), can you use the $\tan^{-1}$ key on your calculator to find cot 13?**

**Got It?** What is the decimal value of each expression? Use the radian mode on your calculator. Round your answers to the nearest thousandth.

**a.** $\cot 13$

**b.** $\csc 6.5$

**c.** $\sec 15°$

**d.** $\sec \frac{3\pi}{2}$

**e. Reasoning** How can you find the cotangent of an angle without using the tangent key on your calculator?

 **Graphing Calculator** **Use a calculator to find each value. Round your answers to the nearest thousandth.**

**3.** sec 2.5

**4.** cot (−32°)

The graphs of reciprocal trigonometric functions have asymptotes where the functions are undefined.

## Problem 3 Sketching a Graph

**Got It?** What are the graphs of $y = \tan x$ and $y = \cot x$ in the interval from 0 to $2\pi$?

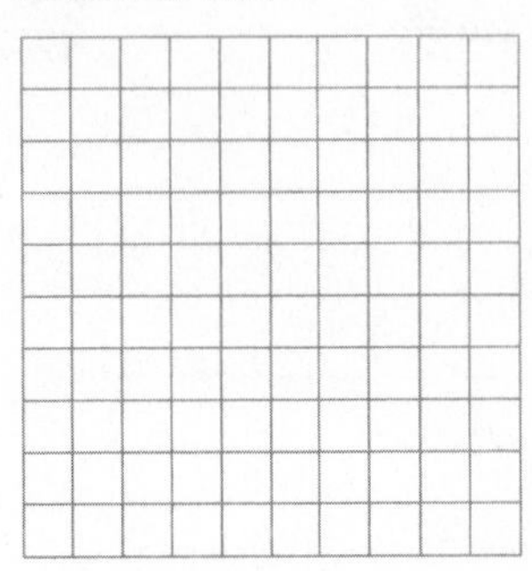

**Think**

**For what values is cot *x* undefined?**

**Practice** **Graph each function in the interval from 0 to $2\pi$.**

**5.** $y = \sec 2\theta$

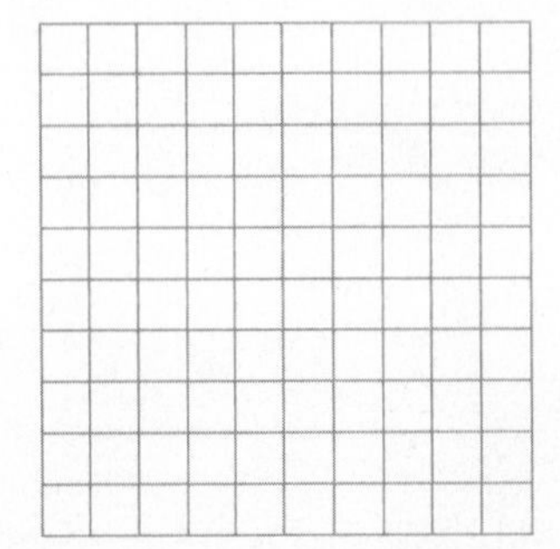

**6.** $y = \csc 2\theta - 1$

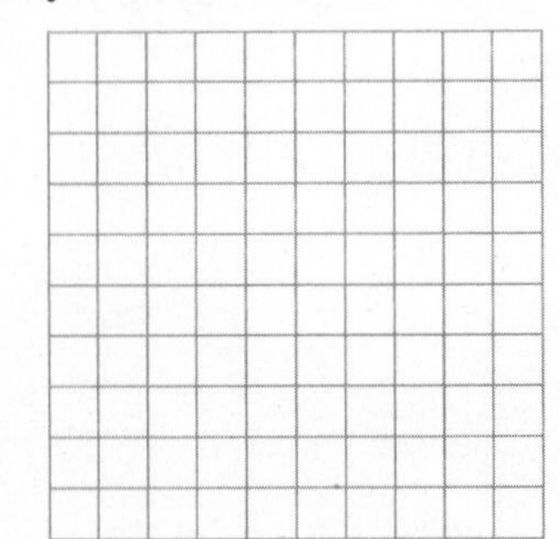

## Problem 4 Using Technology to Graph a Reciprocal Function

**Got It?** What is the value of csc 45°? Use the graph of the reciprocal trigonometric function.

**Practice** **Graphing Calculator** **Use the graph of the appropriate reciprocal trigonometric function to find each value. Round to four decimal places.**

**7.** csc 130°

**8.** cot 30°

You can use a reciprocal trigonometric function to solve a real-world problem.

## Problem 5 Using Reciprocal Functions to Solve a Problem

**Got It?** The 601 in the function in Problem 5 is the diner's height above the ground in feet. If the diner is 553 feet above the ground, how far away are objects sighted at angles of 50° and 80°?

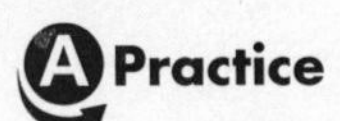

**9. Distance** A woman looks out a window of a building. She is 94 feet above the ground. Her line of sight makes an angle of $\theta$ with the building. The distance in feet of an object from the woman is modeled by the function $d = 94 \sec \theta$. How far away are objects sighted at angles of 25° and 55°?

## Lesson Check

### Do you know HOW?

**Find each value without using a calculator.**

**10.** $\csc \frac{\pi}{2}$

**11.** $\sec\left(-\frac{\pi}{6}\right)$

**Use a calculator to find each value. Round your answers to the nearest thousandth.**

**12.** $\csc 1.5$

**13.** $\sec 42^\circ$

**14.** An extension ladder leans against a building, forming a 50° angle with the ground. Use the function $y = 21 \csc x + 2$ to find $y$, the length of the ladder. Round to the nearest tenth of a foot.

## Do you UNDERSTAND?

**15. Reasoning** Explain why the graph of $y = 5 \sec \theta$ has no zeros.

**16. Error Analysis** On a quiz, a student wrote $\sec \sec 20° + 1 = 0.5155$. The teacher marked it wrong. What error did the student make?

**17. Compare and Contrast** How are the graphs of $y = \sec x$ and $y = \csc x$ alike? How are they different? Could the graph of $y = \csc x$ be a transformation of the graph of $y = \sec x$?

## More Practice and Problem-Solving Exercises

### B Apply

**18. Think About a Plan** A communications tower has wires anchoring it to the ground. Each wire is attached to the tower at a height 20 ft above the ground. The length $y$ of the wire is modeled with the function $y = 20 \csc \theta$, where $\theta$ is the measure of the angle formed by the wire and the ground. Find the length of wire needed to form an angle of 45°.

- Do you need to graph the function?
- How can you rewrite the function so you can use a calculator?

**19. Multiple Representations** Write a cosecant model that has the same graph as $y = \sec \theta$.

**Match each function with its graph.**

**20.** $y = \frac{1}{\sin x}$

**21.** $y = \frac{1}{\cos x}$

**22.** $y = -\frac{1}{\sin x}$

**A.**

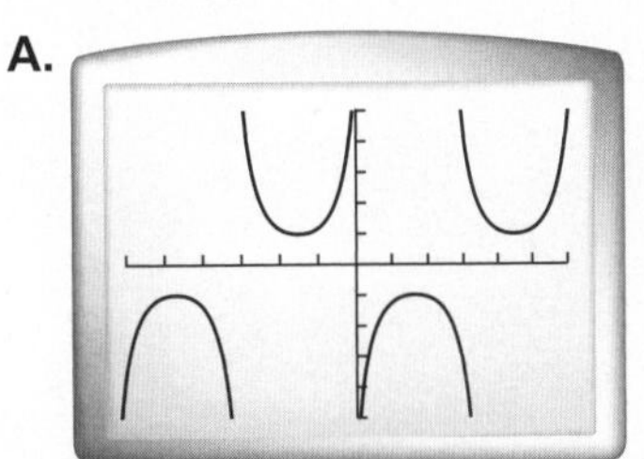

**B.**

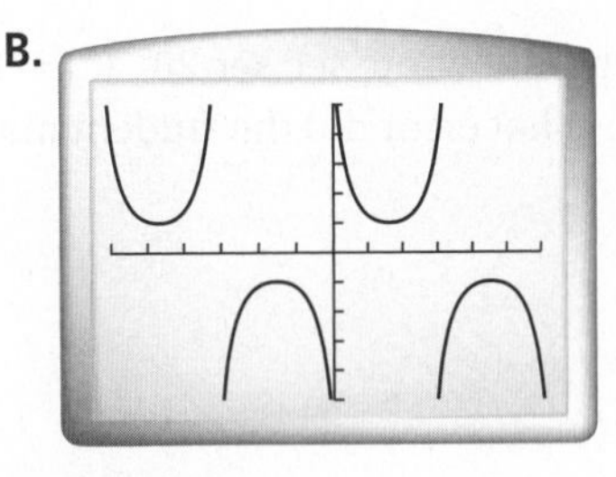

**C.**

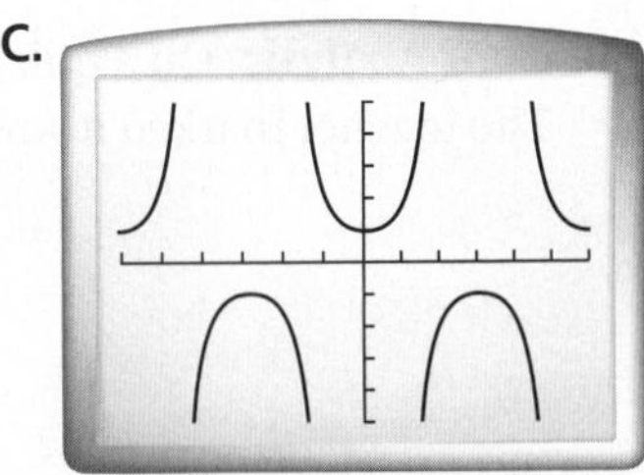

**Graph each function in the interval from 0 to $2\pi$.**

**23.** $y = \csc \theta - \frac{\pi}{2}$

**24.** $y = \sec \frac{1}{4}\theta$

**25.** $y = -\sec \pi\theta$

**26.** $y = \cot \frac{\theta}{3}$

**27. a.** What are the domain, range, and period of $y = \csc x$?

**b.** What is the relative minimum in the interval $0 \leq x \leq \pi$?

**c.** What is the relative maximum in the interval $\pi \leq x \leq 2\pi$?

**28. Reasoning** Use the relationship $\csc x = \frac{1}{\sin x}$ to explain why each statement is true.

**a.** When the graph of $y = \sin x$ is above the $x$-axis, so is the graph of $y = \csc x$.

**b.** When the graph of $y = \sin x$ is near a $y$-value of $-1$, so is the graph of $y = \csc x$.

**Writing** **Explain why each expression is undefined.**

**29.** $\csc 180°$ **30.** $\sec 90°$ **31.** $\cot 0°$

**32. Indirect Measurement** The fire ladder forms an angle of measure $\theta$ with the horizontal. The hinge of the ladder is 35 ft from the building. The function $y = 35 \sec \theta$ models the length $y$ in feet that the fire ladder must be to reach the building.

**a.** Graph the function.

**b.** In the photo, $\theta = 13°$. What is the ladder's length?

**c.** How far is the ladder extended when it forms an angle of 30°?

**d.** Suppose the ladder is extended to its full length of 80 ft. What angle does it form with the horizontal? How far up a building can the ladder reach when fully extended? (*Hint*: Use the information in the photo.)

**33. a.** Graph $y = \tan x$ and $y = \cot x$ on the same axes.

**b.** State the domain, range, and asymptotes of each function.

**c. Compare and Contrast** Compare the two graphs. How are they alike? How are they different?

**d. Geometry** The graph of the tangent function is a reflection image of the graph of the cotangent function. Name at least two reflection lines for such a transformation.

**Graphing Calculator** **Graph each function in the interval from 0 to $2\pi$. Describe any phase shift and vertical shift in the graph.**

**34.** $y = \sec 2\theta + 3$ **35.** $y = \sec 2(\theta + \frac{\pi}{2})$ **36.** $y = -2\sec(x - 4)$

**37.** $f(x) = 3\csc(x + 2) - 1$ **38.** $y = \cot 2(x + \pi) + 3$ **39.** $g(x) = 2\sec\left(3\left(x - \frac{\pi}{6}\right)\right) - 2$

**40. a.** Graph $y = -\cos x$ and $y = -\sec x$ on the same axes.

**b.** State the domain, range, and period of each function.

**c.** For which values of $x$ does $-\cos x = -\sec x$? Justify your answer.

**d. Compare and Contrast** Compare the two graphs. How are they alike? How are they different?

**e. Reasoning** Is the value of $-\sec x$ positive when $-\cos x$ is positive and negative when $-\cos x$ is negative? Justify your answer.

**41. a. Reasoning** Which expression gives the correct value of $\csc 60°$?

**I.** $\sin((60^{-1})^{\circ})$ **II.** $(\sin 60^{\circ})^{-1}$ **III.** $(\cos 60^{\circ})^{-1}$

**b.** Which expression in part (a) represents $\sin\left(\frac{1}{60}\right)^{\circ}$?

## Challenge

**42. Reasoning** Each branch of $y = \sec x$ and $y = \csc x$ is a curve. Explain why these curves cannot be parabolas. (*Hint*: Do parabolas have asymptotes?)

**43. Reasoning** Consider the relationship between the graphs of $y = \cos x$ and $y = \cos 3x$. Use the relationship to explain the distance between successive branches of the graphs of $y = \sec x$ and $y = \sec 3x$.

**44. a.** Graph $y = \cot x$, $y = \cot(2x)$, $y = \cot(-2x)$, and $y = \cot \frac{1}{2}x$ for $x \geq 0$ on the same axes.

**b. Make a Conjecture** Describe how the graph of $y = \cot bx$ changes as the value of $b$ changes.

# 8-9 Trigonometric Identities

**F.TF.8** Prove the Pythagorean identity $\sin^2(\theta) + \cos^2(\theta) = 1$ . . . find $\sin(\theta)$, $\cos(\theta)$, or $\tan(\theta)$, given $\sin(\theta)$, $\cos(\theta)$, or $\tan(\theta)$, and the quadrant of the angle.

**Objective** To verify trigonometric identities

**Solve It!** Write your solution to the Solve It in the space below.

You may recognize $x^2 = 5x - 6$ as an equation that you are to solve to find the few, if any, values of $x$ that make the equation true. On the other hand, you may recognize $\frac{x^5}{x^3} = x^2$ to be an example of an *identity*, an equation in which all values of $x$ make the equation true, except those values for which the expressions in the equation are undefined. (Here, $\frac{x^5}{x^3}$ is not defined for $x = 0$.)

A **trigonometric identity** in one variable is a trigonometric equation that is true for all values of the variable for which all expressions in the equation are defined.

**Essential Understanding** The interrelationships among the six basic trigonometric functions make it possible to write trigonometric expressions in various equivalent forms, some of which can be significantly easier to work with than others in mathematical applications.

Some trigonometric identities are definitions or follow immediately from definitions.

take note

## Key Concept Basic Identities

**Reciprocal Identities** $\csc\theta = \frac{1}{\sin\theta}$ $\sec\theta = \frac{1}{\cos\theta}$ $\tan\theta = \frac{1}{\cot\theta}$

$\sin\theta = \frac{1}{\csc\theta}$ $\cos\theta = \frac{1}{\sec\theta}$ $\cot\theta = \frac{1}{\tan\theta}$

**Tangent Identity** $\tan\theta = \frac{\sin\theta}{\cos\theta}$ **Cotangent Identity** $\cot\theta = \frac{\cos\theta}{\sin\theta}$

The *domain of validity* of an identity is the set of values of the variable for which all expressions in the equation are defined.

## Problem 1 Finding the Domain of Validity

**Got It?** What is the domain of validity of the trigonometric identity $\sin\theta = \frac{1}{\csc\theta}$?

**Plan**
When is $\csc\theta$ undefined?

**Practice** Give the domain of validity for each identity.

**1.** $\cos\theta\cot\theta = \frac{1}{\sin\theta} - \sin\theta$

**2.** $\sin\theta\cot\theta = \cos\theta$

You can use known identities to verify other identities. To verify an identity, you can use previously known identities to transform one side of the equation to look like the other side.

## Problem 2 Verifying an Identity Using Basic Identities

**Got It?** Verify the identity $\frac{\csc\theta}{\sec\theta} = \cot\theta$. What is the domain of validity?

**Plan**
What identities do you know that you can use?

**Practice** Verify each identity. Give the domain of validity for each identity.

3. $\cos\theta \tan\theta = \sin\theta$

4. $\sin\theta \sec\theta = \tan\theta$

You can use the unit circle and the Pythagorean Theorem to verify another identity. The circle with its center at the origin with a radius of 1 is called the unit circle, and has an equation $x^2 + y^2 = 1$.

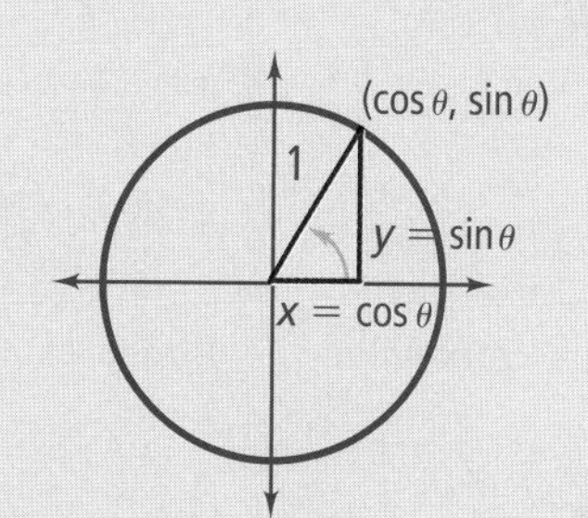


Every angle $\theta$ determines a unique point on the unit circle with $x$- and $y$-coordinates $(x, y) = (\cos\theta, \sin\theta)$.

Therefore, for every angle $\theta$,
$(\cos\theta)^2 + (\sin\theta)^2 = 1$ or $\cos^2\theta + \sin^2\theta = 1$.

This form allows you to write the identity without using parentheses.

This is a Pythagorean identity. You will verify two others in Problem 3.

You can use the basic and Pythagorean identities to verify other identities. To prove identities, transform the expression on one side of the equation to the expression on the other side. It often helps to write everything in terms of sines and cosines.

## Problem 3 Verifying a Pythagorean Identity

**Got It?** a. Verify the third Pythagorean identity, $1 + \cot^2\theta = \csc^2\theta$.

b. **Reasoning** Explain why the domain of validity is not the same for all three Pythagorean identities.

**Practice** Verify each identity. Give the domain of validity for each identity.

5. $\cos\theta \sec\theta = 1$

6. $\tan\theta \cot\theta = 1$

You have now seen all three Pythagorean identities.

take note

## Key Concept Pythagorean Identities

$\cos^2\theta + \sin^2\theta = 1$ $\qquad 1 + \tan^2\theta = \sec^2\theta$ $\qquad 1 + \cot^2\theta = \csc^2\theta$

There are many trigonometric identities. Most do not have specific names.

ONLINE PROBLEMS

## Problem 4 Verifying an Identity

**Got It?** Verify the identity $\sec^2\theta - \sec^2\theta\cos^2\theta = \tan^2\theta$.

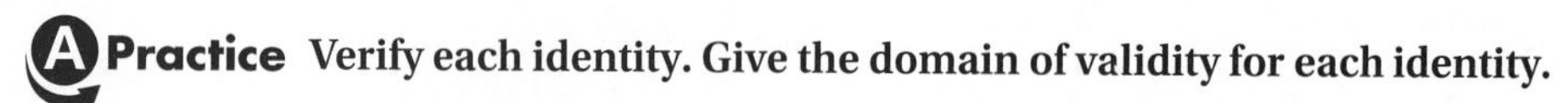

**A Practice** **Verify each identity. Give the domain of validity for each identity.**

**7.** $\cot\theta = \csc\theta\cos\theta$

**8.** $\csc\theta - \sin\theta = \cot\theta\cos\theta$

You can use trigonometric identities to simplify trigonometric expressions.

## Problem 5 Simplifying an Expression

**Got It?** What is a simplified trigonometric expression for $\sec\theta \cot\theta$?

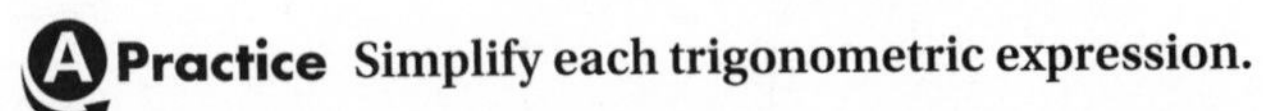

**Practice** **Simplify each trigonometric expression.**

**9.** $\sec\theta \cos\theta \sin\theta$

**10.** $\sec^2\theta - \tan^2\theta$

## Lesson Check

### Do you know HOW?

**Verify each identity.**

**11.** $\tan\theta \csc\theta = \sec\theta$

12. $\csc^2\theta - \cot^2\theta = 1$

13. $\sin\theta\tan\theta = \sec\theta - \cos\theta$

14. Simplify $\tan\theta\cot\theta - \sin^2\theta$.

### Do you UNDERSTAND?

15. **Vocabulary** How does the identity $\cos^2\theta + \sin^2\theta = 1$ relate to the Pythagorean Theorem?

**16. Error Analysis** A student simplified the expression $2 - \cos^2\theta$ to $1 - \sin^2\theta$. What error did the student make? What is the correct simplified expression?

## More Practice and Problem-Solving Exercises

### B Apply

**17. Think About a Plan** Simplify the expression $\frac{\tan\theta}{\sec\theta - \cos\theta}$.

- Can you write everything in terms of $\sin\theta$, $\cos\theta$, or both?
- Are there any trigonometric identities that can help you simplify the expression?

**Simplify each trigonometric expression.**

**18.** $\cos\theta + \sin\theta\tan\theta$

**19.** $\csc\theta\cos\theta\tan\theta$

**20.** $\tan\theta(\cot\theta + \tan\theta)$

**21.** $\sin^2\theta + \cos^2\theta + \tan^2\theta$

**22.** $\sin\theta(1 + \cot^2\theta)$

**23.** $\sin^2\theta\csc\theta\sec\theta$

**24.** $\sec\theta\cos\theta - \cos^2\theta$

**25.** $\csc\theta - \cos\theta\cot\theta$

**26.** $\csc^2\theta(1 - \cos^2\theta)$

**27.** $\frac{\csc\theta}{\sin\theta + \cos\theta\cot\theta}$

**28.** $\frac{\cos\theta\csc\theta}{\cot\theta}$

**29.** $\frac{\sin^2\theta\csc\theta\sec\theta}{\tan\theta}$

**Express the first trigonometric function in terms of the second.**

**30.** $\sin\theta$, $\cos\theta$

**31.** $\tan\theta$, $\cos\theta$

**32.** $\cot\theta$, $\sin\theta$

**33.** $\csc\theta$, $\cot\theta$

**34.** $\cot\theta$, $\csc\theta$

**35.** $\sec\theta$, $\tan\theta$

**Verify each identity.**

**36.** $\sin^2\theta\tan^2\theta = \tan^2\theta - \sin^2\theta$

**37.** $\sec\theta - \sin\theta\tan\theta = \cos\theta$

**38.** $\sin\theta\cos\theta(\tan\theta + \cot\theta) = 1$

**39.** $\frac{1 - \sin\theta}{\cos\theta} = \frac{\cos\theta}{1 + \sin\theta}$

**40.** $\frac{\sec\theta}{\cot\theta + \tan\theta} = \sin\theta$

**41.** $(\cot\theta + 1)^2 = \csc^2\theta + 2\cot\theta$

**42.** Express $\cos\theta\csc\theta\cot\theta$ in terms of $\sin\theta$.

**43.** Express $\frac{\cos\theta}{\sec\theta + \tan\theta}$ in terms of $\sin\theta$.

**Use the identity $\sin^2\theta + \cos^2\theta = 1$ and the basic identities to answer the following questions. Show all your work.**

**44.** Given that $\sin\theta = 0.5$ and $\theta$ is in the first quadrant, what are $\cos\theta$ and $\tan\theta$?

**45.** Given that $\sin\theta = 0.5$ and $\theta$ is in the second quadrant, what are $\cos\theta$ and $\tan\theta$?

**46.** Given that $\cos\theta = -0.6$ and $\theta$ is in the third quadrant, what are $\sin\theta$ and $\tan\theta$?

**47.** Given that $\sin\theta = 0.48$ and $\theta$ is in the second quadrant, what are $\cos\theta$ and $\tan\theta$?

**48.** Given that $\tan\theta = 1.2$ and $\theta$ is in the first quadrant, what are $\sin\theta$ and $\cos\theta$?

**49.** Given that $\tan\theta = 3.6$ and $\theta$ is in the third quadrant, what are $\sin\theta$ and $\cos\theta$?

**50.** Given that $\sin\theta = 0.2$ and $\tan\theta < 0$, what is $\cos\theta$?

## Challenge

**51.** The unit circle is a useful tool for verifying identities. Use the diagram at the right to verify the identity $\sin(\theta + \pi) = -\sin\theta$.

**a.** Explain why the $y$-coordinate of point $P$ is $\sin(\theta + \pi)$.

**b.** Prove that the two triangles shown are congruent.

**c.** Use part (b) to show that the two blue segments are congruent.

**d.** Use part (c) to show that the $y$-coordinate of $P$ is $-\sin\theta$.

**e.** Use parts (a) and (d) to conclude that $\sin(\theta + \pi) = -\sin\theta$.

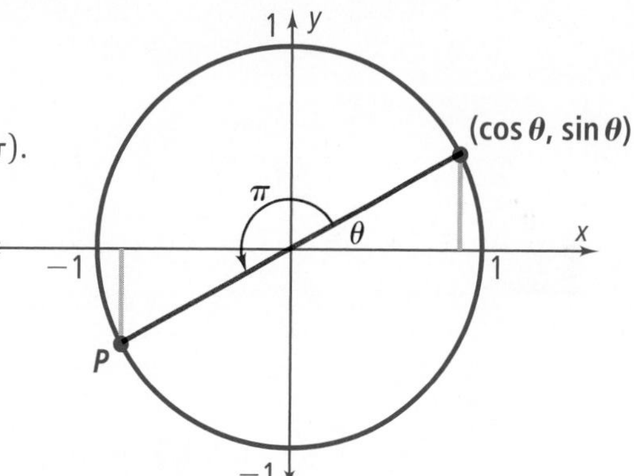


**Use the diagram in Exercise 51 to verify each identity.**

**52.** $\cos(\theta + \pi) = -\cos\theta$

**53.** $\tan(\theta + \pi) = \tan\theta$

**Simplify each trigonometric expression.**

**54.** $\dfrac{\cot^2\theta - \csc^2\theta}{\tan^2\theta - \sec^2\theta}$

**55.** $(1 - \sin\theta)(1 + \sin\theta)\csc^2\theta + 1$

**56. Physics** When a ray of light passes from one medium into a second, the angle of incidence $\theta_1$ and the angle of refraction $\theta_2$ are related by Snell's law: $n_1 \sin\theta_1 = n_2 \sin\theta_2$, where $n_1$ is the index of refraction of the first medium and $n_2$ is the index of refraction of the second medium. How are $\theta_1$ and $\theta_2$ related if $n_2 > n_1$? If $n_2 < n_1$? If $n_2 = n_1$?

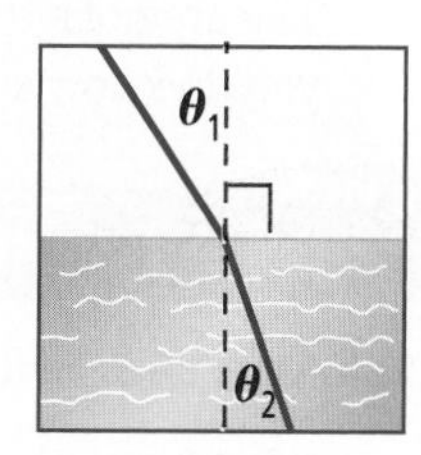

# Area and the Law of Sines

**G.SRT.11** Understand and apply the Law of Sines . . . to find unknown measurements in right and non-right triangles . . . Also **G.SRT.9, G.SRT.10**

**Objectives** To find the area of any triangle
To use the Law of Sines

**Solve It!** Write your solution to the Solve It in the space below.

Recall from geometry that if you know three parts of a triangle then you can sometimes *solve the triangle*; that is, you can determine its complete shape. This is what the congruence statements SAS, ASA, AAS, SSS were all about.

**Essential Understanding** If you know two angles and a side of a triangle, you can use trigonometry to solve the triangle. If you know two sides and the included angle, you can find the area of the triangle.

The area of a triangle with base $b$ and height $h$ is $\frac{1}{2}bh$. When you don't know $h$ but you do know an angle measure, there may be another way to find the area.

**take note**

### Formula Area of a Triangle

Any $\triangle ABC$ with side lengths $a$, $b$, and $c$ has area

$\frac{1}{2}bc \sin A = \frac{1}{2}ac \sin B = \frac{1}{2}ab \sin C.$

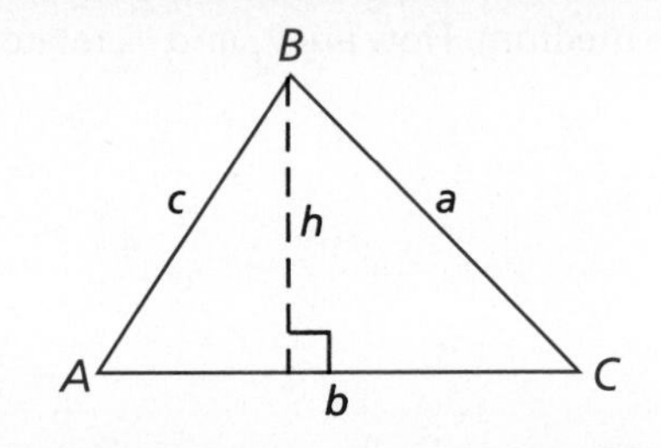


**Here's Why It Works** The area of the triangle above is $\frac{1}{2}bh$ . The altitude $h$ to side $AC$ completes a right triangle. Thus, $\sin A = \frac{h}{c}$, so $h = c \sin A$. Substituting $c \sin A$ for $h$ you get, $\frac{1}{2}bh = \frac{1}{2}bc \sin A$. You can derive $\frac{1}{2}ac \sin B$ and $\frac{1}{2}ab \sin C$ in a similar way.

## Problem 1 Finding the Area of a Triangle

**Got It?** A triangle has sides of 12 in. and 15 in. The measure of the angle between them is 24°. What is the area of the triangle?

**Plan**
**Can you use the area formula?**

**A Practice** **Find the area of each triangle. Round your answer to the nearest tenth.**

**1.**

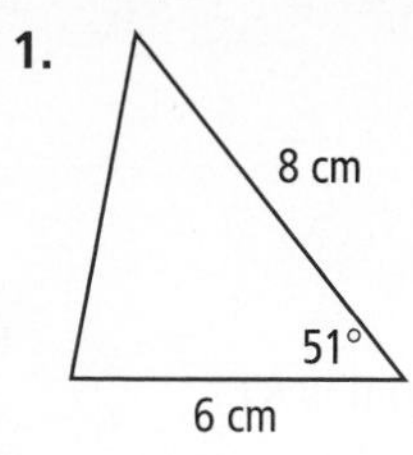


**2.**

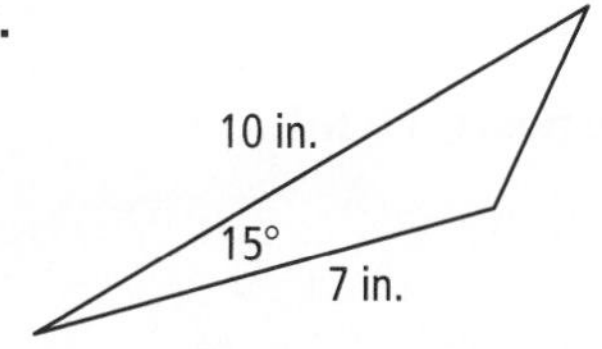


The relationship $\frac{1}{2}bc \sin A = \frac{1}{2}ac \sin B = 12\, ab \sin C$ yields an important formula when you divide each expression by $\frac{1}{2}abc$. The formula, known as the Law of Sines, relates the sines of the angles of a triangle to the lengths of their opposite sides.

take note

### Theorem 109 Law of Sines

In any triangle, the ratio of the sine of each angle to its opposite side is constant. In particular, for $\triangle ABC$, labeled as shown,

$$\frac{\sin A}{a} = \frac{\sin B}{b} = \frac{\sin C}{c}.$$

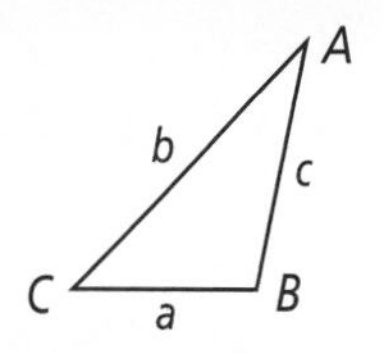

You can use the Law of Sines to find missing measures of any triangle when you know the measures of

- two angles and any side, or
- two sides and an obtuse angle opposite one of them.
- two sides and an acute angle opposite one of them, where the length of the side opposite the known acute angle is greater than or equal to the length of the remaining known side.

In Problem 2, you know the measures of two angles and a side (AAS). In Problem 3, you know the measures of two sides and an obtuse angle opposite one of them (SSA with $A$ obtuse).

## Finding a Side of a Triangle

**Plan**

**How can drawing a diagram help?**

**Got It?** In $\triangle KLM$, $m\angle K = 120^\circ$, $m\angle M = 50^\circ$, and $ML = 35$ yd. What is $KL$?

**Practice** **Use the Law of Sines. Find the measure $x$ to the nearest tenth.**

**3.**

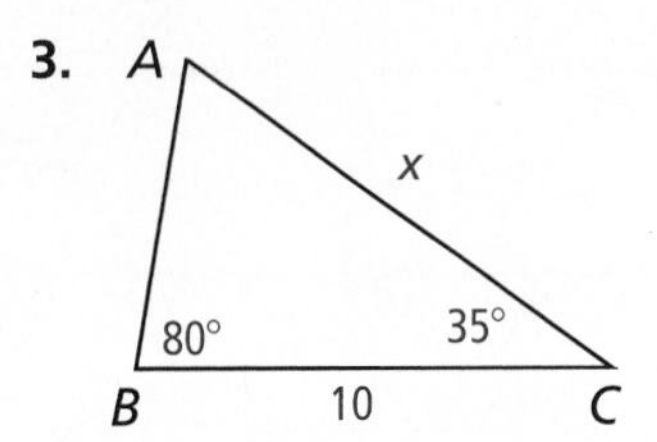


**4.**

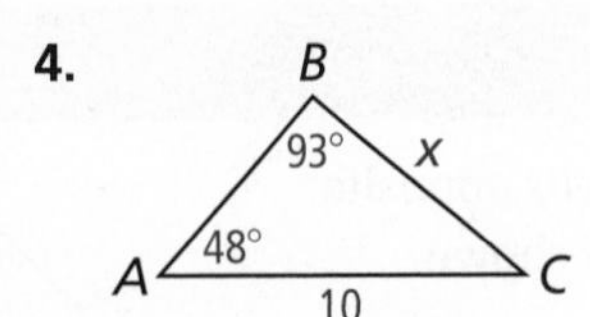

## Problem 3 Finding an Angle of a Triangle

**Got It?** **a.** In $\triangle PQR$, $m\angle R = 97.5°$, $r = 80$, and $p = 75$. What is $m\angle P$?

**b.** In Problem 3, can you use the Law of Sines to find the heights of the triangle? Explain your answer.

**Practice** **Use the Law of Sines. Find the measure $x$ to the nearest tenth.**

**5.**

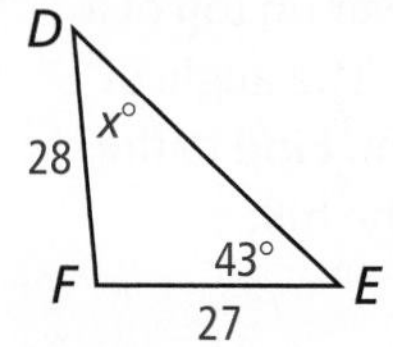


**6.**

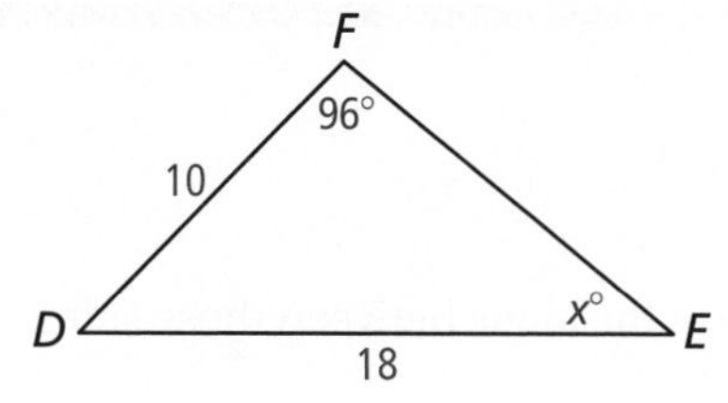

In the SSA case, if the known nonincluded angle is acute, you have an ambiguous situation. Inverse sine is not able to distinguish whether a second angle is, say, 47° or 133°.

In the SAS and SSS congruence situations, the Law of Sines is not useful because you do not have a known angle paired with a known opposite side. You will find out how to solve these triangles in the next lesson.

## Problem 4 Using the Law of Sines to Solve a Problem

**Got It?** A landscaper sights the top of a tree at a 68°angle. She then moves an additional 70 ft directly away from the tree and sights the top at a 43° angle. How tall is the tree to the nearest tenth of a foot?

**Practice** 7. **Surveying** The distance from you to the base of a tower on top of a hill is 2760 ft. The angle of elevation of the base is 26°. The angle of elevation of the top of the tower is 32°. Draw a diagram. Find to the nearest foot the height of the tower above the top of the hill.

## Lesson Check

### Do you know HOW?

**8.** A triangle has sides 2.4 and 9.0 and the measure of the angle between those sides is 98°. What is the area of the triangle?

**9.** In $\triangle PQR$, $m\angle P = 85°$, $m\angle R = 54°$, and $QR = 30$. What is $PR$?

**10.** In $\triangle HJK$, $m\angle J = 14°$, $HK = 6$, and $JK = 11$. What is $m\angle H$?

## Do you UNDERSTAND?

**11. Vocabulary** Suppose you are given information about a triangle according to SSS, SAS, AAS, and ASA. For which of these can you immediately use the Law of Sines to find one of the remaining measures?

**12. Error Analysis** Suppose you used the Law of Sines and wrote $a = \frac{3 \sin 22°}{\sin 45°}$. Is that the same equation as $a = 3 \sin\left(\frac{22}{45}\right)°$? Explain.

## More Practice and Problem-Solving Exercises

### B Apply

13. **Think About a Plan** One of the congruent sides of an isosceles triangle is 10 cm long. One of the congruent angles has a measure of 54°. Find the perimeter of the triangle. Round your answer to the nearest centimeter.
    - Can drawing a diagram help you solve this problem?
    - What information do you need before finding the perimeter?
    - How can you find that information?

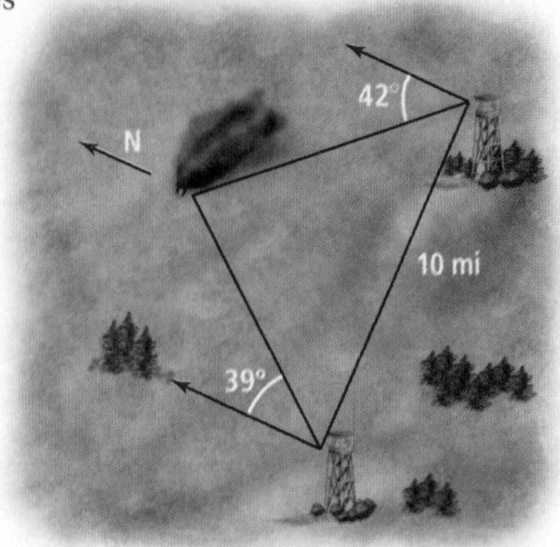


14. **Forestry** A forest ranger in an observation tower sights a fire 39° east of north. A ranger in a tower 10 miles due east of the first tower sights the fire at 42° west of north. How far is the fire from each tower?

15. **Geometry** The sides of a triangle are 15 in., 17 in., and 16 in. The smallest angle has a measure of 54°. Find the measure of the largest angle. Round to the nearest degree.

**Find the remaining sides and angles of $\triangle DEF$. Round your answers to the nearest tenth.**

16. $m\angle D = 54°$, $m\angle E = 54°$, and $d = 20$

17. $m\angle D = 54°$, $e = 8$, and $d = 10$

18. **Reasoning** In $\triangle ABC$, $a = 10$ and $b = 15$.
    a. Does the triangle have a greater area when $m\angle C = 1°$ or when $m\angle C = 50°$?
    b. Does the triangle have a greater area when $m\angle C = 50°$ or when $m\angle C = 179°$?
    c. For what measure of $\angle C$ does $\triangle ABC$ have the greatest area? Explain.

19. **Open-Ended** Sketch a triangle. Specify three of its measures, and then use the Law of Sines to find the remaining measures.

**Find the area of $\triangle ABC$. Round your answer to the nearest tenth.**

20. $m\angle C = 68°$, $b = 12.9$, $c = 15.2$

21. $m\angle A = 52°$, $a = 9.71$, $c = 9.33$

22. $m\angle A = 23°$, $m\angle C = 39°$, $b = 14.6$

23. $m\angle B = 87°$, $a = 10.1$, $c = 9.8$

**In $\triangle ABC$, $m\angle A = 40°$ and $m\angle B = 30°$. Find each value to the nearest tenth.**

24. Find $AC$ for $BC = 10.5$ m.

25. Find $BC$ for $AC = 21.8$ ft.

26. Find $AC$ for $AB = 81.2$ yd.

27. Find $BC$ for $AB = 5.9$ cm.

28. **Measurement** A vacant lot is in the shape of an isosceles triangle. It is between two streets that intersect at an 85.9° angle. Each of the sides of the lot that face these streets is 150 ft long. Find the perimeter of the lot to the nearest foot.

**29. a.** In the diagram at the right, $m\angle A = 30°$, $AB = 10$, and $BC = BD = 6$. Use the Law of Sines to find $m\angle D$, $m\angle ABD$, and $m\angle ABC$.

**b. Reasoning** Notice that two sides and a nonincluded angle of $\triangle ABC$ are congruent to the corresponding parts of $\triangle ABD$, but the triangles are not congruent. Must $\triangle EFG$ be congruent to $\triangle ABD$ if $EF = 10$, $FG = 6$, and $\angle E \approx \angle A$? Explain.

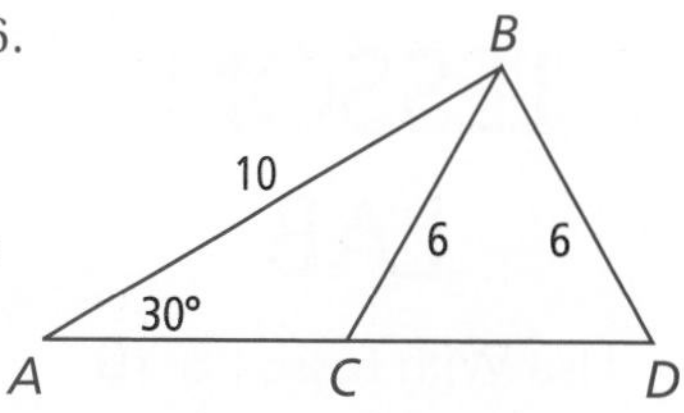


## Challenge

**30. Sailing** Buoys are located in the sea at points $A$, $B$, and $C$. $\angle ACB$ is a right angle. $AC = 3.0$ mi, $BC = 4.0$ mi, and $AB = 5.0$ mi. A ship is located at point $D$ on $\overline{AB}$ so that $m\angle ACD = 30°$. How far is the ship from the buoy at point $C$? Round your answer to the nearest tenth of a mile.

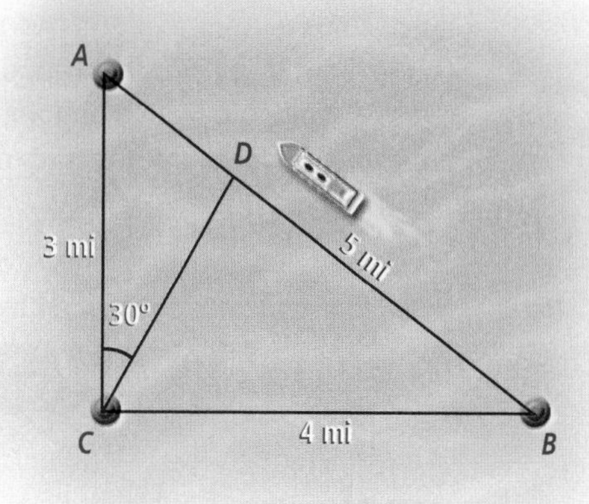


**31. Writing** Suppose you know the measures of all three angles of a triangle. Can you use the Law of Sines to find the lengths of the sides? Explain.

LESSON LAB

Use With Lesson 8-10

# The Ambiguous Case

**G.SRT.11** Understand and apply the Law of Sines . . . to find unknown measurements in right and non-right triangles . . .

The triangles at the right have one pair of congruent angles and two pairs of congruent sides. But the triangles are not congruent. Notice that the congruent angles are not included by the congruent sides.

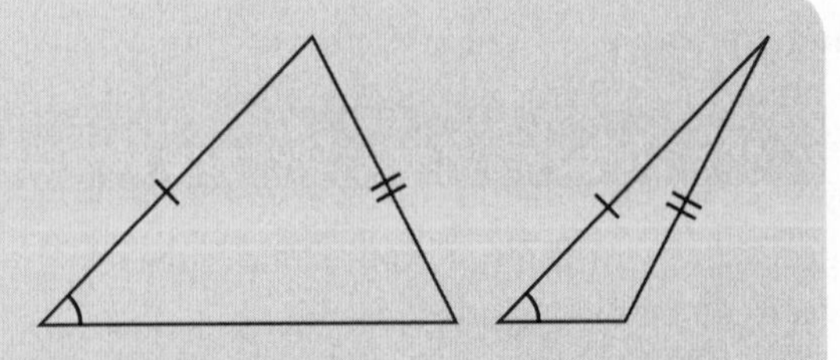

When you know the measures of two sides of a triangle and one of the opposite angles, there may be two triangles with those measurements. You can use the Law of Sines to find the other measures for both triangles.

## Example

**In each $\triangle ABC$ at the right, $m\angle A = 35°$, $a = 11$, and $b = 15$. Find $m\angle B$.**

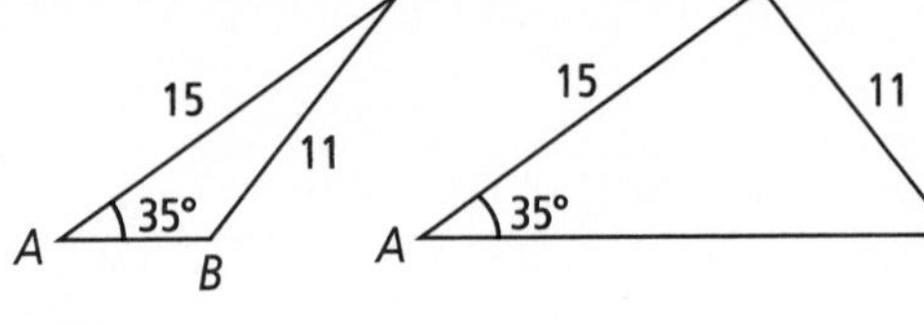


$\frac{\sin A}{a} = \frac{\sin B}{b}$ Law of Sines

$\frac{\sin 35°}{11} = \frac{\sin B}{15}$ Substitute.

$\sin B = \frac{15 \sin 35°}{11}$ Solve for sin *B*.

$m\angle B = \sin^{-1}\left(\frac{15 \sin 35°}{11}\right) \approx 51°$ Solve for $m\angle B$. Use a calculator.

The sine function is also positive in Quadrant II. So another value of $m\angle B$ is about $180° - 51° = 129°$.

Because there are two possible angle measures for $\angle B$, there are two triangles that satisfy the given conditions. In one triangle the angle measures are about 35°, 51°, and 94°. In the other, the angle measures are about 35°, 129°, and 16°.

## Exercises

**In each $\triangle ABC$, find the measures for $\angle B$ and $\angle C$ that satisfy the given conditions. Draw diagrams to help you decide whether two triangles are possible.**

**1.** $m\angle A = 62°$, $a = 30$, and $b = 32$

**2.** $m\angle A = 16°$, $a = 12$, and $b = 37.5$

**3.** $m\angle A = 48°$, $a = 93$, and $b = 125$

**4.** $m\angle A = 112°$, $a = 16.5$, and $b = 5.4$

**5.** $m\angle A = 23.6°$, $a = 9.8$, and $b = 17$

**6.** $m\angle A = 155°$, $a = 12.5$, and $b = 8.4$

**7. Multiple Choice** You can construct a triangle with compass and straightedge when given three parts of the triangle (except for three angles). Which of the following given sets could result in the ambiguous case?

**A** Given: three sides

**B** Given: two sides and an included angle

**C** Given: two angles and a nonincluded side

**D** Given: two sides and a nonincluded angle

# 8-11 The Law of Cosines

G.SRT.10 Prove the Law . . . of Cosines . . . Also G.SRT.11

**Objective** To use the Law of Cosines in finding the measures of sides and angles of a triangle

**Solve It!** Write your solution to the Solve It in the space below.

The measures of all three sides (SSS) or the measures of two sides and the included angle (SAS) determine a triangle. The Law of Sines does not enable you to solve such a triangle, but the Law of Cosines does.

**Essential Understanding** If you know the measures of enough parts of a triangle to completely determine the triangle, you can solve the triangle.

The Law of Cosines relates the length of a side of any triangle to the measure of the opposite angle.

take note

## Theorem 110 Law of Cosines

In $\triangle ABC$, let $a$, $b$, and $c$ represent the lengths of the sides opposite $\angle A$, $\angle B$, and $\angle C$, respectively.

- $a^2 = b^2 + c^2 - 2bc \cos A$
- $b^2 = a^2 + c^2 - 2ac \cos B$
- $c^2 = a^2 + b^2 - 2ab \cos C$

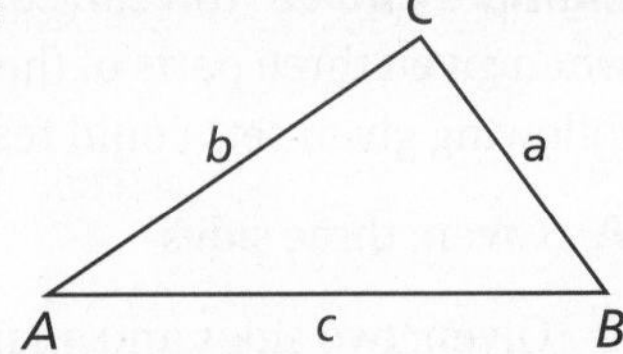

### Here's Why It Works

In this $\triangle ABC$ with altitude $h$, let $AD = x$.

Then $DB = c - x$.

In $\triangle ADC$, $b^2 = x^2 + h^2$

and $\cos A = \frac{x}{b}$ or $x = b \cos A$.

In $\triangle CBD$,

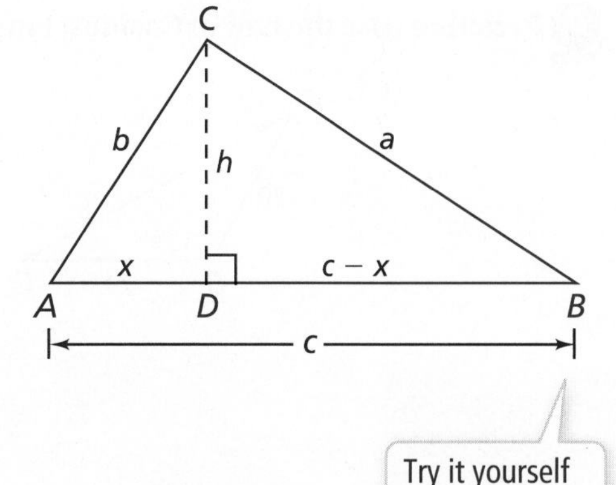


| | |
|---|---|
| $a^2 = (c - x)^2 + h^2$ | Pythagorean Theorem |
| $= c^2 - 2cx + x^2 + h^2$ | Square the binomial. |
| $= c^2 - 2cx + b^2$ | Substitute $b^2$ for $x^2 + h^2$. |
| $= c^2 - 2cb \cos A + b^2$ | Substitute $b \cos A$ for $x$. |
| $= b^2 + c^2 - 2bc \cos A$ | Commutative Properties of Addition and Multiplication |

Try it yourself for obtuse $\angle B$.

The last equation is the Law of Cosines.

ONLINE PROBLEMS

## Problem 1 Using the Law of Cosines to Solve a Problem

**Got It?** **a.** The lengths of two sides of a triangle are 8 and 10, and the measure of the angle between them is 40°. What is the approximate length of the third side?

**b. Reasoning** The measure of the included angle for the course in Problem 1 can be between 0° and 180°. Between what lengths can the length of the third side be? Explain your answer.

**A Practice** **Use the Law of Cosines. Find length $x$ to the nearest tenth.**

1. 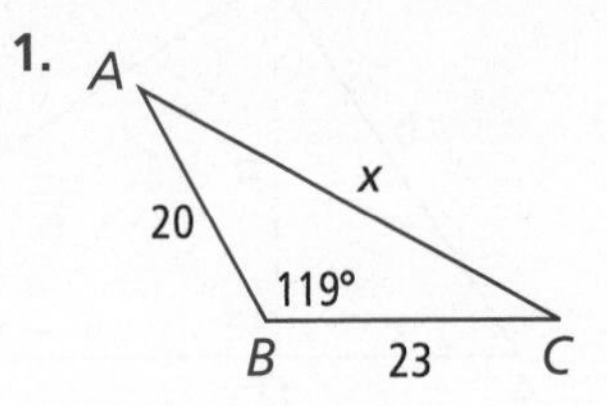


2. 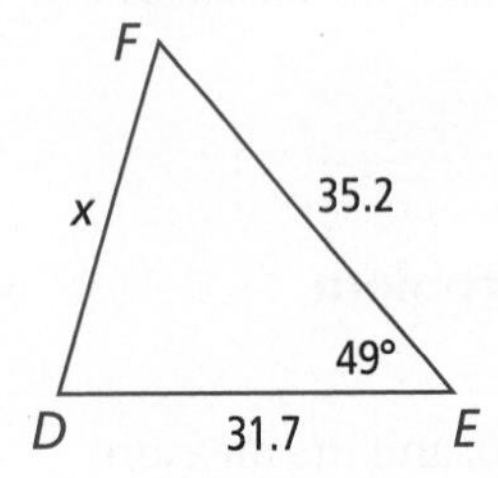


You can also use the Law of Cosines with triangles determined by the measures of all three sides (SSS).

## Problem 2 Finding an Angle Measure

**Got It?** The lengths of the sides of a triangle are 10, 14, and 15. What is the measure of the angle opposite the longest side?

**Plan**
**What form of the Law of Cosines should you use?**

**Practice** **Use the Law of Cosines. Find $x$ to the nearest tenth.**

**3.**

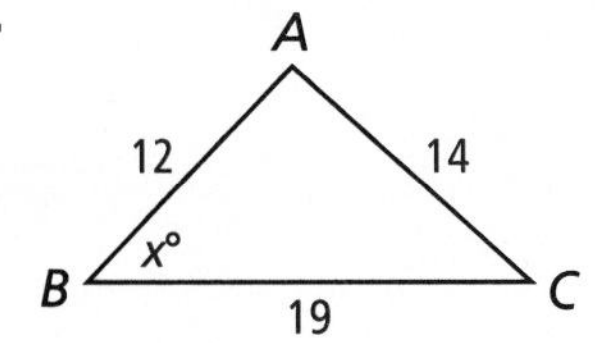


**4.**

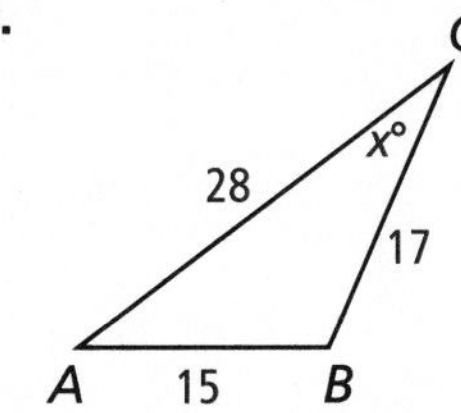


Sometimes you need to use the Law of Cosines followed by the Law of Cosines again or by the Law of Sines.

## Problem 3 Finding an Angle Measure

**Got It?** In $\triangle RST$, $s = 41$, $t = 53$, and $m\angle R = 126°$. What is $m\angle T$?

**Plan**
**How can drawing a figure help?**

**Practice** **Use the Law of Cosines and the Law of Sines. Find $x$ to the nearest tenth.**

**5.**

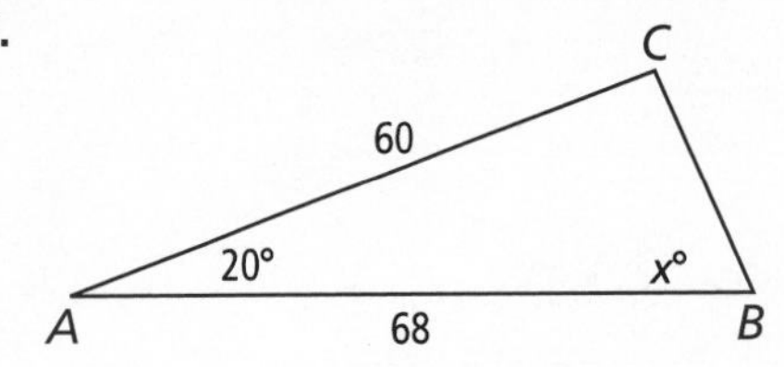


**6.**

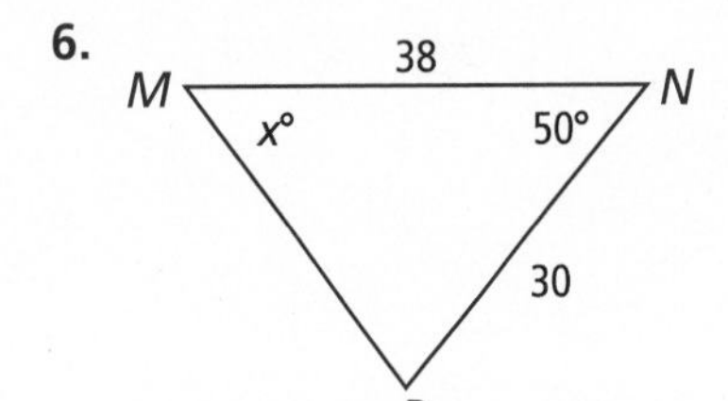

## Lesson Check

### Do you know HOW?

**7.** In $\triangle ABC$, $m\angle B = 26°$, $a = 20$ in., and $c = 10$ in. Find $b$.

**8.** In $\triangle ABC$, $a = 8$ m, $b = 5$ m, and $c = 10$ m. Find $m\angle A$.

**9.** In $\triangle KNP$, $k = 21$ cm, $n = 12$ cm, and $m\angle P = 67°$. Find $m\angle N$.

**10.** In $\triangle WXY$, $w = 7.7$ ft, $x = 6.4$ ft, and $y = 8.5$ ft. Find $m\angle W$.

## Do you UNDERSTAND?

**11. Writing** Explain how you choose between the Law of Sines and the Law of Cosines when finding the measure of a missing angle or side.

**12. Error Analysis** A student solved for $m\angle C$, with $a = 11$ m, $b = 17$ m, and $c = 15$ m. What was the student's mistake?

$$\cos C = \frac{15^2 - 11^2 - 17^2}{2(11)(17)}$$

$$\cos C \approx -0.495$$

$$C = \cos^{-1}(-0.495) \approx 119.7^\circ$$

## More Practice and Problem-Solving Exercises

### B Apply

**For each triangle, write the correct form of the Law of Cosines or the Law of Sines to solve for the measure in red. Use only the information given in blue.**

13.

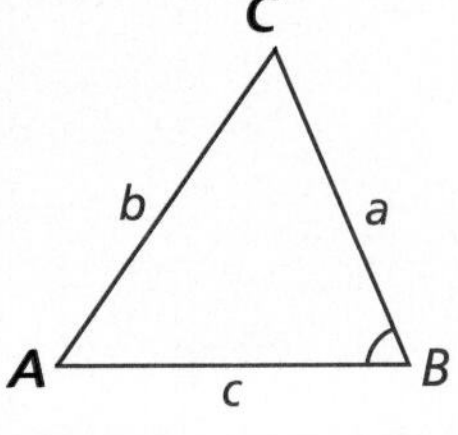


14.

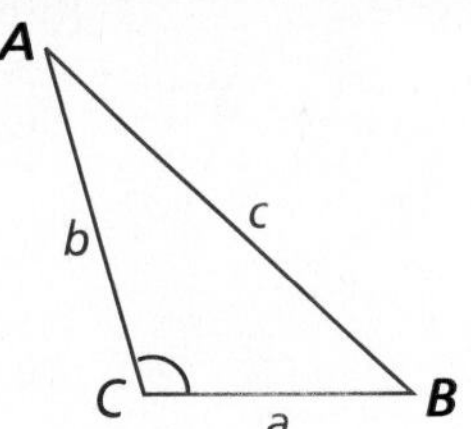


15.

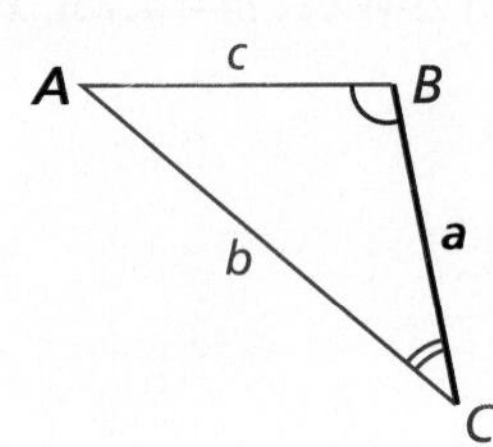


16.

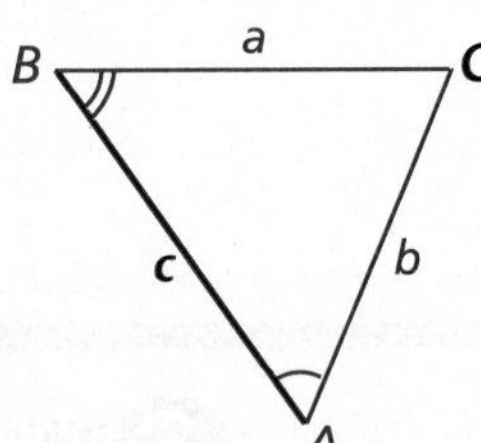


17.

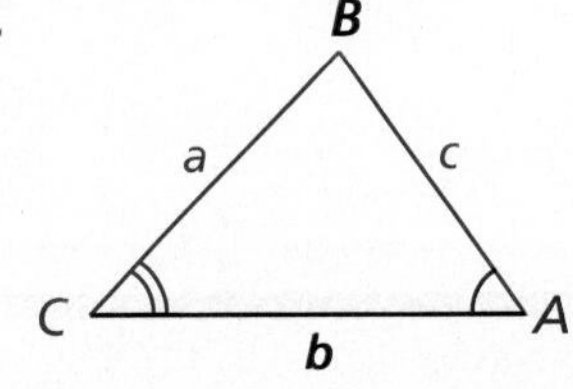


18.

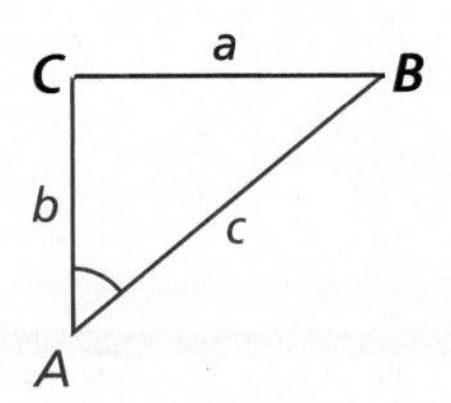


**19. Think About a Plan** A touring boat was heading toward an island 80 nautical miles due south of where it left port. After traveling 15 nautical miles, it headed 8° east of south to avoid a fleet of commercial fishermen. After traveling 6 nautical miles, it turned to head directly toward the island. How far was the boat from the island at the time it turned?

- Can a diagram help you understand the problem?
- What are you asked to find?
- Which measurements do you need to solve the problem?

**20. Sports** A softball diamond is a square that is 65 ft on a side. The pitcher's mound is 46 ft from home plate. How far is the pitcher from third base?

**Find the remaining sides and angles in each triangle. Round your answers to the nearest tenth.**

**21.**

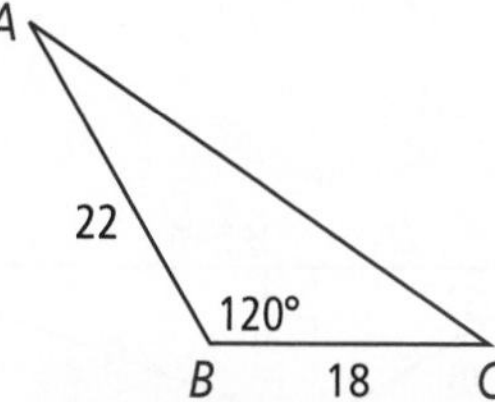


**22.**

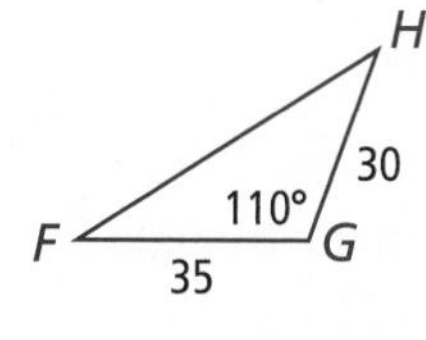


**23.**

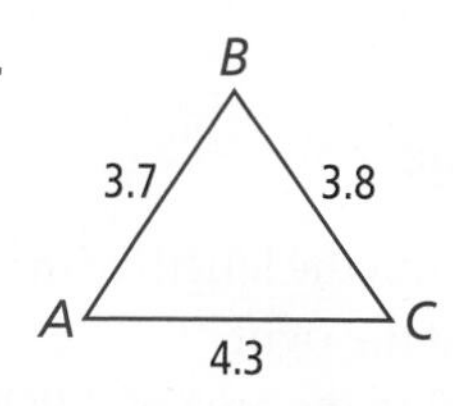


**24. a. Open-Ended** Sketch a triangle. Specify three of its measures so that you can use the Law of Cosines to find the remaining measures.

**b.** Solve for the remaining measures of the triangle.

**25. Writing** Given the measures of three angles of a triangle, explain how to find the ratio of the lengths of two sides of the triangle.

**26. Geometry** The lengths of the sides of a triangle are 7.6 cm, 8.2 cm, and 5.2 cm. Find the measure of the largest angle.

**27. Navigation** A pilot is flying from city A to city B, which is 85 mi due north. After flying 20 mi, the pilot must change course and fly 10° east of north to avoid a cloudbank.

**a.** If the pilot remains on this course for 20 mi, how far will the plane be from city B?

**b.** How many degrees will the pilot have to turn to the left to fly directly to city B? How many degrees from due north is this course?

**In $\triangle ABC$, $m\angle A = 53°$ and $c = 7$ cm. Find each value to the nearest tenth.**

**28.** Find $m\angle B$ for $b = 6.2$ cm.

**29.** Find $a$ for $b = 13.7$ cm.

**30.** Find $a$ for $b = 11$ cm.

**31.** Find $m\angle C$ for $b = 15.2$ cm.

**32.** Find $m\angle B$ for $b = 37$ cm.

**33.** Find $a$ for $b = 16$ cm.

**In $\triangle RST$, $t = 7$ ft and $s = 13$ ft. Find each value to the nearest tenth.**

**34.** Find $m\angle T$ for $r = 11$ ft.

**35.** Find $m\angle T$ for $r = 6.97$ ft.

**36.** Find $m\angle S$ for $r = 14$ ft.

**37.** Find $r$ for $m\angle R = 35°$.

**38.** Find $m\angle S$ for $m\angle R = 87°$.

**39.** Find $m\angle R$ for $m\angle S = 70°$.

**40. Geometry** The lengths of the adjacent sides of a parallelogram are 54 cm and 78 cm. The larger angle measures 110°. What is the length of the longer diagonal? Round your answer to the nearest centimeter.

**41. Geometry** The lengths of the adjacent sides of a parallelogram are 21 cm and 14 cm. The smaller angle measures 58°. What is the length of the shorter diagonal? Round your answer to the nearest centimeter.

**42. Reasoning** Does the Law of Cosines apply to a right triangle? That is, does $c^2 = a^2 + b^2 - 2ab \cos C$ remain true when $\angle C$ is a right angle? Justify your answer.

## Challenge

**43. a.** Find the length of the altitude to $\overline{PQ}$ in the triangle at the right.

**b.** Find the area of $\triangle PQR$.

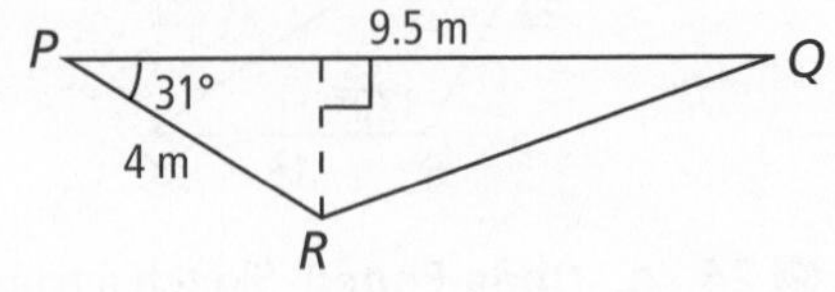


STEM **44. Physics** A pendulum 36 in. long swings 30° from the vertical. How high above the lowest position is the pendulum at the end of its swing? Round your answer to the nearest tenth of an inch.

**45. Reasoning** If you solve for $\cos A$ in the Law of Cosines, you get $\cos A = \frac{b^2 + c^2 - a^2}{2bc}$.

**a.** Use this formula to explain how $\cos A$ can be positive, zero, or negative, depending on how $b^2 + c^2$ compares to $a^2$.

**b.** What does this tell you about $\angle A$ in each case?

# 8 Chapter Review

## 8-1 Exploring Periodic Data

### Quick Review

A **periodic function** repeats a pattern of $y$-values at regular intervals. One complete pattern is called a **cycle.** A cycle may begin at any point on the graph. The **period** of a function is the length of one cycle. The **midline** is the line located midway between the maximum and the minimum values of the function. The **amplitude** of a periodic function is half the difference between its maximum and minimum values.

### Example

**What is the period of the periodic function?**

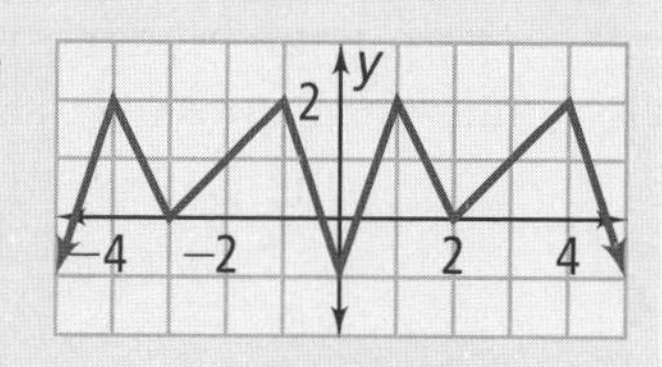

One cycle is 5 units long, so the period of the function is 5.

### Exercises

**1.** Determine whether the function below *is* or *is not* periodic. If it is, identify one cycle in two different ways and find the period and amplitude.

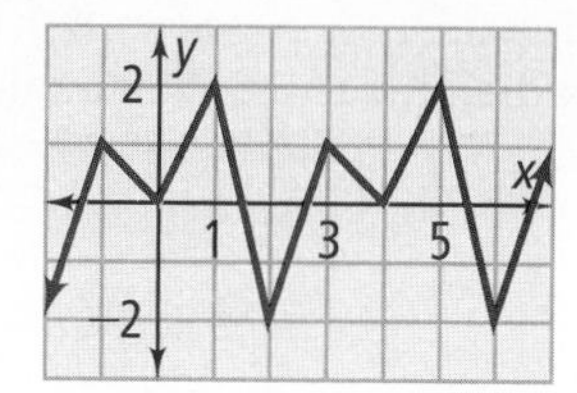

**2.** Sketch the graph of a wave with a period of 2, an amplitude of 4, and a midline of $y = 1$.

**3.** Sketch the graph of a wave with a period of 4, an amplitude of 3, and a midline of $y = 0$.

## 8-2 Angles and the Unit Circle

### Quick Review

An angle is in **standard position** if the vertex is at the origin and one ray, the **initial side**, is on the positive $x$-axis. The other ray is the **terminal side** of the angle. Two angles in standard position are **coterminal** if they have the same terminal side.

The **unit circle** has radius of 1 unit and its center at the origin. The **cosine of $\theta$** ($\cos\theta$) is the $x$-coordinate of the point where the terminal side of the angle intersects the unit circle. The **sine of $\theta$** ($\sin\theta$) is the $y$-coordinate.

### Example

**What are the cosine and sine of $-210°$?**

Sketch an angle of $-210°$ in standard position with a unit circle. The terminal side forms a 30°-60°-90° triangle with hypotenuse $= 1$, shorter leg $= \frac{1}{2}$, and longer leg $= \frac{\sqrt{3}}{2}$.

Since the terminal side lies in Quadrant II, $\cos(-210°)$ is negative and $\sin(-210°)$ is positive. $\cos(-210°) = -\frac{\sqrt{3}}{2}$ and $\sin(-210°) = \frac{1}{2}$.

### Exercises

**4.** Find the measurement of the angle in standard position below.

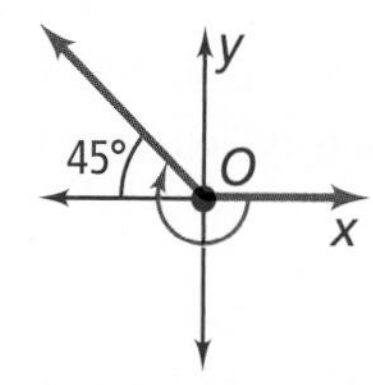


**5.** Sketch a $-30°$ angle in standard position.

**6.** Find the measure of an angle between 0° and 360° coterminal with a $-120°$ angle.

**7.** Find the exact values of the sine and cosine of 315° and $-315°$. Then find the decimal equivalents. Round your answers to the nearest hundredth.

## 8-3 Radian Measure

### Quick Review

A **central angle** of a circle is an angle whose vertex is at the center of a circle and whose sides are radii of the circle. An **intercepted arc** is the portion of the circle whose endpoints are on the sides of the angle and whose remaining points lie in the interior of the angle. A **radian** is the measure of a central angle that intercepts an arc equal in length to a radius of the circle.

### Example

**What is the radian measure of an angle of $-210°$?**

$$-210° = -210° \cdot \frac{\pi}{180°} \text{ radians} = -\frac{7\pi}{6} \text{ radians}$$

### Exercises

**The measure $\theta$ of an angle in standard position is given.**

**a. Write each degree measure in radians and each radian measure in degrees rounded to the nearest degree.**

**b. Find the exact values of $\cos\theta$ and $\sin\theta$ for each angle measure.**

**8.** $60°$

**9.** $-45°$

**10.** $180°$

**11.** $2\pi$ radians

**12.** $\frac{5\pi}{6}$ radians

**13.** $-\frac{3\pi}{4}$ radians

**14.** Use the circle to find the length of the indicated arc. Round your answer to the nearest tenth.

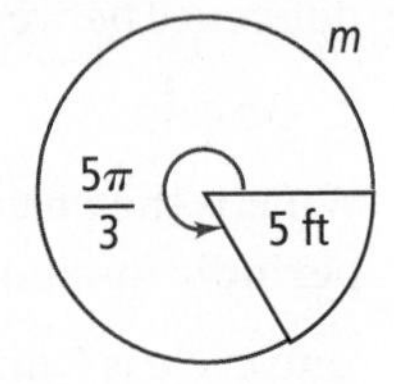


## 8-4 The Sine Function

### Quick Review

The **sine function** $y = \sin\theta$ matches the measure $\theta$ of an angle in standard position with the $y$-coordinate of a point on the unit circle. This point is where the terminal side of the angle intersects the unit circle. The graph of a sine function is called a **sine curve.**

For the sine function $y = a\sin b\theta$, the amplitude equals $|a|$, there are $b$ cycles from 0 to $2\pi$, and the period is $\frac{2\pi}{b}$.

### Example

**Determine the number of cycles the sine function $y = -7\sin 3\theta$ has in the interval from 0 to $2\pi$. Find the amplitude and period of the function.**

For $y = -7\sin 3\theta$, $a = -7$ and $b = 3$. Therefore there are 3 cycles from 0 to $2\pi$. The amplitude is $|a| = |-7| = 7$. The period is $\frac{2\pi}{b} = \frac{2\pi}{3}$.

### Exercises

**Sketch the graph of each function in the interval from 0 to $2\pi$.**

**15.** $y = 3\sin\theta$

**16.** $y = \sin 4\theta$

**17.** Write an equation of a sine function with $a > 0$, amplitude 4, and period $0.5\pi$.

## 8-5 The Cosine Function

### Quick Review

The **cosine function** $y = \cos\theta$ matches the measure $\theta$ of an angle in standard position with the $x$-coordinate of a point on the unit circle. This point is where the terminal side of the angle intersects the unit circle.

For the cosine function $y = a\cos b\theta$, the amplitude equals $|a|$, there are $b$ cycles from 0 to $2\pi$, and the period is $\frac{2\pi}{b}$.

### Example

**Find all solutions to $5\cos\theta = -4$ in the interval from 0 to $2\pi$. Round each answer to the nearest hundredth.**

On a graphing calculator graph the equations $y = -4$ and $y = 5\cos\theta$.

Use the Intersect feature to find the points at which the two graphs intersect. The graph shows two solutions in the interval. They are $\theta \approx 2.50$ and 3.79.

### Exercises

**Sketch the graph of each function in the interval from 0 to $2\pi$.**

**18.** $y = 2\cos\left(\frac{\pi}{2}\theta\right)$

**19.** $y = -\cos 2\theta$

**20.** Write an equation of a cosine function with $a > 0$, amplitude 3, and period $\pi$.

**Solve each equation in the interval from 0 to $2\pi$. Round your answer to the nearest hundredth.**

**21.** $3\cos 4\theta = -2$

**22.** $\cos(\pi\theta) = -0.6$

## 8-6 The Tangent Function

### Quick Review

The **tangent** of an angle $\theta$ in standard position is the $y$-coordinate of the point where the terminal side of the angle intersects the tangent line $x = 1$. A **tangent function** in the form $y = a\tan b\theta$ has a period of $\frac{\pi}{b}$.

Unlike the graphs of the sine and the cosine, the tangent is periodically undefined. At these points, the graph has vertical asymptotes.

### Example

**What is the period of $y = \tan\frac{\pi}{4}\theta$? Tell where two asymptotes occur.**

$$\text{Period} = \frac{\pi}{b} = \frac{\pi}{\frac{\pi}{4}} = 4$$

One cycle occurs in the interval from $-2$ to 2, so there are asymptotes at $\theta = -2$ and $\theta = 2$.

### Exercises

**Graph each function in the interval from 0 to $2\pi$. Then evaluate the function at $t = \frac{\pi}{4}$ and $t = \frac{\pi}{2}$. If the tangent is undefined at that point, write *undefined*.**

**23.** $y = \tan\frac{1}{2}t$

**24.** $y = \tan 3t$

**25.** $y = 2\tan t$

**26.** $y = 4\tan 2t$

## 8-7 Translating Sine and Cosine Functions

### Quick Review

Each horizontal translation of certain periodic functions is a **phase shift.** When $g(x) = f(x - h) + k$, the value of $h$ is the amount of the horizontal shift and the value of $k$ is the amount of the vertical shift. $y = k$ is the midline of the graph.

### Example

**What is an equation for the translation of $y = \sin x$, 2 units to the right and 1 unit up?**

2 units to the right means $h = 2$, and 1 unit up means $k = 1$.

An equation is $y = \sin(x - 2) + 1$.

### Exercises

**Graph each function in the interval from 0 to $2\pi$.**

**27.** $y = \cos\left(x + \frac{\pi}{2}\right)$

**28.** $y = 2\sin x - 4$

**29.** $y = \sin(x - \pi) + 3$

**30.** $y = \cos(x + \pi) - 1$

**Write an equation for each translation.**

**31.** $y = \sin x$, $\frac{\pi}{4}$ units to the right

**32.** $y = \cos x$, 2 units down

## 8-8 Reciprocal Trigonometric Functions

### Quick Review

The **cosecant** (csc), **secant** (sec), and **cotangent** (cot) functions are defined as reciprocals for all real numbers $\theta$ (except those that make a denominator zero).

$$\csc\theta = \frac{1}{\sin\theta} \qquad \sec\theta = \frac{1}{\cos\theta} \qquad \cot\theta = \frac{1}{\tan\theta}$$

### Example

**Suppose $\sin\theta = -\frac{3}{5}$. Find $\csc\theta$.**

$$\csc\theta = \frac{1}{\sin\theta} = \frac{1}{-\frac{3}{5}} = -\frac{5}{3}$$

### Exercises

**Evaluate each expression. Write your answer in exact form.**

**33.** $\sec(-45^\circ)$

**34.** $\cot 120^\circ$

**35.** $\csc 150^\circ$

**36.** $\cot(-150^\circ)$

**Graph each function in the interval from 0 to $4\pi$.**

**37.** $y = 2\csc\theta$

**38.** $y = \sec\theta - 1$

**39.** $y = \cot\frac{1}{4}\theta$

**40.** $y = \csc\frac{1}{2}\theta + 2$

## 8-9 Trigonometric Identities

### Quick Review

A **trigonometric identity** is a trigonometric equation that is true for all values except those for which the expressions on either side of the equal sign are undefined.

**Reciprocal Identities**

$\csc\theta = \frac{1}{\sin\theta}$ $\quad$ $\sec\theta = \frac{1}{\cos\theta}$ $\quad$ $\cot\theta = \frac{1}{\tan\theta}$

**Tangent and Cotangent Identities**

$\tan\theta = \frac{\sin\theta}{\cos\theta}$ $\quad$ $\cot\theta = \frac{\cos\theta}{\sin\theta}$

**Pythagorean Identities**

$\cos^2\theta + \sin^2\theta = 1$ $\quad$ $1 + \tan^2\theta = \sec^2\theta$

$1 + \cot^2\theta = \csc^2\theta$

### Example

**Simplify the trigonometric expression $\cot\theta\sec\theta$.**

| | |
|---|---|
| $\cot\theta\sec\theta = \frac{\cos\theta}{\sin\theta} \cdot \sec\theta$ | Cotangent identity |
| $= \frac{\cos\theta}{\sin\theta} \cdot \frac{1}{\cos\theta}$ | Reciprocal identity |
| $= \frac{1}{\sin\theta}$ | Simplify. |
| $= \csc\theta$ | Reciprocal identity |

### Exercises

**Verify each identity. Give the domain of validity for each identity.**

**41.** $\sin\theta\tan\theta = \frac{1}{\cos\theta} - \cos\theta$

**42.** $\cos^2\theta\cot^2\theta = \cot^2\theta - \cos^2\theta$

**Simplify each trigonometric expression.**

**43.** $1 - \sin^2\theta$

**44.** $\frac{\cos\theta}{\sin\theta\cot\theta}$

**45.** $\csc^2\theta - \cot^2\theta$

**46.** $\cos^2\theta - 1$

**47.** $\frac{\sin\theta\cos\theta}{\tan\theta}$

**48.** $\sec\theta\sin\theta\cot\theta$

## 8-10 and 8-11 Law of Sines and Law of Cosines

### Quick Review

You can use the Law of Sines and the Law of Cosines to find missing measures of a triangle. For $\triangle ABC$:

The **Law of Sines** states that $\frac{\sin A}{a} = \frac{\sin B}{b} = \frac{\sin C}{c}$

The **Law of Cosines**

$a^2 = b^2 + c^2 - 2bc\cos A$ $\quad$ $b^2 = a^2 + c^2 - 2ac\cos B$

$c^2 = a^2 + b^2 - 2ab\cos C$

### Example

**In $\triangle ABC$, $m\angle B = 60°$, $a = 12$, and $c = 8$. What is $b$ to the nearest tenth?**

| | |
|---|---|
| $b^2 = 12^2 + 8^2 - 2(12)(8)\cos 60°$ | Law of Cosines |
| $b^2 = 112$ | Simplify. |
| $b \approx 10.6$ | Use a calculator. |

### Exercises

**49.** Find the area of the triangle. Round your answer to the nearest hundredth.

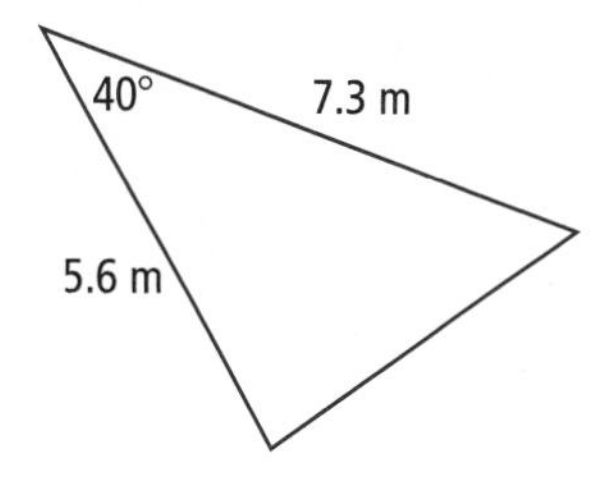


**50.** In $\triangle LMN$, $m\angle L = 67°$, $m\angle N = 24°$, and $MN = 16$ in. Find $LM$ to the nearest tenth.

**51.** In $\triangle DEF$, $d = 25$ in., $e = 28$ in., and $f = 20$ in. Find $m\angle F$ to the nearest tenth.

**52.** In $\triangle GHI$, $h = 8$, $i = 12$, and $m\angle G = 96°$. Find $m\angle I$ to the nearest tenth.

# *Pull It* All Together

ASSESSMENT

## Animating a Game

Suzanne is designing a computer game. She uses a coordinate grid and graph, as shown below, to help her design the layout. In the game, a dragonfly will start at the bottom of the circle and then move counterclockwise around it. It will complete one cycle around the circle in 5 seconds.

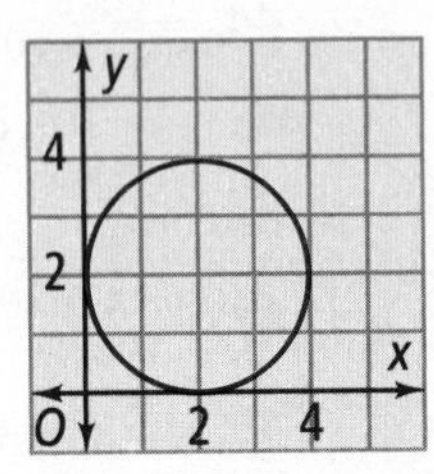


After 8 seconds, a frog jumps out and eats the dragonfly. Suzanne wants to determine the location of the dragonfly when this occurs.

## Task Description

**Determine the coordinates of the dragonfly when the frog eats it. Round each coordinate to the nearest hundredth.**

CHAPTER 9

# Get Ready!

## Evaluating Functions

**For each function, find $f(1)$, $f(2)$, $f(3)$, and $f(4)$.**

**1.** $f(x) = 2x + 7$

**2.** $f(x) = 5x - 4$

**3.** $f(x) = 0.2x + 0.7$

**4.** $f(x) = -5x + 3$

**5.** $f(x) = 4x - \frac{2}{3}$

**6.** $f(x) = -3x - 9$

## Identifying Mathematical Patterns

**Identify a pattern and find the next three numbers in the pattern.**

**7.** 9, 4, −1, −6, . . .

**8.** 1, 2, 4, 8, . . .

**9.** 18, 9, 10, 1, 2, . . .

**10.** 7, 10, 13, 16, . . .

## Simplifying Complex Fractions

**Simplify each complex fraction.**

**11.** $\dfrac{1 - \frac{1}{3}}{\frac{1}{2}}$

**12.** $\dfrac{\frac{1}{3} + \frac{1}{6}}{\frac{2}{3}}$

**13.** $\dfrac{1}{1 - \frac{2}{5}}$

**14.** $\dfrac{1 - \frac{3}{8}}{2 + \frac{1}{4}}$

## Looking Ahead Vocabulary

**15.** Think of a function and evaluate the function for the input numbers 1, 2, 3, 4, and 5. List the five outputs in order. This list is a *sequence* of numbers. The *sequence* can be infinitely long.

**16.** Use a linear function to generate a sequence of five numbers. Beginning with the second number, subtract the number that precedes it. Continue doing this until you have found all four differences. Are the results the same? If so, you have discovered that your sequence has a *common difference*.

**17.** Now use an exponential function to define your sequence of five numbers. Instead of subtracting, divide each number by the number that precedes it. Do this until you find all four quotients. Are these four results the same? If so, you have discovered that your sequence has a *common ratio*.

# Sequences and Series

## Big Ideas

**1 Variable**

**Essential Question** How can you represent the terms of a sequence explicitly? How can you represent them recursively?

**2 Equivalence**

**Essential Question** What are equivalent explicit and recursive definitions for an arithmetic sequence?

**3 Modeling**

**Essential Question** How can you model a geometric sequence? How can you model its sum?

## © Domain

- Seeing Structure in Expressions

## Chapter Preview


9-1 Mathematical Patterns

9-2 Arithmetic Sequences

9-3 Geometric Sequences

9-4 Arithmetic Series

9-5 Geometric Series

Log in to **pearsonsuccessnet.com** and click on Interactive Digital Path to access the Solve Its and animated Problems.

## Vocabulary

**English/Spanish Vocabulary Audio Online:**

| English | Spanish |
|---|---|
| arithmetic sequence, *p. 696* | progresión aritmética |
| arithmetic series, *p. 711* | serie aritmética |
| common difference, *p. 696* | diferencia común |
| common ratio, *p. 703* | razón común |
| converge, *p. 725* | convergir |
| diverge, *p. 725* | divergir |
| explicit formula, *p. 687* | fórmula explícita |
| geometric sequence, *p. 703* | progresión geométrica |
| geometric series, *p. 723* | serie geométrica |
| limits, *p. 714* | límites |
| recursive formula, *p. 688* | formula recursiva |

# 9-1 Mathematical Patterns

F.BF.1.a Determine an explicit expression, a recursive process, or steps for calculation . . .

**Objectives** To identify mathematical patterns found in a sequence
To use a formula to find the $n$th term of a sequence

**Solve It!** Write your solution to the Solve It in the space below.

Sometimes you can state a rule to describe a pattern. At other times, you have to do a bit of work to find a rule.

**Essential Understanding** If the numbers in a list follow a pattern, you may be able to relate each number in the list to its numerical position in the list with a rule.

A **sequence** is an ordered list of numbers. Each number in a sequence is a **term of a sequence**. You can represent a term of a sequence by using a variable with a subscript number to indicate its position in the sequence. For example, $a_5$ is the fifth term in the sequence $a_1, a_2, a_3, a_4, \ldots$.

The subscripts of sequence terms are often positive integers starting with 1. If so, you can generalize a term as $a_n$, the $n$th term in the sequence.

| 1st term | 2nd term | 3rd term | ... | $n-1$ term | $n$th term | $n+1$ term | ... |
|---|---|---|---|---|---|---|---|
| ↓ | ↓ | ↓ | | ↓ | ↓ | ↓ | |
| $a_1$ | $a_2$ | $a_3$ | ... | $a_{n-1}$ | $a_n$ | $a_{n+1}$ | ... |

An **explicit formula** describes the $n$th term of a sequence using the number $n$.

For example, in the sequence 2, 4, 6, 8, 10, . . . , the $n$th term is twice the value of $n$. You write this as $a_n = 2n$. The table shows how to find $a_n$ by substituting the value of $n$ into the explicit formula.

| $n$ | $n$th term |
|---|---|
| 1 | $a_1 = 2(1) = 2$ |
| 2 | $a_2 = 2(2) = 4$ |
| 3 | $a_3 = 2(3) = 6$ |
| 4 | $a_4 = 2(4) = 8$ |

ONLINE PROBLEMS

## Problem 1 Generating a Sequence Using an Explicit Formula

**Plan**

**How does the explicit formula help you find the value of a term?**

**Got It?** A sequence has an explicit formula $a_n = 12n + 3$. What is term $a_{12}$ in the sequence?

**A Practice** **Find the first six terms of each sequence.**

**1.** $a_n = -5n + 1$

**2.** $a_n = \frac{1}{2}n^3 - 1$

Sometimes you can see the pattern in a sequence by comparing each term to the one that came before it. For example, in the sequence 133, 130, 127, 124, . . . , each term after the first term is equal to three less than the previous term.

A recursive definition for this sequence contains two parts.

(a) an initial condition (the value of the first term): $a_1 = 133$

(b) a **recursive formula** (relates each term after the first term to the one before it): $a_n = a_{n-1} - 3$, for $n > 1$

## Problem 2 Writing a Recursive Definition for a Sequence

**Got It?** What is a recursive definition for each sequence? (*Hint:* Look for simple addition or multiplication patterns to relate consecutive terms.)

**a.** 1, 2, 6, 24, 120, 720, . . .

**b.** 1, 5, 14, 30, 55, . . .

**Think**
**What pattern do you see in the differences of successive terms?**

**Practice** Write a recursive definition for each sequence.

**3.** 100, 10, 1, 0.1, 0.01, . . .

**4.** 4, −8, 16, −32, 64, . . .

Recursive definitions can be very helpful when you look at a small section of a sequence. However, if you want to know both $a_3$ and $a_{5000}$ of a sequence, an explicit formula often works better.

## Problem 3 Writing an Explicit Formula for a Sequence

**Got It?** **a.** What is an explicit formula for the sequence 0, 3, 8, 15, 24, . . . ? What is the 20th term?

**b. Reasoning** Why is using an explicit formula often more efficient than using a recursive definition?

**Practice** **5.** Write an explicit formula for the sequence $\frac{1}{2}, -\frac{1}{4}, \frac{1}{8}, -\frac{1}{16} \ldots$ Find the tenth term.

**6.** Find the eighth term of the sequence 2, 1, −2, −7, −14, . . . .

## Problem 4 Using Formulas to Find Terms of a Sequence

**Got It?** In the scenario in Problem 4, if the credit card company were to allow Pierre to continue making no payments, after how many months would his balance exceed $1000?

**7. Exercise** You walk 1 mile the first day of your training, 1.2 miles the second day, 1.6 miles the third day, and 2.4 miles the fourth day. If you continue this pattern, how many miles do you walk on the seventh day?

## Lesson Check

### Do you know HOW?

**Find the first five terms of each sequence.**

**8.** $a_n = 5n - 3$

**9.** $a_n = n^2 - 2n$

**10.** What is a recursive definition for the sequence 3, 6, 12, 24, . . . ?

**11.** What is an explicit formula for the sequence 5, 8, 11, 14, . . . ?

## Do you UNDERSTAND?

**12. Vocabulary** Explain the difference between an explicit formula and a recursive definition. Give an example of each.

**13. Error Analysis** A student writes that $a_n = 3n + 1$ is an explicit formula for the sequence 1, 4, 7, 10, .... Explain the student's error and write a correct explicit formula for the sequence.

## More Practice and Problem-Solving Exercises

### Apply

**Determine whether each formula is *explicit* or *recursive*. Then find the first five terms of each sequence.**

**14.** $a_n = 2a_{n-1} + 3$, where $a_1 = 3$

**15.** $a_n = \frac{1}{2}(n)(n-1)$

**16.** $a_n = (n-5)(n+5)$

**17.** $a_n = -3a_{n-1}$, where $a_1 = -2$

**18.** $a_n = -4n^2 - 2$

**19.** $a_n = 2n^2 + 1$

**Use the given rule to write the 4th, 5th, 6th, and 7th terms of each sequence.**

**20.** $a_n = (n+1)^2$

**21.** $a_n = 2(n-1)^3$

**22.** $a_n = \frac{n^2}{n+1}$

**23.** $a_n = \frac{n+1}{n+2}$

24. **Think About a Plan** You invested money in a company and each month you receive a payment for your investment. Over the first four months, you received \$50, \$52, \$56, and \$62. If this pattern continues, how much do you receive in the tenth month?

- What pattern do you see between consecutive terms?
- Can you write a recursive or explicit formula to describe the pattern?
- How can you use your formula to find the amount you receive in the tenth month?

25. **Entertainment** Suppose you are building towers of cards with levels as displayed below. Copy and complete the table, assuming the pattern continues.

| Number of Levels | Cards Needed |
|---|---|
| 1 | 2 |
| 2 | 7 |
| 3 | ■ |
| 4 | ■ |
| 5 | ■ |

**Find the next two terms in each sequence. Write a formula for the *n*th term. Identify each formula as *explicit* or *recursive*.**

26. 5, 8, 11, 14, 17, ...

27. 3, 6, 12, 24, 48, ...

28. 1, 8, 27, 64, 125, ...

29. 4, 16, 64, 256, 1024, ...

30. 49, 64, 81, 100, 121, ...

31. $-1, 1, -1, 1, -1, 1, \ldots$

32. $-16, -8, -4, -2, \ldots$

33. $-75, -68, -61, -54, \ldots$

34. $21, 13, 5, -3, \ldots$

35. a. **Open-Ended** Write four terms of a sequence of numbers that you can describe both recursively and explicitly.
b. Write a recursive definition and an explicit formula for your sequence.
c. Find the 20th term of the sequence by evaluating one of your formulas. Use the other formula to check your work.

36. **Geometry** Suppose you are stacking boxes in levels that form squares. The numbers of boxes in successive levels form a sequence. The figure at the right shows the top four levels as viewed from above.

a. How many boxes of equal size would you need for the next lower level?
b. How many boxes of equal size would you need to add three levels?
c. Suppose you are stacking a total of 285 boxes. How many levels will you have?

## Challenge

**37. Geometry** The triangular numbers form a sequence. The diagram represents the first three triangular numbers: 1, 3, 6.

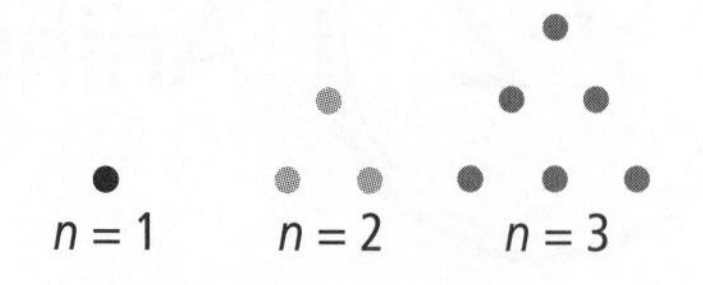


**a.** Find the fourth and fifth triangular numbers.

**b.** Write a recursive formula for the $n$th triangular number.

**c.** Is the explicit formula $a_n = \frac{1}{2}(n^2 + n)$ the correct formula for this sequence? Explain.

**Use each recursive definition to write an explicit formula for the sequence.**

**38.** $a_1 = 10, a_n = 2a_{n-1}$

**39.** $a_1 = -5, a_n = a_{n-1} - 1$

**40.** $a_1 = 1, a_n = a_{n-1} + 4$

**41. Finance** Use the information in the ad.

**a.** Suppose you start a savings account. Write a recursive definition and an explicit formula for the amount of money you would have in the bank at the end of any week.

**b.** How much money would you have in the bank after four weeks?

**c.** Assume the bank pays interest every four weeks. To calculate your interest, multiply the balance at the end of the four weeks by 0.005. Then add that amount to your account on the last day of the four-week period. Write a recursive formula for the amount of money you have after each interest payment.

**d. Reasoning** What is the bank's annual interest rate?

# 9-2 Arithmetic Sequences

**F.BF.1.a** Determine an explicit expression, a recursive process, or steps for calculation . . .

**Objective** To define, identify, and apply arithmetic sequences

**Solve It!** Write your solution to the Solve It in the space below.

It is sometimes helpful to represent a situation with a sequence of numbers. There are different types of numerical sequences.

**Essential Understanding** In an *arithmetic sequence*, the difference between any two consecutive terms is always the same number. You can build an arithmetic sequence by adding the same number to each term.

An **arithmetic sequence** is a sequence in which the difference between consecutive terms is constant. This difference is the **common difference**.

take note

### Key Concept: Arithmetic Sequence

An arithmetic sequence with a starting value $a$ and common difference $d$ is a sequence of the form

$$a, a + d, a + 2d, a + 3d, \ldots$$

A recursive definition for this sequence has two parts:

$a_1 = a$ initial condition

$a_n = a_{n-1} + d$, for $n > 1$ recursive formula

An explicit definition for this sequence is a single formula:

$a_n = a + (n - 1)d$, for $n \geq 1$

## Problem 1 Identifying Arithmetic Sequences

**Got It?** Is the sequence an arithmetic sequence?

**a.** 2, 4, 8, 16, . . .

**b.** 1, 5, 9, 13, 17, . . .

**Practice** **Determine whether each sequence is arithmetic. If so, identify the common difference.**

**1.** $-21, -18, -15, -12, \ldots$

**2.** 3, 7, 11, 15, . . .

## Problem 2 Analyzing Arithmetic Sequences

**Got It?** **a.** What is the 46th term of the arithmetic sequence that begins 3, 5, 7, . . . ?

**Think**

**What do you need to find additional terms of an arithmetic sequence?**

**b.** What are the second and third terms of this arithmetic sequence?

80, ______, ______, 125, . . .

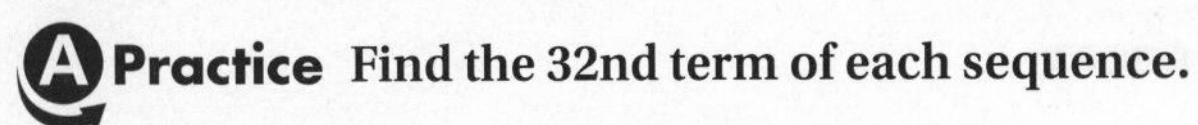

**Practice** **Find the 32nd term of each sequence.**

**3.** $-9, -8.7, -8.4, \ldots$

**4.** $101, 105, 109, 113, \ldots$

The **arithmetic mean**, or average, of two numbers $x$ and $y$ is $\frac{x + y}{2}$.

In an arithmetic sequence, the middle term of any three consecutive terms is the arithmetic mean of the other two terms.

## Problem 3 Using the Arithmetic Mean

**Got It?** **a.** The 9th and 11th terms of an arithmetic sequence are 132 and 98. What is the 10th term?

**b. Reasoning** If you know the 5th and 6th terms of an arithmetic sequence, how can you find term 7 using the arithmetic mean?

**Practice** Find the missing term of each arithmetic sequence.

**5.** $-15, \_\_\_\_\_\_, 1, \ldots$

**6.** $25, \_\_\_\_\_\_, -10, \ldots$

## Problem 4 Using an Explicit Formula for an Arithmetic Sequence

**Got It?** The numbers of seats in the first 16 rows in a curved section of another arena form an arithmetic sequence. If there are 20 seats in Row 1 and 23 seats in Row 2, how many seats are in Row 16?

**Think**
How can you find the common difference of the arithmetic sequence?

**Practice** **7. Savings** A student deposits the same amount of money into her bank account each week. At the end of the second week she has $30 in her account. At the end of the third week she has $45 in her account. How much will she have in her bank account at the end of the ninth week?

## Lesson Check

### Do you know HOW?

**Find the tenth term of each arithmetic sequence.**

**8.** 2, 8, 14, 20, . . .

**9.** 15, 23, 31, . . .

**Find the missing term of each arithmetic sequence.**

**10.** . . . 4, ______, 22, . . .

**11.** . . . 25, ______, 53, . . .

### Do you UNDERSTAND?

**12. Vocabulary** Explain what it means for a sequence to be an arithmetic sequence.

**13. Open-Ended** Give an example of a sequence that is not an arithmetic sequence.

## More Practice and Problem-Solving Exercises

### B Apply

**Find the 17th term of each sequence.**

**14.** $a_{16} = 18, d = 5$
**15.** $a_{16} = 21, d = -3$
**16.** $a_{18} = -5, d = 12$
**17.** $a_{18} = 32, d = -4$
**18.** $a_{16} = \frac{1}{5}, d = \frac{1}{2}$
**19.** $a_{18} = -9, d = -11$

**20. Think About a Plan** The arithmetic mean of the monthly salaries of two employees is \$3210. One employee earns \$3470 per month. What is the monthly salary of the other employee?
- What is the given information and what is the unknown?
- What equation can you use to find the other monthly salary?

**21. Error Analysis** A student claims that the next term of the arithmetic sequence 0, 2, 4, . . . is 8. Explain and correct the student's error.

**Find the arithmetic mean $a_n$ of the given terms.**

**22.** $a_{n-1} = 7, a_{n+1} = 1$
**23.** $a_{n-1} = 100, a_{n+1} = 140$
**24.** $a_{n-1} = 4, a_{n+1} = -3$
**25.** $a_{n-1} = 0.3, a_{n+1} = 1.9$
**26.** $a_{n-1} = r, a_{n+1} = s$
**27.** $a_{n-1} = -2x, a_{n+1} = 2x$

**28. a. Graphing Calculator** Use your calculator to generate an arithmetic sequence with a common difference of $-7$. How could you use a calculator to find the 6th term? The 8th term? The 20th term?

**b. Reasoning** Explain how your answer to part (a) relates to the explicit formula $a_n = a + (n - 1)d$.

**Write an explicit and a recursive formula for each sequence.**

**29.** 2, 4, 6, 8, 10, . . .
**30.** 0, 6, 12, 18, 24, . . .
**31.** $-5, -4, -3, -2, -1, \ldots$
**32.** $-4, -8, -12, -16, -20, \ldots$
**33.** $-5, -3.5, -2, -0.5, 1, \ldots$
**34.** $-32, -20, -8, 4, 16, \ldots$
**35.** $1, 1\frac{1}{3}, 1\frac{2}{3}, 2, \ldots$
**36.** $0, \frac{1}{8}, \frac{1}{4}, \frac{3}{8}, \ldots$
**37.** $27, 15, 3, -9, -21, \ldots$

**38. Reasoning** What information do you need to find a term of a sequence using an explicit formula?

**39. Writing** Describe some advantages and some disadvantages of a recursive formula and an explicit formula. When is it appropriate to use each formula?

**40. Transportation** Suppose a trolley stops at a certain intersection every 14 min. The first trolley of the day gets to the stop at 6:43 A.M. How long do you have to wait for a trolley if you get to the stop at 8:15 A.M.? At 3:20 P.M.?

**Find the missing terms of each arithmetic sequence. (*Hint:* The arithmetic mean of the first and fifth terms is the third term.)**

**41.** $2, a_2, a_3, a_4, -22, \ldots$

**42.** $10, a_2, a_3, a_4, -11.6, \ldots$

**43.** $1, a_2, a_3, a_4, -35, \ldots$

**44.** $\ldots \frac{13}{5}, a_6, a_7, a_8, \frac{37}{5}, \ldots$

**45.** $17, a_2, a_3, a_4, 17, \ldots$

**46.** $660, a_2, a_3, a_4, 744, \ldots$

**47.** $\ldots -17, a_4, a_5, a_6, 1, \ldots$

**48.** $\ldots a + 1, a_3, a_4, a_5, a + 17, \ldots$

**49. Income** The arithmetic mean of the monthly salaries of two people is \$4475. One person earns \$3895 per month. What is the monthly salary of the other person?

**50. Reasoning** Suppose you turn the water on in an empty bathtub with vertical sides. After 20 s, the water has reached a level of 1.15 in. You then leave the room. You want to turn the water off when the level in the bathtub is 8.5 in. How many minutes later should you return? (*Hint:* Begin by identifying two terms of an arithmetic sequence.)

## Challenge

**51.** In an arithmetic sequence with $a_1 = 4$ and $d = 9$, which term is 184?

**52.** In an arithmetic sequence with $a_1 = 2$ and $d = -2$, which term is $-82$?

**53.** The arithmetic mean of two terms in an arithmetic sequence is 42. One term is 30. Find the other term.

**54.** The arithmetic mean of two terms in an arithmetic sequence is $-6$. One term is $-20$. Find the other term.

**Given two terms of each arithmetic sequence, find $a_1$ and $d$.**

**55.** $a_3 = 5$ and $a_5 = 11$

**56.** $a_4 = 8$ and $a_7 = 20$

**57.** $a_3 = 32$ and $a_7 = -8$

**58.** $a_{10} = 17$ and $a_{14} = 34$

**59.** $a_4 = -34.5$ and $a_5 = -12.5$

**60.** $a_4 = -2.4$ and $a_6 = 2$

**Find the indicated term of each arithmetic sequence in terms of $k$.**

**61.** $a_1 = k, d = k + 4; a_9$

**62.** $a_1 = k + 7, d = 2k - 5; a_{11}$

# 9-3 Geometric Sequences

**F.BF.1.a** Determine an explicit expression, a recursive process, or steps for calculation . . .

**Objective** To define, identify, and apply geometric sequences

**Solve It!** Write your solution to the Solve It in the space below.

You build a *geometric sequence* by multiplying each term by a constant.

**Essential Understanding** In a *geometric sequence*, the ratio of any term to its preceding term is a constant value.

take note

### Key Concept Geometric Sequence

A **geometric sequence** with a starting value $a$ and a **common ratio** $r$ is a sequence of the form

$$a, ar, ar^2, ar^3, \ldots$$

A recursive definition for the sequence has two parts:

$a_1 = a$ initial condition

$a_n = a_{n-1} \cdot r$, for $n > 1$ recursive formula

An explicit definition for this sequence is a single formula:

$a_n = a_1 \cdot r^{n-1}$, for $n \geq 1$

## Problem 1 Identifying Geometric Sequences

**Got It?** Is the sequence geometric? If it is, what are $a_1$ and $r$?

**Think**
How do you find the ratios between consecutive terms?

**a.** $2, 4, 8, 16, \ldots$

**b.** $1, 5, 9, 13, 17, \ldots$

**c.** $2^3, 2^7, 2^{11}, 2^{15}, \ldots$

**A Practice** **Determine whether each sequence is geometric. If so, find the common ratio.**

**1.** $1, \frac{1}{2}, \frac{1}{3}, \frac{1}{4}, \ldots$

**2.** 10, 15, 22.5, 33.75, . . .

## Problem 2 Analyzing Geometric Sequences

**Got It?** What is the 2nd term of the geometric sequence 3, ■, 12, . . . ?

**Practice** **Find the eighth term of each geometric sequence.**

**3.** 10, 5, 2.5, . . .

**4.** $-30, 7\frac{1}{2}, -1\frac{7}{8}, \ldots$

## Problem 3 Using a Geometric Sequence

**Got It?** a. **Reasoning** In Problem 3, to find the height of the 10th bounce, would you use the recursive or the explicit formula? Explain.

b. What are the heights of the 6th and 10th bounces?

**Practice** STEM

5. **Science** When radioactive substances decay, the amount remaining will form a geometric sequence when measured over constant intervals of time. The table shows the amount of Np-240, a radioactive isotope of Neptunium, initially and after 2 hours. What are the amounts left after 1 hour, 3 hours, and 4 hours?

| Hours Elapsed | 0 | 1 | 2 | 3 | 4 |
|---|---|---|---|---|---|
| Grams of Np-240 | 1244 | ■ | 346 | ■ | ■ |

In a geometric sequence, the square of the middle term of any three consecutive terms is equal to the product of the other two terms. For example, examine the sequence 2, −6, 18, −54, . . . .

$$(-6)^2 = 2 \cdot 18 = 36$$

$$2, \mathbf{-6}, 18, \mathbf{-54}, \ldots$$

$$18^2 = \mathbf{(-6)(-54)} = 324$$

In an arithmetic sequence, recall that the middle term of any three consecutive terms is the arithmetic mean of the other two terms.

The **geometric mean** of two positive numbers $x$ and $y$ is $\sqrt{xy}$.

Note that the geometric mean is positive by definition. While there are two possible values for the missing term in the geometric sequence 3, ▨, 12, . . . , there is only one geometric mean. The geometric mean is one possible value to fill in the geometric sequence. The opposite of the geometric mean is the other.

## Problem 4 Using the Geometric Mean

**Got It?** The 9th and 11th terms of a geometric sequence are 45 and 80. What are possible values for the 10th term?

**Think**
**Is it necessary to find the first term to answer this question?**

**A Practice** **Find the missing term of each geometric sequence. It could be the geometric mean or its opposite.**

**6.** 9180, ______, 255, . . .

**7.** 5, ______, 2.8125, . . .

## Lesson Check

### Do you know HOW?

**Determine whether each sequence is geometric. If so, find the common ratio.**

**8.** 5, 10, 15, . . .

**9.** 10, 20, 40, . . .

**Find the seventh term of each geometric sequence.**

**10.** 1, −3, 9, . . .

**11.** 100, 20, 4, . . .

### Do you UNDERSTAND?

**12. Error Analysis** To find the third term of the geometric sequence 5, 10, ■, ■, 80, your friend says that there are two possible answers—the geometric mean of 5 and 80, and its opposite. Explain your friend's error.

**13. Compare and Contrast** How is finding a missing term of a geometric sequence using the geometric mean similar to finding a missing term of an arithmetic sequence using the arithmetic mean? How is it different?

## More Practice and Problem-Solving Exercises

### B Apply

**Write an explicit formula for each sequence. Then generate the first five terms.**

**14.** $a_1 = 1, r = 0.5$

**15.** $a_1 = 100, r = -20$

**16.** $a_1 = 7, r = 1$

**17.** $a_1 = 1024, r = 0.5$

**18.** $a_1 = 4, r = 0.1$

**19.** $a_1 = 10, r = -1$

**Identify each sequence as *arithmetic, geometric,* or *neither*. Then find the next two terms.**

**20.** 45, 90, 180, 360, . . .

**21.** 25, 50, 75, 100, . . .

**22.** 3, −3, 3, −3, . . .

**23.** −5, 10, −20, 40, . . .

**24.** 2, 1, 0.5, 0.25, . . .

**25.** 1, 4, 9, 16, . . .

**Find the missing terms of each geometric sequence. If necessary, round to the nearest hundredth. (*Hint:* The geometric mean of the first and fifth terms is the third term. Some terms might be negative.)**

**26.** 972, ■, ■, ■, 12, . . .

**27.** 2.5, ■, ■, ■, 202.5, . . .

**28.** 12.5, ■, ■, ■, 5.12, . . .

**29.** −4, ■, ■, ■, $-20\frac{1}{4}$

**30. Think About a Plan** Suppose a balloon is filled with 5000 $cm^3$ of helium. It then loses one fourth of its helium each day. How much helium will be left in the balloon at the start of the tenth day?

- How can you write a sequence of numbers to represent this situation?
- Is the sequence arithmetic, geometric, or neither?
- How can you write a formula for this sequence?

**31. Athletics** During your first week of training for a 100-mile bike event, you bike a total of 10 miles. You increase the distance you bike each week by twenty percent. How many miles do you bike during your twelfth week of training?

**32. a. Open-Ended** Choose two positive numbers. Find their geometric mean.

**b.** Find the common ratio for a geometric sequence that includes the terms from part (a) as its first three terms.

**c.** Find the 9th term of the geometric sequence from part (b).

**d.** Find the geometric mean of the term from part (c) and the first term of your sequence. What term of the sequence have you just found?

**For the geometric sequence 3, 12, 48, 192, . . . , find the indicated term.**

**33.** 5th term **34.** 17th term **35.** 20th term **36.** $n$th term

**Find the 10th term of each geometric sequence.**

**37.** $a_9 = 8$, $r = \frac{1}{2}$

**38.** $a_9 = -5$, $r = -\frac{1}{2}$

**39.** $a_{11} = -5$, $r = -\frac{1}{2}$

**40.** $a_9 = -\frac{1}{3}$, $r = \frac{1}{2}$

**41. Writing** Describe the similarities and differences between a common difference and a common ratio.

## Challenge

**42. Banking** Copy and complete the table below. Use the geometric mean. Assume compound interest is earned and no withdrawals are made.

| Period 1 | Period 2 | Period 3 |
|---|---|---|
| $140.00 | ■ | $145.64 |
| $600.00 | ■ | $627.49 |
| $25.00 | ■ | $32.76 |
| $57.50 | ■ | $60.37 |
| $100.00 | ■ | $111.98 |
| $250.00 | ■ | $276.55 |

**Find $a_1$ for a geometric sequence with the given terms.**

**43.** $a_5 = 112$ and $a_7 = 448$

**44.** $a_9 = \frac{1}{2}$ and $a_{12} = \frac{1}{16}$

# 9-4 Arithmetic Series

**F.BF.1.a** Determine an explicit expression, a recursive process, or steps for calculation . . .

**Objective** To define arithmetic series and find their sums

**Solve It!** Write your solution to the Solve It in the space below.

Just as you found formulas for terms of sequences, you can find formulas for the sums of the terms of sequences.

**Essential Understanding** When you know two terms and the number of terms in a finite arithmetic sequence, you can find the sum of the terms.

A **series** is the indicated sum of the terms of a sequence. A **finite series**, like a finite sequence, has a first term and a last term, while an **infinite series** continues without end.

| **Finite sequence** | **Finite series** |
|---|---|
| 6, 9, 12, 15, 18 | $6 + 9 + 12 + 15 + 18$ (The sum is 60.) |
| **Infinite sequence** | **Infinite series** |
| 3, 7, 11, 15, . . . | $3 + 7 + 11 + 15 + \cdots$ |

An **arithmetic series** is a series whose terms form an arithmetic sequence (as shown above). When a series has a finite number of terms, you can use a formula involving the first and last term to evaluate the sum.

take note

**Property** Sum of a Finite Arithmetic Series

The sum $S_n$ of a finite arithmetic series $a_1 + a_2 + a_3 + \cdots + a_n$ is

$$S_n = \frac{n}{2}(a_1 + a_n)$$

where $a_1$ is the first term, $a_n$ is the $n$th term, and $n$ is the number of terms.

## Problem 1 Finding the Sum of a Finite Arithmetic Series

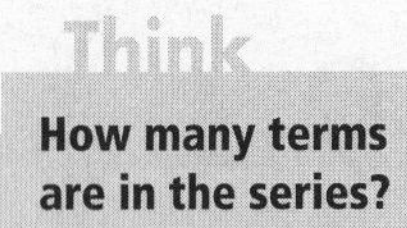


How many terms are in the series?

**Got It?** **a.** What is the sum of the finite arithmetic series $4 + 9 + 14 + 19 + 24 + \cdots + 99$?

**b. Reasoning** Will the sum of a sequence of even numbers always be an even number? Will the sum of a sequence of odd numbers always be an odd number? Explain.

**Practice** Find the sum of each finite arithmetic series.

**1.** $7 + 14 + 21 + \cdots + 105$

**2.** $(-3) + (-6) + (-9) + \cdots + (-30)$

## Problem 2 Using the Sum of a Finite Arithmetic Series

**Got It?** The company in Problem 2 has an alternative bonus plan. It pays a \$5000 bonus if a new salesperson makes 10 sales in the first week and then improves by *one* sale per week each week thereafter. One salesperson qualified for this bonus with the minimum number of sales. How many sales did the salesperson make in week 50? In all 50 weeks?

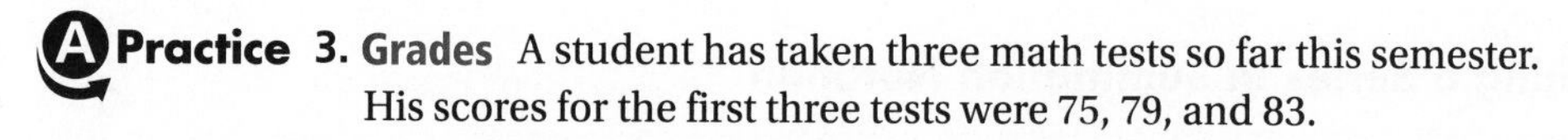

**Practice** 3. **Grades** A student has taken three math tests so far this semester. His scores for the first three tests were 75, 79, and 83.

**a.** Suppose his test scores continue to improve at the same rate. What will his grade on the sixth (and final) test be?

**b.** What will his total score for all six tests be?

You can use the Greek capital letter sigma, $\Sigma$, to indicate a sum. With it, you use *limits* to indicate how many terms you are adding. **Limits** are the least and greatest values of $n$ in the series. You write the limits below and above the $\Sigma$ to indicate the least and greatest values of $n$.

For example, you can write the series $3^2 + 4^2 + 5^2 + \cdots + 108^2$ as $\sum_{n=3}^{108} n^2$.

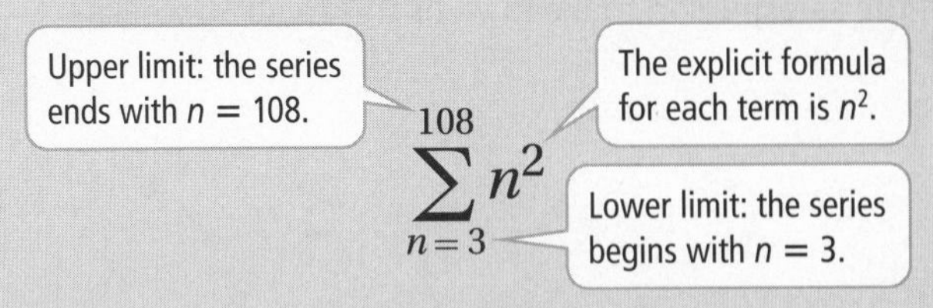


For an infinite series, summation notation shows $\infty$ as the upper limit.

To find the number of terms in a series written in $\Sigma$ form, subtract the lower limit from the upper limit and add 1.

The number of terms in the series above is $108 - 3 + 1 = 106$.

## Problem 3 Writing a Series in Summation Notation

**Got It?** What is summation notation for the series?

**a.** $-5 + 2 + 9 + 16 + \cdots + 261 + 268$

**Plan**

**What do you need to write a series in summation notation?**

**b.** $500 + 490 + 480 + \cdots + 20 + 10$

**Practice** Write each arithmetic series in summation notation.

**4.** $5 + 8 + 11 + \cdots + 38$

**5.** $105 + 97 + 89 + \cdots + (-71)$

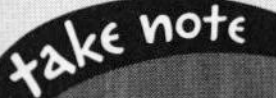


## Key Concept Summation Notation and Linear Functions

If the explicit formula for the $n$th term in summation notation is a *linear* function of $n$, then the series is arithmetic. The slope of the linear function is the common difference between terms of the series.

## Problem 4 Finding the Sum of a Series

**Got It?** What is the sum of each finite series?

**a.** $\sum_{n=1}^{40} (3n - 8)$ **b.** $\sum_{n=1}^{4} n^3$ **c.** $\sum_{n=0}^{100} (-1)^n$

**Practice** Find the sum of each finite series.

6. $\sum_{n=1}^{10}(3n - 4)$

7. $\sum_{n=1}^{3}(-1)^n \cdot 2$

On a graphing calculator, you can find the sum of a finite series by using commands from the **LIST** menu.

## Problem 5 Using a Graphing Calculator to Find the Sum of a Series

**Got It?** Use a graphing calculator. What is $\sum_{n=1}^{50}(n^2 - n)$?

**Practice** Use a graphing calculator to find the sum of each series.

8. $\sum_{n=1}^{20}(n^3 - 10n^2)$

9. $\sum_{n=5}^{25}(n^2 - 14n + 32)$

## Lesson Check

### Do you know HOW?

**Find the sum of each finite arithmetic series.**

**10.** $4 + 7 + 10 + 13 + 16 + 19 + 22$

**11.** $10 + 20 + 30 + \cdots + 110 + 120$

**Write each arithmetic series in summation notation.**

**12.** $3 + 6 + 9 + 12 + 15 + 18 + 21$

**13.** $1 + 5 + 9 + \cdots + 41 + 45$

## Do you UNDERSTAND?

**14. Vocabulary** What is the difference between an arithmetic sequence and an arithmetic series?

**15. Error Analysis** A student writes the arithmetic series $3 + 8 + 13 + \cdots + 43$ in summation notation as $\sum_{n=3}^{8}(3 + 5n)$. Describe and correct the error.

**16. Reasoning** Is it possible to have more than one arithmetic series with four terms whose sum is 44? Explain.

## More Practice and Problem-Solving Exercises

### B Apply

**17. Think About a Plan** A meeting room is set up with 16 rows of seats. The number of seats in a row increases by two with each successive row. The first row has 12 seats. What is the total number of seats?

- How can you find the number of seats in each row using an explicit formula?
- What is the number of seats in the 16th row?
- How can you find the sum of the seats in 16 rows?

**Determine whether each list is a *sequence* or a *series* and *finite* or *infinite*.**

**18.** $1, 2, 4, 8, 16, 32, \ldots$

**19.** $1, 0.5, 0.25, 0.125, 0.0625$

**20.** $5 + 10 + \cdots + 25$

**21.** $-0.5 - 0.25 - 0.125 - \cdots$

**22.** $\frac{4}{3}, \frac{7}{3}, \frac{10}{3}, \frac{13}{3}, \frac{16}{3}, \ldots$

**23.** $2.3 + 4.6 + 9.2 + 18.4$

**Each sequence has eight terms. Evaluate each related series.**

**24.** $\frac{1}{2}, \frac{3}{2}, \frac{5}{2}, \ldots, \frac{15}{2}$

**25.** $1, -1, -3, \ldots, -13$

**26.** $5, 13, 21, \ldots, 61$

**27.** $-3.5, -1.25, 1, \ldots, 12.25$

**28.** $1765, 1414, 1063, \ldots, -692$

**29.** $-13, -14.5, -16, \ldots, -23.5$

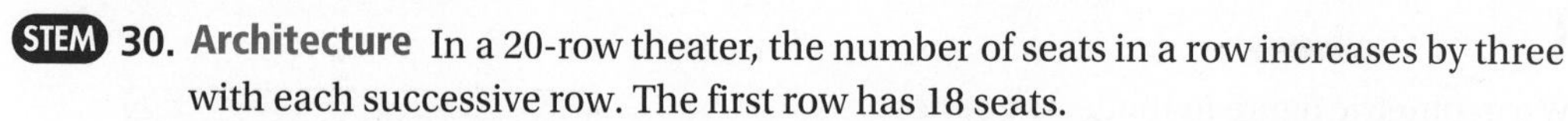

STEM **30. Architecture** In a 20-row theater, the number of seats in a row increases by three with each successive row. The first row has 18 seats.

**a.** Write an arithmetic series to represent the number of seats in the theater.

**b.** Find the total seating capacity of the theater.

**c.** Front-row tickets for a concert cost \$60. After every 5 rows, the ticket price goes down by \$5. What is the total amount of money generated by a full house?

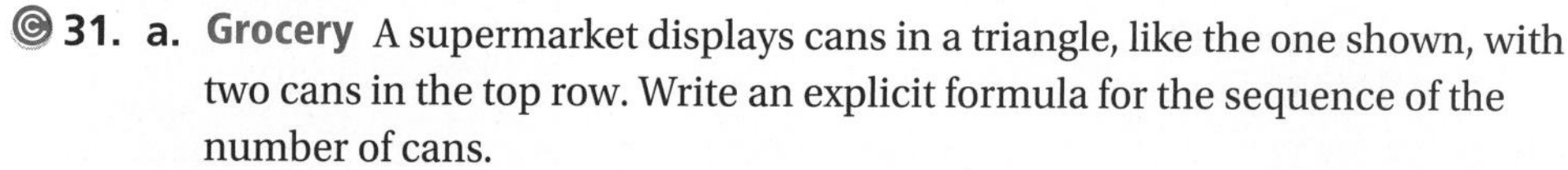

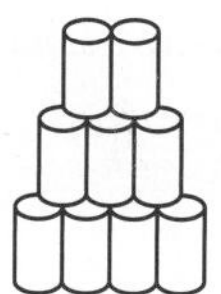

**31. a. Grocery** A supermarket displays cans in a triangle, like the one shown, with two cans in the top row. Write an explicit formula for the sequence of the number of cans.

**b.** Use summation notation to write the related series for a triangle with 10 cans in the bottom row.

**c.** Suppose the triangle had 17 rows. How many cans would be in the 17th row?

**d. Reasoning** Could the triangle have 110 cans? 140 cans? Explain.

**Evaluate each series to the given term.**

**32.** $2 + 4 + 6 + 8 + \cdots$ ; 10th term

**33.** $-5, -25, -45, - \cdots$ ; 9th term

**34. a. Open-Ended** Write two explicit formulas for arithmetic sequences.

**b.** Write the first five terms of each related series.

**c.** Use summation notation to rewrite each series.

**d.** Evaluate each series.

## Challenge

**Use the values of $a_1$ and $S_n$ to find the value of $a_n$.**

**35.** $a_1 = 4$ and $S_{40} = 6080$; $a_{40}$

**36.** $a_1 = -6$ and $S_{50} = -5150$; $a_{50}$

**Find $a_1$ for each arithmetic series.**

**37.** $S_8 = 440$ and $d = 6$

**38.** $S_{30} = 240$ and $d = -2$

**39.** Evaluate $S_{10}$ for the series $x + (x + y) + (x + 2y) + \cdots$

**40.** Evaluate $S_{15}$ for the series $3x + (3x - 2y) + (3x - 4y) + \cdots$

ACTIVITY LAB

Use With Lesson 9-5

# Geometry and Infinite Series

**A.SSE.4** Derive the formula for the sum of a finite geometric series (when the common ratio is not 1), and use the formula to solve problems.

You can use geometric figures to model some infinite series.

## Example 1

**Geometry** Draw a geometric figure to model the series.

$\frac{1}{2} + \left(\frac{1}{2}\right)^2 + \left(\frac{1}{2}\right)^3 + \ldots + \left(\frac{1}{2}\right)^n + \ldots$

Draw a square. Shade one half of the square. Then shade one half of the remaining unshaded region. Continue until the square is full.

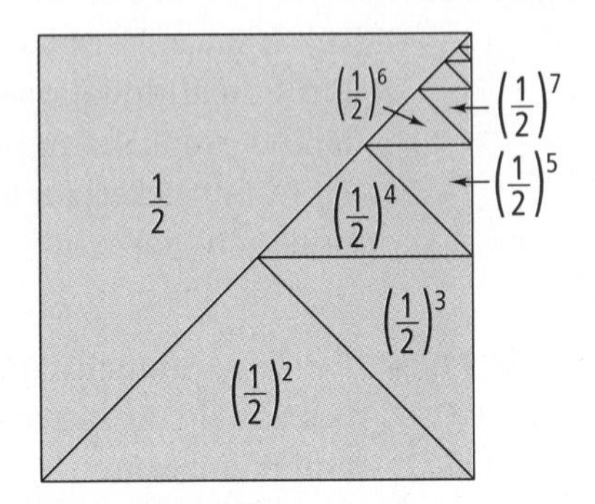


So the series appears to have a sum of 1.

You can write an infinite series from a geometric model.

## Example 2

**Geometry** Write the series modeled by the trapezoids. Estimate the sum of the series. Explain your reasoning.

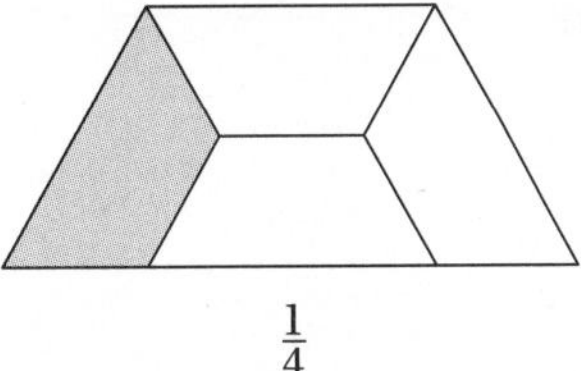
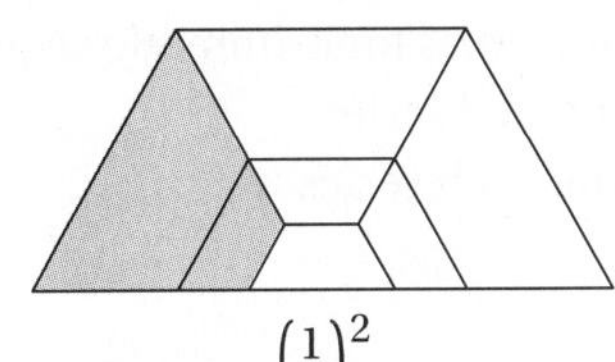
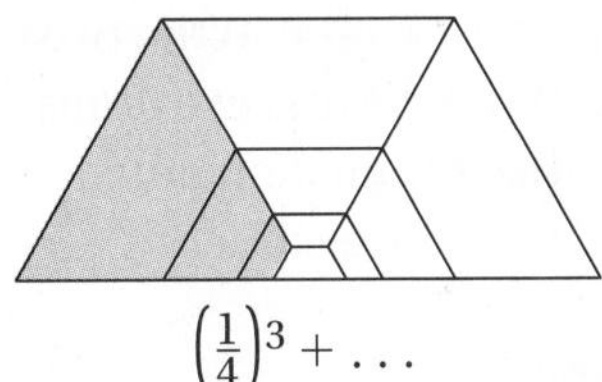

$\frac{1}{4} \quad + \quad \left(\frac{1}{4}\right)^2 \quad + \quad \left(\frac{1}{4}\right)^3 + \ldots$

The shaded region approaches one third of the figure.

So the series $\frac{1}{4} + \left(\frac{1}{4}\right)^2 + \left(\frac{1}{4}\right)^3 + \ldots + \left(\frac{1}{4}\right)^n + \ldots$ appears to have a sum of $\frac{1}{3}$.

## Exercises

**1. a.** Write the series modeled by the figure at the right.

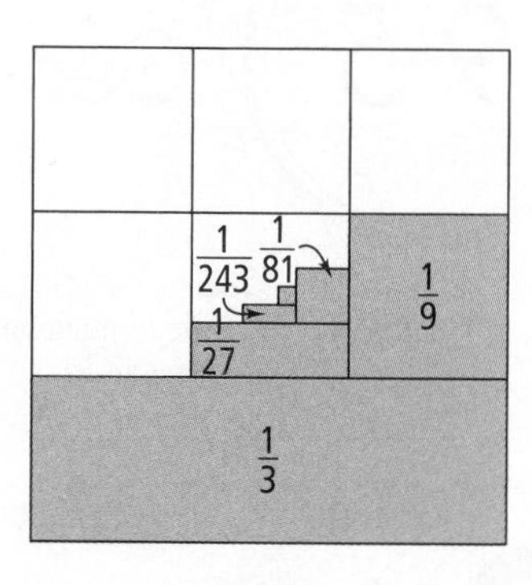


**b.** Evaluate the series. Explain your reasoning.

**2.** Draw a figure to model the series. $\frac{1}{5} + \left(\frac{1}{5}\right)^2 + \left(\frac{1}{5}\right)^3 + \ldots + \left(\frac{1}{5}\right)^n + \ldots$

**3. Make a Conjecture** Consider the series. $\frac{1}{c} + \left(\frac{1}{c}\right)^2 + \left(\frac{1}{c}\right)^3 + \ldots + \left(\frac{1}{c}\right)^n + \ldots, c > 1$

What is the sum of the series? Explain your reasoning.

# 9-5 Geometric Series

**A.SSE.4** Derive the formula for the sum of a finite geometric series . . . and use the formula to solve problems.

**Objective** To define geometric series and find their sums

**Solve It!** Write your solution to the Solve It in the space below.

You can write any whole number that has the same digit in every place as the sum of the terms of a geometric sequence. For example,

$$4444 = 4(10)^0 + 4(10)^1 + 4(10)^2 + 4(10)^3$$

You can write any rational number as an infinite repeating decimal.

For example, $\frac{47}{90} = 0.5222\ldots$

Therefore, you can write any rational number as a number plus the sum of an infinite geometric sequence.

$$0.5222\ldots = 0.5 + 2(0.1)^2 + 2(0.1)^3 + 2(0.1)^4 + \cdots$$

**Essential Understanding** Just as with finite arithmetic series, you can find the sum of a finite geometric series using a formula. You need to know the first term, the number of terms, and the common ratio.

A **geometric series** is the sum of the terms of a geometric sequence.

take note

## Key Concept Sum of a Finite Geometric Series

The sum $S_n$ of a finite geometric series $a_1 + a_1r + a_1r^2 + \cdots + a_1r^{n-1}$, $r \neq 1$, is

$$S_n = \frac{a_1(1 - r^n)}{1 - r}$$

where $a_1$ is the first term, $r$ is the common ratio, and $n$ is the number of terms.

ONLINE PROBLEMS

## Problem 1 Finding the Sums of Finite Geometric Series

**Got It?** What is the sum of the finite geometric series?

**a.** $-15 + 30 - 60 + 120 - 240 + 480$

**Plan**
How do you find the common ratio in each of these series?

**b.** $\sum_{n=1}^{10} 5 \cdot (-2)^{n-1}$

**Practice** Evaluate the sum of the finite geometric series.

1. $-5 - 10 - 20 - 40 - \cdots - 2560$

2. $\sum_{n=1}^{4} \left(\frac{2}{3}\right)^{n-1}$

**The Soldier's Reasonable Request** A famous story involves a soldier who rescues his king in battle. The king grants him any prize "within reason" from the riches of the kingdom. The soldier asks for a chessboard with a single kernel of wheat on the first square, two kernels of wheat on the second square, then four, then eight, and so on for all 64 squares of the chessboard. The king decides that the request is reasonable.

See Problem 2 for the outcome.

## Problem 2 Using the Geometric Series Formula

**Got It?** To save money for a vacation, you set aside \$100. For each month thereafter, you plan to set aside 10% more than the previous month. How much money will you save in 12 months?

**A Practice** **3. Financial Planning** In March, a family starts saving for a vacation they are planning for the end of August. The family expects the vacation to cost \$1375. They start with \$125. Each month they plan to deposit 20% more than the previous month. Will they have enough money for their trip? If not, how much more do they need?

**The Rest of the Story** A bushel of wheat contains about a million kernels. The total US output of wheat in a recent year was just over 2.1 billion bushels. How many years of production at that level would it take the United States to produce enough wheat to satisfy the soldier's "reasonable" request?

The terms of a geometric series grow rapidly when the common ratio is greater than 1. Likewise, they diminish rapidly when the common ratio is between 0 and 1. In fact, they diminish so rapidly that an *infinite geometric series* has a finite sum.

take note

### Key Concept Infinite Geometric Series

An infinite geometric series with first term $a_1$ and common ratio $|r| < 1$ has a finite sum

$$S = \frac{a_1}{1 - r}.$$

An infinite geometric series with $|r| \geq 1$ does not have a finite sum.

To say that an infinite series $a_1 + a_2 + a_3 + \cdots$ has a sum means that the *sequence of partial sums* $S_1 = a_1$, $S_2 = a_1 + a_2$, $S_3 = a_1 + a_2 + a_3, \ldots,$ $S_n = a_1 + a_2 + \cdots + a_n, \ldots$ **converges** to a number $S$ as $n$ gets very large.

When an infinite series does not converge to a sum, the series **diverges**. An infinite geometric series with $|r| \geq 1$ diverges.

## Problem 3 Analyzing Infinite Geometric Series

**Got It?** Does the infinite series *converge* or *diverge*? If it converges, what is the sum?

**a.** $\frac{1}{2} + \frac{3}{4} + \frac{9}{8} + \cdots$

**Think**
**When does an infinite geometric series converge?**

**b.** $\frac{1}{3} - \frac{1}{9} + \frac{1}{27} - \frac{1}{81} + \cdots$

**c.** $\sum_{n=1}^{\infty} \left(\frac{2}{3}\right)^n$

**d. Reasoning** Will an infinite geometric series either converge or diverge? Explain.

**Practice** Determine whether each infinite geometric series *diverges* or *converges*. If the series converges, state the sum.

**4.** $4 + 2 + 1 + \cdots$

**5.** $\frac{1}{4} + \frac{1}{2} + 1 + 2 + \cdots$

Evaluate the infinite geometric series.

**6.** $3 + 2 + \frac{4}{3} + \frac{8}{9} + \cdots$

## Lesson Check

### Do you know HOW?

Evaluate each finite geometric series.

**7.** $\frac{1}{5} + \frac{1}{10} + \frac{1}{20} + \frac{1}{40} + \frac{1}{80}$

**8.** $9 - 6 + 4 - \frac{8}{3} + \frac{16}{9}$

**Determine whether each infinite geometric series *diverges* or *converges*.**

**9.** $1 - \frac{1}{6} + \frac{1}{36} - \frac{1}{216} + \cdots$

**10.** $\frac{1}{64} + \frac{1}{32} + \frac{1}{16} + \cdots$

## Do you UNDERSTAND?

**11. Error Analysis** A classmate uses the formula for the sum of an infinite geometric series to evaluate $1 + 1.1 + 1.21 + 1.331 + \cdots$ and gets $-10$. What error did your classmate make?

**12. Writing** Explain how you can determine whether an infinite geometric series has a sum.

**13. Compare and Contrast** How are the formulas for the sum of a finite arithmetic series and the sum of a finite geometric series similar? How are they different?

## More Practice and Problem-Solving Exercises

**Determine whether each series is *arithmetic* or *geometric*. Then evaluate the finite series for the specified number of terms.**

**14.** $2 + 4 + 8 + 16 + \cdots; n = 10$

**15.** $2 + 4 + 6 + 8 + \cdots; n = 20$

**16.** $-5 + 25 - 125 + 625 - \cdots; n = 9$

**17.** $6.4 + 8 + 10 + 12.5 + \cdots; n = 7$

**18.** $1 + 2 + 3 + 4 + \cdots; n = 1000$

**19.** $81 + 27 + 9 + 3 + \cdots; n = 200$

**20. Think About a Plan** The height a ball bounces is less than the height of the previous bounce due to friction. The heights of the bounces form a geometric sequence. Suppose a ball is dropped from one meter and rebounds to 95% of the height of the previous bounce. What is the total distance traveled by the ball when it comes to rest?

- Does the problem give you enough information to solve the problem?
- How can you write the general term of the sequence?
- What formula should you use to calculate the total distance?

**21. Communications** Many companies use a telephone chain to notify employees of a closing due to bad weather. Suppose a company's CEO (Chief Executive Officer) calls four people. Then each of these people calls four others, and so on.

**a.** Make a diagram to show the first three stages in the telephone chain. How many calls are made at each stage?

**b.** Write the series that represents the total number of calls made through the first six stages.

**c.** How many employees have been notified after stage six?

**22. Graphing Calculator** The graph models the sum of the first $n$ terms in the infinite geometric series with $a_1 = 20$ and $r = 0.9$.

**a.** Write the first four sums of the series.

**b.** Use the graph to evaluate the series to the 47th term.

**c.** Write and evaluate the formula for the sum of the series.

**d.** Graph the formula using the window values shown. Use the graph to verify your answer to part (b).

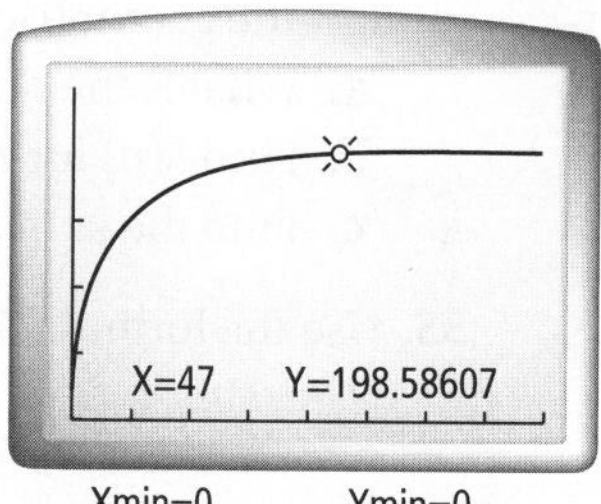


Xmin=0 Ymin=0
Xmax=94 Ymax=250
Xscl=10 Yscl=50

**Evaluate each infinite series that has a sum.**

**23.** $\sum_{n=1}^{\infty} \left(\frac{1}{5}\right)^{n-1}$

**24.** $\sum_{n=1}^{\infty} 3\left(\frac{1}{4}\right)^{n-1}$

**25.** $\sum_{n=1}^{\infty} \left(-\frac{1}{3}\right)^{n-1}$

**26.** $\sum_{n=1}^{\infty} 7(2)^{n-1}$

**27.** $\sum_{n=1}^{\infty} (-0.2)^{n-1}$

**28. Open-Ended** Write an infinite geometric series that converges to 3. Use the formula to evaluate the series.

**29. Reasoning** Find the specified value for each infinite geometric series.

**a.** $a_1 = 12, S = 96$; find $r$

**b.** $S = 12, r = \frac{1}{6}$, find $a_1$

**30. Writing** Suppose you are to receive an allowance each week for the next 26 weeks. Would you rather receive (a) $1000 per week or (b) $.02 the first week, $.04 the second week, $.08 the third week, and so on for the 26 weeks? Justify your answer.

**31.** The sum of an infinite geometric series is twice its first term.

**a. Error Analysis** A student says the common ratio of the series is $\frac{3}{2}$. What is the student's error?

**b.** Find the common ratio of the series.

**32. Physics** Because of friction and air resistance, each swing of a pendulum is a little shorter than the previous one. The lengths of the swings form a geometric sequence. Suppose the first swing of a pendulum has a length of 100 cm and the return swing is 99 cm.

**a.** On which swing will the arc first have a length less than 50 cm?

**b.** What is the total distance the pendulum has traveled when it comes to rest?

**33.** Where did the formula for summing finite geometric series come from? Suppose the geometric series has first term $a_1$ and constant ratio $r$, so that

$$S_n = a_1 + a_1r + a_1r^2 + \cdots + a_1r^{n-1}.$$

**a.** Show that $rS_n = a_1r + a_1r^2 + a_1r^3 + \cdots + a_1r^n$.

**b.** Use part (a) to show that $S_n - rS_n = a_1 - a_1r^n$.

**c.** Use part (b) to show that $S_n = \frac{a_1 - a_1r^n}{1 - r} = \frac{a_1(1 - r^n)}{1 - r}$.

## Challenge

**34.** The function $S(n) = \frac{10(1 - 0.8^n)}{0.2}$ represents the sum of the first $n$ terms of an infinite geometric series.

**a.** What is the domain of the function?

**b.** Find $S(n)$ for $n = 1, 2, 3, \ldots, 10$. Sketch the graph of the function.

**c.** Find the sum $S$ of the infinite geometric series.

**35.** Use the formula for the sum of an infinite geometric series to show that $0.\overline{9} = 1$. (*Hint:* $0.\overline{9} = \frac{9}{10} + \frac{9}{100} + \frac{9}{1000} + \cdots$)

# 9 Chapter Review

## 9-1 Mathematical Patterns

### Quick Review

A **sequence** is an ordered list of numbers called **terms.**

A **recursive definition** gives the first term and defines the other terms by relating each term after the first term to the one before it.

An **explicit formula** expresses the $n$th term in a sequence in terms of $n$, where $n$ is a positive integer.

### Example

**A sequence has an explicit formula $a_n = n^2$. What are the first three terms of this sequence?**

$a_1 = (1)^2 = 1$ Substitute 1 for $n$ and evaluate.

$a_2 = (2)^2 = 4$ Substitute 2 for $n$ and evaluate.

$a_3 = (3)^2 = 9$ Substitute 3 for $n$ and evaluate.

The first three terms are 1, 4, and 9.

### Exercises

**Find the first five terms of each sequence.**

**1.** $a_n = -2n + 3$

**2.** $a_n = -n^2 + 2n$

**3.** $a_n = 2a_{n-1} - 1$, where $a_1 = 2$

**4.** $a_n = \frac{1}{2}a_{n-1}$, where $a_1 = 20$

**Write a recursive definition for each sequence.**

**5.** 5, 22, 39, 56, ...

**6.** −2, 7, 16, 25, ...

**Write an explicit formula for each sequence.**

**7.** 1, 4, 7, 10, ...

**8.** 4, 1.5, −1, −3.5, ...

## 9-2 Arithmetic Sequences

### Quick Review

In an **arithmetic sequence**, the difference between consecutive terms is constant. This difference is the **common difference.**

For an arithmetic sequence, $a$ is the first term, $a_n$ is the $n$th term, $n$ is the number of the term, and $d$ is the common difference.

An explicit formula is $a_n = a + (n - 1)d$.

A recursive formula is $a_n = a_{n-1} + d$, with $a_1 = a$.

The **arithmetic mean** of two numbers $x$ and $y$ is the average of the two numbers $\frac{x+y}{2}$.

### Example

**What is the missing term of the arithmetic sequence 11, ■, 27, ... ?**

$$\text{arithmetic mean} = \frac{11 + 27}{2} = \frac{38}{2} = 19$$

The missing term is 19.

### Exercises

**Determine whether each sequence is arithmetic. If so, identify the common difference and find the 32nd term of the sequence.**

**9.** 2, 4, 7, 10, ...

**10.** 3, 18, 33, 48, ...

**11.** 7, 10, 13, 16, ...

**12.** 2, 5, 9, 14, ...

**Find the missing term(s) of each arithmetic sequence.**

**13.** 1, ■, 9, ...

**14.** 104, ■, 99, ...

**15.** −1, ■, 11 ...

**16.** −4.6, ■, −5.2, ...

**17.** −13, ■, ■, ■, −3, ...

**18.** 2, ■, ■, ■, −0.4, ...

**Write an explicit formula for each arithmetic sequence.**

**19.** −2, 7, 16, 25, ...

**20.** 62, 59, 56, 53, ...

# 9-3 Geometric Sequences

## Quick Review

In a **geometric sequence**, the ratio of consecutive terms is constant. This ratio is the **common ratio.**

For a geometric sequence, $a$ is the first term, $a_n$ is the $n$th term, $n$ is the number of the term, and $r$ is the common ratio.

An explicit formula is $a_n = a \cdot r^{n-1}$.

A recursive formula is $a_n = a_{n-1} \cdot r$, with $a_1 = a$.

The geometric mean of two positive numbers $x$ and $y$ is $\sqrt{xy}$.

## Example

**What is the sixth term of the geometric sequence that begins 2, 6, 18, . . . ?**

$a_1 = 2$ and $r = 6 \div 2 = 3$

$a_6 = 2 \cdot 3^{6-1}$ Substitute 6 for $n$, 2 for $a_1$, and 3 for $r$.

$= 486$

The sixth term is 486.

## Exercises

**Determine whether each sequence is geometric. If so, identify the common ratio and find the next two terms.**

**21.** $1, \frac{1}{2}, \frac{1}{4}, \frac{1}{8}, \ldots$

**22.** $1, 3, 5, 7, \ldots$

**23.** $3, 3.6, 4.32, 5.184, \ldots$

**Find the missing term(s) of each geometric sequence.**

**24.** 3, ■, 12, . . .

**25.** 0.004, ■, 0.4, . . .

**26.** −20, ■, ■, ■, −1.25, . . .

**Write an explicit formula for each geometric sequence.**

**27.** $1, 2, 4, 8, \ldots$

**28.** $25, 5, 1, \frac{1}{5}, \ldots$

**Use an explicit formula to find the 10th term of each geometric sequence.**

**29.** $5, 10, 20, 40, \ldots$

**30.** $-3, 6, -12, 24, \ldots$

# 9-4 Arithmetic Series

## Quick Review

A **series** is the expression for the sum of the terms of a sequence.

An **arithmetic series** is the sum of the terms of an arithmetic sequence. The sum $S_n$ of the first $n$ terms of an arithmetic series is $S_n = \frac{n}{2}(a_1 + a_n)$. You can use a summation symbol, $\Sigma$, and lower and upper **limits** to write a series. The lower limit is the least value of $n$ and the upper limit is the greatest value of $n$.

## Example

**What is the sum of the arithmetic series?**

$2 + 5 + 8 + 11 + 14 + 17 + 20$

$a_1 = 2$, $a_7 = 20$, and $n = 7$.

$S_7 = \frac{7}{2}(2 + 20)$ Substitute 7 for $n$, 2 for $a_1$, and 20 for $a_7$.

$= 77$ Evaluate.

The sum is 77.

## Exercises

**Use summation notation to write each arithmetic series for the specified number of terms. Then evaluate the sum.**

**31.** $10 + 7 + 4 + \cdots; n = 5$

**32.** $50 + 55 + 60 + \cdots; n = 7$

**33.** $6 + 7.4 + 8.8 + \cdots; n = 11$

**34.** $21 + 19 + 17 + \cdots; n = 8$

**Find the number of terms in each series, the first term, and the last term. Then evaluate the sum.**

**35.** $\sum_{n=1}^{3}(17n - 25)$

**36.** $\sum_{n=2}^{10}\left(\frac{1}{2}n + 3\right)$

# 9-5 Geometric Series

## Quick Review

A **geometric series** is the sum of the terms of a geometric sequence. The sum $S_n$ of the first $n$ terms of a geometric series is $S_n = \frac{a_1(1 - r^n)}{1 - r}$, $r \neq 1$.

When an infinite series has a finite sum, the series **converges**. When the series does not converge, the series **diverges**.

In a geometric series, when $|r| < 1$, the series converges to $S = \frac{a_1}{1 - r}$. When $|r| \geq 1$, the series diverges.

## Example

**What is the sum of the geometric series?**

$5 + 10 + 20 + 40 + 80 + 160$

$n = 6$, $a_1 = 5$, and $r = 10 \div 5 = 2$.

$S_6 = \frac{5(1 - 2^6)}{1 - 2}$ Substitute 6 for $n$, 5 for $a_1$, and 2 for $r$.

$= 315$ Evaluate.

The sum is 315.

## Exercises

**Evaluate each finite series for the specified number of terms.**

**37.** $1 + 2 + 4 + \cdots; n = 5$

**38.** $80 - 40 + 20 - \cdots; n = 8$

**39.** $12 + 2 + \frac{1}{3} + \cdots; n = 4$

**Determine whether each infinite geometric series *converges* or *diverges*. If the series converges, state the sum.**

**40.** $150 + 30 + 6 + \cdots$

**41.** $2.2 + 2.42 + 2.662 + \cdots$

**42.** $-10 - 20 - 40 - \cdots$

**43.** $\frac{2}{3} + \frac{4}{9} + \frac{8}{27} + \cdots$

# *Pull It* All Together

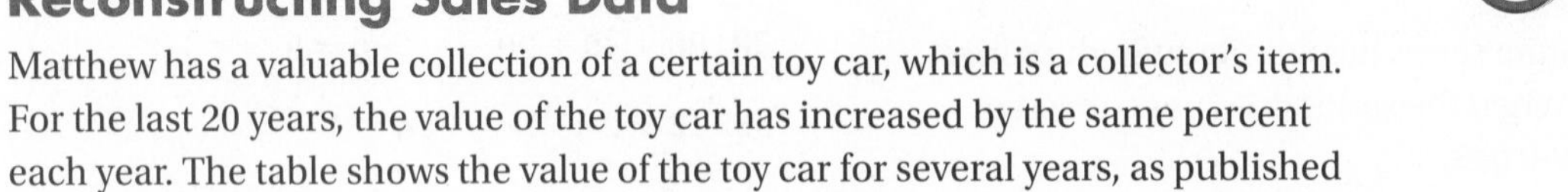

ASSESSMENT

## Reconstructing Sales Data

Matthew has a valuable collection of a certain toy car, which is a collector's item. For the last 20 years, the value of the toy car has increased by the same percent each year. The table shows the value of the toy car for several years, as published in a collector's magazine.

| Year | Value |
|---|---|
| 2003 | $76.00 |
| 2004 | $79.04 |
| 2005 | $82.20 |
| 2006 | $85.49 |
| 2007 | $88.91 |
| 2008 | $92.47 |

Over a span of 7 years, Matthew sold 7 toy cars, with each sale occurring one year after the previous sale and at the published price. His total revenue from the sales was $533.64. However, he cannot remember when he sold the cars, and he is wondering how he can figure this out.

## Task Description

**Determine the years in which the toy cars were sold.**

# Get Ready!

## Squaring Numbers and Finding Square Roots

**Simplify.**

**1.** $3^2$

**2.** $8^2$

**3.** $12^2$

**4.** $15^2$

**5.** $\sqrt{16}$

**6.** $\sqrt{64}$

**7.** $\sqrt{100}$

**8.** $\sqrt{169}$

**Solve each quadratic equation.**

**9.** $x^2 = 64$

**10.** $b^2 - 225 = 0$

**11.** $a^2 = 144$

## Simplifying Radicals

**Simplify. Leave your answers in simplified radical form.**

**12.** $\sqrt{8}$

**13.** $\sqrt{27}$

**14.** $\sqrt{75}$

**15.** $4\sqrt{72}$

## Area

**16.** A garden that is 6 ft by 8 ft has a walkway that is 3 ft wide around it. What is the ratio of the area of the garden to the area of the garden and walkway? Write your answer in simplest form.

**17.** A rectangular rose garden is 8 m by 10 m. One bag of fertilizer can cover 16 m². How many bags of fertilizer will be needed to cover the entire garden?

## Classifying Quadrilaterals

**Classify each quadrilateral as specifically as possible.**

**18.**

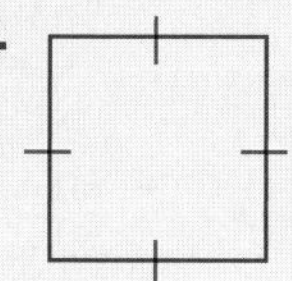

**19.**

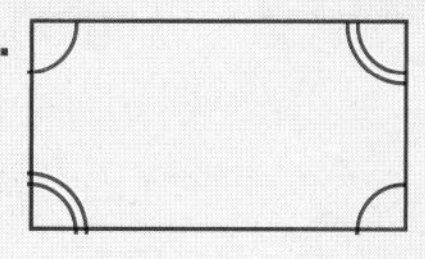

**20.**

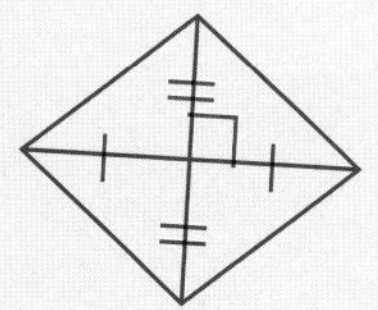

## Looking Ahead Vocabulary

**21.** Polygons are two-dimensional figures made up of edges and vertices. How can three-dimensional figures be made up of faces, edges, and vertices?

**22.** The word *locus* comes from the Latin word for "place" or "location." What is the *locus* of a set of points?

# Applying Geometric Concepts

## Big Ideas

**1 Similarity**

**Essential Questions:** How do perimeters and areas of similar polygons compare? How do surface areas and volumes of similar solids compare?

**2 Measurement**

**Essential Question:** How do you find the area of a polygon?

**3 Visualization**

**Essential Question:** How can you determine the intersection of a solid and a plane?

## Domains

- Congruence
- Geometric Measurement and Dimension
- Modeling with Geometry

## Chapter Preview


10-1 Applying Constructions
10-2 Solving Density and Design Problems
10-3 Perimeters and Areas of Similar Figures
10-4 Geometric Probability
10-5 Space Figures and Cross Sections
10-6 Areas and Volumes of Similar Solids
10-7 Locus: A Set of Points

## Vocabulary

**English/Spanish Vocabulary Audio Online:**

| English | Spanish |
|---|---|
| cross section, *p. 778* | sección de corte |
| edge, *p. 774* | arista |
| face, *p. 774* | cara |
| geometric probability, *p. 765* | probabilidad geométrica |
| locus, *p. 794* | lugar geométrico |
| polyhedron, *p. 774* | poliedro |
| similar solids, *p. 785* | cuerpos geométricos semejantes |
| vertex, *p. 774* | vértice |

# Applying Constructions

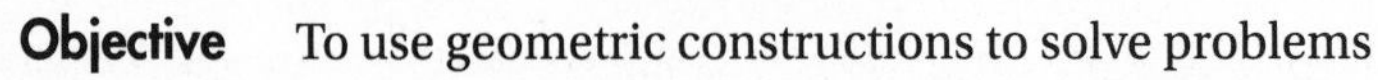

**G.CO.12** Make formal geometric constructions with . . . compass and straightedge . . . Also **G.CO.13, G.C.3**

**Objective** To use geometric constructions to solve problems

**Solve It!** Write your solution to the Solve It in the space below.

The Solve It involves constructing a square. There are other ways to apply constructions in addition to folding paper.

**Essential Understanding** You can use a compass, protractor, and straightedge to construct geometric figures.

To **bisect** an angle or segment means to divide the angle or segment into two equal parts.

## Problem 1 Bisecting an Angle

**Got It?** Follow the steps to construct the bisector of $\overline{CD}$.

- Put the compass point on point $C$. Draw arcs to the left and to the right of $\overline{CD}$.
- Put the compass point on point $D$. Using the same compass setting, draw an arc to the left and to the right of $\overline{CD}$. Be sure the arcs intersect.
- Draw the line connecting the points of intersections of the arcs.

C

D

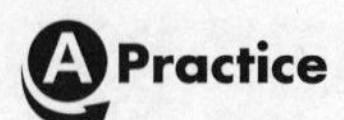

**Practice** **1.** Draw a 60°-angle. Then bisect the angle.

**2.** Draw a 3-inch line segment. Then bisect the segment.

Recall that perpendicular lines form right angles.

## Problem 2 Constructing Perpendicular Lines

**Think**

**Which segment do you need to bisect?**

**Got It?** First Street is the perpendicular bisector of the section of Front Street between the school and the intersection of Main Street and Front Street. Draw First Street.

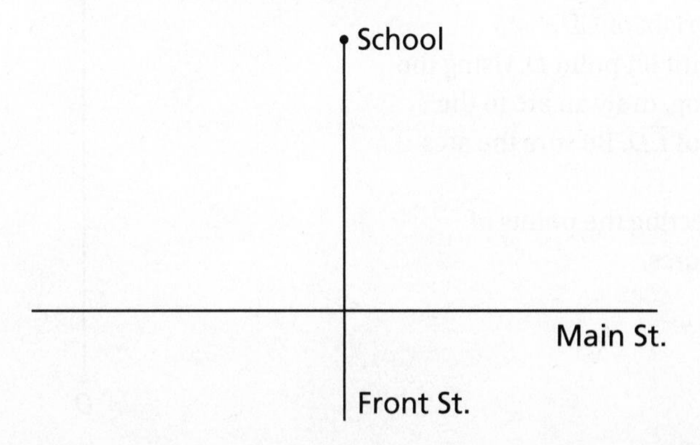

**3.** The figure below shows the vertical beam of a telephone pole. The points shows the location where the horizontal beam is attached to the vertical beam. Construct the horizontal beam.

**4.** Explain how to prove that the telephone pole beams drawn in Exercise 3 are perpendicular.

Recall that parallel lines never instersect.

## Problem 3 Constructing Parallel Lines

**Got It?** Construct a line parallel to the line below through the given point by constructing two perpendicular lines.

**Think**

**How do you know that the second line you construct is parallel to the given line?**

5. A city worker is painting yellow road lines on a highway. The left road line is shown below. Construct the right road line parallel to the given line.

6. Prove that the roads constructed in Exercise 5 are parallel.

To *circumscribe* means to "draw around." A **circumscribed circle** is a circle that passes through each vertex of a given polygon.

## Problem 4 Circumscribing a Circle About a Polygon

**Got It?** A circle can also be *inscribed* in certain polygons. This means that the circle touches each side of a given polygon. Use the steps below to construct an inscribed circle in $\triangle MNP$.

- Bisect $\angle M$ and $\angle P$. Label the intersection of the angle bisectors point $Q$.
- Construct a line through $Q$ perpendicular to $\overline{MP}$. Label the intersection of the perpendicular line and $\overline{MP}$ as point $R$.
- Draw a circle with center $Q$ that passes through $R$.

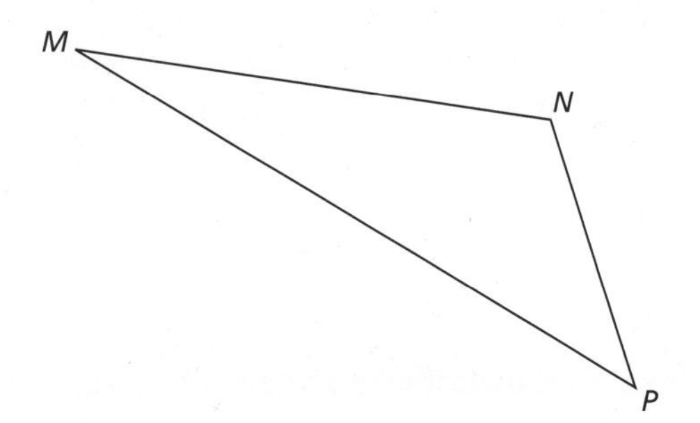


**A Practice** 7. Construct a circle circumscribed about the isosceles right triangle below.

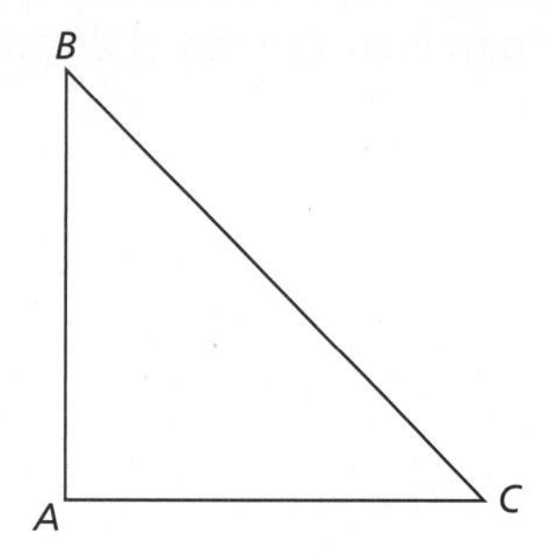

**8.** Explain how you constructed a circle circumscribed about the right triangle in Exercise 7.

To *inscribe* means to draw inside. An **inscribed polygon** is a polygon in which all vertices of the polygon are on a given circle.

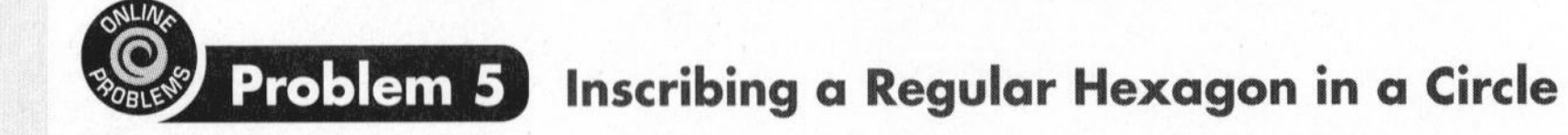


## Problem 5 Inscribing a Regular Hexagon in a Circle

**Got It?** You decide to change the company logo from Problem 5 to be an equilateral triangle inscribed in a circle. Explain how you could use the existing logo to create the new logo. Construct the new logo.

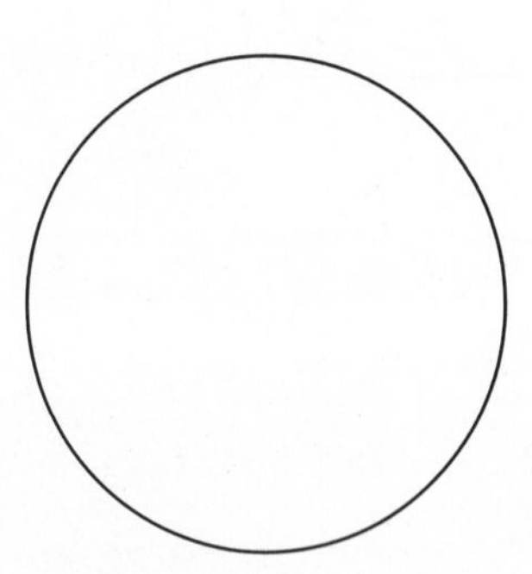

9. **Graphic Design** Damon is drawing a logo for his new business. He wants the logo to be a square inscribed in a circle. The circular outline of the logo is shown below. Construct the square inscribed in the circle.

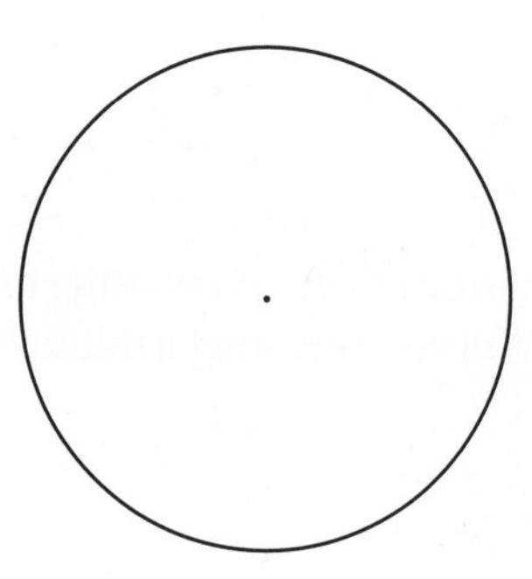

10. Explain how to prove the figure you drew inside the circle is a square.

## Lesson Check

### Do you know HOW?

11. Construct a copy of $\angle ABC$.

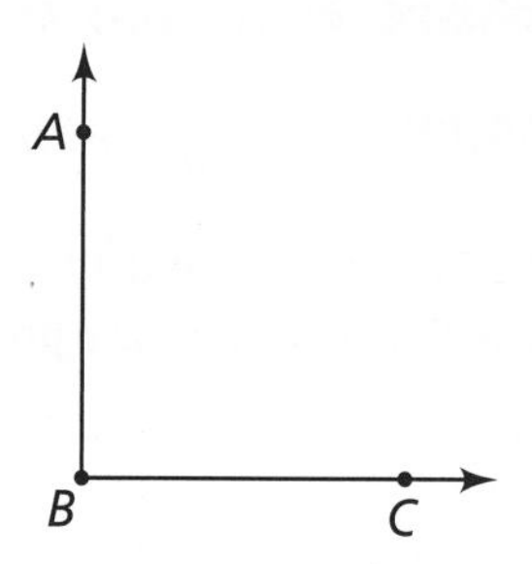


12. Construct the angle bisector of $\angle ABC$. (Use your copy from Exercise 11.)

## Do you UNDERSTAND?

**13. Vocabulary** What is the difference between a circumscribed circle and an inscribed polygon.

**14. Reasoning** Suppose you used a narrower compass setting to construct the angle bisector of $\angle ABC$ in Exercise 12. Will you construct a different angle bisector? Explain.

**15. Compare and Contrast** How are the constructions in Problem 4 and its Got It similar? How are they different?

## More Practice and Problem-Solving Exercises

### B Apply

**In Exercises 16 and 17, construct a figure congruent to the figure given. Check your work with a ruler or a protractor.**

**16.**

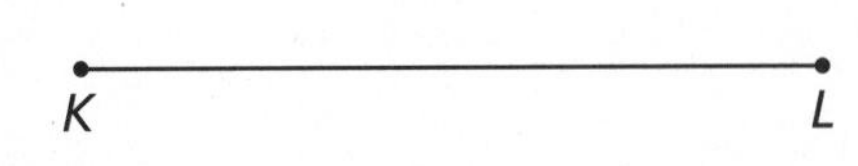


**17.**

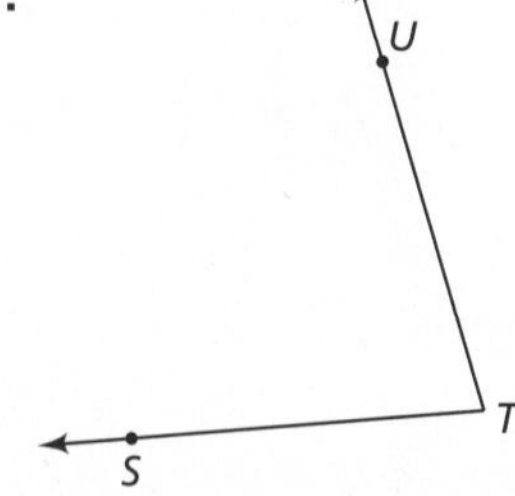

**18.** Describe how to bisect a segment.

**19. Think About a Plan** The 2-inch line segment represents the one side of a square table. Copy the segment, then construct a scale model of the top view of the table.

- How can you copy the segment?
- How do you construct lines perpendicular to the segment through the endpoints of the segment?
- How can make sure that each side of the tabletop is the same length?

**20.** Draw a line segment. Construct an equilateral triangle with the segment as one side. Describe the steps in your construction.

**21.** Construct a 30°-60°-90° triangle. (*Hint*: Use the construction from Exercise 20.)

**22. Sports** An indoor soccer field has a length that is twice its width.

**a.** Construct a drawing of the soccer field.

**b.** Describe the steps in your construction.

**23. a.** Construct a circle inscribed in a square.

**b.** Describe the steps in your construction from part (a).

**24.** Draw $\overline{ST}$.

**a.** Construct a trisection of $\overline{ST}$ by following the steps below.

- Draw $\overrightarrow{SR}$ to form $\angle RST$.
- Choose a point $X$ on $\overrightarrow{SR}$.
- Copy $\overline{SX}$ with endpoint at $X$ along $\overrightarrow{SR}$ in the opposite direction of point $S$. Label the new endpoint of the copied segment point $Y$.
- Copy $\overline{SX}$ with endpoint $Y$ along $\overrightarrow{SR}$ in the opposite direction of point $S$. Label the new endpoint of the copied segment point $Z$.
- Draw $\overline{ZT}$. Construct lines through points $X$ and $Y$ that are parallel to $\overline{ZT}$.

**b.** Show that the parallel lines in the last step of the construction trisect $\overline{ST}$.

**25.** Copy the number line below, and the point $X$ on the number line.

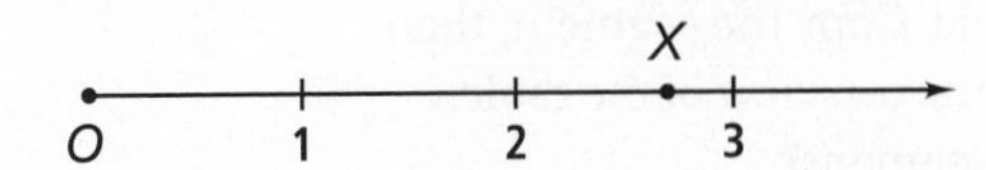


**a.** Construct $\sqrt{X}$ by following the steps below.

- Draw a circle of radius 1 with center $O$.
- Extend the number line to the left so that it intersects the circle at point $P$.
- Find the midpoint of $\overline{XP}$. Label the midpoint $Q$.
- Draw a circle with center $Q$ and radius $QP$.
- Construct a line through $O$ perpendicular to the number line. Let the intersection of this line and the circle from the previous step be $R$. The length of $\overline{RO}$ is $\sqrt{X}$.

**b.** Prove that $RO = \sqrt{X}$. (*Hint*: Draw $\overline{RP}$ and $\overline{RX}$. Use the fact that $\triangle PRO \sim \triangle RXO$ to write a proportion of side lengths of the two triangles.)

**26. Golden Rectangle** Rectangles in which the ratio of the length to the width is $1 + \sqrt{5} : 2$ are *golden rectangles.* A golden rectangle can be divided into a square and a rectangle that is similar to the original rectangle.

**a.** Construct a golden rectangle by following the steps below.

- Draw square $FGHJ$.
- Construct the midpoint of $\overline{FJ}$. Label the midpoint $I$.
- Extend $\overline{FJ}$ in the direction of $J$.
- Place the compass at $I$. Make the width of the compass $IH$. Draw an arc that intersects the extended segment. Label the intersection $K$.
- Construct a line at $K$ perpendicular to $\overline{FK}$.
- Extend $\overline{GH}$ to intersect the perpendicular line constructed in the previous step at point $L$. $GLKF$ is a golden rectangle, where rectangle $JHLK$ is similar to rectangle $GLKF$.

**b.** Show that $IK = \frac{\sqrt{5}}{2}FJ$. (*Hint*: Consider $\triangle IHJ$.)

**c.** Show that $JK = \frac{\sqrt{5}-1}{2}FJ$.

**d.** Show that $FGLK$ is similar to $HJKL$ by showing that $\frac{FK}{GF} = \frac{HJ}{JK}$.

# 10-2 Solving Density and Design Problems

G.MG.2 Apply concepts of density based on area and volume in modeling situations . . . Also **G.MG.3**

**Objective** To find the density of objects

**Solve It!** Write your solution to the Solve It in the space below.

The Solve It involves finding the area per person of your classroom. *Density* is a measure based on area or volume that you can use to describe real-world situations.

**Essential Understanding** You can use geometric methods to solve real-world problems.

To find the **density** of an object, divide its mass by its volume. To find **population density**, divide the number of individuals in the population by the total area or volume that they occupy.

## Problem 1 Finding Population Density

**Plan**

**What do you need to know to find the population density?**

**Got It?** A fish tank is shown below. There are 36 fish in the tank. What is the population density of the fish tank?

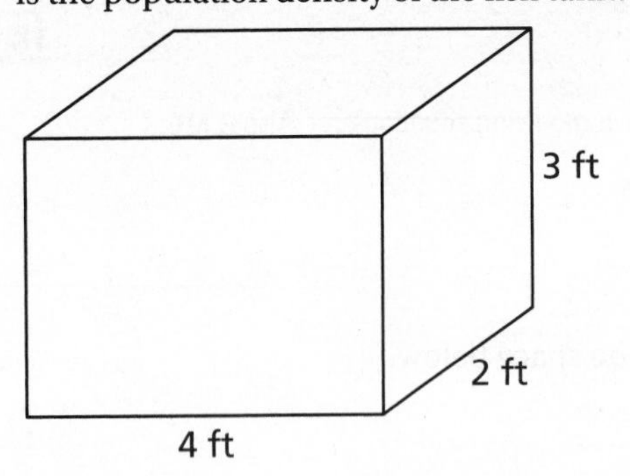


**Practice** 1. An outline of a city map is shown. The population of the city is 23,023 people. What is the population density of the city?

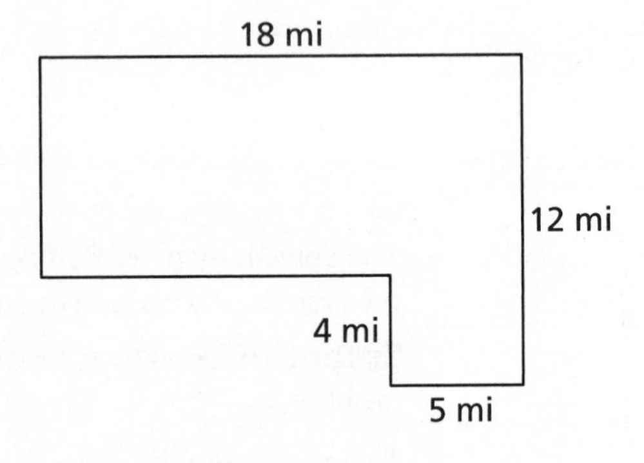

**2.** The aquarium can accommodate medium-size fish.

**a.** What is the population density of the aquarium if it holds two fish?

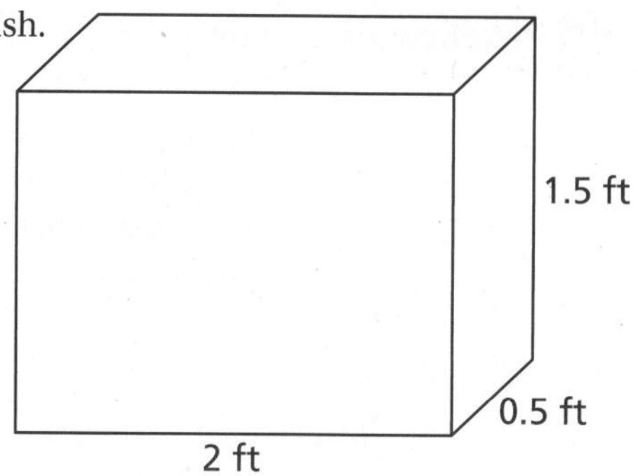


**b.** An aquarium in the shape of a cube has 2 ft edges. Based on the population density you found in part (a), how many medium size fish can this aquarium hold?

You can also use geometric methods to solve design problems.

## Problem 2 Solving a Design Problem

**Think**

**How do you find the surface area and volume of the prism?**

**Got It?** The company in Problem 2 decides to change the base of the block of cheese to be an isosceles right triangle while maintaining its volume. What dimensions should the company choose for the blocks of cheese in order to minimize the surface area? Round your answer to the nearest tenth.

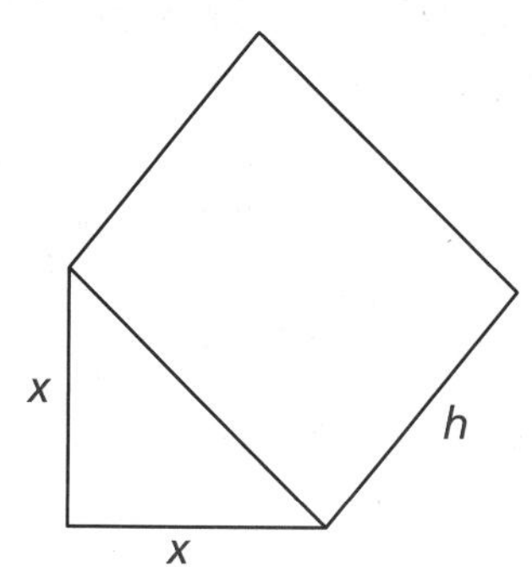

3. A company wants to manufacture packaging boxes in the shape of rectangular prisms. Each box will have a volume of 12,000 cubic inches. The company wants to choose the dimensions of a box with side lengths $h$ in., $8x$ in., and $12x$ in., so that the box's surface area is minimized. What dimensions should the company choose for the boxes? Round your answer to the nearest tenth.

4. A designer wants to manufacture storage crates in the shape of rectangular prisms with an open top. Each crate will have a volume of 1944 cubic inches. The designer wants to choose the dimensions of a crate with length $1.5x$ in., width $x$ in., and height $h$ in., so that the crate's surface area is minimized. What dimensions should the company choose for the boxes? Round your answer to the nearest tenth.

## Lesson Check

### Do you know HOW?

**5.** What two measures are needed to find the density of an object?

**6.** How can you minimize the surface area of an object with a fixed volume?

**7.** How do you find population density?

### Do you UNDERSTAND?

**8. Vocabulary** What does *population* refer to in the term *population density*?

9. **Open-Ended** Describe a situation in which you might want to minimize the surface area of an object with a fixed volume.

10. **Error Analysis** The volume of a block of iron is 12 $cm^3$ and its mass is 94.44 grams. A classmate said the density of iron was 0.13 $g/cm^3$. Explain his error.

## More Practice and Problem-Solving Exercises

11. New York City has an area of 303 square miles. In 2011, New York City had a population of 8,244,910. What was the population density of New York City in 2011?

12. The state of Connecticut has an area of 4,845 square miles. In 2011, Connecticut had a population of 3,580,709. What was the population density of Connecticut in 2011?

13. **Think About a Plan** You want to manufacture soup cans in the shape of a cylinder. Each can will have a volume of 1099 cubic centimeters. You want to choose the dimensions so that the surface area is minimized. What dimensions should you choose for the cans?
    - What formula should you use for the volume of a cylinder?
    - What formula should you use for the surface area of a cylinder?
    - How can you use a calculator to find the dimensions for each can?

**14.** A designer wants to manufacture storage bins in the shape of rectangular prisms. Each bin will have a volume of 9 cubic feet. The designer wants to choose the dimensions of a bin so that the bases of the prism are squares and the bin's surface area is minimized. What dimensions should the designer choose for the bins?

**15. Error Analysis** The population of a city is 293,908 and the area is 142 square miles. A classmate said the population density can be found by dividing 142 square miles by 293,908 people. What is her mistake?

STEM **16. Metals** The table shows the mass and volume of different metals. Find the density of each.

**Density**

| Substance | Mass (grams) | Volume ($cm^3$) |
|---|---|---|
| Aluminum | 135 | 50 |
| Cesium | 308.8 | 160 |
| Gold | 482.5 | 25 |
| Lead | 339 | 30 |

**a.** Aluminum
**b.** Cesium
**c.** Gold
**d.** Lead

**17.** The table shows the population and area of several countries.

| Country | Population | Area ($km^2$) |
|---|---|---|
| Singapore | 5,183,700 | 710 |
| Bhutan | 738,267 | 38,394 |
| Bangladesh | 152,518,015 | 147,570 |
| South Korea | 48,456,369 | 99,538 |

**a.** What is the population density of Singapore?
**b.** What is the population density of Bhutan?
**c.** What is the population density of Bangladesh?
**d.** What is the population density of South Korea?

**18.** A florist recommends that you should grow 4 Flower *A* plants per square foot, and 9 Flower *B* plants per square foot. If you want to grow 50 plants each of Flower *A* and Flower *B*, how many more square feet of garden space do you need for the Flower *A* plants than the Flower *B* plants?

**19.** Japan has 127,960,000 people living on 377,944 square kilometers of land. Belgium has 11,007,020 people living on 30,528 square kilometers of land. How many fewer people live on a square kilometer of land in Japan than in Belgium?

20. **Buoyancy** Buoyancy is the upward force that a fluid applies to an object less dense than itself. This means an object will float if the density of the object is less than the density of the fluid is displaces. Water has a density of 1 g/cm$^3$.
   a. A beach ball has a volume of 1800 cm$^3$ and a mass of 630 grams. What is the density of the beach ball?
   b. Will the beach ball float? Explain.

STEM 21. **Energy** Natural gas is measured by volume, in cubic feet. A cubic foot of gas is the amount of gas needed to fill a volume of one cubic foot under certain conditions of pressure and temperature. The energy content of natural gas is measured in British Thermal Units, or BTUs. One BTU is the amount of heat needed to raise one pound of water 1°F. One cubic foot of propane has 2516 BTUs, and one cubic foot of natural gas has 1030 BTUs.
   a. How much natural gas will a 100,000 BTU/hr furnace will use in one hour? Explain.
   b. How much propane gas will a 100,000 BTU/hr furnace will use in one hour? Explain.
   c. How many times more energy does propane contain than natural gas, using a 100,000 BTU/hr furnace? Explain.

# 10-3 Perimeters and Areas of Similar Figures

**G.MG.1** Use geometric shapes, their measures, and their properties to describe objects . . . Also **G.MG.2, G.MG.3**

**Objective** To find the perimeters and areas of similar polygons

**Solve It!** Write your solution to the Solve It in the space below.

In the Solve It, you compared the areas of similar figures.

**Essential Understanding** You can use ratios to compare the perimeters and areas of similar figures.

take note

### Theorem 111 Perimeters and Areas of Similar Figures

If the scale factor of two similar figures is $\frac{a}{b}$, then

(1) the ratio of their perimeters is $\frac{a}{b}$, and

(2) the ratio of their areas is $\frac{a^2}{b^2}$.

## Problem 1 Finding Ratios in Similar Figures

**Got It?** Two similar polygons have corresponding sides in the ratio 5 : 7.

**a.** What is the ratio (larger to smaller) of their perimeters?

**b.** What is the ratio (larger to smaller) of their areas?

**A Practice** **The figures in each pair are similar. Compare the first figure to the second. Give the ratio of the perimeters and the ratio of the areas.**

**1.**

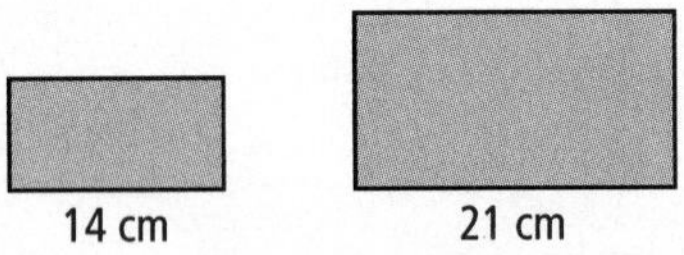

14 cm

21 cm

2.

15 in. 25 in.

When you know the area of one of two similar polygons, you can use a proportion to find the area of the other polygon.

## Problem 2 Finding Areas Using Similar Figures

**Think**

**What is the ratio of the areas?**

**Got It?** The scale factor of two similar parallelograms is $\frac{3}{4}$. The area of the larger parallelogram is 96 in.$^2$. What is the area of the smaller parallelogram?

**A Practice** **The figures in each pair are similar. The area of one figure is given. Find the area of the other figure to the nearest whole number.**

**3.**

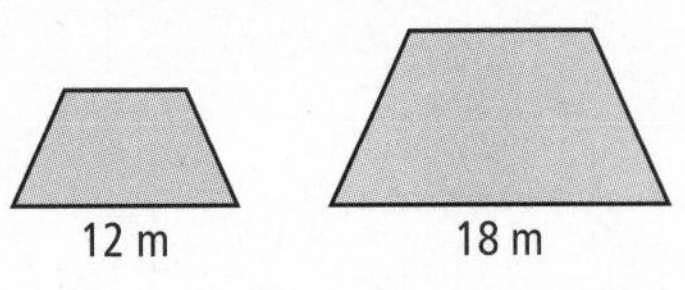


Area of larger trapezoid $= 121 \text{ m}^2$

**4.**

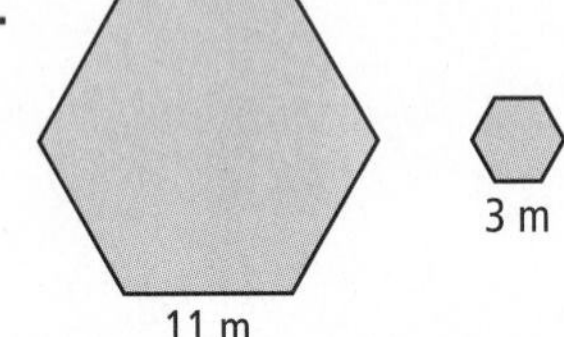


Area of smaller hexagon $= 23 \text{ m}^2$

## Problem 3 Applying Area Ratios

**Got It?** **a.** The scale factor of the dimensions of two similar pieces of window glass is 3 : 5. The smaller piece costs $2.50. How much should the larger piece cost?

**b. Reasoning** In Problem 3, why is it important that *each* dimension is 2.5 times the corresponding dimension of the original plot? Explain.

**5. Remodeling** The scale factor of the dimensions of two similar wood floors is 4:3. It costs $216 to refinish the smaller wood floor. At that rate, how much would it cost to refinish the larger wood floor?

**6. Decorating** An embroidered placemat costs $3.95. An embroidered tablecloth is similar to the placemat, but four times as long and four times as wide. How much would you expect to pay for the tablecloth?

When you know the ratio of the areas of two similar figures, you can work backward to find the ratio of their perimeters.

## Problem 4 Finding Perimeter Ratios

**Got It?** The areas of two similar rectangles are 1875 $ft^2$ and 135 $ft^2$. What is the ratio of their perimeters?

**Plan**
**How can you find the scale factor?**

**Practice** **Find the scale factor and the ratio of perimeters for each pair of similar figures.**

**7.** two trapezoids with areas 49 $cm^2$ and 9 $cm^2$

**8.** two equilateral triangles with areas $16\sqrt{3}$ $ft^2$ and $\sqrt{3}$ $ft^2$

## Lesson Check

### Do you know HOW?

**The figures in each pair are similar. What is the ratio of the perimeters and the ratio of the areas?**

**9.**

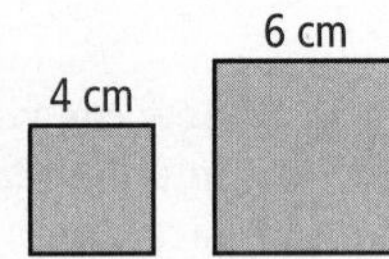


**10.**

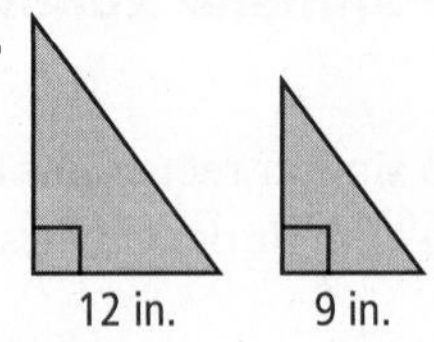

**11.** In Exercise 10, if the area of the smaller triangle is about 39 $ft^2$, what is the area of the larger triangle to the nearest tenth?

**12.** The areas of two similar rhombuses are 48 $m^2$ and 128 $m^2$. What is the ratio of their perimeters?

## Do you UNDERSTAND?

**13. Reasoning** How does the ratio of the areas of two similar figures compare to the ratio of their perimeters? Explain.

**14. Reasoning** The area of one rectangle is twice the area of another. What is the ratio of their perimeters? How do you know?

**15. Error Analysis** Your friend says that since the ratio of the perimeters of two polygons is $\frac{1}{2}$, the area of the smaller polygon must be one half the area of the larger polygon. What is wrong with this statement? Explain.

**16. Compare and Contrast** How is the relationship between the areas of two congruent figures different from the relationship between the areas of two similar figures?

## More Practice and Problem-Solving Exercises

### B Apply

**The scale factor of two similar polygons is given. Find the ratio of their perimeters and the ratio of their areas.**

**17.** $3:1$ **18.** $2:5$ **19.** $\frac{2}{3}$ **20.** $\frac{7}{4}$ **21.** $6:1$

**22.** The area of a regular decagon is $50\text{ cm}^2$. What is the area of a regular decagon with sides four times the sides of the smaller decagon?

**A** $200\text{ cm}^2$ **B** $500\text{ cm}^2$ **C** $800\text{ cm}^2$ **D** $2000\text{ cm}^2$

**23. Error Analysis** A reporter used the graphic below to show that the number of houses with more than two televisions had doubled in the past few years. Explain why this graphic is misleading.

**24. Think About a Plan** Two similar rectangles have areas 27 in.$^2$ and 48 in.$^2$. The length of one side of the larger rectangle is 16 in. What are the dimensions of both rectangles?

- How does the ratio of the areas of the similar rectangles compare to their scale factor?
- How can you use the dimensions of the larger rectangle to find the dimensions of the smaller rectangle?

**25.** The longer sides of a parallelogram are 5 m. The longer sides of a similar parallelogram are 15 m. The area of the smaller parallelogram is 28 m$^2$. What is the area of the larger parallelogram?

**Algebra Find the values of $x$ and $y$ when the smaller triangle shown here has the given area.**

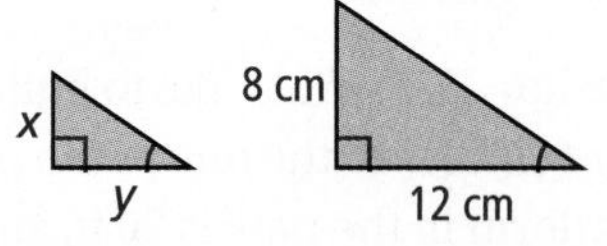


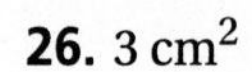

**26.** 3 cm$^2$ **27.** 6 cm$^2$ **28.** 12 cm$^2$

**29.** 16 cm$^2$ **30.** 24 cm$^2$ **31.** 48 cm$^2$

STEM **32. Medicine** For some medical imaging, the scale of the image is 3 : 1. That means that if an image is 3 cm long, the corresponding length on the person's body is 1 cm. Find the actual area of a lesion if its image has area 2.7 cm$^2$.

**33.** In $\triangle RST$, $RS = 20$ m, $ST = 25$ m, and $RT = 40$ m.

**a. Open-Ended** Choose a convenient scale. Then use a ruler and compass to draw $\triangle R'S'T' \sim \triangle RST$.

**b. Constructions** Construct an altitude of $\triangle R'S'T'$ and measure its length. Find the area of $\triangle R'S'T'$.

**c. Estimation** Estimate the area of $\triangle RST$.

**Compare the blue figure to the red figure. Find the ratios of (a) their perimeters and (b) their areas.**

**34.**

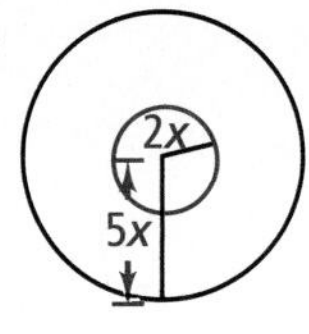


**35.**

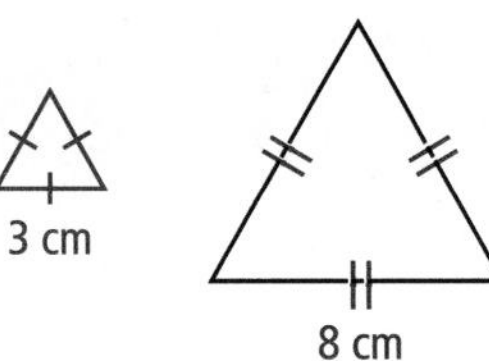


**36.**

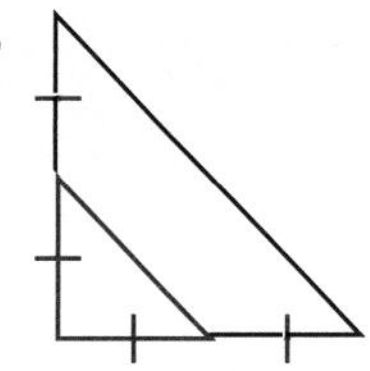

**37. a.** Find the area of a regular hexagon with sides 2 cm long. Leave your answer in simplest radical form.

**b.** Use your answer to part (a) and Theorem 111 to find the areas of the regular hexagons shown at the right.

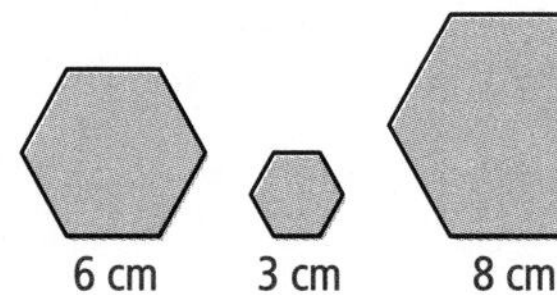


**38. Writing** The enrollment at an elementary school is going to increase from 200 students to 395 students. A parents' group is planning to increase the 100 ft-by-200 ft playground area to a larger area that is 200 ft by 400 ft. What would you tell the parents' group when they asked your opinion about whether the new playground will be large enough?

STEM **39.** **a.** **Surveying** A surveyor measured one side and two angles of a field, as shown in the diagram. Use a ruler and a protractor to draw a similar triangle.

**b.** Measure the sides and altitude of your triangle and find its perimeter and area.

**c.** **Estimation** Estimate the perimeter and area of the field.

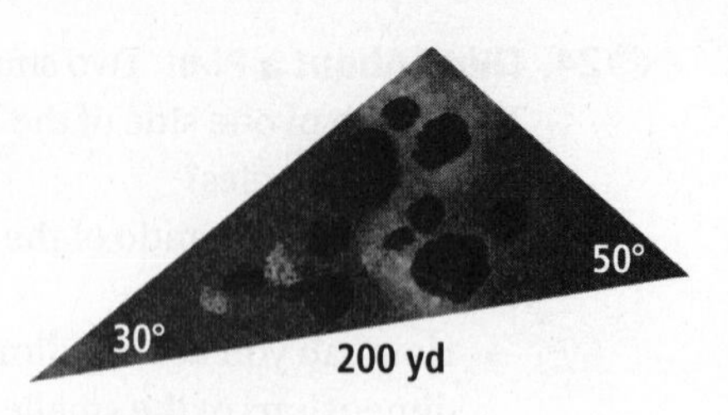


**40.** **Gardening** You have a triangular garden that you want to expand. The larger garden will be similar to the smaller garden, and the ratio of the side lengths will be 5 : 8. If you can grow 8 pea plants per square foot, and you were able to grow 55 pea plants in the smaller garden, how many pea plants can you grow in the larger garden?

**41.** **Design** You would like to build a rectangular skateboarding platform in your yard similar to the one in the park, but on a smaller scale. The length of the platform in the park is 20 ft, and the area is 192 ft$^2$. The length of the platform you are building in your yard is 15 ft. What will the area of the new skateboarding platform be after it is built?

## Challenge

**Reasoning** **Complete each statement with *always, sometimes,* or *never*. Justify your answers.**

**42.** Two similar rectangles with the same perimeter are _?_ congruent.

**43.** Two rectangles with the same area are _?_ similar.

**44.** Two rectangles with the same area and different perimeters are _?_ similar.

**45.** Similar figures _?_ have the same area.

# 10-4 Geometric Probability

**G.MG.1** Use geometric shapes, their measures, and their properties to describe objects . . .

**Objective** To use segment and area models to find the probabilities of events

**Solve It!** Write your solution to the Solve It in the space below.

In the Solve It, you found a probability involving a coin. In this lesson you will find probabilities based on lengths and areas. The probability of an event, written $P$(event), is the likelihood that the event will occur.

When the possible outcomes are equally likely, the theoretical probability of an event is the ratio of the number of favorable outcomes to the number of possible outcomes.

$$P(\text{event}) = \frac{\text{number of favorable outcomes}}{\text{number of possible outcomes}}$$

Recall that a probability can be expressed as a fraction, a decimal, or a percent.

**Essential Understanding** You can use geometric models to solve certain types of probability problems.

In **geometric probability**, points on a segment or in a region of a plane represent outcomes. The geometric probability of an event is a ratio that involves geometric measures such as length or area.

take note

## Key Concept Probability and Length

Point $S$ on $\overline{AD}$ is chosen at random. The probability that $S$ is on $\overline{BC}$ is the ratio of the length of $\overline{BC}$ to the length of $\overline{AD}$.

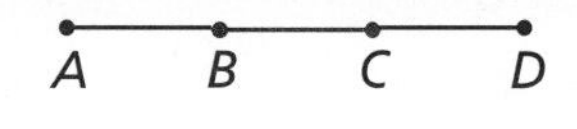


$$P(S \text{ on } \overline{BC}) = \frac{BC}{AD}$$

## Problem 1 Using Segments to Find Probability

**Got It?** Use the diagram below. Point $H$ on $\overline{ST}$ is selected at random. What is the probability that $H$ lies on $\overline{SR}$?

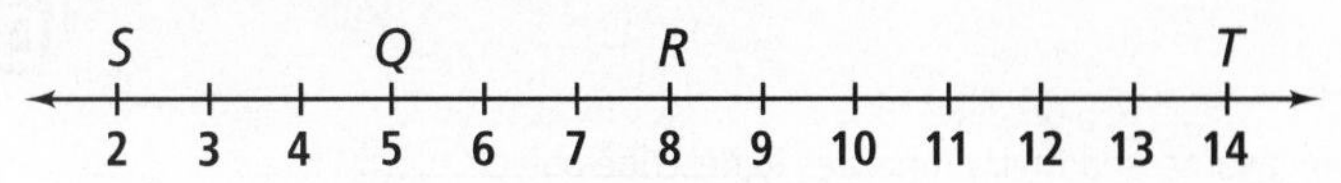


**Practice** **A point on $\overline{AK}$ is chosen at random. Find the probability that the point lies on the given segment.**

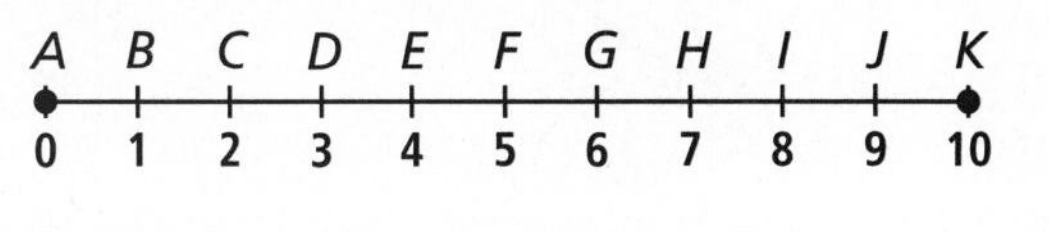


**1.** $\overline{DJ}$

**2.** $\overline{AK}$

## Problem 2 Using Segments to Find Probability

**Got It?** **Transportation** A commuter train runs every 25 min. If a commuter arrives at the station at a random time, what is the probability that a commuter will have to wait no more than 5 min for the train?

**Think**

**What segment represents a wait of 5 minutes or less?**

**3. Traffic Lights** The cycle of the traffic light on Main Street at the intersection of Main Street and Commercial Street is 40 seconds green, 5 seconds yellow, and 30 seconds red. If you reach the intersection at a random time, what is the probability that the light is red?

**4. Communication** Your friend is supposed to call you between 3 P.M. and 4 P.M. At 3:20 P.M., you realize that your cell phone is off and you immediately turn it on. What is the probability that you missed your friend's call?

When the points of a region represent equally likely outcomes, you can find probabilities by comparing areas.

take note

## Key Concept Probability and Area

Point $S$ in region $R$ is chosen at random. The probability that $S$ is in region $N$ is the ratio of the area of region $N$ to the area of region $R$.

$$P(S \text{ in region } N) = \frac{\text{area of region } N}{\text{area of region } R}$$

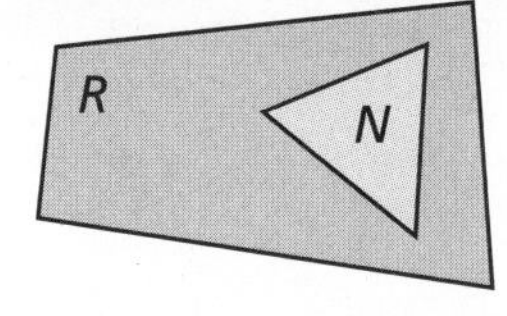

## Problem 3 Using Area to Find Probability

**Got It?** A triangle is inscribed in a square. Point $T$ in the square is selected at random. What is the probability that $T$ lies in the shaded region?

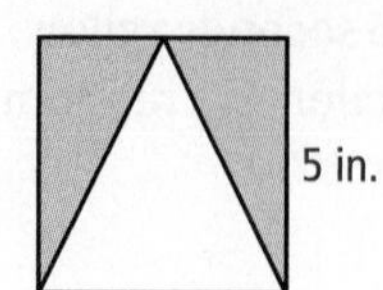


**Think**

**What two areas must you compare to find the probability?**

**Practice** **A point in the figure is chosen at random. Find the probability that the point lies in the shaded region.**

**5.**

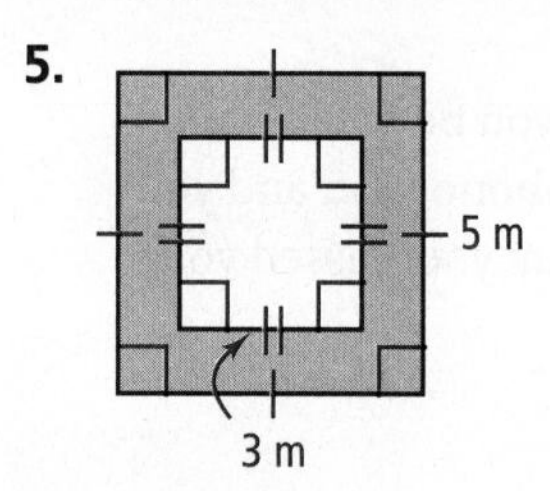


**6.**

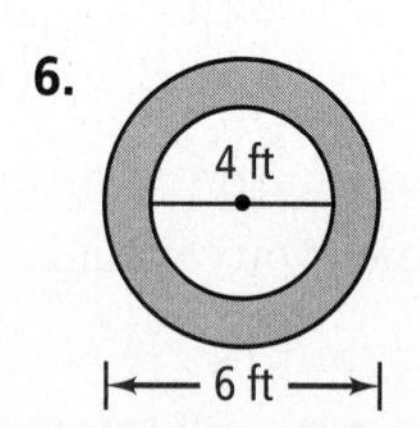

## Problem 4 Using Area to Find Probability

**Got It?** **a.** What is the probability that an arrow hits the yellow zone in Problem 4?

**b. Reasoning** If an arrow hits the target at a random point, is it more likely to hit the black zone or the red zone? Explain.

**Practice** **Target Game** **A target with a diameter of 14 cm has 4 scoring zones formed by concentric circles. The diameter of the center circle is 2 cm. The width of each ring is 2 cm. A dart hits the target at a random point. Find the probability that it will hit a point in the indicated region.**

**7.** the center region

**8.** either the blue or the red region

## Lesson Check

### Do you know HOW?

**Point $T$ on $\overline{AD}$ is chosen at random. What is the probability that $T$ lies on the given segment?**

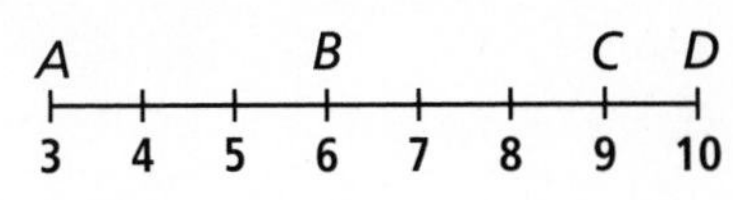


**9.** $\overline{AB}$

**10.** $\overline{AC}$

**11.** $\overline{BD}$

**12.** $\overline{BC}$

**13.** A point $K$ in the regular hexagon is chosen at random. What is the probability that $K$ lies in the region that is *not* shaded?

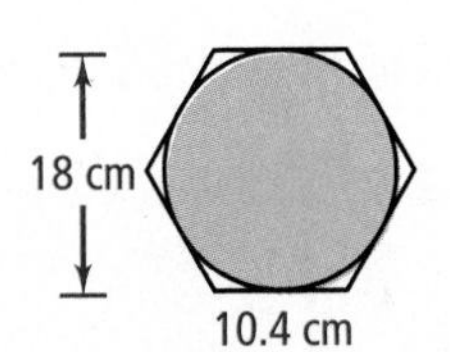


### Do you UNDERSTAND?

MATHEMATICAL PRACTICES

**14. Reasoning** In the figure at the right, $\frac{SQ}{QT} = \frac{1}{2}$. What is the probability that a point on $\overline{ST}$ chosen at random will lie on $\overline{QT}$? Explain.

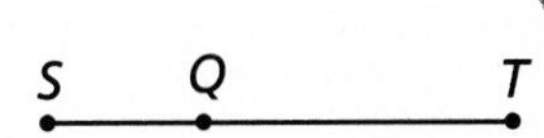

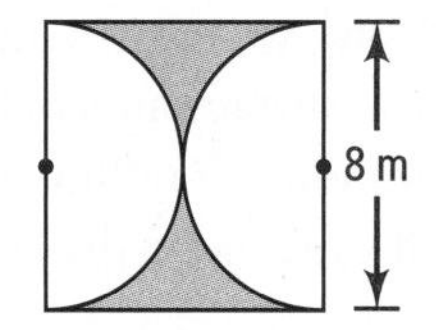


**15. Error Analysis** Your class needs to find the probability that a point $A$ in the square chosen at random lies in the shaded region. Your classmate's work is shown below. What is the error? Explain.

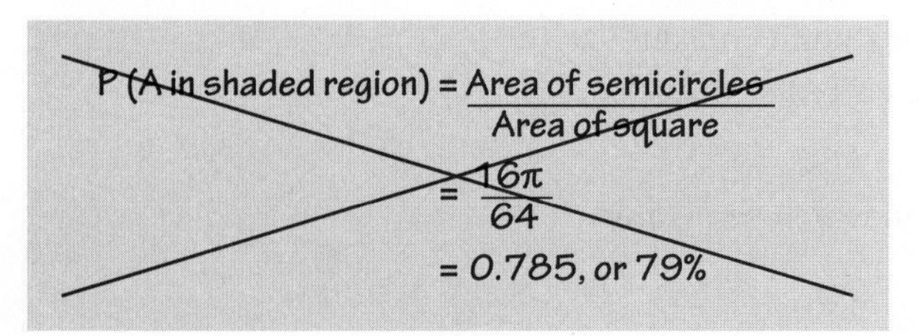


## Practice and Problem-Solving Exercises

**16.** Points $M$ and $N$ are on $\overline{ZB}$ with $M$ between $Z$ and $N$. $ZM = 5$, $NB = 9$, and $ZB = 20$. A point on $\overline{ZB}$ is chosen at random. What is the probability that the point is on $\overline{MN}$?

**17.** $\overline{BZ}$ contains $\overline{MN}$, and $BZ = 20$. A point on $\overline{BZ}$ is chosen at random. The probability that the point is also on $\overline{MN}$ is 0.3, or 30%. Find $MN$.

**18. Think About a Plan** Every 20 min from 4:00 P.M. to 7:00 P.M., a commuter train crosses Boston Road. For 3 min, a gate stops cars from crossing over the tracks as the train goes by. What is the probability that a motorist randomly arriving at the train crossing during this time interval will have to stop for a train?

- How can you represent the situation visually?
- What ratio can you use to solve the problem?

**19. Reasoning** Suppose a point in the regular pentagon is chosen at random. What is the probability that the point is *not* in the shaded region? Explain.

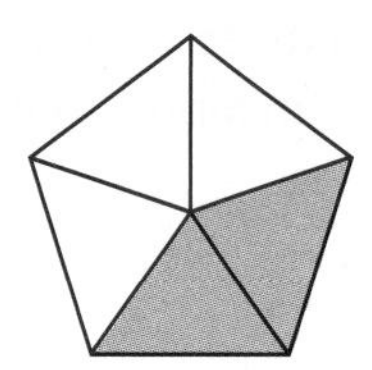

**20. Commuting** A bus arrives at a stop every 16 min and waits 3 min before leaving. What is the probability that a person arriving at the bus stop at a random time has to wait more than 10 min for a bus to leave?

STEM **21. Astronomy** Meteorites (mostly dust-particle size) are continually bombarding Earth. The surface area of Earth is about 65.7 million mi$^2$. The area of the United States is about 3.7 million mi$^2$. What is the probability that a meteorite landing on Earth will land in the United States?

**22. Reasoning** What is the probability that a point chosen at random on the circumference of the circle lies on $\overset{\frown}{AB}$? Explain how you know.

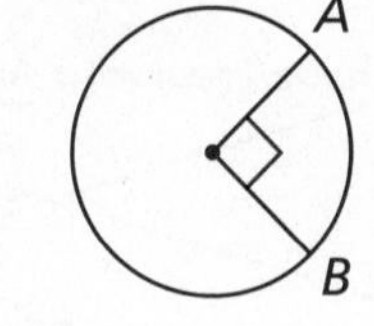


**23. Writing** Describe a real-life situation in which you would use geometric probability.

**Algebra Find the probability that coordinate $x$ of a point chosen at random on $\overline{AK}$ satisfies the inequality.**

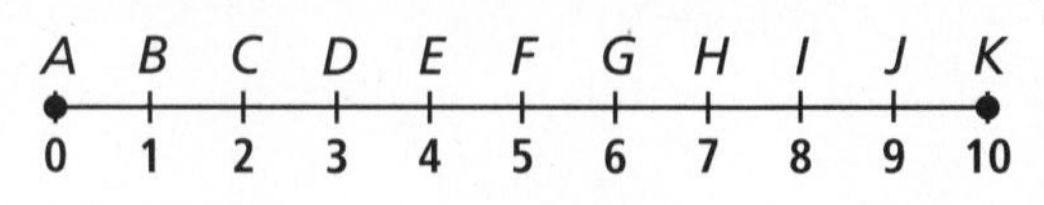


**24.** $2 \leq x \leq 8$

**25.** $2x \leq 8$

**26.** $5 \leq 11 - 6x$

**27.** $\frac{1}{2}x - 5 > 0$

**28.** $2 \leq 4x \leq 3$

**29.** $-7 \leq 1 - 2x \leq 1$

**30.** One type of dartboard is a square of radius 10 in. You throw a dart and hit the target. What is the probability that the dart lies within $\sqrt{10}$ in. of the square's center?

**31. Games** To win a prize at a carnival game, you must toss a quarter so that it lands entirely within a circle, as shown at the right. Assume that the center of a tossed quarter is equally likely to land at any point within the 8-in. square.

**a.** What is the probability that the quarter lands entirely in the circle in one toss?

**b. Reasoning** On average, how many coins must you toss to win a prize? Explain.

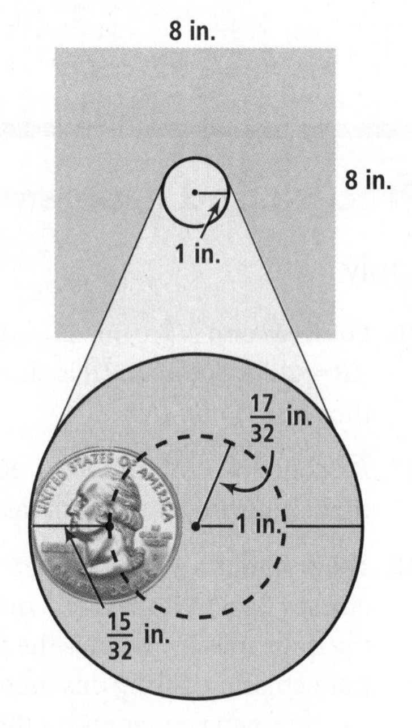


**32. Traffic Patterns** The traffic lights at Fourth and State Streets repeat themselves in 1-min cycles. A motorist will face a red light 60% of the time. Use this information to estimate how long the Fourth Street light is red during each 1-min cycle.

**33.** You have a 4-in. straw and a 6-in. straw. You want to cut the 6-in. straw into two pieces so that the three pieces form a triangle.

**a.** If you cut the straw to get two 3-in. pieces, can you form a triangle?

**b.** If the two pieces are 1 in. and 5 in., can you form a triangle?

**c.** If you cut the straw at a random point, what is the probability that you can form a triangle?

**34. Target Game** Assume that a dart you throw will land on the 12 in.-by-12 in. square dartboard and is equally likely to land at any point on the board. The diameter of the center circle is 2 in., and the width of each ring is 1 in.

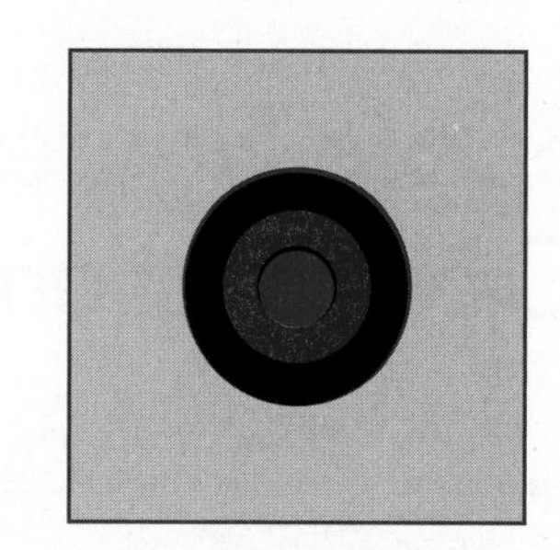

**a.** What is the probability of hitting either the dark blue or the red region?

**b.** What is the probability the dart will *not* hit the light blue region?

## Challenge

**35. Graphing Calculator** A circular dartboard has radius 1 m and a yellow circle in the center. Assume you hit the target at a random point. For what radius of the yellow center region would *P*(hitting yellow) equal each of the following? Use the table feature of a calculator to generate all six answers. Round to the nearest centimeter.

**a.** 0.2 **b.** 0.4 **c.** 0.5

**d.** 0.6 **e.** 0.8 **f.** 1.0

**36.** You and your friend agree to meet for lunch between 12 P.M. and 1 P.M. Each of you agrees to wait 15 min for the other before giving up and eating lunch alone. If you arrive at 12:20, what is the probability that you and your friend will eat lunch together?

# 10-5 Space Figures and Cross Sections

G.GMD.4 Identify the shapes of two-dimensional cross-sections of three-dimensional objects . . .

**Objectives** To recognize polyhedra and their parts
To visualize cross sections of space figures

**Solve It!** Write your solution to the Solve It in the space below.

In the Solve It, you used two-dimensional nets to represent a three-dimensional object.

A **polyhedron** is a space figure, or three-dimensional figure, whose surfaces are polygons. Each polygon is a **face** of the polyhedron. An **edge** is a segment that is formed by the intersection of two faces. A **vertex** is a point where three or more edges intersect.

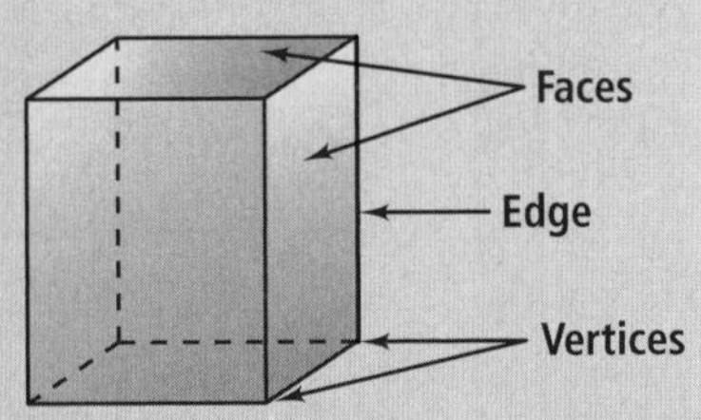


**Essential Understanding** You can analyze a three-dimensional figure by using the relationships among its vertices, edges, and faces.

## Problem 1 Identifying Vertices, Edges, and Faces

**Got It?** **a.** How many vertices, edges, and faces are in the polyhedron at the right? List them.

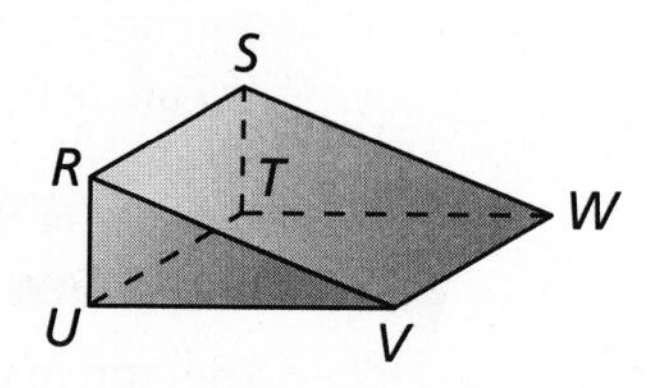


**b. Reasoning** Is $\overline{TV}$ an edge? Explain why or why not.

**Practice** **For each polyhedron, how many vertices, edges, and faces are there? List them.**

**1.**

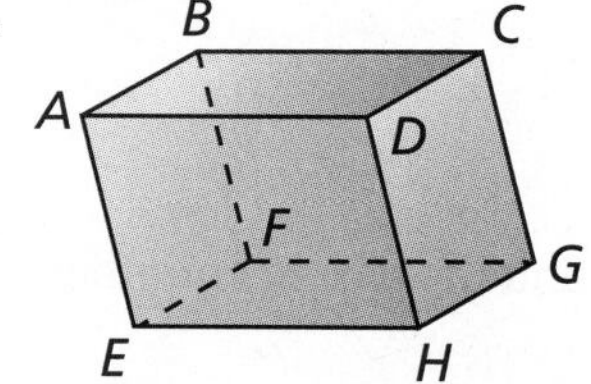


**2.**

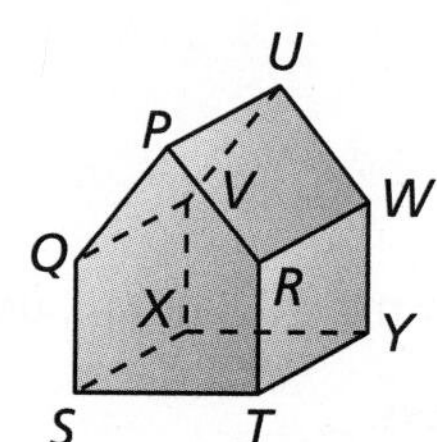

Leonhard Euler, a Swiss mathematician, discovered a relationship among the numbers of faces, vertices, and edges of any polyhedron. The result is known as Euler's Formula.

take note

## Key Concept Euler's Formula

The sum of the number of faces ($F$) and vertices ($V$) of a polyhedron is two more than the number of its edges ($E$).

$$F + V = E + 2$$

ONLINE PROBLEMS

## Problem 2 Using Euler's Formula

**Got It?** For each polyhedron, use Euler's Formula to find the missing number.

**a.**

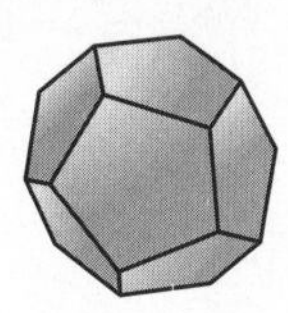

faces: ______

edges: 30

vertices: 20

**b.**

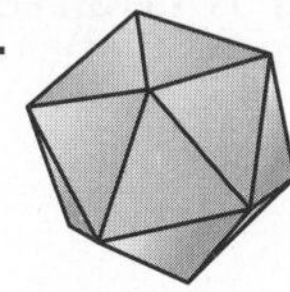

faces: 20

edges: ______

vertices: 12

**A Practice** **3.** For the polyhedron, use Euler's Formula to find the missing number.

faces: ______

edges: 15

vertices: 9

**4.** Use Euler's Formula to find the number of vertices of a polyhedron made up of 1 octagon and 8 triangles.

In two dimensions, Euler's Formula reduces to $F + V = E + 1$, where $F$ is the number of regions formed by $V$ vertices linked by $E$ segments.

## Problem 3 Verifying Euler's Formula in Two Dimensions

**Got It?** Use the solid at the right.

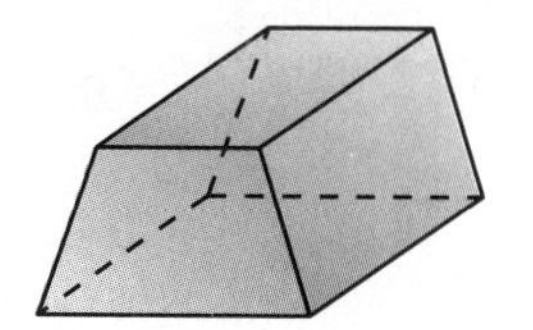

**a.** How can you verify Euler's Formula $F + V = E + 2$ for the solid?

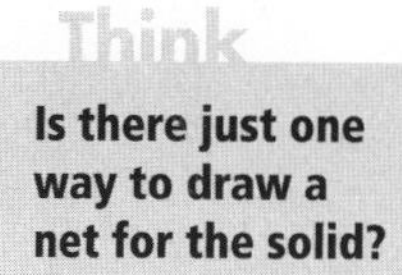

**Think**

**Is there just one way to draw a net for the solid?**

**b.** Draw a net for the solid.

**c.** How can you verify Euler's Formula $F + V = E + 1$ for your two-dimensional net?

**Verify Euler's Formula for each polyhedron. Then draw a net for the figure and verify Euler's Formula for the two-dimensional figure.**

**5.**

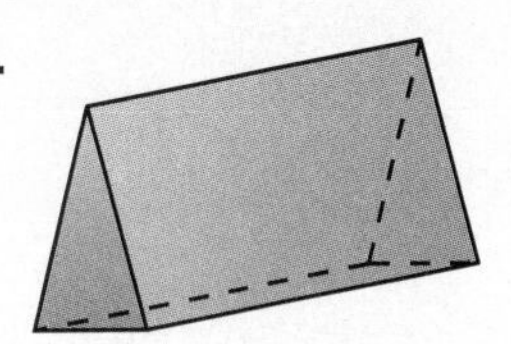

**6.**

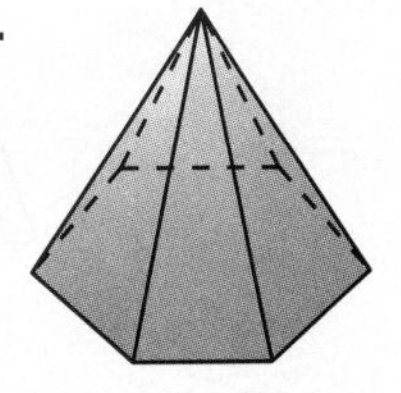

A **cross section** is the intersection of a solid and a plane. You can think of a cross section as a very thin slice of the solid.

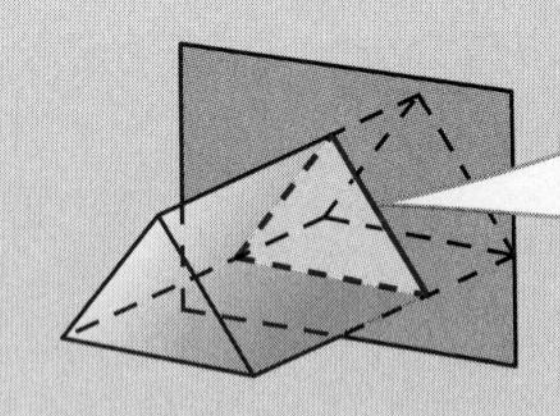

## Problem 4 Describing a Cross Section

**Got It?** For the solid at the right, what is the cross section formed by each of the following planes?

**a.** a horizontal plane

**b.** a vertical plane that divides the solid in half

**Think**

**How can you see the cross section more clearly?**

**Practice** **Describe each cross section.**

**7.**

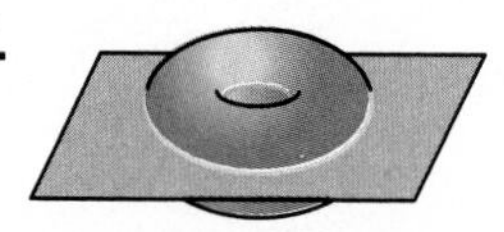

**8.**

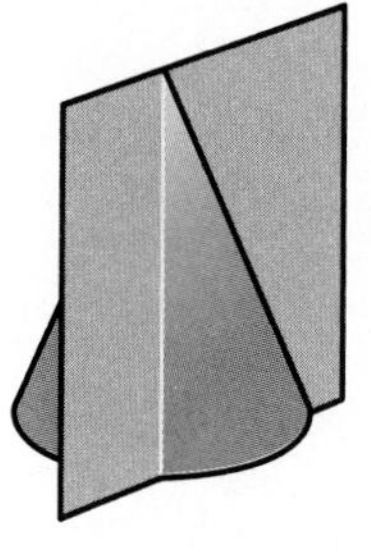

To draw a cross section, you can sometimes use the idea from Postulate 3 that the intersection of two planes is exactly one line.

## Problem 5 Drawing a Cross Section

**Got It?** Draw the cross section formed by a horizontal plane intersecting the left and right faces of the cube. What shape is the cross section?

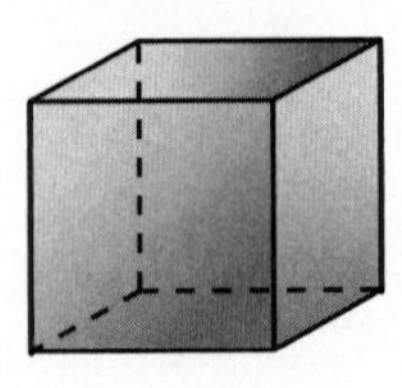

**Practice** **Visualization** **Draw and describe a cross section formed by a vertical plane intersecting the cube above as follows.**

**9.** The vertical plane intersects the front and left faces of the cube.

**10.** The vertical plane contains the red edges of the cube.

## Lesson Check

### Do you know HOW?

**11.** How many faces, edges, and vertices are in the solid? List them.

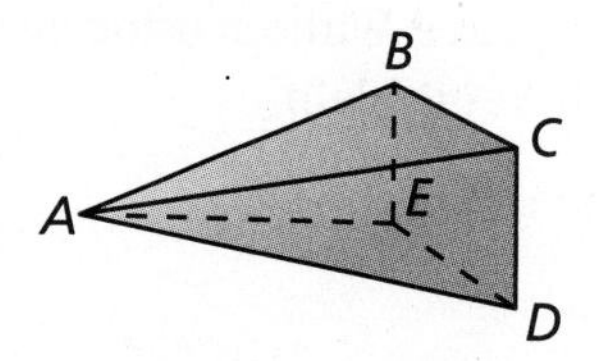


**12.** What is a net for the solid in Exercise 11? Verify Euler's Formula for the net.

**13.** What is the cross section of the cube formed by the plane containing the diagonals of a pair of opposite faces?

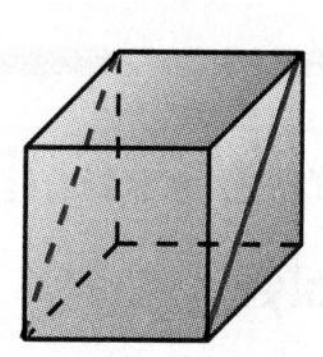

## Do you UNDERSTAND?

**14. Vocabulary** Suppose you built a polyhedron from two octagons and eight squares. Without using Euler's Formula, how many edges would the solid have? Explain.

**15. Error Analysis** Your math class is drawing polyhedrons. Which figure does not belong in the diagram below? Explain.

## More Practice and Problem-Solving Exercises

### B Apply

**16. a. Open-Ended** Sketch a polyhedron whose faces are all rectangles. Label the lengths of its edges.

**b.** Use graph paper to draw two different nets for the polyhedron.

**17.** For the figure shown at the right, sketch each of following.

**a.** a horizontal cross section

**b.** a vertical cross section that contains the vertical line of symmetry

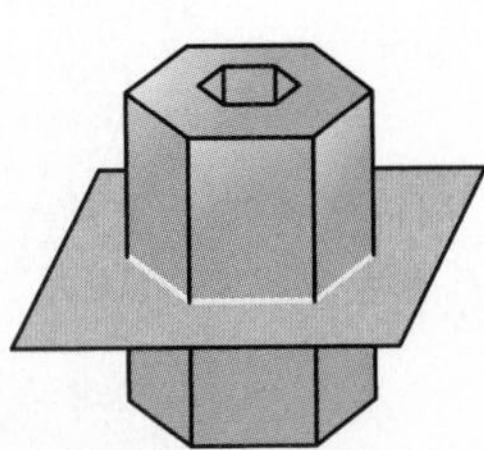

**18. Reasoning** Can you find a cross section of a cube that forms a triangle? Explain.

19. **Reasoning** Suppose the number of faces in a certain polyhedron is equal to the number of vertices. Can the polyhedron have nine edges? Explain.

**Visualization Draw and describe a cross section formed by a plane intersecting the cube as follows.**

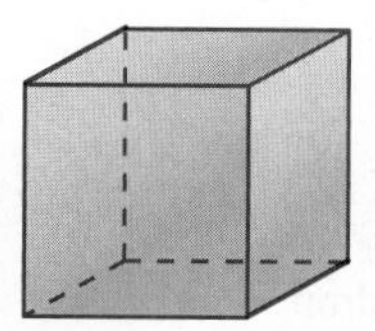

20. The plane is tilted and intersects the left and right faces of the cube.

21. The plane contains the red edges of the cube.

22. The plane cuts off a corner of the cube.

**Visualization A plane region that revolves completely about a line sweeps out a solid of revolution. Use the sample to help you describe the *solid of revolution* you get by revolving each region about line $\ell$.**

**Sample:** Revolve the rectangular region about the line $\ell$. You get a cylinder as the solid of revolution.

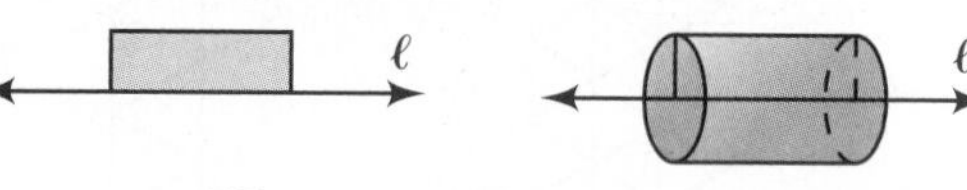


23.

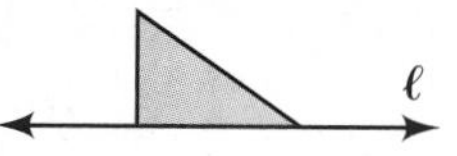


24.

25.

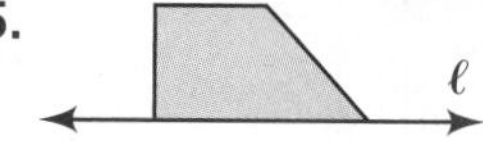


26. **Think About a Plan** Some balls are made from panels that suggest polygons. A soccer ball suggests a polyhedron with 20 regular hexagons and 12 regular pentagons. How many vertices does this polyhedron have?
- How can you determine the number of edges in a solid if you know the types of polygons that form the faces?
- What relationship can you use to find the number of vertices?

**Euler's Formula $F + V = E + 1$ applies to any two-dimensional network where $F$ is the number of regions formed by $V$ vertices linked by $E$ edges (or paths). Verify Euler's Formula for each network shown.**

27.

28.

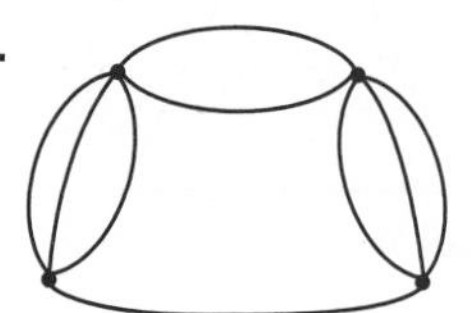

29.

**30. Platonic Solids** There are five regular polyhedrons. They are called *regular* because all their faces are congruent regular polygons, and the same number of faces meet at each vertex. They are also called *Platonic solids* after the Greek philosopher Plato, who first described them in his work *Timaeus* (about 350 B.C.).

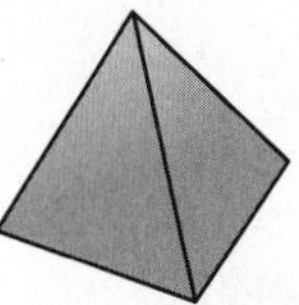
Tetrahedron

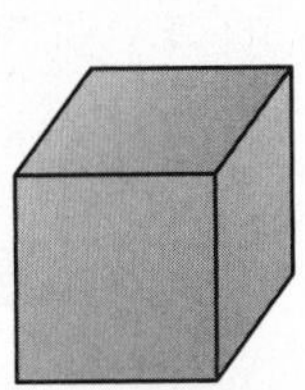
Hexahedron

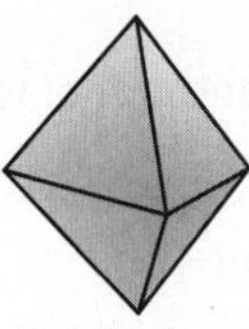
Octahedron

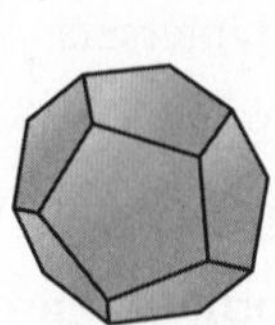
Dodecahedron

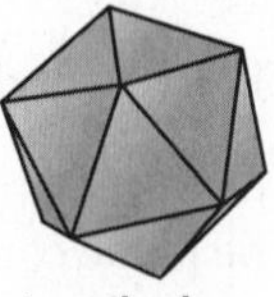
Icosahedron

**a.** Match each net below with a Platonic solid.

**A.** 

**B.** 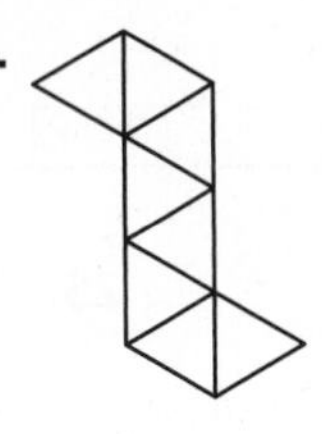

**C.** 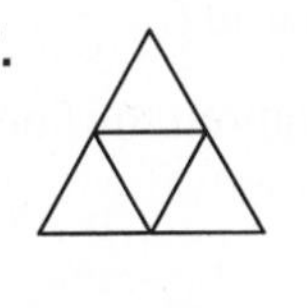

**D.** 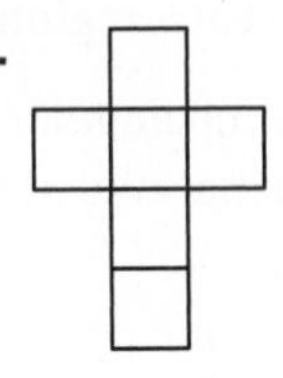

**E.** 

**b.** The first two Platonic solids also have more familiar names. What are they?

**c.** Verify that Euler's Formula is true for the first three Platonic solids.

**31.** A cube has a net with area 216 $\text{in.}^2$. How long is an edge of the cube?

**32. Writing** Cross sections are used in medical training and research. Research and write a paragraph on how magnetic resonance imaging (MRI) is used to study cross sections of the brain.

## Challenge

**33. Open-Ended** Draw a single solid that has the following three cross sections.

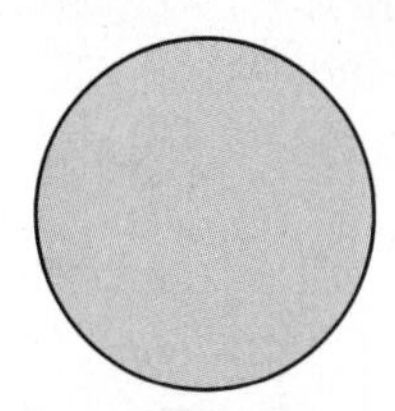
Horizontal

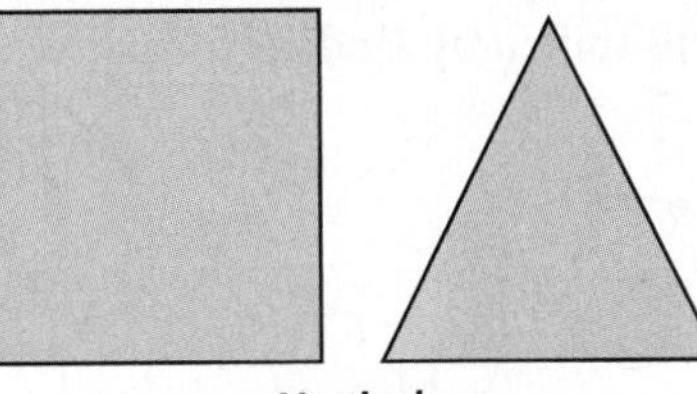
Vertical

**Visualization Draw a plane intersecting a cube to get the cross section indicated.**

**34.** scalene triangle

**35.** isosceles triangle

**36.** equilateral triangle

**37.** trapezoid

**38.** isosceles trapezoid

**39.** parallelogram

**40.** rhombus

**41.** pentagon

**42.** hexagon

# 10-6 Areas and Volumes of Similar Solids

G.MG.1 Use geometric shapes, their measures, and their properties to describe objects . . . Also G.MG.2, G.MG.3

**Objective** To compare and find the areas and volumes of similar solids

**Solve It!** Write your solution to the Solve It in the space below.

**Essential Understanding** You can use ratios to compare the areas and volumes of similar solids.

**Similar solids** have the same shape, and all their corresponding dimensions are proportional. The ratio of corresponding linear dimensions of two similar solids is the scale factor. Any two cubes are similar, as are any two spheres.

## Problem 1 Identifying Similar Solids

**Got It?** Are the two cylinders similar? If so, what is the scale factor of the first figure to the second figure?

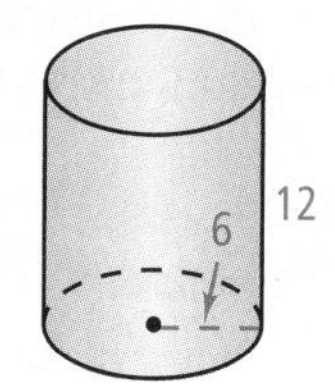


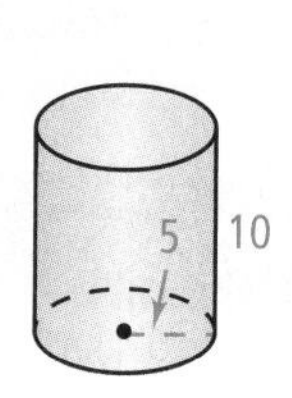

**A Practice** **For Exercises 1 and 2, are the two figures similar? If so, give the scale factor of the first figure to the second figure.**

**1.**

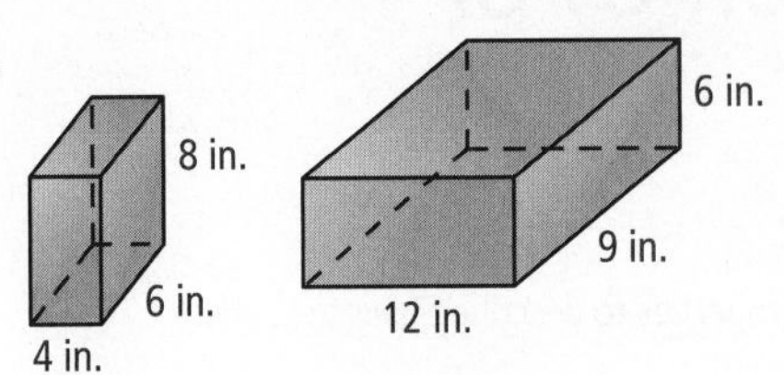


**2.** a cylinder and a square prism, both with 3-in. radius and 1-in. height

The two similar prisms shown here suggest two important relationships for similar solids.

The ratio of the side lengths is 1 : 2.

The ratio of the surface areas is 22 : 88, or 1 : 4.

The ratio of the volumes is 6 : 48, or 1 : 8.

The ratio of the surface areas is the square of the scale factor. The ratio of the volumes is the cube of the scale factor. These two facts apply to all similar solids.

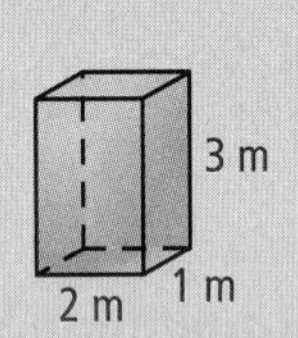


S.A. = 22 $m^2$
$V$ = 6 $m^3$

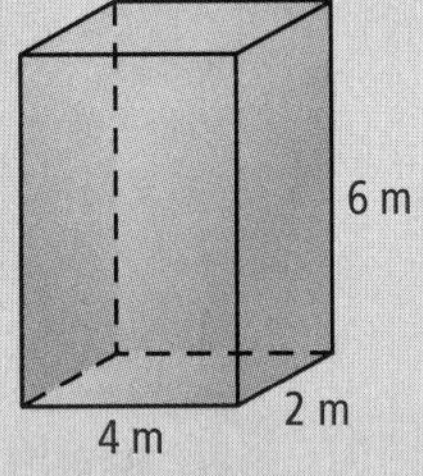


S.A. = 88 $m^2$
$V$ = 48 $m^3$

take note

### Theorem 112 Areas and Volumes of Similar Solids

If the scale factor of two similar solids is $a : b$, then

- the ratio of their corresponding areas is $a^2 : b^2$, and
- the ratio of their volumes is $a^3 : b^3$.

## Problem 2 Finding the Scale Factor

**Got It?** **a.** What is the scale factor of two similar prisms with surface areas $144\ \text{m}^2$ and $324\ \text{m}^2$?

**b. Reasoning** Are any two square prisms similar? Explain.

**Practice** **Each pair of figures is similar. Use the given information to find the scale factor of the smaller figure to the larger figure.**

**3.**

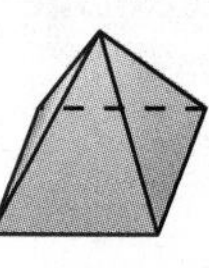

$V = 216\ \text{in.}^3$

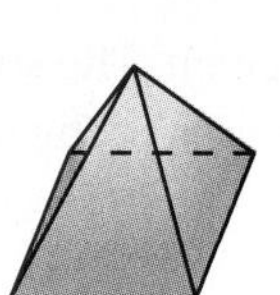

$V = 343\ \text{in.}^3$

**4.**

S.A. $= 20\pi\ \text{yd}^2$

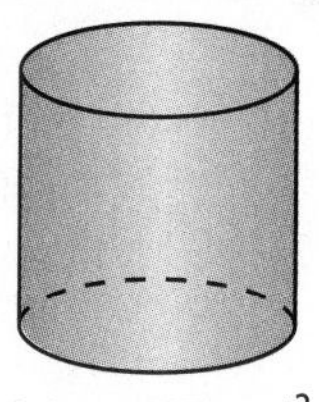

S.A. $= 125\pi\ \text{yd}^2$

## Problem 3 Using a Scale Factor

**Got It?** The volumes of two similar solids are $128 \text{ m}^3$ and $250 \text{ m}^3$. The surface area of the larger solid is $250 \text{ m}^2$. What is the surface area of the smaller solid?

**Plan**
**How can you find the scale factor?**

**A Practice** 5. The surface areas of two similar figures are given. The volume of the larger figure is given. Find the volume of the smaller figure.

S.A. $= 192 \text{ m}^2$

S.A. $= 1728 \text{ m}^2$

$V = 4860 \text{ m}^3$

6. The volumes of two similar figures are given. The surface area of the smaller figure is given. Find the surface area of the larger figure.

$V = 2 \text{ yd}^3$

$V = 250 \text{ yd}^3$

S.A. $= 13 \text{ yd}^2$

You can compare the capacities and weights of similar objects. The capacity of an object is the amount of fluid the object can hold. The capacities and weights of similar objects made of the same material are proportional to their volumes.

## Problem 4 Using a Scale Factor to Find Capacity

**Got It?** STEM A marble paperweight shaped like a pyramid weighs 0.15 lb. How much does a similarly shaped marble paperweight weigh if each dimension is three times as large?

**Think**
**How does weight relate to volume?**

**A Practice** STEM **7. Packaging** A cylinder with a 4-in. diameter and a 6-in. height holds 1 lb of oatmeal. To the nearest ounce, how much oatmeal will a similar 10-in.-high cylinder hold? (*Hint*: 1 lb = 16 oz)

**8. Compare and Contrast** A regular pentagonal prism has 9-cm base edges. A larger, similar prism of the same material has 36-cm base edges. How does each indicated measurement for the larger prism compare to the same measurement for the smaller prism?

**a.** the volume

**b.** the weight

# Lesson Check

## Do you know HOW?

**9.** Which two of the following cones are similar? What is their scale factor?

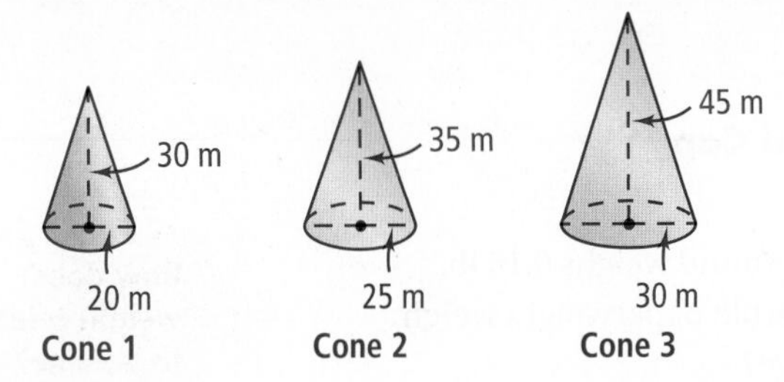


**10.** The volumes of two similar containers are 115 in.$^3$ and 67 in.$^3$. The surface area of the smaller container is 108 in.$^2$. What is the surface area of the larger container?

## Do you UNDERSTAND?

**11. Vocabulary** How are similar solids different from similar polygons? Explain.

**12. Error Analysis** Two cubes have surface areas 49 $cm^2$ and 64 $cm^2$. Your classmate tried to find the scale factor of the larger cube to the smaller cube. Explain and correct your classmate's error.

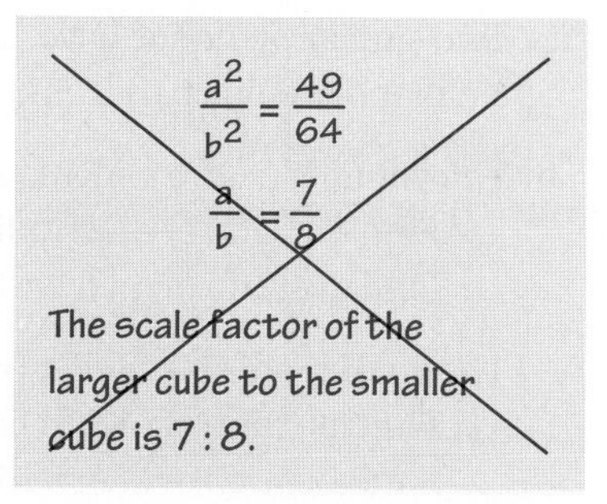


## More Practice and Problem-Solving Exercises

### B Apply

**13.** Two similar prisms have heights 4 cm and 10 cm.

**a.** What is their scale factor?

**b.** What is the ratio of their surface areas?

**c.** What is the ratio of their volumes?

**14. Think About a Plan** A company announced that it had developed the technology to reduce the size of its atomic clock, which is used in electronic devices that transmit data. The company claims that the smaller clock will be similar to the existing clock made of the same material. The dimensions of the smaller clock will be $\frac{1}{10}$ the dimensions of the company's existing atomic clocks, and it will be $\frac{1}{100}$ the weight. Do these ratios make sense? Explain.

- What is the scale factor of the smaller clock to the larger clock?
- How are the weights of the two objects related to their scale factor?

**15. Reasoning** Is there a value of $x$ for which the rectangular prisms at the right are similar? Explain.

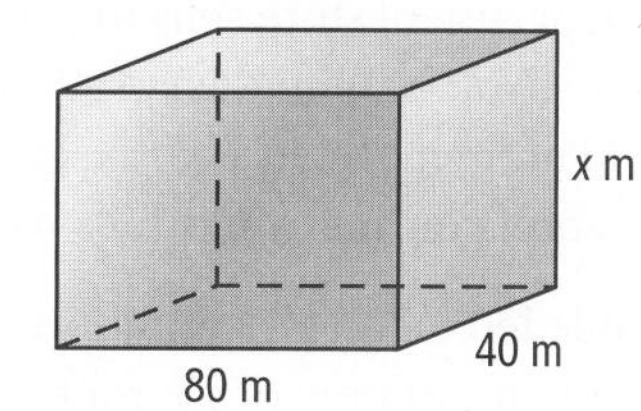


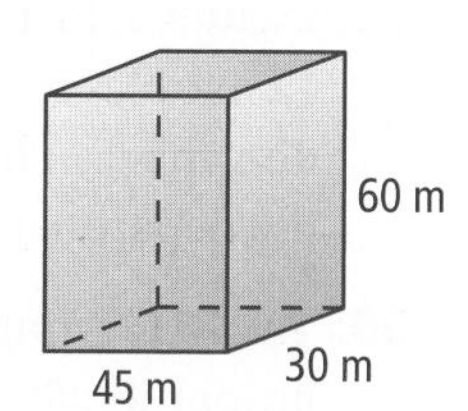


**16.** The volume of a spherical balloon with radius 3.1 cm is about 125 $cm^3$. Estimate the volume of a similar balloon with radius 6.2 cm.

**17. Writing** Are all spheres similar? Explain.

**18. Reasoning** A carpenter is making a blanket chest based on an antique chest. Both chests have the shape of a rectangular prism. The length, width, and height of the new chest will all be 4 in. greater than the respective dimensions of the antique. Will the chests be similar? Explain.

**19.** Two similar pyramids have lateral areas 20 $ft^2$ and 45 $ft^2$. The volume of the smaller pyramid is 8 $ft^3$. Find the volume of the larger pyramid.

**20.** The volumes of two spheres are 729 $in.^3$ and 27 $in.^3$.

**a.** Find the ratio of their radii.

**b.** Find the ratio of their surface areas.

**21.** The volumes of two similar pyramids are 1331 $cm^3$ and 2744 $cm^3$.

**a.** Find the ratio of their heights.

**b.** Find the ratio of their surface areas.

**22.** A clown's face on a balloon is 4 in. tall when the balloon holds 108 $in.^3$ of air. How much air must the balloon hold for the face to be 8 in. tall?

**Copy and complete the table for the similar solids.**

| | Similarity Ratio | Ratio of Surface Areas | Ratio of Volumes |
|---|---|---|---|
| **23.** | 1 : 2 | ■ : ■ | ■ : ■ |
| **24.** | 3 : 5 | ■ : ■ | ■ : ■ |
| **25.** | ■ : ■ | 49 : 81 | ■ : ■ |
| **26.** | ■ : ■ | ■ : ■ | 125 : 512 |

**27. Literature** In *Gulliver's Travels*, by Jonathan Swift, Gulliver first traveled to Lilliput. The Lilliputian average height was one twelfth of Gulliver's height.

**a.** How many Lilliputian coats could be made from the material in Gulliver's coat? (*Hint*: Use the ratio of surface areas.)

**b.** How many Lilliputian meals would be needed to make a meal for Gulliver? (*Hint*: Use the ratio of volumes.)

**28.** The trunk of an oak tree is 15 ft high. A cylindrical model of the oak tree trunk has a height of 1 foot and a surface area of about 0.838 $ft^2$.

**a.** What is the scale factor of the cylindrical model and the oak tree trunk?

**b.** Use the cylindrical model to approximate the surface area of the trunk of the oak tree. Round to the nearest tenth.

**29. Design** A local department store sells marbles that come in small boxes, 12 marbles to a box. You want to design a larger container, similar to the small one, that can hold more marbles. If you tripled the dimensions of the box from the department store, how many marbles would your new box hold?

**30.** The BTU rating needed for an air conditioner to cool a room increases proportionally with the volume of the room. An air conditioner rated at 6000 BTUs can cool a room that is 1500 cubic feet. If another room has dimensions that are each 1.2 times greater than the first room, what rating must an air conditioner have to cool the larger room?

## Challenge

31. **Indirect Reasoning** Some stories say that Paul Bunyan was ten times as tall as the average human. Assume that Paul Bunyan's bone structure was proportional to that of ordinary people.

   a. Strength of bones is proportional to the area of their cross section. How many times as strong as the average person's bones would Paul Bunyan's bones have been?
   b. Weights of objects made of like material are proportional to their volumes. How many times the average person's weight would Paul Bunyan's weight have been?
   c. Human leg bones can support about 6 times the average person's weight. Use your answers to parts (a) and (b) to explain why Paul Bunyan could not have existed with a bone structure that was proportional to that of ordinary people.

32. Square pyramids $A$ and $B$ are similar. In pyramid $A$, each base edge is 12 cm. In pyramid $B$, each base edge is 3 cm, and the volume is 6 $cm^3$.
   a. Find the volume of pyramid $A$.
   b. Find the ratio of the surface area of $A$ to the surface area of $B$.
   c. Find the surface area of each pyramid.

33. A cone is cut by a plane parallel to its base. The small cone on top is similar to the large cone. The ratio of the slant heights of the cones is 1 : 2. Find each ratio. (For parts (b) and (c), a *frustum* of a cone is the part that remains when the cone is cut off by a plane parallel to the base.)

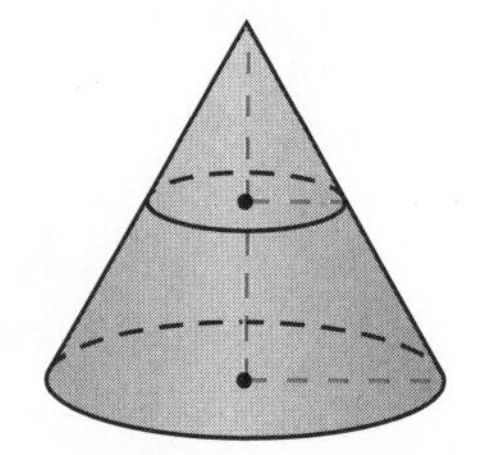

   a. the surface area of the large cone to the surface area of the small cone
   b. the volume of the large cone to the volume of the small cone
   c. the surface area of the frustum to the surface area of the large cone and to the surface area of the small cone
   d. the volume of the frustum to the volume of the large cone and to the volume of the small cone

# 10-7 Locus: A Set of Points

**G.GMD.4** . . . identify three-dimensional objects generated by rotations of two-dimensional objects.

**Objective** To draw and describe a locus

**Solve It!** Write your solution to the Solve It in the space below.

In the Solve It, you described the possible locations based on a certain condition. A **locus** is a set of points, all of which meet a stated condition. *Loci* is the plural of locus.

**Essential Understanding** You can use the description of a locus to sketch a geometric relationship.

## Problem 1 Describing a Locus in a Plane

**Got It?** **Reasoning** If the question for part (b) of Problem 1 had asked for the locus of points in a plane 1 cm from $\overleftrightarrow{AB}$, how would the sketch change?

**Practice** **Sketch and describe each locus of points in a plane.**

**1.** points equidistant from two perpendicular lines

**2.** midpoints of radii of a circle with radius 2 cm

You can use locus descriptions for geometric terms.

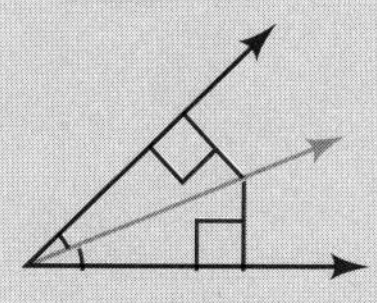

The locus of points in the interior of an angle that are equidistant from the sides of the angle is an angle bisector.

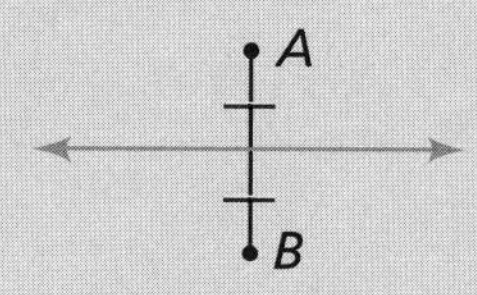


In a plane, the locus of points that are equidistant from a segment's endpoints is the perpendicular bisector of the segment.

Sometimes a locus is described by two conditions. You can draw the locus by first drawing the points that satisfy each condition. Then find their intersection.

## Problem 2 Drawing a Locus for Two Conditions

**Got It?** What is a sketch of the locus of points in a plane that satisfy these conditions?

- the points equidistant from two points $X$ and $Y$
- the points 2 cm from the midpoint of $\overline{XY}$

**Think**

**What is the locus of points in a plane that are equidistant from $X$ and $Y$?**

**Practice** **For Exercises 3 and 4, sketch the locus of points in a plane that satisfy the given conditions.**

**3.** 3 cm from $\overline{GH}$ and 5 cm from $G$, where $GH = 4.5$ cm

**4.** equidistant from the sides of $\angle JKL$ and on $\odot C$

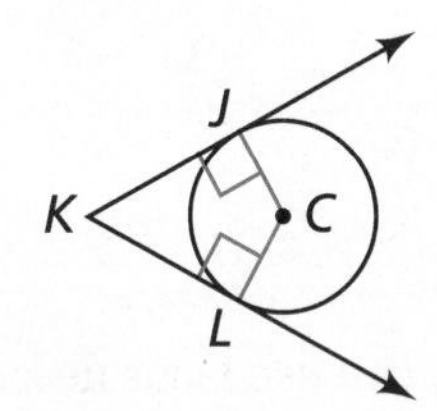

## Problem 3 Describing a Locus in Space

**Got It?** What is each locus of points?

**Think**
**How can making a sketch help?**

**a.** in a plane, the points that are equidistant from two parallel lines

**b.** in space, the points that are equidistant from two parallel planes

**Practice** **Describe each locus of points in space.**

**5.** points 3 cm from a point $F$

**6.** points 5 mm from $\overrightarrow{PQ}$

## Lesson Check

### Do you know HOW?

**What is a sketch and description for each locus of points in a plane?**

**7.** points 4 cm from a point $X$

**8.** points 2 in. from $\overline{UV}$

**9.** points 3 mm from $\overleftrightarrow{LM}$

**10.** points 1 in. from a circle with radius 3 in.

## Do you UNDERSTAND?

**11. Vocabulary** How are the words *locus* and *location* related?

**12. Compare and Contrast** How are the descriptions of the locus of points for each situation alike? How are they different?

- in a plane, the points equidistant from points $J$ and $K$
- in space, the points equidistant from points $J$ and $K$

## More Practice and Problem-Solving Exercises

### B Apply

**Describe the locus that each light blue figure represents.**

13.

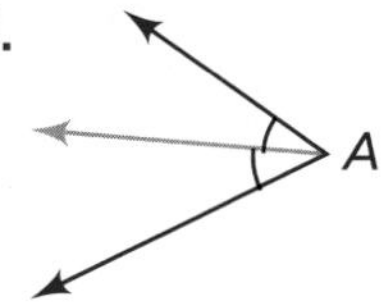


14.

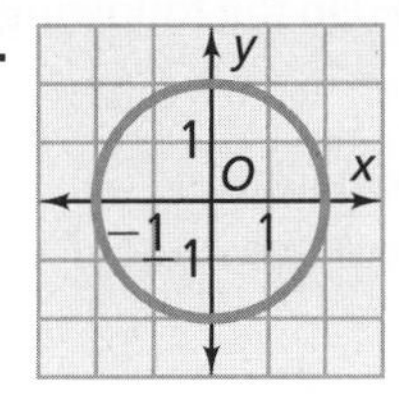


15.

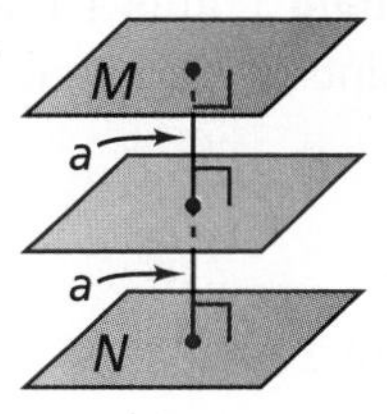


**16. Open-Ended** Give two examples of loci from everyday life, one in a plane and one in space.

**17. Writing** A classmate says that it is impossible to find a point equidistant from three collinear points. Is she correct? Explain.

**18. Think About a Plan** Write a locus description of the red points on the coordinate plane.

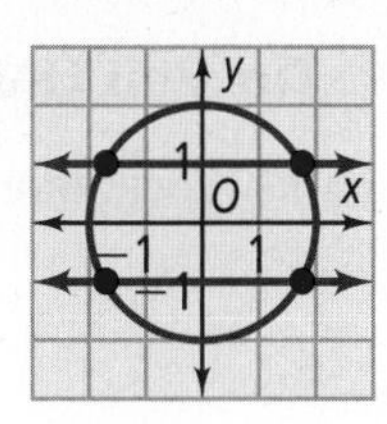


- How many conditions will be involved?
- What is the condition with respect to the origin?
- What are the conditions with respect to the $x$- and $y$-axes?

**Coordinate Geometry Write an equation for the locus of points in a plane equidistant from the two given points.**

**19.** $A(0, 2)$ and $B(2, 0)$ **20.** $P(1, 3)$ and $Q(5, 1)$ **21.** $T(2, -3)$ and $V(6, 1)$

**22. Meteorology** An anemometer measures wind speed and wind direction. In an anemometer, there are three cups mounted on an axis. Consider a point on the edge of one of the cups.

**a.** Describe the locus that this point traces as the cup spins in the wind.

**b.** Suppose the distance of the point from the axis of the anemometer is 2 in. Write an equation for the locus of part (a). Use the axis as the origin.

**23. Landscaping** The school board plans to construct a fountain in front of the school. What are all the possible locations for a fountain such that the fountain is 8 ft from the statue and 16 ft from the flagpole?

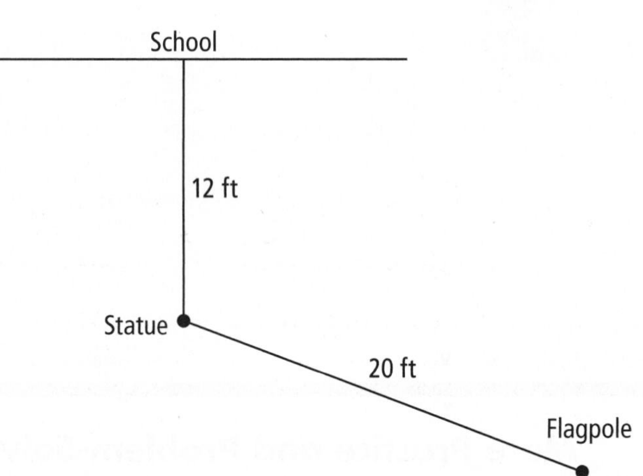


**Make a drawing of each locus.**

**24.** the path of a car as it turns to the right

**25.** the path of a doorknob as a door opens

**26.** the path of a knot in the middle of a jump-rope as it is being used

**27.** the path of the tip of your nose as you turn your head

**28.** the path of a fast-pitched softball

**29. Reasoning** Points $A$ and $B$ are 5 cm apart. Do the following loci in a plane have any points in common?

the points 3 cm from $A$
the points 4 cm from $\overline{AB}$

Illustrate your answer with a sketch.

**Coordinate Geometry** **Draw each locus on the coordinate plane.**

**30.** all points 3 units from the origin

**31.** all points 2 units from $(-1, 3)$

**32.** all points 4 units from the $y$-axis

**33.** all points 5 units from $x = 2$

**34.** all points equidistant from $y = 3$ and $y = -1$

**35.** all points equidistant from $x = 4$ and $x = 5$

**36.** all points equidistant from the $x$- and $y$-axes

**37.** all points equidistant from $x = 3$ and $y = 2$

**38.** **a.** Draw a segment to represent the base of an isosceles triangle. Locate three points that could be the vertex of the isosceles triangle.
**b.** Describe the locus of possible vertices for the isosceles triangle.
**c.** **Writing** Explain why points in the locus you described are the only possibilities for the vertex of the isosceles triangle.

**39.** Describe the locus of points in a plane 3 cm from the points on a circle with radius 8 cm.

**40.** Describe the locus of points in a plane 8 cm from the points on a circle with radius 3 cm.

**41.** Sketch the locus of points for the air valve on the tire of a bicycle as the bicycle moves down a straight path.

## Challenge

**42.** In the diagram, Moesha, Jan, and Leandra are seated at uniform distances around a circular table. Copy the diagram. Shade the points on the table that are closer to Moesha than to Jan or Leandra. (Moesha is seated at the right of the table.)

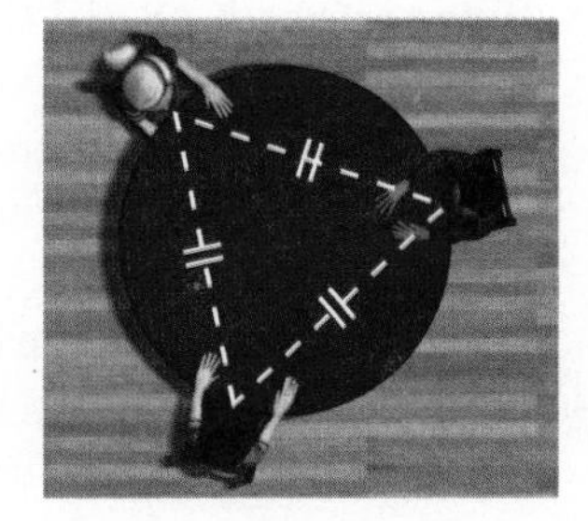

**Playground Equipment** **Think about the path of a child on each piece of playground equipment. Draw the path from (a) a top view, (b) a front view, and (c) a side view.**

**43.** a swing

**44.** a straight slide

**45.** a corkscrew slide

**46.** a merry-go-round

**47.** a firefighters' pole

# 10 Chapter Review

## 10-1 Applying Constructions

### Quick Review

You can use a compass, protractor, and straightedge to apply constructions.

### Example

**Follow the steps to construct a line parallel to $\overline{AB}$ through point *C*.**

C

- Draw a line through *C*. Label the intersection of this line and $\overline{AB}$ as point *D*.
- Place the point of a compass on *D*. Draw an arc that intersects both $\overline{AB}$ and $\overline{CD}$.
- Use the same compass width. Draw an arc at *C*.
- Set the compass width from the intersection of $\overline{CD}$ and the first arc to the intersection of $\overline{AB}$ and the first arc.
- Place the compass at the intersection of $\overline{CD}$ and the second arc. Draw an arc. Label the intersection *E*.
- Draw a line through *C* and *E*.

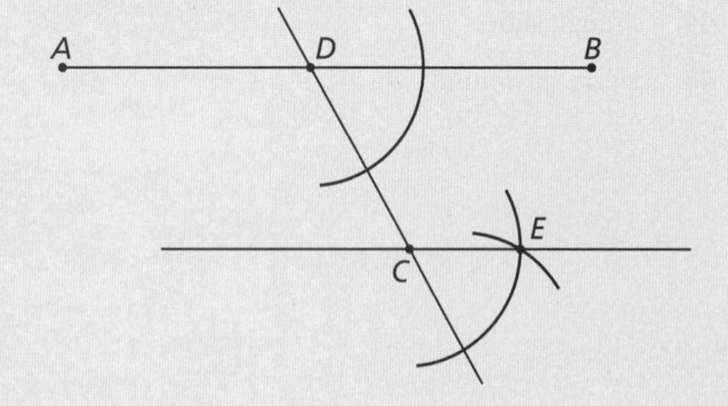


### Exercises

1. Use a straightedge and compass to copy $\overline{HJ}$.

   H J

2. Copy $\overline{RT}$. Then use a straightedge and compass to construct a 30° angle on $\overline{RT}$ with vertex at *R*.

   R T

3. **Design** The shape of the triangle below is used in a local high school's logo. The school wants to use the logo on key chains to sell at a fundraiser. You need to supply the maker of the key chains with a drawing of the logo. Use a straightedge and compass to copy the triangle used in the school's logo.

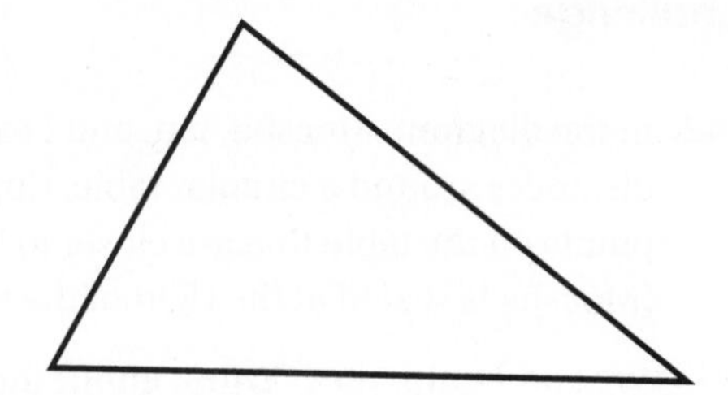

## 10-2 Solving Density and Design Problems

### Quick Review

To find the **density** of an object, divide its mass by its volume. To find **population density,** divide the number of individuals in the population by the total area or volume that they occupy.

### Example

**A calcium tablet has a volume of 12 $cm^3$ and a mass of 18.48 grams. What is the density of the calcium tablet?**

Density $= \frac{m}{V}$

$= \frac{18.48}{12}$ Substitute 18.48 for $m$ and 12 for $V$.

$= 1.54\ g/cm^3$ Simplify.

### Exercises

**4.** Japan has an area of 377,944 square kilometers. The population of Japan is 127,960,000. What was the population density of Japan?

**5. Gift Box** A company wants to manufacture gift boxes in the shape of rectangular prisms. Each gift box will have a volume of 84 cubic inches. The base of the rectangular prism should be twice as long as it is wide. What dimensions should the company choose for the gift boxes in order to minimize the surface area of each box?

## 10-3 Perimeters and Areas of Similar Figures

### Quick Review

If the scale factor of two similar figures is $\frac{a}{b}$, then the ratio of their perimeters is $\frac{a}{b}$, and the ratio of their areas is $\frac{a^2}{b^2}$.

### Example

**If the ratio of the areas of two similar figures is $\frac{4}{9}$, what is the ratio of their perimeters?**

Find the scale factor.

$\frac{\sqrt{4}}{\sqrt{9}} = \frac{2}{3}$ Take the square root of the ratio of areas.

The ratio of the perimeters is the same as the ratio of corresponding sides, $\frac{2}{3}$.

### Exercises

**For each pair of similar figures, find the ratio of the area of the first figure to the area of the second.**

**6.** 8 12

**7.** 6 4

**8.** 3 6

**9.** 14 mm 7 mm

**10.** If the ratio of the areas of two similar hexagons is 8 : 25, what is the ratio of their perimeters?

## 10-4 Geometric Probability

### Quick Review

**Geometric probability** uses geometric figures to represent occurrences of events. You can use a segment model or an area model. Compare the part that represents favorable outcomes to the whole, which represents all outcomes.

### Example

**A ball hits the target at a random point. What is the probability that it lands in the shaded region?**

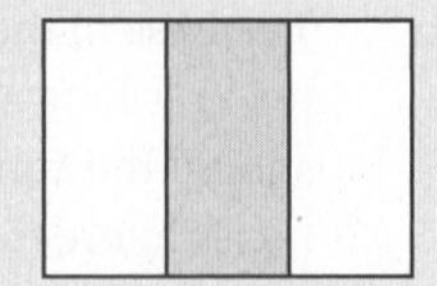

Since $\frac{1}{3}$ of the target is shaded, the probability that the ball hits the shaded region is $\frac{1}{3}$.

### Exercises

**A dart hits each dartboard at a random point. Find the probability that it lands in the shaded region.**

**11.**

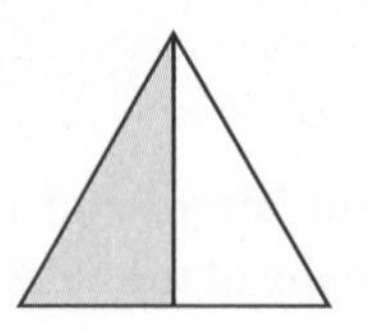

**12.**

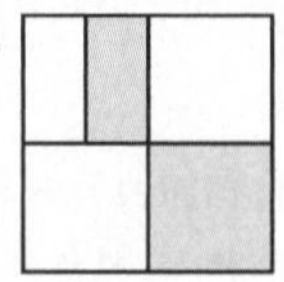

**13.**

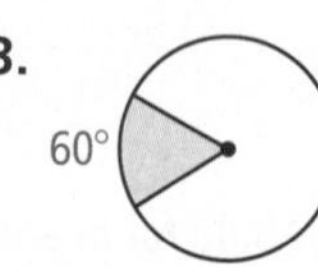


**14.**

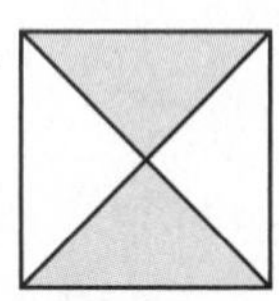

**15.**

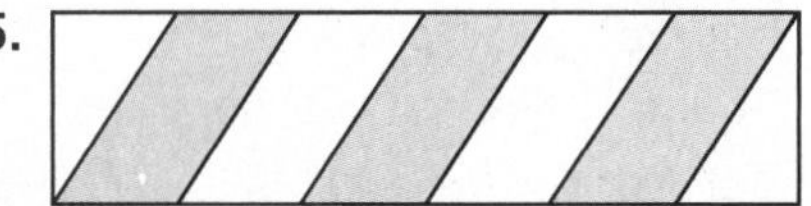

## 10-5 Space Figures and Cross Sections

### Quick Review

A **polyhedron** is a three-dimensional figure whose surfaces are polygons. The polygons are **faces** of the polyhedron. An **edge** is a segment that is the intersection of two faces. A **vertex** is a point where three or more edges intersect. A **cross section** is the intersection of a solid and a plane.

### Example

**How many faces and edges does the polyhedron have?**

The polyhedron has 2 triangular bases and 3 rectangular faces for a total of 5 faces.

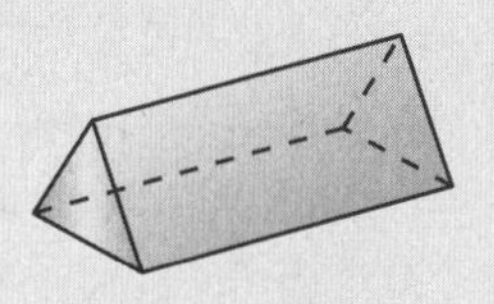

The 2 triangles have a total of 6 edges. The 3 rectangles have a total of 12 edges. The total number of edges in the polyhedron is one half the total of 18 edges, or 9.

### Exercises

**Draw a net for each three-dimensional figure.**

**16.**

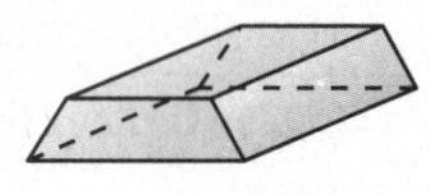

**17.**

**Use Euler's Formula to find the missing number.**

**18.** $F = 5$, $V = 5$, $E = ■$ **19.** $F = 6$, $V = ■$, $E = 12$

**20.** How many vertices are there in a solid with 4 triangular faces and 1 square base?

**21.** Describe the cross section in the figure at the right.

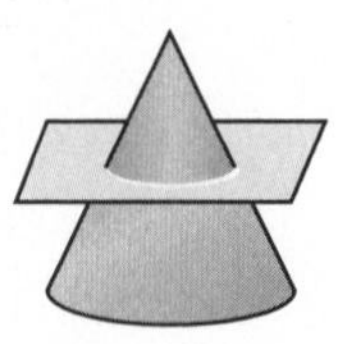

**22.** Sketch a cube with an equilateral triangle cross section.

## 10-6 Areas and Volumes of Similar Solids

### Quick Review

**Similar solids** have the same shape, and all their corresponding dimensions are proportional.

If the scale factor of two similar solids is $a : b$, then the ratio of their corresponding surface areas is $a^2 : b^2$, and the ratio of their volumes is $a^3 : b^3$.

### Example

**Is a cylinder with radius 4 in. and height 12 in. similar to a cylinder with radius 14 in. and height 35 in.? If so, give the scale factor.**

$\frac{4}{14} \neq \frac{12}{35}$

The cylinders are not similar because the ratios of corresponding linear dimensions are not equal.

### Exercises

**23. Open-Ended** Sketch two similar solids whose surface areas are in the ratio 16 : 25. Include dimensions.

**For each pair of similar solids, find the ratio of the volume of the first figure to the volume of the second.**

**24.**

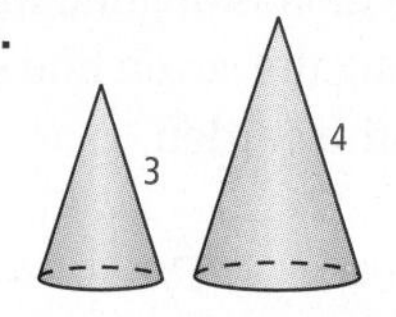


**25.**

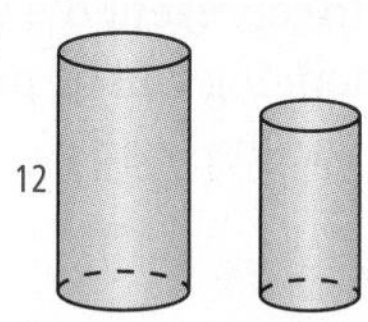


**26. Packaging** There are 12 pencils in a regular-sized box. If a jumbo box is made by tripling all the dimensions of the regular-sized box, how many pencils will the jumbo box hold?

## 10-7 Locus: A Set of Points

### Quick Review

A **locus** is a set of points that satisfies a stated condition.

### Example

**Sketch and describe the locus of points in a plane equidistant from points *A* and *B*.**

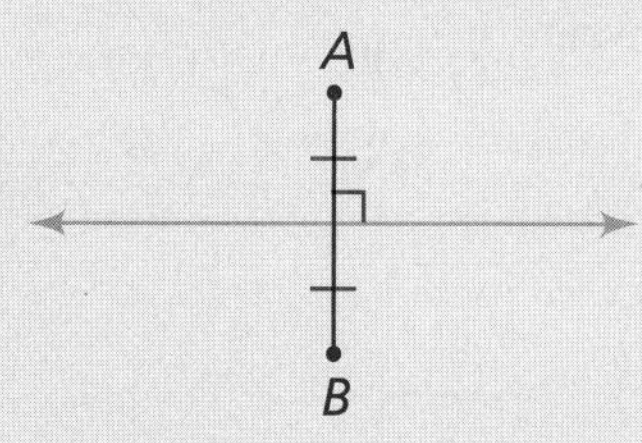


The locus is the perpendicular bisector of $\overline{AB}$.

### Exercises

**Describe each locus of points.**

**27.** The set of all points in a plane that are in the interior of an angle and equidistant from the sides of the angle.

**28.** The set of all points in a plane that are 5 cm from a circle with radius 2 cm.

**29.** The set of all points in a plane at a distance 8 in. from a given line.

**30.** The set of all points in space that are 6 in. from $\overline{AB}$.

# Pull It All Together

## Calculating the Cost of a Gardening Project

Frank is at the nursery buying fencing and fertilizer for his garden. Fencing costs \$5.00 per foot and fertilizer costs \$.01 per square foot. Frank made the sketch below to represent the garden, which is divided into two trapezoid-shaped sections. The fencing will be placed along the seven line segments shown in the sketch, and the fertilizer will cover the entire garden.

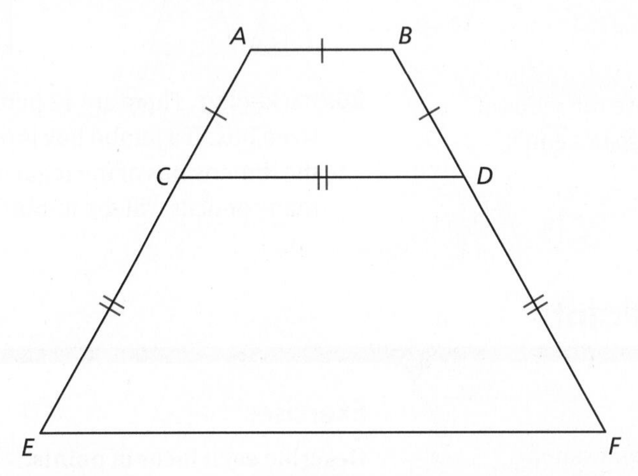


Unfortunately, Frank forgot to label his sketch with measurements, and he does not want to drive home to measure the garden again. However, Frank recalls some additional information:

- The two trapezoids are similar, with corresponding side lengths in the ratio 2 : 1.
- The total outer perimeter of the garden (not including the separation between the two sections) is 66 feet.

### Task Description

**Determine the total cost of the fencing and fertilizer.**

# Get Ready!

## Squaring Numbers

**Simplify.**

**1.** $6^2$ **2.** $5^2$ **3.** $12^2$

## Simplifying Expressions

**Simplify each expression. Use 3.14 for $\pi$.**

**4.** $3 \cdot 2.5 + 3 \cdot 1.5$ **5.** $\pi(2)^2$ **6.** $\sqrt{8^2 + 15^2}$

## Evaluating Expressions

**Evaluate the following expressions for $a = -3$ and $b = 7$.**

**7.** $\frac{a + b}{2}$ **8.** $\frac{b - 8}{4 + a}$ **9.** $\sqrt{(2 - a)^2 + (-5 - b)^2}$

## Finding Absolute Value

**Simplify each absolute value expression.**

**10.** $|-4|$ **11.** $|1 - 10|$ **12.** $|-6 - (-5)|$

## Solving Equations

**Algebra** **Solve each equation.**

**13.** $8 = 3x - 7$ **14.** $4x - 5 = 7 - 2x$ **15.** $-1 - 3x = 5 - 3(2x + 4)$

## Looking Ahead Vocabulary

**16.** A building or a monument can have a *base* and a *height*. What are the *base* and the *height* of a parallelogram?

**17.** The *altitude* of an airplane is the height of the airplane above ground. What do you think an *altitude* of a parallelogram is?

# Connecting Algebra and Geometry

## Big Ideas

**1 Measurement**
**Essential Question** How do you find the area and perimeter of a polygon?

**2 Coordinate Geometry**
**Essential Question** How can you use coordinate geometry to prove general relationships?

## Domains

- Expressing Geometric Properties with Equations
- Quantities

## Chapter Preview

**11-1** Perimeter and Area in the Coordinate Plane
**11-2** Areas of Parallelograms and Triangles
**11-3** Areas of Trapezoids, Rhombuses, and Kites
**11-4** Polygons in the Coordinate Plane

**Interactive Digital Path**

Log in to **pearsonsuccessnet.com** and click on Interactive Digital Path to access the Solve Its and animated Problems.

## Vocabulary

**English/Spanish Vocabulary Audio Online:**

| English | Spanish |
|---|---|
| area, *p. 809* | segmentos congruentes |
| base of a parallelogram, *p. 823* | base de paralelogramo |
| base of a triangle, *p. 825* | base de un triangulo |
| height of a parallelogram, *p. 823* | alture de un paralelogramo |
| height of a trapezoid, *p. 832* | altura de un trapecio |
| height of a triangle, *p. 825* | altura de un triangulo |
| perimeter, *p. 809* | perímetro |

# 11-1 Perimeter and Area in the Coordinate Plane

G.GPE.7 Use coordinates to compute perimeters of polygons and areas of triangles and rectangles . . . Also N.Q.1

**Objectives** To find the perimeter or circumference of basic shapes
To find the area of basic shapes

**Solve It!** Write your solution to the Solve It in the space below.

In the Solve It, you considered various ideas of what it means to take up space on a flat surface.

**Essential Understanding** Perimeter and area are two different ways of measuring geometric figures.

The **perimeter** $P$ of a polygon is the sum of the lengths of its sides. The **area** $A$ of a polygon is the number of square units it encloses. For figures such as squares, rectangles, triangles, and circles, you can use formulas for perimeter (or *circumference* $C$ for circles) and area.

take note

## Key Concept Perimeter, Circumference, and Area

**Square**

side length $s$

$P = 4s$

$A = s^2$

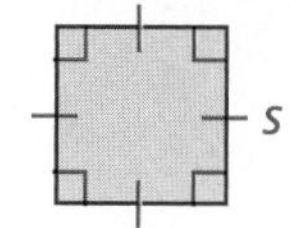


**Triangle**

side lengths $a$, $b$, and $c$, base $b$, and height $h$

$P = a + b + c$

$A = \frac{1}{2}bh$

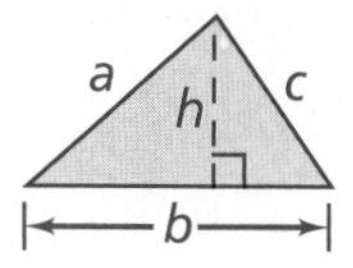


**Rectangle**

base $b$ and height $h$

$P = 2b + 2h$, or $2(b + h)$

$A = bh$

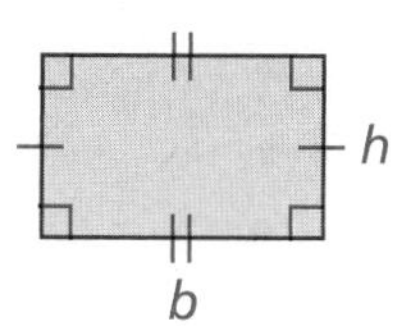


**Circle**

radius $r$ and diameter $d$

$C = \pi d$, or $C = 2\pi r$

$A = \pi r^2$

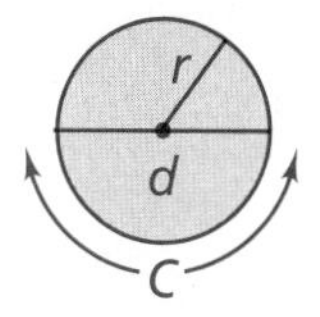

The units of measurement for perimeter and circumference include inches, feet, yards, miles, centimeters, and meters. When measuring area, use square units such as square inches ($in.^2$), square feet ($ft^2$), square yards ($yd^2$), square miles ($mi^2$), square centimeters ($cm^2$), and square meters ($m^2$).

## Problem 1 Finding the Perimeter and Area of a Rectangle in the Coordinate Plane

**Got It?** Rectangle $HIJK$ has vertices $H(-5, -3)$, $I(-5, 2)$, $J(2, 2)$, and $K(2, -3)$. What is the perimeter of rectangle $HIJK$? What is the area of rectangle $HIJK$?

**Practice** **Find the perimeter and area of each rectangle.**

**1.** rectangle $ABCD$ with vertices $A(2, 4)$, $B(2, 9)$, $C(5, 9)$, and $D(5, 4)$

**2.** rectangle $EFGH$ with vertices $E(-3, 1)$, $F(-3, 6)$, $G(2, 6)$, and $H(2, 1)$

You can name a circle with the symbol $\odot$. For example, the circle with center $A$ is written $\odot A$.

The formulas for a circle involve the special number *pi* ($\pi$). Pi is the ratio of any circle's circumference to its diameter. Since $\pi$ is an irrational number,

$$\pi = 3.1415926\ldots,$$

you cannot write it as a terminating decimal. For an approximate answer, you can use 3.14 or $\frac{22}{7}$ for $\pi$. You can also use the $\pi$ key on your calculator to get a rounded decimal for $\pi$. For an exact answer, leave the result in terms of $\pi$.

## Problem 2 Finding Circumference

**Plan**

**How do you decide which formula to use?**

**Got It?** **a.** What is the circumference of a circle with radius 24 m in terms of $\pi$?

**b.** What is the circumference of a circle with diameter 24 m to the nearest tenth?

**Practice** **Find the circumference of $\odot C$ in terms of $\pi$.**

**3.**

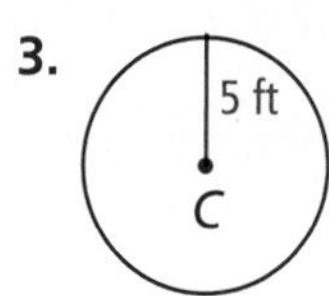

**4.**

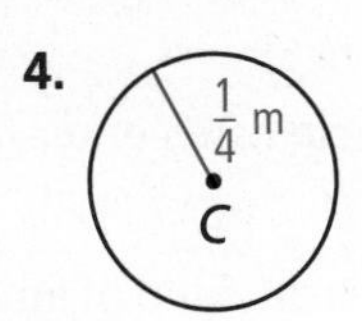

## Problem 3 Finding Perimeter and Area of a Triangle in the Coordinate Plane

**Got It?** Triangle $ABC$ has vertices $A(-6, 4)$, $B(6, 4)$, and $C(-6, -1)$. What is the perimeter of $\triangle ABC$? What is the area of $\triangle ABC$?

**A Practice** **Find the perimeter and area of each triangle.**

**5.** triangle $JKL$ with vertices $J(1, -1)$, $K(1, 5)$, and $L(9, -1)$

**6.** triangle $MNP$ with vertices $M(-5, -3)$, $N(5, 2)$, and $P(5, -3)$

## Problem 4 Finding the Perimeter of a Pentagon in the Coordinate Plane

**Got It?** Pentagon $JKLMN$ has vertices $J(-2, 5)$, $K(1, 1)$, $L(1, -4)$, $M(-5, -4)$, and $N(-5, 1)$. What is the perimeter of $JKLMN$?

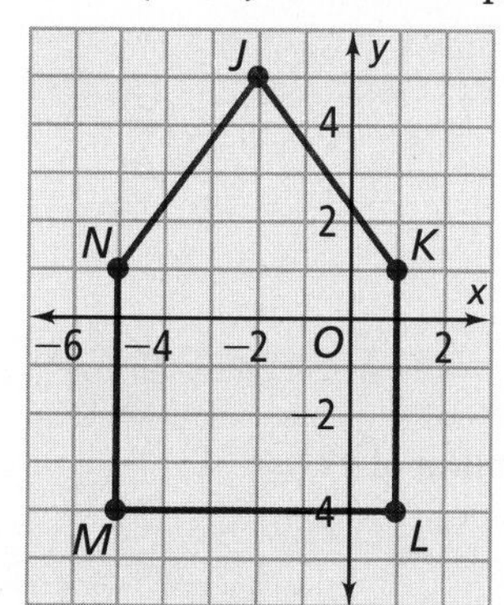


**Think**

**Do you need to calculate the length of each side?**

**Practice** **In Exercises 7 and 8, find the perimeter of each pentagon.**

**7.** pentagon $MNPQR$ with vertices $M(1, 6)$, $N(5, 10)$, $P(9, 6)$, $Q(9, 1)$, and $R(1, 1)$

8. pentagon $RSTUV$ with vertices $R(-6, 2)$, $S(-3, 6)$, $T(5, 6)$, $U(5, -2)$, and $V(-3, -2)$

## Problem 5 Finding Area of a Circle

**Got It?** The diameter of a circle is 14 ft.

**a.** What is the area of the circle in terms of $\pi$?

**b.** What is the area of the circle using an approximation of $\pi$?

**c. Reasoning** Which approximation of $\pi$ did you use in part (b)? Why?

**Practice** **Find the area of each circle in terms of $\pi$.**

9.

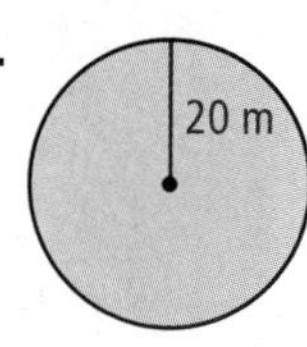


10.

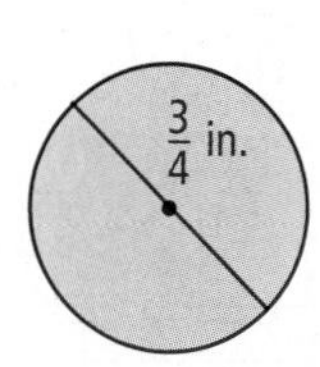


The following postulate is useful in finding areas of figures with irregular shapes.

take note

**Postulate 10 Area Addition Postulate**

The area of a region is the sum of the areas of its nonoverlapping parts.

## Problem 6 Finding Area of an Irregular Shape

**Got It?** **a. Reasoning** What is another way to separate the figure in Problem 6?

**b.** What is the area of the figure at the right?

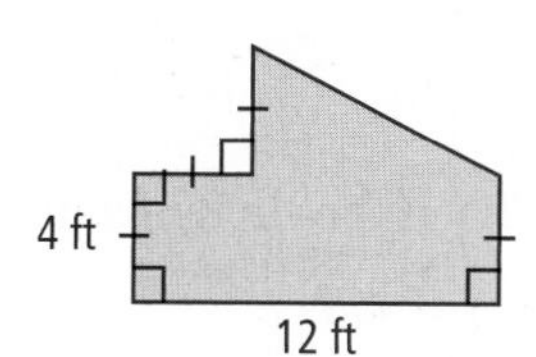

 **Practice** Find the area of the shaded region. All angles are right angles.

**11.**

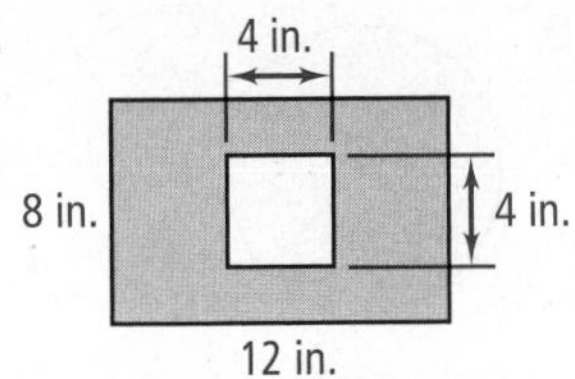


**12.**

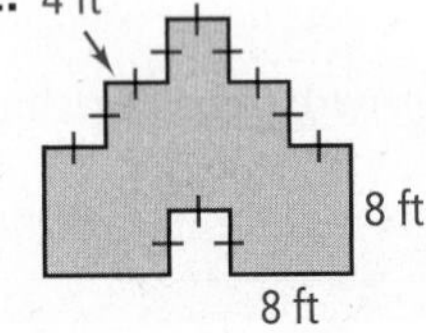


## Lesson Check

### Do you know HOW?

**13.** What is the perimeter and area of a rectangle with base 3 in. and height 7 in.?

**14.** What is the circumference and area of each circle to the nearest tenth?

**a.** $r = 9$ in.

**b.** $d = 7.3$ m

**15.** What is the perimeter and area of the figure at the right?

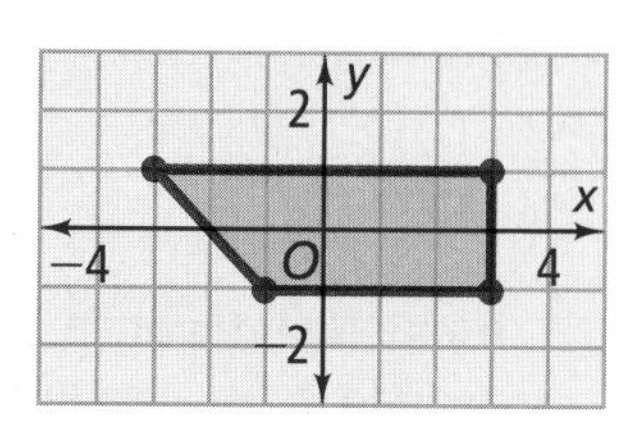


## Do you UNDERSTAND?

**16. Writing** Describe a real-world situation in which you would need to find a perimeter. Then describe a situation in which you would need to find an area.

**17. Compare and Contrast** Your friend can't remember whether $2\pi r$ computes the circumference or the area of a circle. How would you help your friend? Explain.

**18. Error Analysis** A classmate finds the area of a circle with radius 30 in. to be 900 in.$^2$. What error did your classmate make?

## More Practice and Problem-Solving Exercises

### B Apply

**Home Maintenance** **To determine how much of each item to buy, tell whether you need to know area or perimeter. Explain your choice.**

**19.** wallpaper for a bedroom

**20.** crown molding for a ceiling

**21.** fencing for a backyard

**22.** paint for a basement floor

**23.** **Think About a Plan** A light-year unit describes the distance that one photon of light travels in one year. The Milky Way galaxy has a diameter of about 100,000 light-years. The distance to Earth from the center of the Milky Way galaxy is about 30,000 light-years. How many more light-years does a star on the outermost edge of the Milky Way travel in one full revolution around the galaxy compared to Earth?

- What do you know about the shape of each orbital path?
- Are you looking for circumference or area?
- How do you compare the paths using algebraic expressions?

**24.** **a.** What is the area of a square with sides 12 in. long? 1 ft long?
**b.** How many square inches are in a square foot?

**25.** **a.** Count squares to find the area of the entire figure at the right.
**b.** Use a formula to find the area of each square outlined in red.
**c.** **Writing** How does the sum of your results in part (b) compare to your result in part (a)? Which postulate does this support?

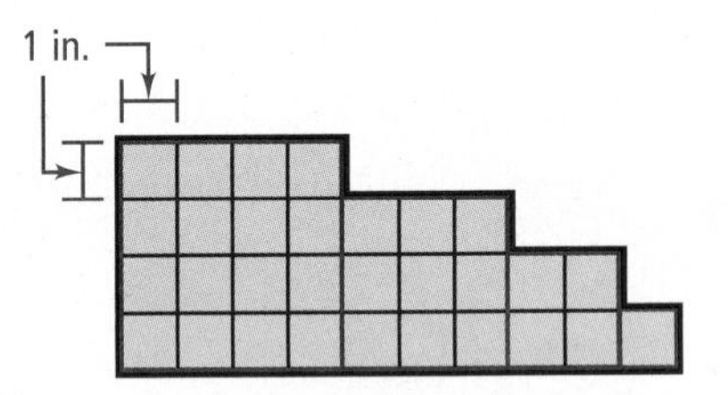


**26.** The area of an 11-cm-wide rectangle is 176 $cm^2$. What is its length?

**27.** **Garden** A scale drawing on a coordinate plane shows a rectangular garden. One unit represents one yard. The vertices of the garden are located at $(-12, -6)$, $(-12, -1)$, $(-2, -1)$, and $(-2, -6)$. What are the perimeter and area of the garden?

**28.** **Tiling** A scale drawing on a coordinate plane shows the plans for a rectangular kitchen. One unit represents one foot. The vertices of the kitchen are at $(-6, 7)$, $(2, 7)$, $(2, -5)$, and $(-6, -5)$. You want to tile the kitchen floor. Each tile is 2 feet by 2 feet. How many tiles will you need for the kitchen floor?

**29.** A square and a rectangle have equal areas. The rectangle is 64 cm by 81 cm. What is the perimeter of the square?

**30.** A rectangle has perimeter 40 cm and base 12 cm. What is its area?

**Find the area of each shaded figure.**

**31.** compact disc

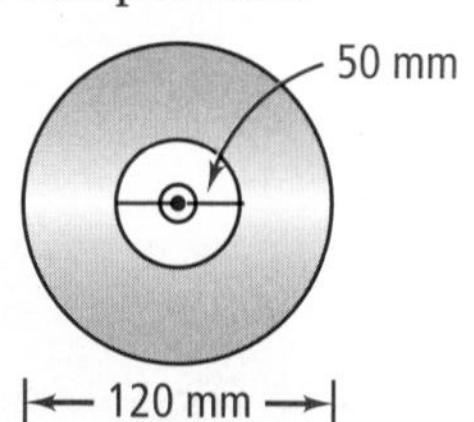


**32.** drafting triangle

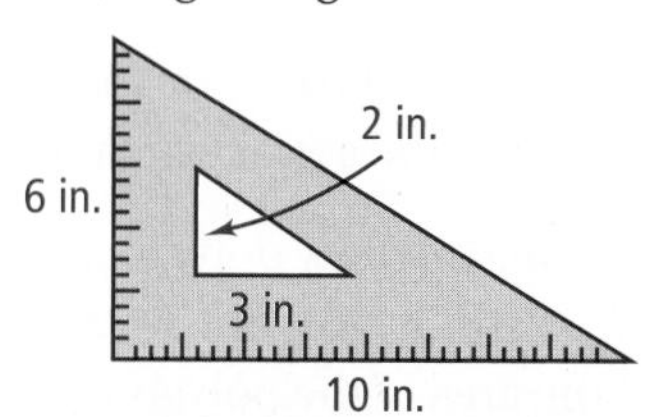


**33.** picture frame

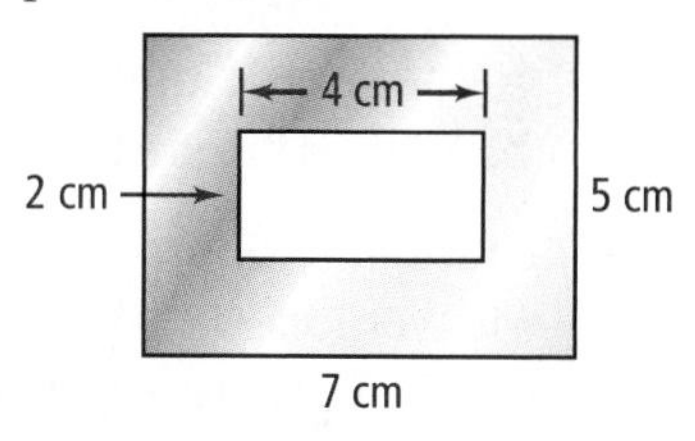


**34. Open-Ended** Draw a right triangle on a coordinate plane that has an area of 27 square units.

**35. Baseball** Sarah drew the outline of a pentagonal home plate on a coordinate plane where each unit represents one centimeter. The vertices of home plate are $(-22.5, 0)$, $(-22.5, 22)$, $(0, 44.5)$, $(22.5, 22)$, and $(22.5, 0)$. What is the perimeter of the home plate? Round to the nearest tenth.

**36. a. Reasoning** Can you use the formula for the perimeter of a rectangle to find the perimeter of any square? Explain.

**b.** Can you use the formula for the perimeter of a square to find the perimeter of any rectangle? Explain.

**c.** Use the formula for the perimeter of a square to write a formula for the area of a square in terms of its perimeter.

**37. Estimation** On an art trip to England, a student sketches the floor plan of the main body of Salisbury Cathedral. The shape of the floor plan is called the building's "footprint." The student estimates the dimensions of the cathedral on her sketch at the right. Use the student's lengths to estimate the area of Salisbury Cathedral's footprint.

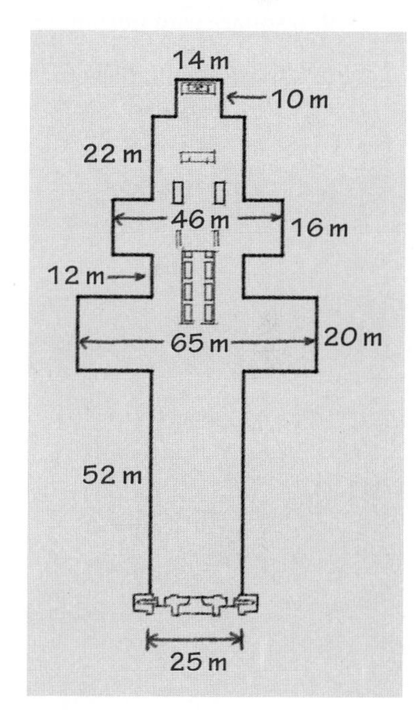


**38. Coordinate Geometry** The endpoints of a diameter of a circle are $A(2, 1)$ and $B(5, 5)$. Find the area of the circle in terms of $\pi$.

**39. Algebra** A rectangle has a base of $x$ units. The area is $(4x^2 - 2x)$ square units. What is the height of the rectangle in terms of $x$?

Ⓐ $(4 - x)$ units
Ⓑ $(4x^3 - 2x^2)$ units
Ⓒ $(x - 2)$ units
Ⓓ $(4x - 2)$ units

**Coordinate Geometry Graph each rectangle in the coordinate plane. Find its perimeter and area.**

**40.** $A(-3, 2)$, $B(-2, 2)$, $C(-2, -2)$, $D(-3, -2)$

**41.** $A(-2, -6)$, $B(-2, -3)$, $C(3, -3)$, $D(3, -6)$

**42.** You are drawing a right triangle on a coordinate plane. Two of the vertices are $(3, 0)$ and $(3, -4)$. Name a third point that you can plot so that the perimeter of the right triangle is 12 units.

**43.** You are drawing a pentagon on a coordinate plane. Four of the vertices are $(-1, 5)$, $(3, 5)$, $(3, -3)$, and $(-1, -3)$. Name a fifth point that can you can plot so that the perimeter of the pentagon is 26 units.

**44.** The surface area of a three-dimensional figure is the sum of the areas of all of its surfaces. You can find the surface area by finding the area of a net for the figure.

**a.** Draw a net for the solid shown. Label the dimensions.

**b.** What is the area of the net? What is the surface area of the solid?

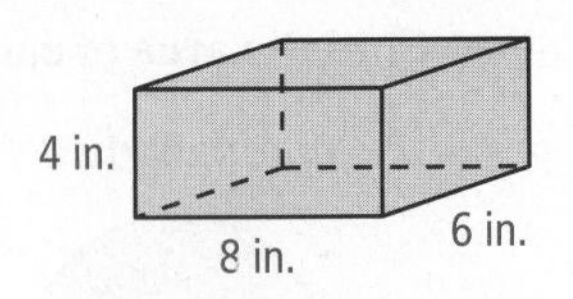


**45. Coordinate Geometry** On graph paper, draw polygon $ABCDEFG$ with vertices $A(1, 1)$, $B(10, 1)$, $C(10, 8)$, $D(7, 5)$, $E(4, 5)$, $F(4, 8)$, and $G(1, 8)$. Find the perimeter and the area of the polygon.

**46. Pet Care** You want to adopt a puppy from your local animal shelter. First, you plan to build an outdoor playpen along the side of your house, as shown on the right. You want to lay down special dog grass for the pen's floor. If dog grass costs $1.70 per square foot, how much will you spend?

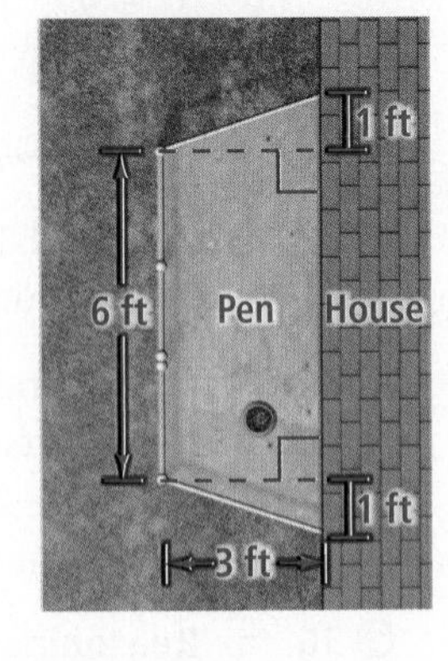


**47.** A rectangular garden has an 8-ft walkway around it. How many more feet is the outer perimeter of the walkway than the perimeter of the garden?

## Challenge

**Algebra Find the area of each figure.**

**48.** a rectangle with side lengths $\frac{2a}{5b}$ units and $\frac{3b}{8}$ units

**49.** a square with perimeter $10n$ units

**50.** a triangle with base $(5x - 2y)$ units and height $(4x + 3y)$ units

LESSON LAB

Use With Lesson 11-1

# Partitioning a Segment

G.GPE.6 Find the point on a directed line segment . . . that partitions the segment in a given ratio.

You have used the Midpoint Formula to find an endpoint of a segment. You can also use proportional reasoning to find points on a segment other than the endpoints.

## Example

**The endpoints of $\overline{LM}$ are $L(-4, 1)$ and $M(5, -5)$. Point $N$ lies on $\overline{LM}$ and is $\frac{2}{3}$ of the way from $L$ to $M$. What are the coordinates of point $N$?**

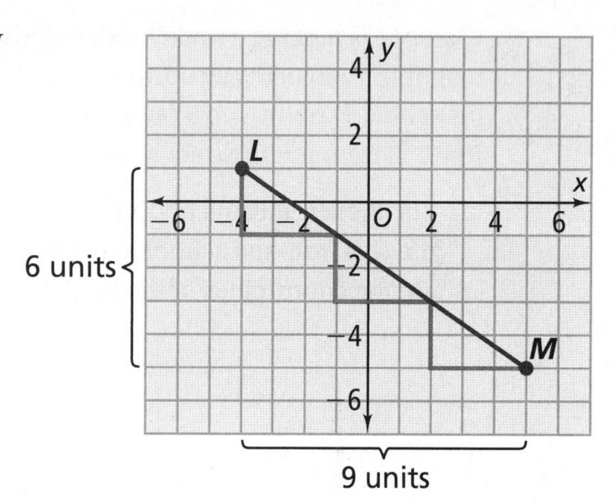


**Step 1** Plot $\overline{LM}$ on a coordinate plane.

**Step 2** Notice that the segment drops 6 units vertically and runs 9 units horizontally as you go from $L$ to $M$.

Divide the horizontal and vertical distances by 3 to break $\overline{LM}$ into thirds.

vertical distance: $\frac{6}{3} = 2$

horizontal distance: $\frac{9}{3} = 3$

**Step 3** Beginning at point $L$, drop 2 units down and move 3 units to the right to arrive at $(-1, -1)$. Repeat this process twice more to find the points $(2, -3)$ and $M(5, -5)$.

The points $(-1, -1)$ and $(2, -3)$ divide $\overline{LM}$ into thirds. The point $(2, -3)$ lies on $\overline{LM}$ and is $\frac{2}{3}$ of the way from $L$ to $M$. The coordinates of point $N$ are $(2, -3)$.

## Exercises

1. The endpoints of $\overline{RS}$ are $R(-5, -2)$ and $S(3, 2)$. Point $T$ lies on $\overline{RS}$ and is $\frac{1}{4}$ of the way from $R$ to $S$. What are the coordinates of point $T$?

**2.** The endpoints of $\overline{CD}$ are $C(-6, -2)$ and $D(6, 4)$. Point $E$ lies on $\overline{CD}$ and is $\frac{1}{3}$ of the way from $C$ to $D$. What are the coordinates of point $E$?

**3.** Clarence is making a scale model of his neighborhood using a coordinate grid. He plots his school at point $S(4, 5)$ and the park at point $P(16, 11)$ along Elm Street as shown.

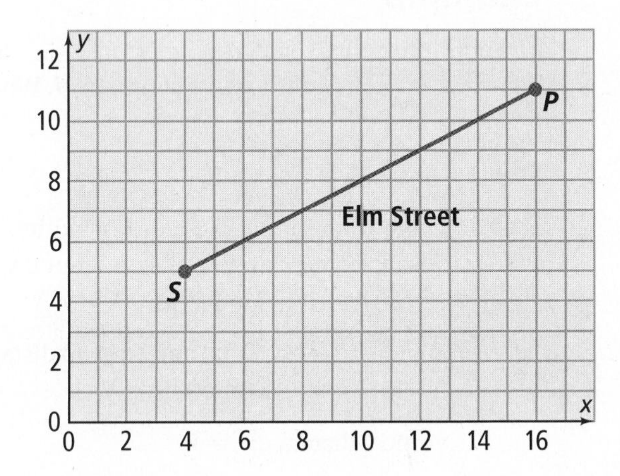


**a.** The bank is located on Elm Street and is $\frac{1}{6}$ of the way from the school to the park. What are the coordinates of the bank?

**b.** The grocery store is located on Elm Street and is $\frac{2}{3}$ of the way from the school to the park. What are the coordinates of the grocery store?

# 11-2 Areas of Parallelograms and Triangles

**G.GPE.7** Use coordinates to compute perimeters of polygons and areas of triangles and rectangles . . . Also **G.MG.1**

**Objective** To find the area of parallelograms and triangles

**Solve It!** Write your solution to the Solve It in the space below.

**Essential Understanding** You can find the area of a parallelogram or a triangle when you know the length of its base and its height.

A parallelogram with the same base and height as a rectangle has the same area as the rectangle.

take note

### Key Concept Area of a Rectangle

The area of a rectangle is the product of its base and height.

$A = bh$

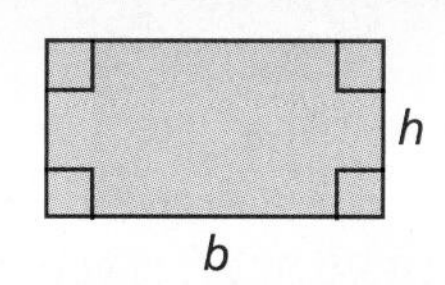


### Key Concept Area of a Parallelogram

The area of a parallelogram is the product of a base and the corresponding height.

$A = bh$

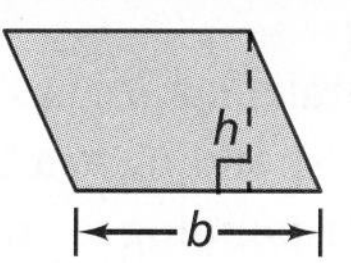


A **base of a parallelogram** can be any one of its sides. The corresponding **altitude** is a segment perpendicular to the line containing that base, drawn from the side opposite the base. The **height** is the length of an altitude.

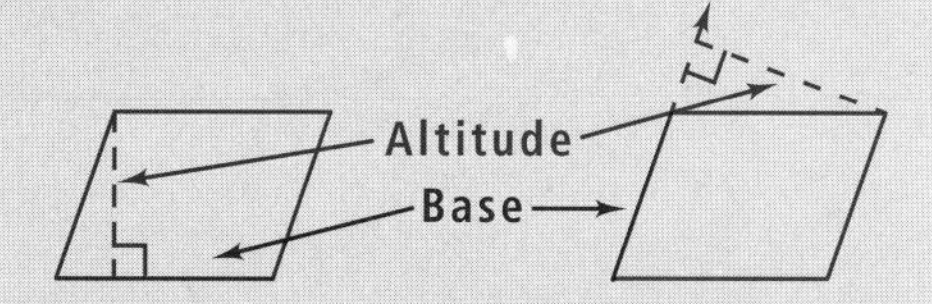

## Problem 1 Finding the Area of a Parallelogram

**Got It?** What is the area of a parallelogram with base length 12 m and height 9 m?

**Practice** Find the area of each parallelogram.

**1.**

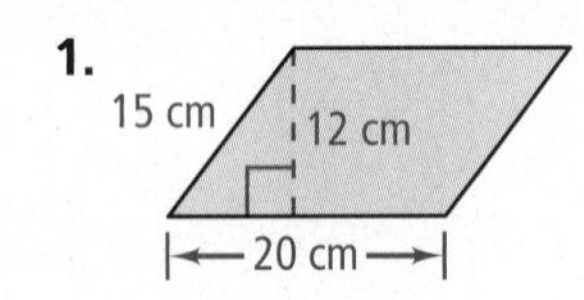


**2.**

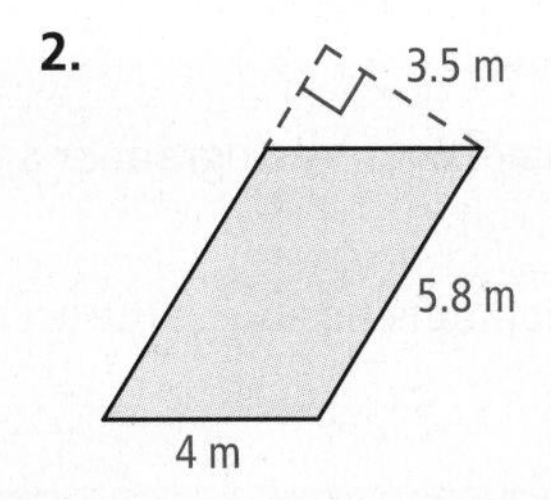

## Problem 2 Finding a Missing Dimension

**Got It?** A parallelogram has sides of length 15 cm and 18 cm. The height corresponding to a 15-cm base is 9 cm. What is the height corresponding to an 18-cm base?

**Think**
How can a diagram help you visualize the problem?

**Practice** **Find the value of $h$ for each parallelogram.**

**3.**

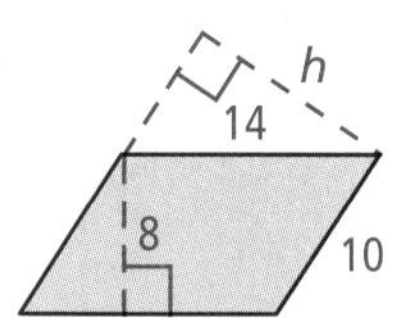


**4.**

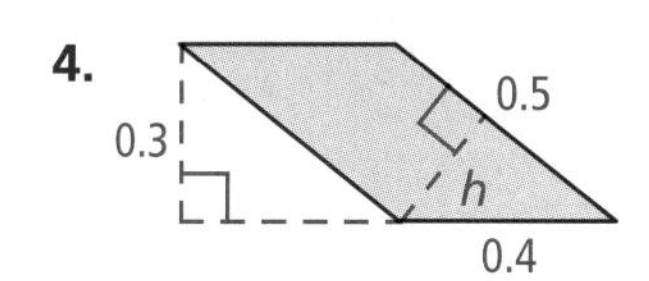


You can rotate a triangle about the midpoint of a side to form a parallelogram.

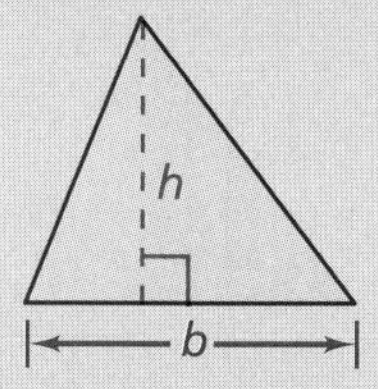


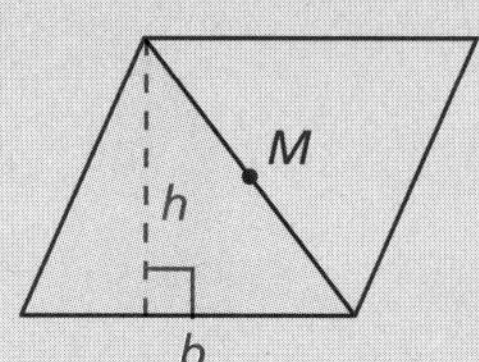


The area of the triangle is half the area of the parallelogram.

take note

## Key Concept Area of a Triangle

The area of a triangle is half the product of a base and the corresponding height.

$A = \frac{1}{2}bh$

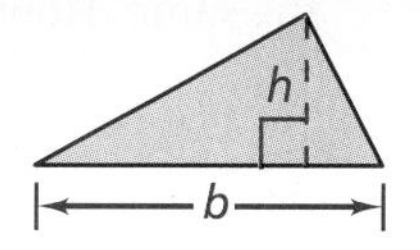


A **base of a triangle** can be any of its sides. The corresponding **height** is the length of the altitude to the line containing that base.

## Problem 3 Finding the Area of a Triangle

**Got It?** What is the area of the triangle?

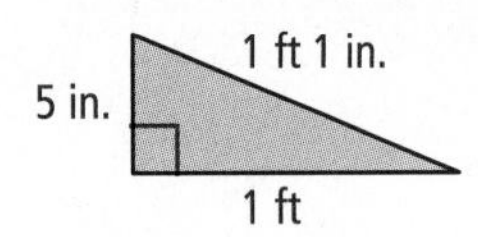


**Think**

**In what units should your final answer be written?**

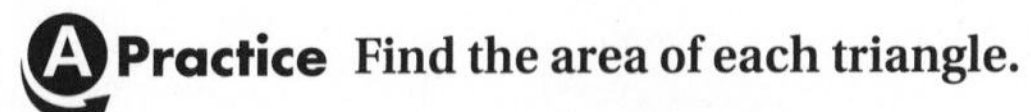


**Practice** Find the area of each triangle.

**5.**

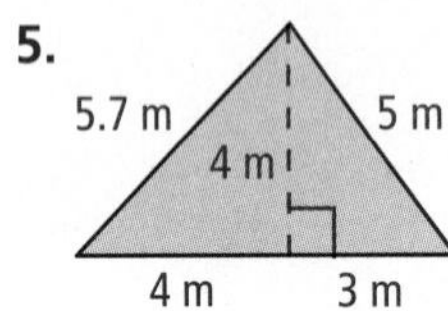


**6.**

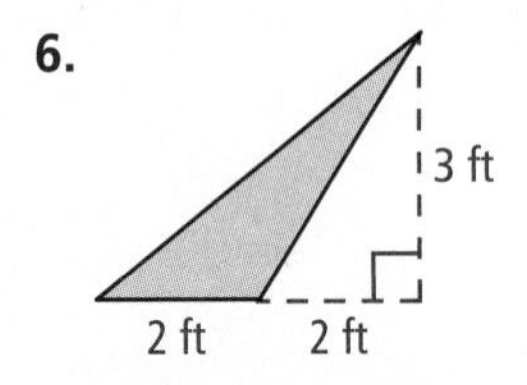


## Problem 4 Finding the Area of an Irregular Figure

**Got It?** **Reasoning** Suppose the base lengths of the square and triangle in Problem 4 are doubled to 12 in., but the height of each polygon remains the same. How is the area of the figure affected?

7. **Urban Design** A bakery has a 50 ft-by-31 ft parking lot. The four parking spaces are parallelograms with the same dimensions, the driving region is a rectangle, and the two areas for flowers are triangles with the same dimensions.

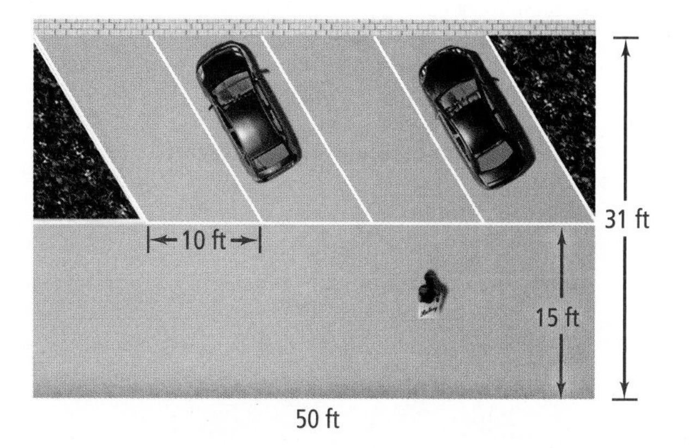


a. Find the area of the paved surface by adding the areas of the driving region and the four parking spaces.

b. Describe another method for finding the area of the paved surface.

c. Use your method from part (b) to find the area. Then compare answers from parts (a) and (b) to check your work.

## Lesson Check

### Do you know HOW?

**Find the area of each parallelogram.**

**8.** 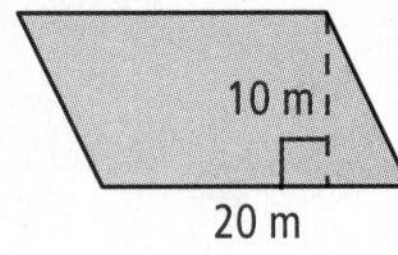


**9.** 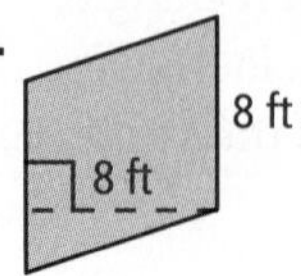


**Find the area of each triangle.**

**10.** 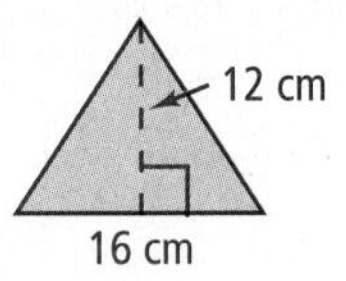


**11.** 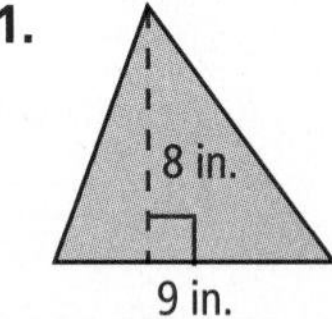


### Do you UNDERSTAND?

**12. Vocabulary** Does an altitude of a triangle have to lie inside the triangle? Explain.

**13. Writing** How can you show that a parallelogram and a rectangle with the same bases and heights have equal areas?

**14.** $\square ABCD$ is divided into two triangles along diagonal $\overline{AC}$. If you know the area of the parallelogram, how do you find the area of $\triangle ABC$?

## More Practice and Problem-Solving Exercises

### B Apply

**15.** The area of a parallelogram is 24 in.$^2$ and the height is 6 in. Find the length of the corresponding base.

**16.** What is the area of the figure shown at the right?

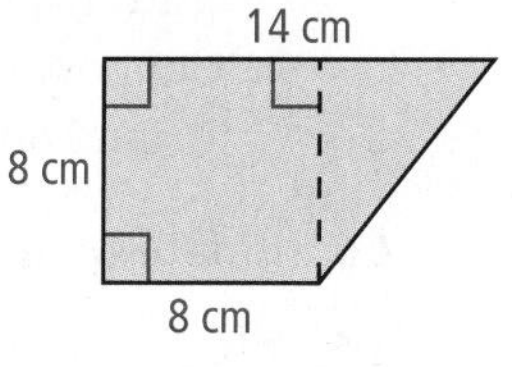


Ⓐ 64 cm$^2$

Ⓑ 88 cm$^2$

Ⓒ 96 cm$^2$

Ⓓ 112 cm$^2$

**17.** A right isosceles triangle has area 98 cm$^2$. Find the length of each leg.

**18. Algebra** The area of a triangle is 108 in.$^2$. A base and corresponding height are in the ratio 3 : 2. Find the length of the base and the corresponding height.

**19. Think About a Plan** Ki used geometry software to create the figure shown at the right. She constructed $\overleftrightarrow{AB}$ and a point $C$ not on $\overleftrightarrow{AB}$. Then she constructed line $k$ parallel to $\overleftrightarrow{AB}$ through point $C$. Next, Ki constructed point $D$ on line $k$ as well as $\overline{AD}$ and $\overline{BD}$. She dragged point $D$ along line $k$ to manipulate $\triangle ABD$. How does the area of $\triangle ABD$ change? Explain.

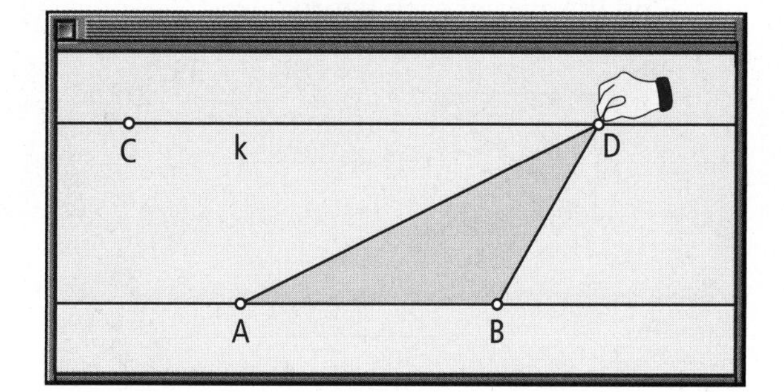


- Which dimensions of the triangle change when Ki drags point $D$?
- Do the lengths of $\overline{AD}$ and $\overline{BD}$ matter when calculating area?

**20. Open-Ended** Using graph paper, draw an acute triangle, an obtuse triangle, and a right triangle, each with area 12 units$^2$.

**Find the area of each figure.**

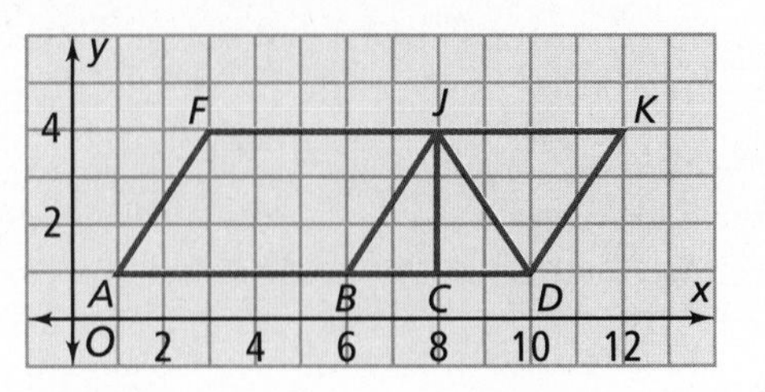


21. $\square ABJF$
22. $\triangle BDJ$
23. $\triangle DKJ$
24. $\square BDKJ$
25. $\square ADKF$
26. $\triangle BCJ$
27. trapezoid $ADJF$

**28. Reasoning** Suppose the height of a triangle is tripled. How does this affect the area of the triangle? Explain.

**For Exercises 29–32, (a) graph the lines and (b) find the area of the triangle enclosed by the lines.**

29. $y = x,\ x = 0,\ y = 7$
30. $y = x + 2,\ y = 2,\ x = 6$
31. $y = -\frac{1}{2}x + 3,\ y = 0,\ x = -2$
32. $y = \frac{3}{4}x - 2,\ y = -2,\ x = 4$

**33. Probability** Your friend drew these three figures on a grid. A fly lands at random at a point on the grid.

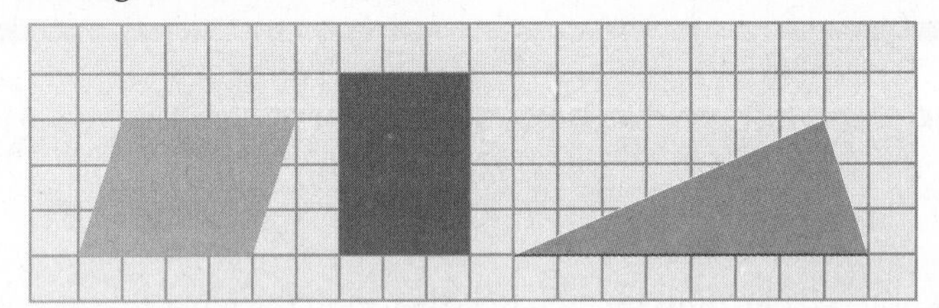

a. **Writing** Is the fly more likely to land on one of the figures or on the blank grid? Explain.

b. Suppose you know the fly lands on one of the figures. Is the fly more likely to land on one figure than on another? Explain.

**Coordinate Geometry** **Find the area of a polygon with the given vertices.**

34. $A(3, 9), B(8, 9), C(2, -3), D(-3, -3)$
35. $E(1, 1), F(4, 5), G(11, 5), H(8, 1)$
36. $D(0, 0), E(2, 4), F(6, 4), G(6, 0)$
37. $K(-7, -2), L(-7, 6), M(1, 6), N(7, -2)$

**Find the area of each figure.**

38.

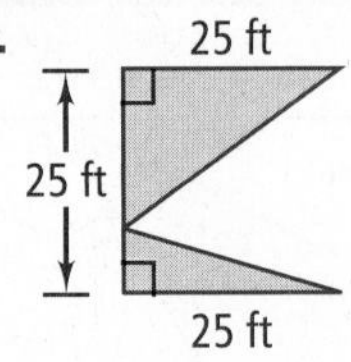


39.

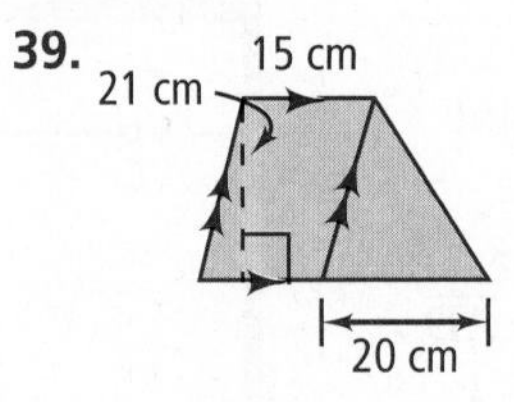


40.

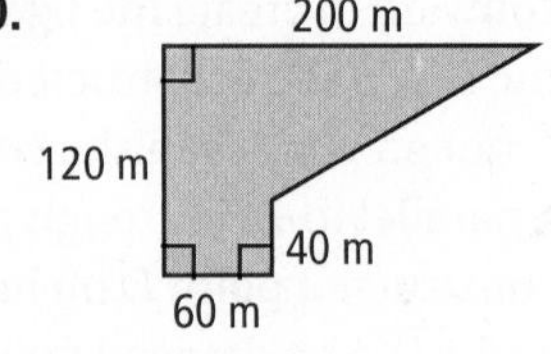

**History** **The Greek mathematician Heron is most famous for this formula for the area of a triangle in terms of the lengths of its sides $a$, $b$, and $c$.**

$$A = \sqrt{s(s-a)(s-b)(s-c)}, \text{ where } s = \tfrac{1}{2}(a+b+c)$$

**Use Heron's Formula and a calculator to find the area of each triangle. Round your answer to the nearest whole number.**

**41.** $a = 8$ in., $b = 9$ in., $c = 10$ in.

**42.** $a = 15$ m, $b = 17$ m, $c = 21$ m

**43.** **a.** Use Heron's Formula to find the area of this triangle.
**b.** Verify your answer to part (a) by using the formula $A = \frac{1}{2}bh$.

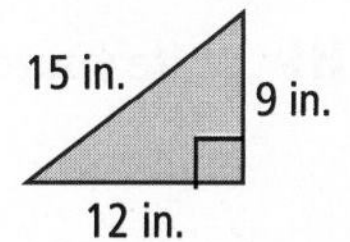

# Areas of Trapezoids, Rhombuses, and Kites

**G.MG.1** Use geometric shapes, their measures, and their properties to describe objects . . . Also Extends **G.GPE.7**

**Objective** To find the area of a trapezoid, rhombus, or kite

**Solve It!** Write your solution to the Solve It in the space below.

**Essential Understanding** You can find the area of a trapezoid when you know its height and the lengths of its bases.

The **height of a trapezoid** is the perpendicular distance between the bases.

take note

## Key Concept Area of a Trapezoid

The area of a trapezoid is half the product of the height and the sum of the bases.

$A = \frac{1}{2}h(b_1 + b_2)$

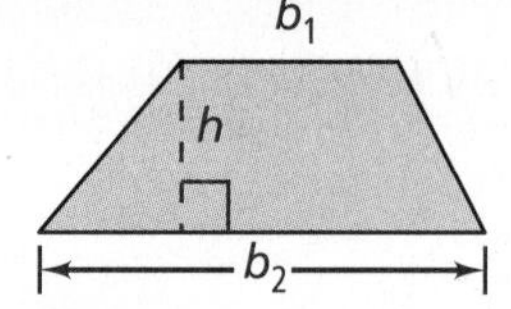

## Problem 1 Area of a Trapezoid

**Got It?** What is the area of a trapezoid with height 7 cm and bases 12 cm and 15 cm?

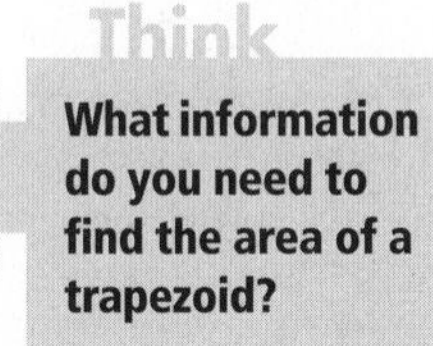

**Practice** Find the area of each trapezoid.

1\.

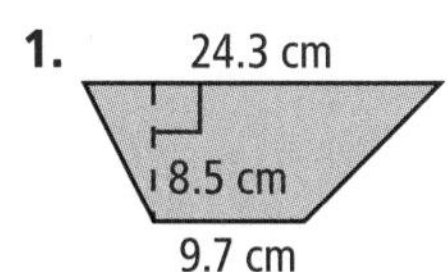


2\.

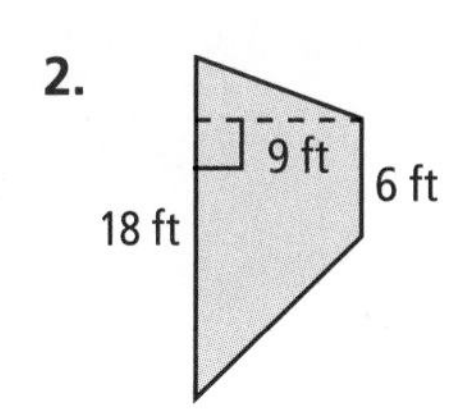


**Essential Understanding** You can find the area of a rhombus or a kite when you know the lengths of its diagonals.

take note

## Key Concept Area of a Rhombus or a Kite

The area of a rhombus or a kite is half the product of the lengths of its diagonals.

$A = \frac{1}{2}d_1d_2$

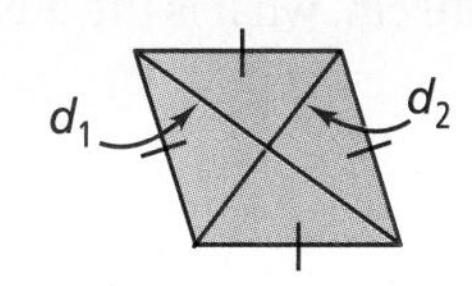


Rhombus

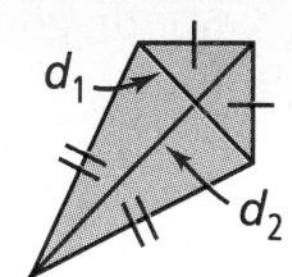


Kite

## Problem 2 Finding the Area of a Kite

**Got It?** What is the area of a kite with diagonals that are 12 in. and 9 in. long?

**Practice** Find the area of each kite.

3.

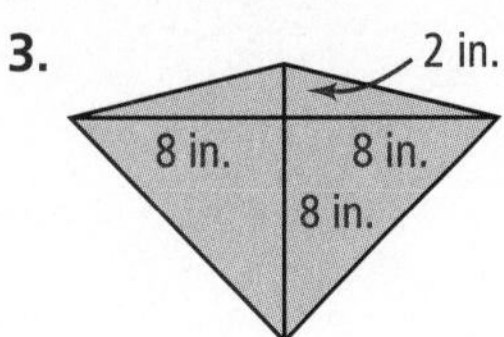


4.

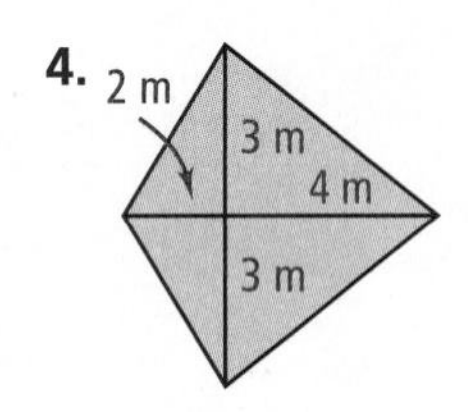


## Problem 3 Finding the Area of a Rhombus

**Got It?** A rhombus has sides 10 cm long. If the length of the longer diagonal is 16 cm, what is the area of the rhombus?

**Think**
How can drawing a diagram help you visualize the problem?

**Practice** Find the area of each rhombus.

5.

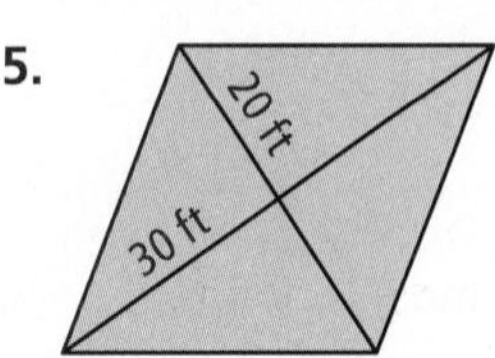

**6.**

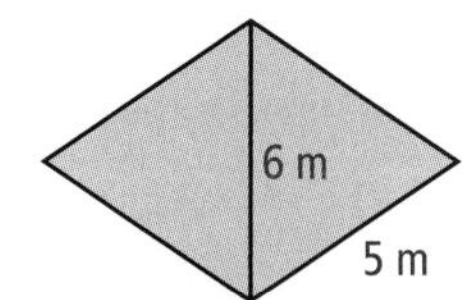

## Lesson Check

### Do you know HOW?

**Find the area of each figure.**

**7.**

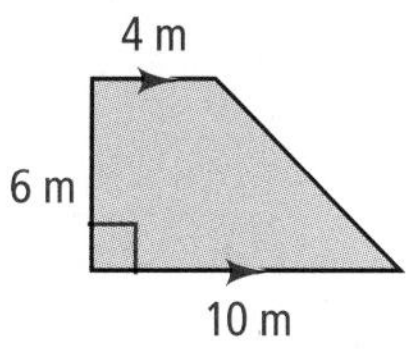


**8.**

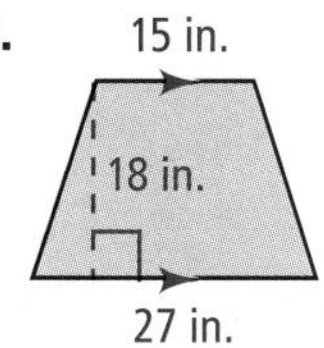


**9.**

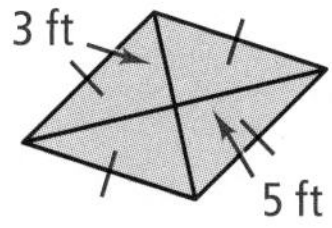


**10.**

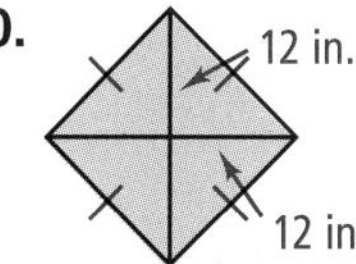

**11.**

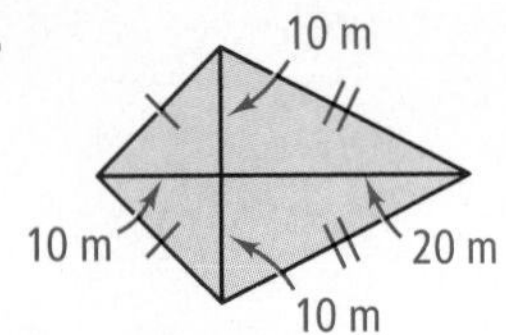


**12.**

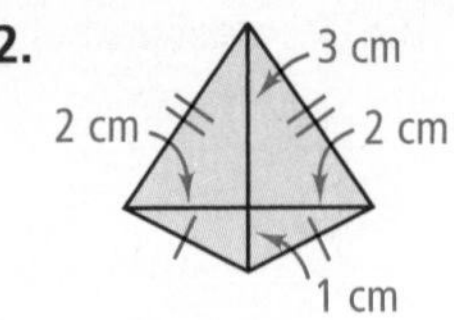


## Do you UNDERSTAND?

MATHEMATICAL PRACTICES

**13. Vocabulary** Can a trapezoid and a parallelogram with the same base and height have the same area? Explain.

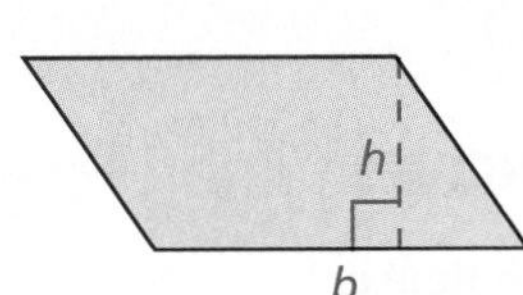


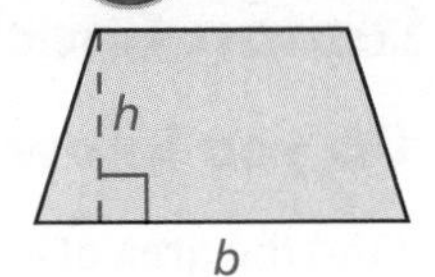


**14. Reasoning** Do you need to know all the side lengths to find the area of a trapezoid?

**15. Reasoning** Can you find the area of a rhombus if you only know the lengths of its sides? Explain.

**16. Reasoning** Do you need to know the lengths of the sides to find the area of a kite? Explain.

## More Practice and Problem-Solving Exercises

### B Apply

**17. Think About a Plan** A trapezoid has two right angles, 12-m and 18-m bases, and an 8-m height. Sketch the trapezoid and find its perimeter and area.

- Are the right angles consecutive or opposite angles?
- How does knowing the height help you find the perimeter?

**18. Metallurgy** The end of a gold bar has the shape of a trapezoid with the measurements shown. Find the area of the end.

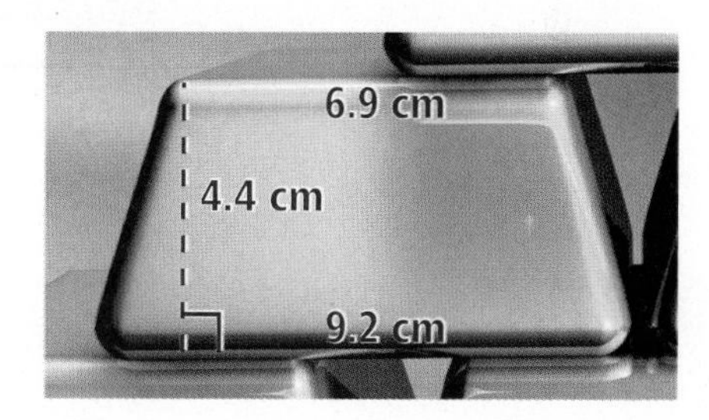


**19. Open-Ended** Draw a kite. Find the lengths of its diagonals. Find its area.

**Find the area of each trapezoid to the nearest tenth.**

20.

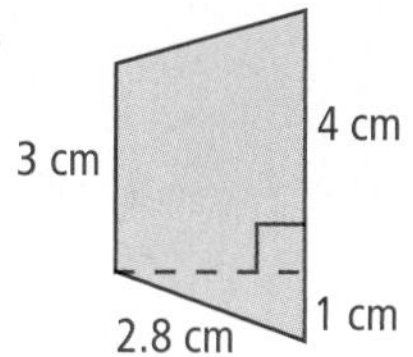


21.

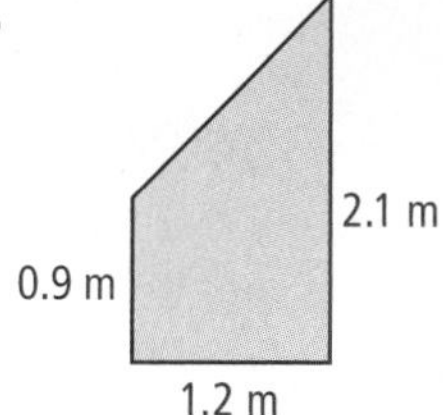


**Coordinate Geometry** **Find the area of quadrilateral *QRST*.**

22.

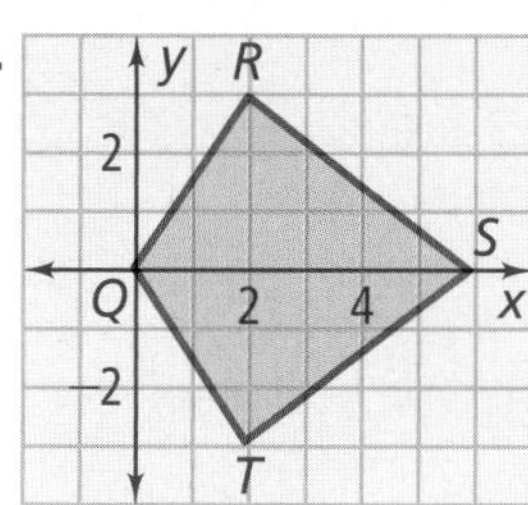


23.

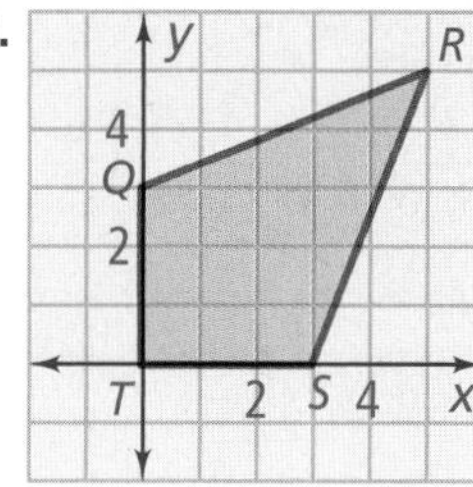


24.

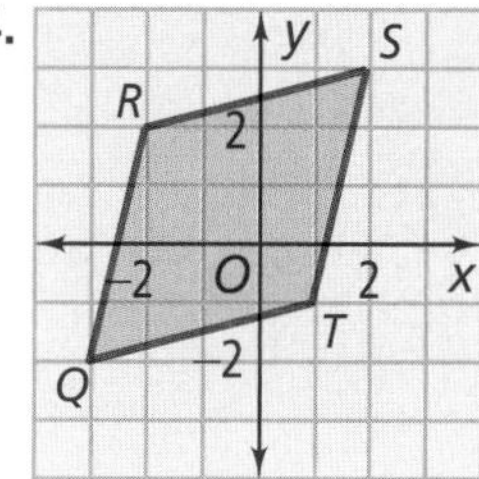


25. a. **Coordinate Geometry** Graph the lines $x = 0$, $x = 6$, $y = 0$, and $y = x + 4$.

b. What type of quadrilateral do the lines form?

c. Find the area of the quadrilateral.

**26. Visualization** The kite has diagonals $d_1$ and $d_2$ congruent to the sides of the rectangle. Explain why the area of the kite is $\frac{1}{2}d_1d_2$.

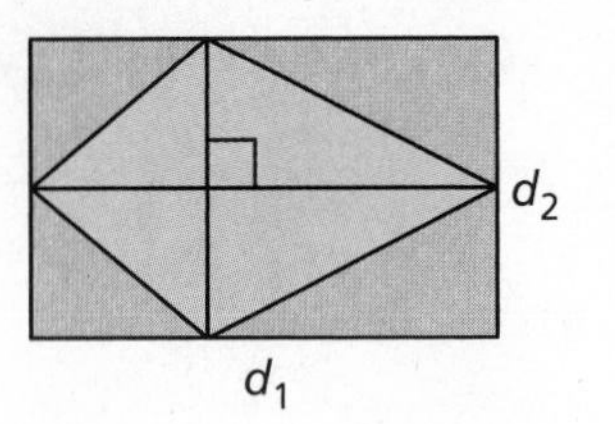


**27.** Draw a trapezoid. Label its bases $b_1$ and $b_2$ and its height $h$. Then draw a diagonal of the trapezoid.

**a.** Write equations for the area of each of the two triangles formed.

**b. Writing** Explain how you can justify the trapezoid area formula using the areas of the two triangles.

## Challenge

**28. Algebra** One base of a trapezoid is twice the other. The height is the average of the two bases. The area is 324 cm². Find the height and the bases. (*Hint:* Let the smaller base be $x$.)

**29. Sports** Ty wants to paint one side of the skateboarding ramp he built. The ramp is 4 m wide. Its surface is modeled by the equation $y = 0.25x^2$. Use the trapezoids and triangles shown to estimate the area to be painted.

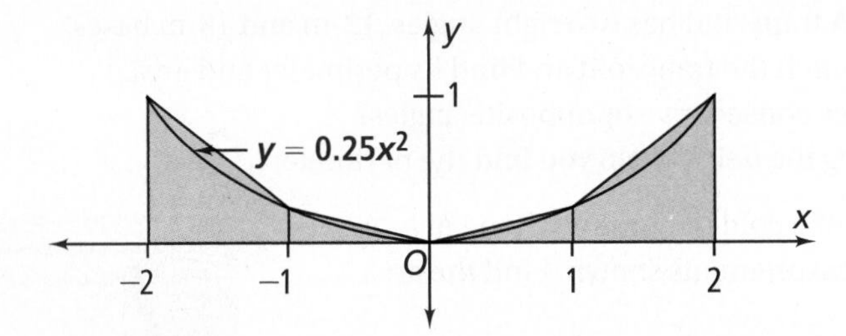

ACTIVITY LAB

Use With Lesson 11-4

# Proving Slope Criteria for Parallel and Perpendicular Lines

**G.GPE.5** Prove the slope criteria for parallel and perpendicular lines and use them to solve geometric problems . . .

You can determine whether two nonvertical lines on a coordinate plane are parallel by examining their slopes.

## Activity 1

Let two nonvertical parallel lines in the coordinate plane be given in slope-intercept form by the equations $y = m_1x + b_1$ and $y = m_2x + b_2$.

**1.** How are $b_1$ and $b_2$ related? Can $b_2 - b_1$ be equal to 0? Explain.

**2.** How many solutions does the equation $m_1x + b_1 = m_2x + b_2$ have? Explain.

**3.** Show that the equation in Exercise 2 is equivalent to $(m_1 - m_2)x = b_2 - b_1$.

**4.** When are there no solutions to the equation in Exercise 3? Explain.

**5.** Explain how your answer to Exercise 4 shows that if nonvertical lines are parallel, then their slopes are equal.

**6.** Show that if two distinct lines have the same slope, then they are parallel by showing that the equation $mx + b_1 = mx + b_2$ has no solutions when $b_1 \neq b_2$.

You can also determine whether two nonvertical lines on a coordinate plane are perpendicular by examining their slopes.

## Activity 2

Let two perpendicular lines, neither of which is vertical, be given in slope-intercept form by the equations $y = m_1x + b_1$ and $y = m_2x + b_2$. Let the point of intersection be point $A$. Draw a horizontal segment $\overline{AP}$ with length 1. Draw a vertical line through point $P$ that intersects the two perpendicular lines at points $B$ and $C$. This is shown in the figure at the right.

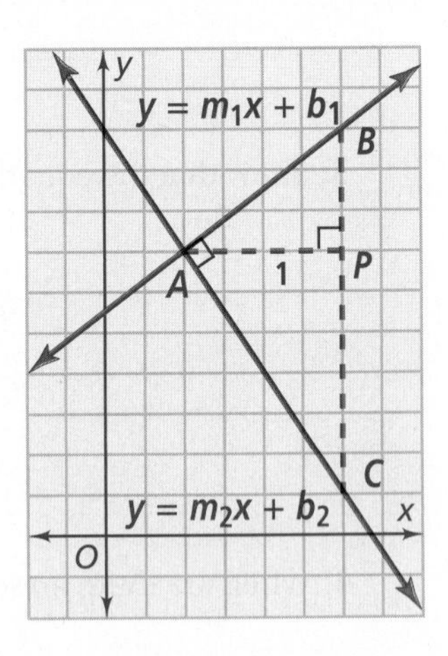


**7.** Use the slopes of the perpendicular lines to find the lengths of $\overline{BP}$ and $\overline{CP}$.

**8.** Use your results from Exercise 7 to find the lengths of $\overline{AB}$ and $\overline{AC}$.

**9.** Let the coordinates of $A$ be $(p, q)$. Show that the $y$-coordinates of $B$ and $C$ are $q + m_1$ and $q + m_2$, respectively.

**10.** Use your results from Exercise 9 to find the length of $\overline{BC}$.

**11.** Use the Pythagorean theorem to show that $m_1 m_2 = -1$.

## Exercises

**Determine whether the lines are *parallel, perpendicular,* or *neither*.**

**12.** $y = 3x + 1$
$y = -\frac{1}{3}x - 1$

**13.** $y = \frac{1}{2}x + \frac{3}{2}$
$y = \frac{1}{2}x - \frac{2}{3}$

**14.** $y = \frac{2}{3}x - 4$
$y = \frac{3}{2}x - 4$

**15.** $y - 2 = 2(x + 1)$
$4x - 2y = -8$

**16. Reasoning** Can you use slope criteria for determining whether lines are parallel or perpendicular if one of the lines is vertical? Explain.

# Polygons in the Coordinate Plane

G.GPE.4 . . . Prove simple geometric theorems algebraically.

**Objective** To classify polygons in the coordinate plane

**Solve It!** Write your solution to the Solve It in the space below.

In the Solve It, you formed a polygon on a grid. In this lesson, you will classify polygons in the coordinate plane.

**Essential Understanding** You can classify figures in the coordinate plane using the formulas for slope, distance, and midpoint.

The chart below reviews these formulas and tells when to use them.

take note

## Key Concept Formulas and the Coordinate Plane

| Formula | When to Use It |
|---|---|
| Distance Formula<br>$d = \sqrt{(x_2 - x_1)^2 + (y_2 - y_1)^2}$ | To determine whether<br>• sides are congruent<br>• diagonals are congruent |
| Midpoint Formula<br>$M = \left(\frac{x_1 + x_2}{2}, \frac{y_1 + y_2}{2}\right)$ | To determine<br>• the coordinates of the midpoint of a side<br>• whether diagonals bisect each other |
| Slope Formula<br>$m = \frac{y_2 - y_1}{x_2 - x_1}$ | To determine whether<br>• opposite sides are parallel<br>• diagonals are perpendicular<br>• sides are perpendicular |

## Problem 1 Classifying a Triangle

**Got It?** $\triangle DEF$ has vertices $D(0, 0)$, $E(1, 4)$, and $F(5, 2)$. Show that $\triangle DEF$ is scalene.

**Think**
**What formula should you use?**

**Practice** Determine whether $\triangle ABC$ is *scalene, isosceles,* or *equilateral.* Explain.

**1.**

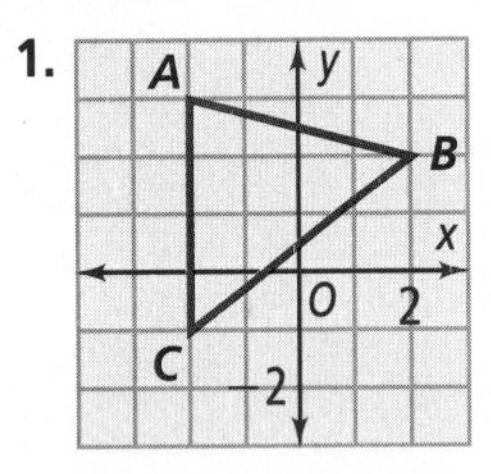


**2.**

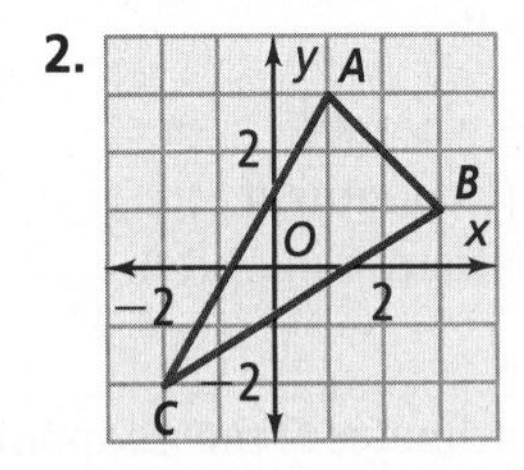

## Problem 2 Classifying a Quadrilateral

**Got It?** Parallelogram $MNPQ$ has vertices $M(0, 1)$, $N(-1, 4)$, $P(2, 5)$, and $Q(3, 2)$. Show that $\square MNPQ$ is a rectangle.

**Think**
How can you use slope to get information about the sides of a figure?

**Practice** Show that the parallelogram with the given vertices is a rhombus.

**3.** $L(1, 2)$, $M(3, 3)$, $N(5, 2)$, $P(3, 1)$

**4.** $S(1, 3)$, $P(4, 4)$, $A(3, 1)$, $T(0, 0)$

## Problem 3 Classifying a Quadrilateral

**Got It?** An isosceles trapezoid has vertices $A(0, 0)$, $B(2, 4)$, $C(6, 4)$, and $D(8, 0)$. Show that the quadrilateral formed by connecting the midpoints of the sides of $ABCD$ is a rhombus.

**What is the most precise classification of the quadrilateral formed by connecting the consecutive midpoints of each figure below?**

**5.** rectangle *EFGH*

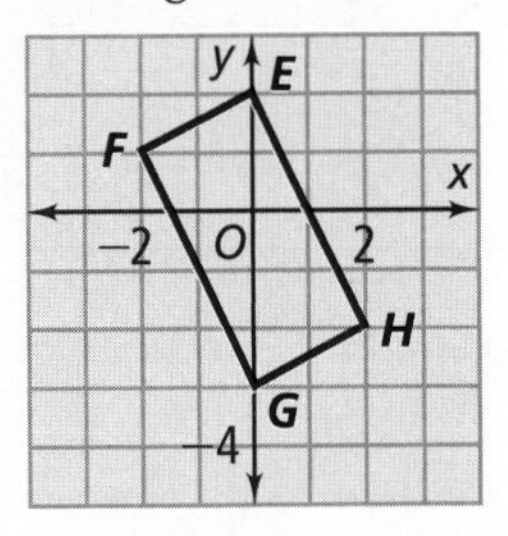


**6.** isosceles trapezoid *JKLM*

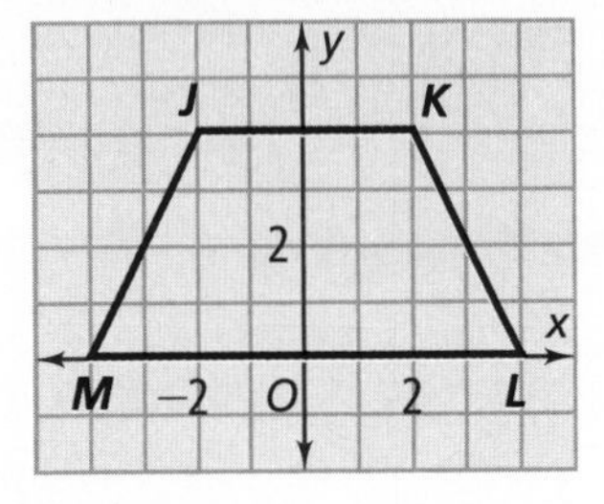

## Lesson Check

### Do you know HOW?

**7.** $\triangle TRI$ has vertices $T(-3, 4)$, $R(3, 4)$, and $I(0, 0)$. Is $\triangle TRI$ *scalene, isosceles,* or *equilateral*?

**8.** Is *QRST* at the right a rectangle? Explain.

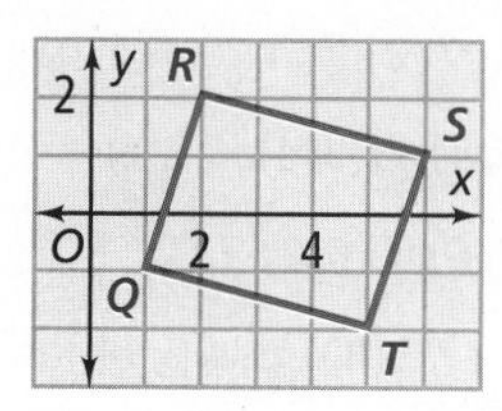


### Do you UNDERSTAND?

MATHEMATICAL PRACTICES

**9. Writing** In the figure at the right, the blue points bisect the sides of the triangle. Describe how you would determine whether the lengths of the blue segments are equal.

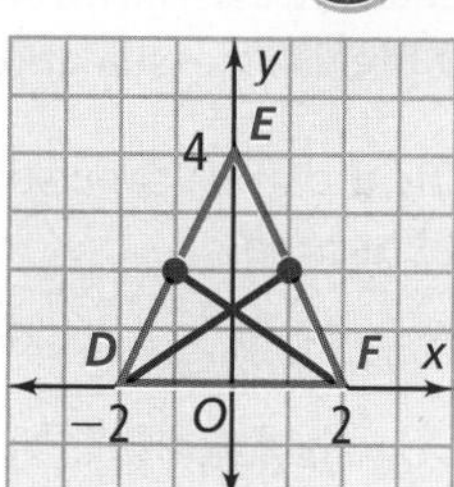


**10. Error Analysis** A student says that the quadrilateral with vertices $D(1, 2)$, $E(2, 0)$, $F(5, 4)$, and $G(6, 2)$ is a square because it has four right angles. What is the student's error?

## More Practice and Problem-Solving Exercises

### B Apply

**Graph and label each triangle with the given vertices. Determine whether each triangle is *scalene, isosceles,* or *equilateral.* Then tell whether each triangle is a right triangle.**

**11.** $T(1, 1)$, $R(3, 8)$, $I(6, 4)$

**12.** $J(-5, 0)$, $K(5, 8)$, $L(4, -1)$

**13.** $A(3, 2)$, $B(-10, 4)$, $C(-5, -8)$

**14.** $H(1, -2)$, $B(-1, 4)$, $F(5, 6)$

**Graph and label each quadrilateral with the given vertices. Then determine the most precise name for each quadrilateral.**

**15.** $P(-5, 0)$, $Q(-3, 2)$, $R(3, 2)$, $S(5, 0)$

**16.** $S(0, 0)$, $T(4, 0)$, $U(3, 2)$, $V(-1, 2)$

**17.** $F(0, 0)$, $G(5, 5)$, $H(8, 4)$, $I(7, 1)$

**18.** $M(-14, 4)$, $N(1, 6)$, $P(3, -9)$, $Q(-12, -11)$

**19.** $A(3, 5)$, $B(7, 6)$, $C(6, 2)$, $D(2, 1)$

**20.** $N(-6, 4)$, $P(-3, 1)$, $Q(0, 2)$, $R(-3, 5)$

**21.** $J(2, 1)$, $K(5, 4)$, $L(8, 1)$, $M(2, -3)$

**22.** $H(-2, -3)$, $I(4, 0)$, $J(3, 2)$, $K(-3, -1)$

**23.** $W(-1, 1)$, $X(0, 2)$, $Y(1, 1)$, $Z(0, -2)$

**24.** $D(-3, 1)$, $E(-7, -3)$, $F(6, -3)$, $G(2, 1)$

**25. Think About a Plan** Do the triangles at the right have the same side lengths? How do you know?
- Which formula should you use?
- What are the corresponding sides?

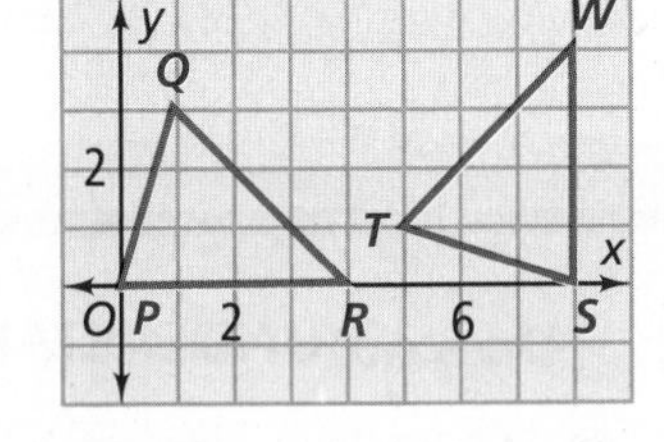


**26. Reasoning** A quadrilateral has opposite sides with equal slopes and consecutive sides with slopes that are negative reciprocals. What is the most precise classification of the quadrilateral? Explain.

**Determine the most precise name for the quadrilateral with the given vertices. Then find its area.**

**27.** $A(0, 2)$, $B(4, 2)$, $C(-3, -4)$, $D(-7, -4)$

**28.** $J(1, -3)$, $K(3, 1)$, $L(7, -1)$, $M(5, -5)$

**29. Interior Design** Interior designers often use grids to plan the placement of furniture in a room. The design at the right shows four chairs around a coffee table. The designer plans for cutouts of chairs on lattice points, where the grid lines intersect. She wants the chairs oriented at the vertices of a parallelogram. Does she need to fix her plan? If so, describe the change(s) she should make.

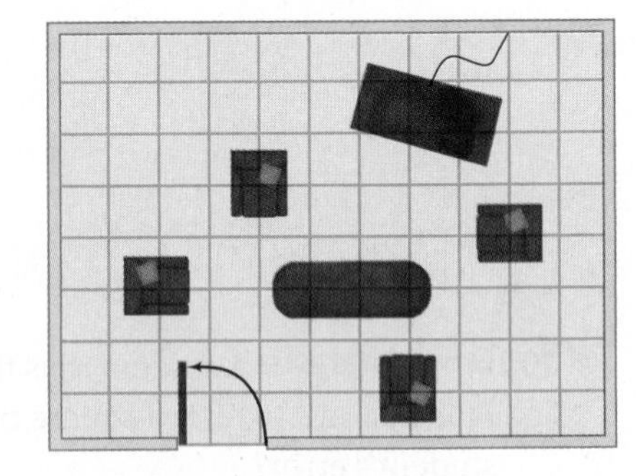

**30.** Use the diagram at the right.

**a.** What is the most precise classification of *ABCD*?

**b.** What is the most precise classification of *EFGH*?

**c.** Do *ABCD* and *EFGH* have the same side lengths and angle measures? Explain.

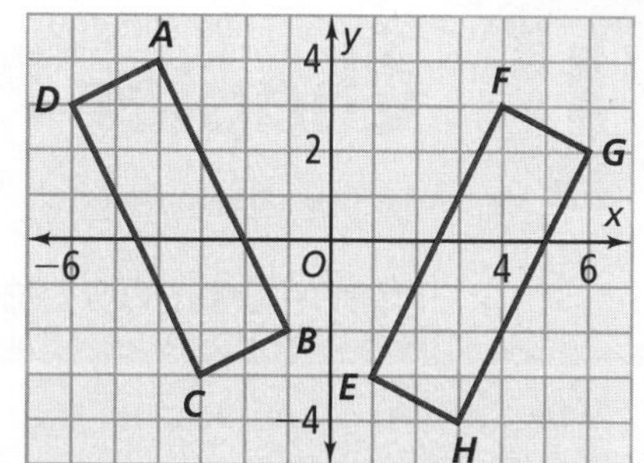


## Challenge

**31. Coordinate Geometry** The diagonals of quadrilateral *EFGH* intersect at *D*(−1, 4). *EFGH* has vertices at *E*(2, 7) and *F*(−3, 5). What must be the coordinates of *G* and *H* to ensure that *EFGH* is a parallelogram?

**The endpoints of $\overline{AB}$ are *A*(−3, 5) and *B*(9, 15). Find the coordinates of the points that divide $\overline{AB}$ into the given number of congruent segments.**

**32.** 4 **33.** 6 **34.** 10 **35.** 50 **36.** *n*

# 11 Chapter Review

## 11-1 Perimeter and Area in the Coordinate Plane

### Quick Review

The perimeter $P$ of a polygon is the sum of the lengths of its sides. Circles have a circumference $C$. The area $A$ of a polygon or a circle is the number of square units it encloses.

Square: $P = 4s;\ A = s^2$

Rectangle: $P = 2b + 2h;\ A = bh$

Triangle: $P = a + b + c;\ A = \frac{1}{2}bh$

Circle: $C = \pi d$ or $C = 2\pi r;\ A = \pi r^2$

### Example

**Find the perimeter and area of a rectangle with $b = 12$ m and $h = 8$ m.**

$P = 2b + 2h$ $\quad\quad$ $A = bh$

$= 2(12) + 2(8)$ $\quad\quad$ $= 12 \cdot 8$

$= 40$ $\quad\quad$ $= 96$

The perimeter is 40 m and the area is 96 m².

### Exercises

**Find the perimeter and area of each figure.**

1.

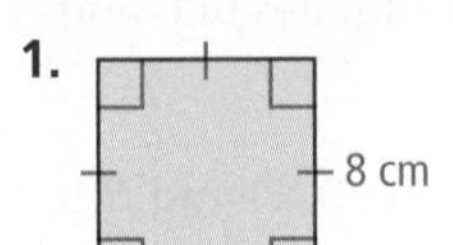


2.

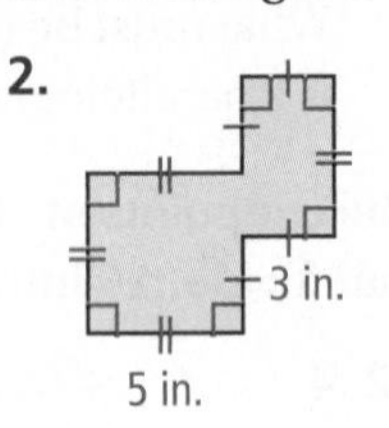


**Find the circumference and the area for each circle in terms of $\pi$.**

3. $r = 3$ in.

4. $d = 15$ m

## 11-2 Areas of Parallelograms and Triangles

### Quick Review

You can find the area of a rectangle, a parallelogram, or a triangle if you know the **base** $b$ and the **height** $h$.

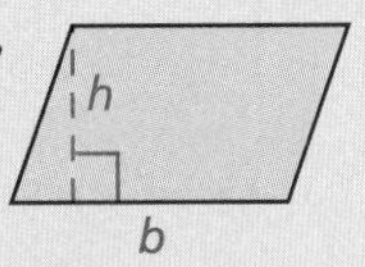


The area of a rectangle or parallelogram is $A = bh$.

The area of a triangle is $A = \frac{1}{2}bh$.

### Example

**What is area of the parallelogram?**

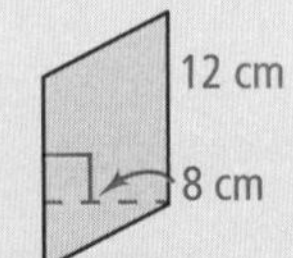


$A = bh$ $\quad$ Use the area formula.

$= (12)(8) = 96$ $\quad$ Substitute and simplify.

The area of the parallelogram is 96 cm².

### Exercises

**Find the area of each figure.**

5.

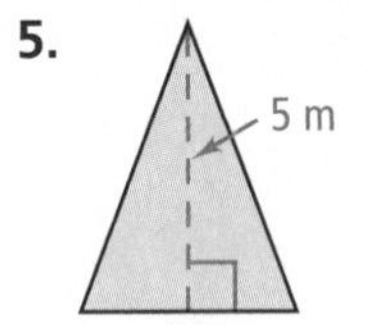


6.

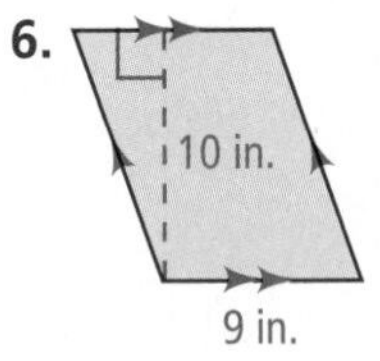


7.

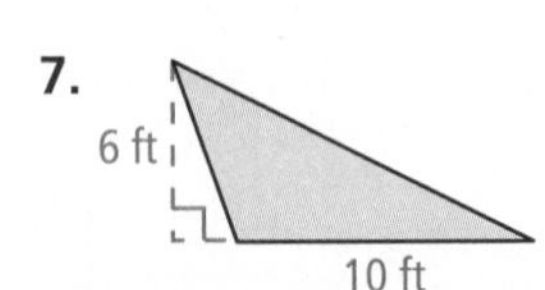


8.

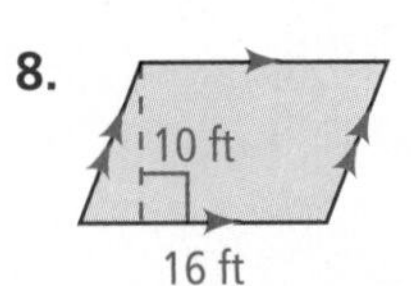


9. A right triangle has legs measuring 5 ft and 12 ft, and hypotenuse measuring 13 ft. What is its area?

# 11-3 Areas of Trapezoids, Rhombuses, and Kites

## Quick Review

The **height of a trapezoid** $h$ is the perpendicular distance between the bases, $b_1$ and $b_2$.

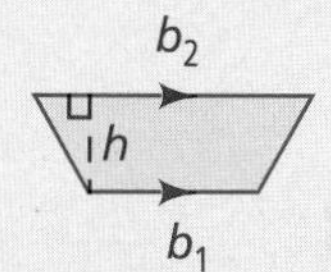


The area of a trapezoid is $A = \frac{1}{2}h(b_1 + b_2)$.

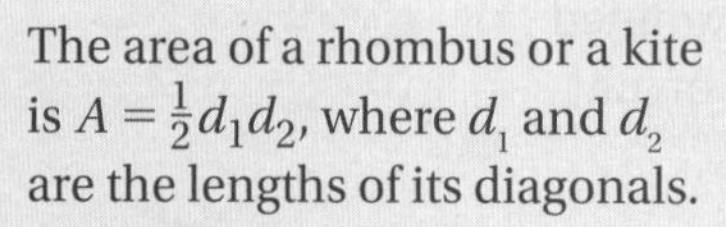

The area of a rhombus or a kite is $A = \frac{1}{2}d_1d_2$, where $d_1$ and $d_2$ are the lengths of its diagonals.

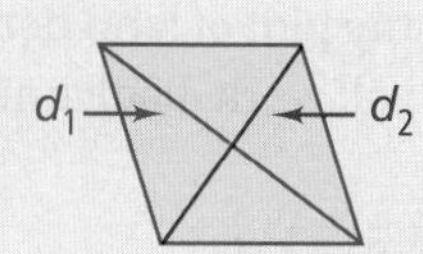


## Example

**What is the area of the trapezoid?**

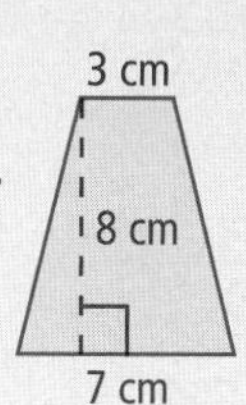


$A = \frac{1}{2}h(b_1 + b_2)$ Use the area formula.

$= \frac{1}{2}(8)(7 + 3)$ Substitute.

$= 40$ Simplify.

The area of the trapezoid is 40 $cm^2$.

## Exercises

**Find the area of each figure. If necessary, leave your answer in simplest radical form.**

**10.** **11.**

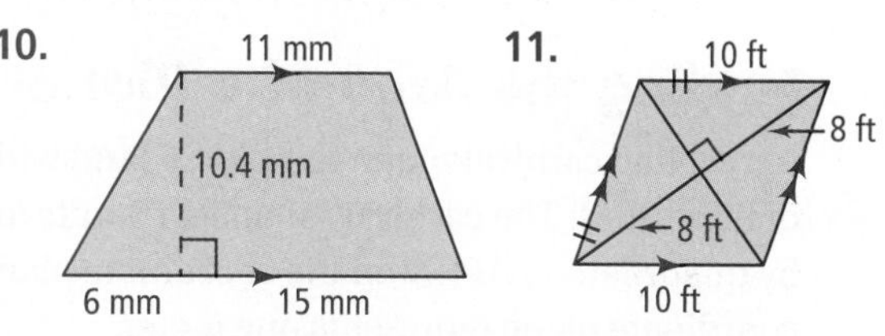


**12.** **13.**

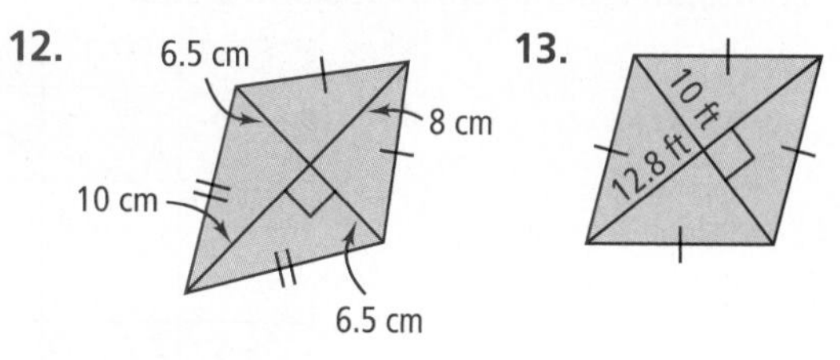


**14.** A trapezoid has a height of 6 m. The length of one base is three times the length of the other base. The sum of the base lengths is 18 m. What is the area of the trapezoid?

# 11-4 Polygons in the Coordinate Plane

## Quick Review

To determine whether sides or diagonals are congruent, use the Distance Formula. To determine the coordinates of the midpoint of a side, or whether the diagonals bisect each other, use the Midpoint Formula. To determine whether opposite sides are parallel, or whether diagonals or sides are perpendicular, use the Slope Formula.

## Example

**$\triangle XYZ$ has vertices $X(1, 0)$, $Y(-2, -4)$, and $Z(4, -4)$. Is $\triangle XYZ$ *scalene, isosceles,* or *equilateral*?**

**To find the lengths of the legs, use the Distance Formula.**

$XY = \sqrt{(-2 - 1)^2 + (-4 - 0)^2} = \sqrt{9 + 16} = 5$

$YZ = \sqrt{(4 - (-2))^2 + (-4 - (-4))^2} = \sqrt{36 + 0} = 6$

$XZ = \sqrt{(4 - 1)^2 + (-4 - 0)^2} = \sqrt{9 + 16} = 5$

Two side lengths are equal, so $\triangle XYZ$ is isosceles.

## Exercises

**Determine whether $\triangle ABC$ is *scalene, isosceles,* or *equilateral*.**

**15.**

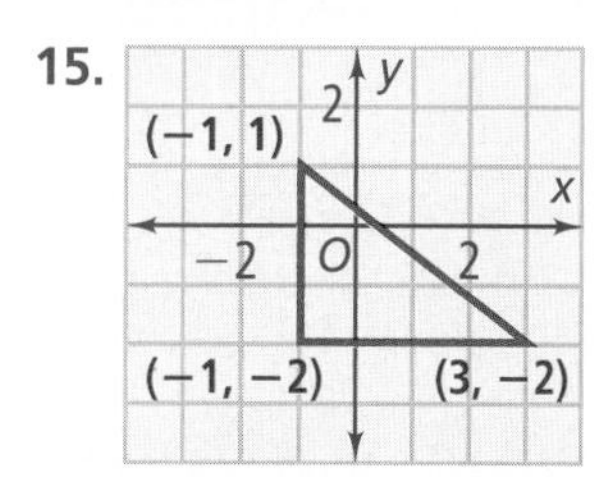


**16.**

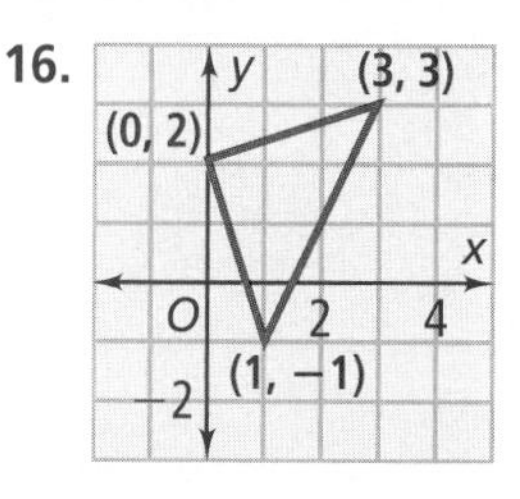


**What is the most precise classification of the quadrilateral with the given vertices?**

**17.** $G(2, 5)$, $R(5, 8)$, $A(-2, 12)$, $D(-5, 9)$

**18.** $F(-13, 7)$, $I(1, 12)$, $N(15, 7)$, $E(1, -5)$

**19.** $Q(4, 5)$, $U(12, 14)$, $A(20, 5)$, $D(12, -4)$

**20.** $W(-11, 4)$, $H(-9, 10)$, $A(2, 10)$, $T(4, 4)$

# Pull It All Together

## Finding the Area of a Plot of Land

A traveling carnival requires a plot of land with an area of at least 45 $m^2$ to set up one of their rides. The carnival's manager wants to know if the plot of land determined by quadrilateral *ABCD* on the coordinate plane below will work. Each unit of the coordinate plane represents one meter.

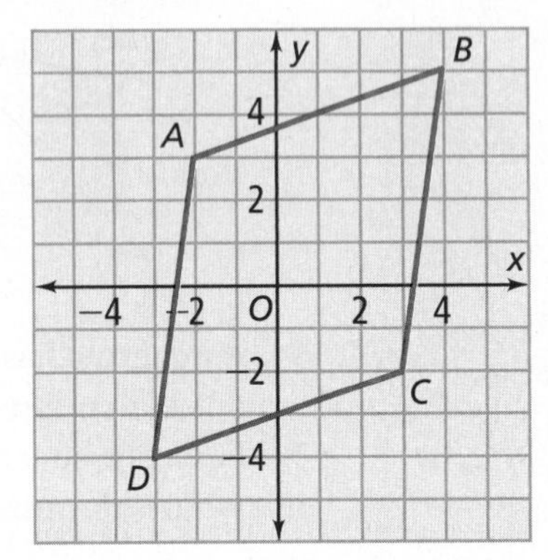


### Task Description

**Decide whether the plot of land determined by quadrilateral *ABCD* meets the carnival's requirements.**

- How can you determine the type of quadrilateral formed by vertices *A*, *B*, *C*, and *D*?
- What lengths do you need to know in order to calculate the area of the quadrilateral?

CHAPTER 12

# Get Ready!

## Solving Equations

**Algebra** **Solve for $x$.**

1. $\frac{1}{2}(x + 42) = 62$
2. $(5 + 3)8 = (4 + x)6$
3. $(9 + x)2 = (12 + 4)3$

## Isosceles and Equilateral Triangles

**Algebra** **Find the value of $x$.**

4. 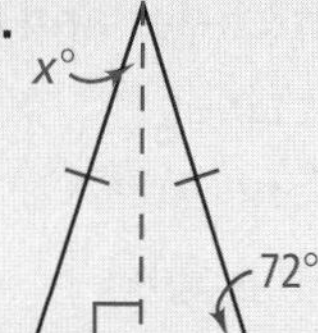


5. 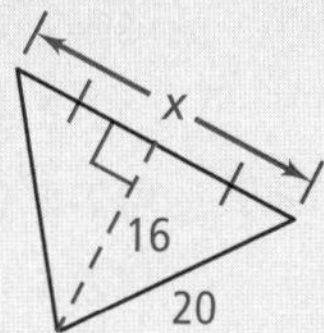


6. 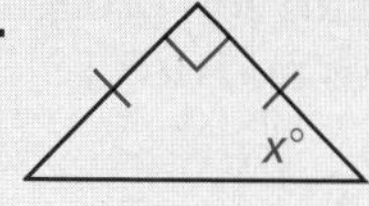


7. 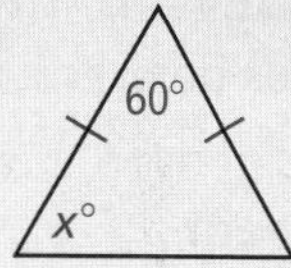


## The Pythagorean Theorem

**Algebra** **Find the value of $x$. Leave your answer in simplest radical form.**

8. 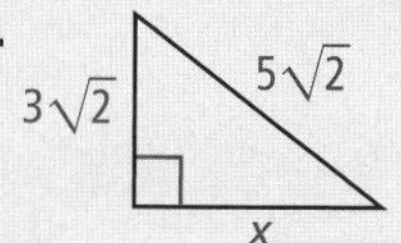


9. 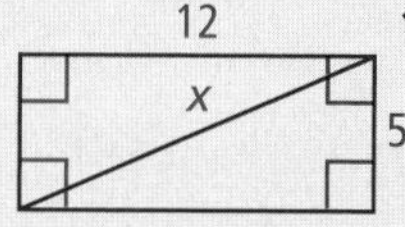


10. 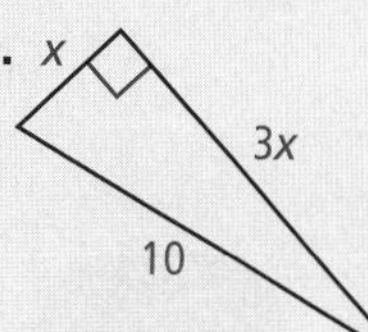


11. 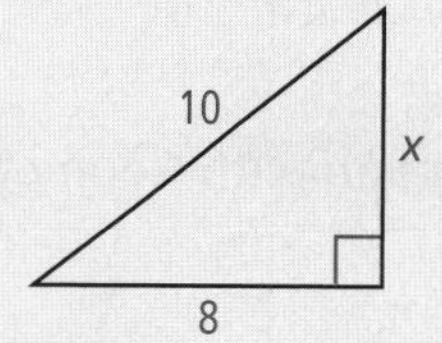

## Looking Ahead Vocabulary

12. When you are in a conversation and you go off on a *tangent,* you are leading the conversation away from the main topic. What do you think a line that is *tangent* to a circle might look like?
13. You learned how to *inscribe* a triangle in a circle in an earlier course. What do you think an *inscribed* angle is?
14. A defensive player *intercepts* a pass when he catches the football before it reaches the intended receiver. On a circle, what might an *intercepted* arc of an angle be?

# Circles

## Big Ideas

**1 Reasoning and Proof**
**Essential Question:** How can you prove relationships between angles and arcs in a circle?

**2 Measurement**
**Essential Question:** When lines intersect a circle or within a circle, how do you find the measures of resulting angles, arcs, and segments?

## Domains

- Circles
- Modeling with Geometry

## Chapter Preview

12-1 Circles and Arcs
12-2 Areas of Circles and Sectors
12-3 Tangent Lines
12-4 Chords and Arcs
12-5 Inscribed Angles
12-6 Angle Measures and Segment Lengths

**Interactive Digital Path**

Log in to **pearsonsuccessnet.com** and click on Interactive Digital Path to access the Solve Its and animated Problems.

## Vocabulary

**English/Spanish Vocabulary Audio Online:**

| English | Spanish |
|---|---|
| central angle, *p. 855* | ángulo central |
| chord, *p. 886* | cuerda |
| concentric circles, *p. 858* | círculos concéntricos |
| diameter, *p. 855* | diámetro |
| inscribed angle, *p. 897* | ángulo inscrito |
| intercepted arc, *p. 897* | arco interceptor |
| major arc, *p. 855* | arco mayor |
| minor arc, *p. 855* | arco menor |
| secant, *p. 907* | secante |
| sector of a circle, *p. 867* | sector de un círculo |
| segment of a circle, *p. 868* | segmento de un círculo |
| tangent to a circle, *p. 876* | tagente de un círculo |

# 12-1 Circles and Arcs

**G.C.1** Prove . . . all circles are similar. Also **G.C.2, G.C.5**

**Objectives** To find the measures of central angles and arcs
To find the circumference and arc length

**Solve It!** Write your solution to the Solve It in the space below.

In a plane, a **circle** is the set of all points equidistant from a given point called the **center**. You name a circle by its center. Circle $P$ ($\odot P$) is shown below.

A **diameter** is a segment that contains the center of a circle and has both endpoints on the circle. A **radius** is a segment that has one endpoint at the center and the other endpoint on the circle. **Congruent circles** have congruent radii. A **central angle** is an angle whose vertex is the center of the circle.

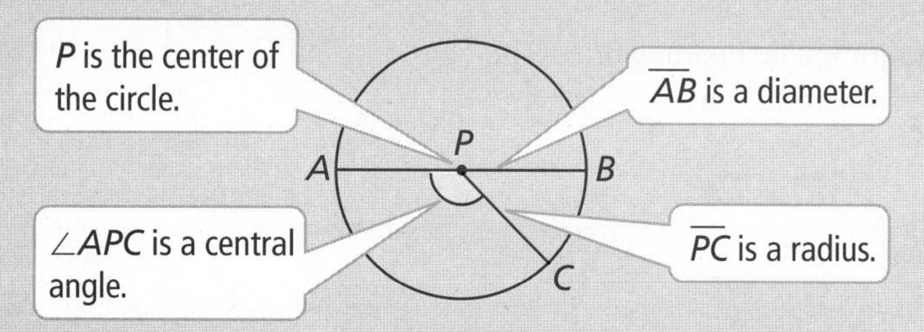


**Essential Understanding** You can find the length of part of a circle's circumference by relating it to an angle in the circle.

An arc is a part of a circle. One type of arc, a **semicircle**, is half of a circle. A **minor arc** is smaller than a semicircle. A **major arc** is larger than a semicircle. You name a minor arc by its endpoints and a major arc or a semicircle by its endpoints and another point on the arc.

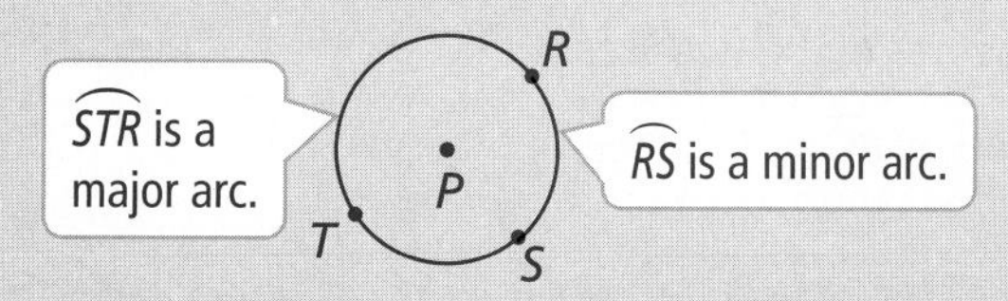

## Problem 1 Naming Arcs

**Think**

**How can you identify the minor arcs?**

**Got It?** **a.** What are the minor arcs of $\odot A$?

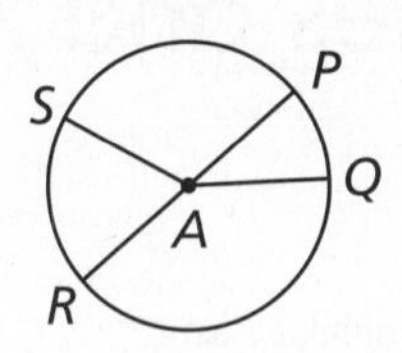


**b.** What are the semicircles of $\odot A$?

**c.** What are the major arcs of $\odot A$ that contain point $Q$?

**Practice** Name the following in $\odot O$.

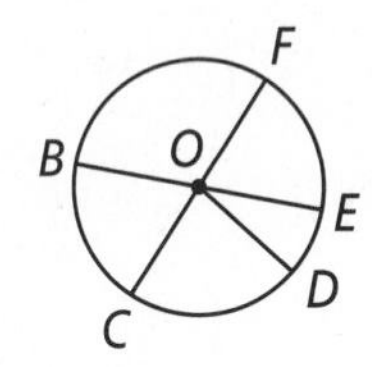


**1.** the major arcs

**2.** the semicircles

take note

## Key Concept Arc Measure

**Arc Measure**

The measure of a minor arc is equal to the measure of its corresponding central angle.

The measure of a major arc is the measure of the related minor arc subtracted from 360.

The measure of a semicircle is 180.

**Example**

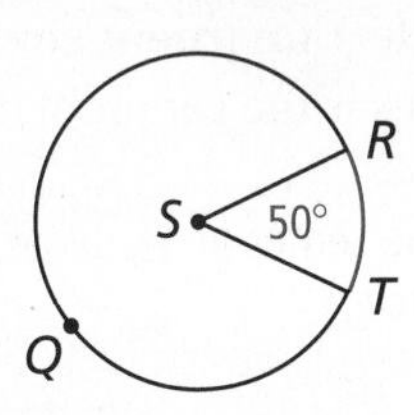


$m\widehat{RT} = m\angle RST = 50$

$m\widehat{TQR} = 360 - m\widehat{RT}$

$= 310$

**Adjacent arcs** are arcs of the same circle that have exactly one point in common. You can add the measures of adjacent arcs just as you can add the measures of adjacent angles.

take note

## Postulate 19 Arc Addition Postulate

The measure of the arc formed by two adjacent arcs is the sum of the measures of the two arcs.

$m\widehat{ABC} = m\widehat{AB} + m\widehat{BC}$

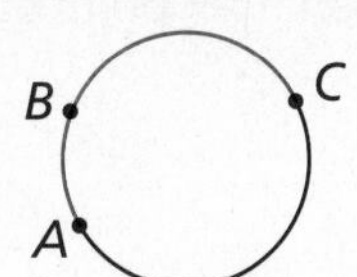

## Problem 2 Finding the Measures of Arcs

**Got It?** What is the measure of each arc in $\odot C$?

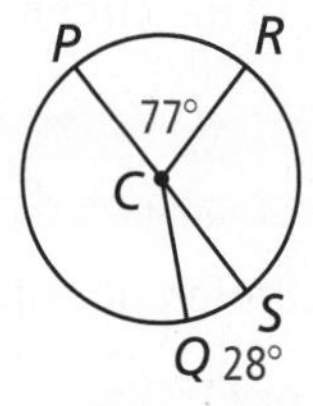


**a.** $m\overparen{PR}$

**b.** $m\overparen{RS}$

**c.** $m\overparen{PRQ}$

**d.** $m\overparen{PQR}$

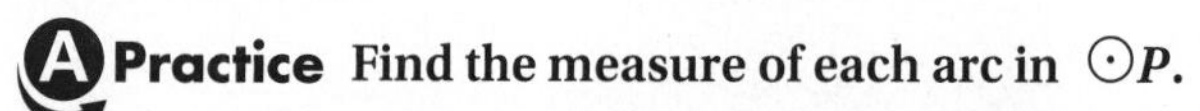

**Practice** Find the measure of each arc in $\odot P$.

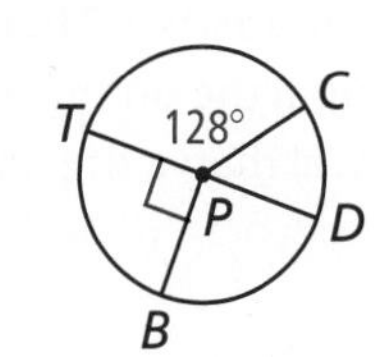


**3.** $\overparen{CBD}$

**4.** $\overparen{BCD}$

The **circumference** of a circle is the distance around the circle. The number **pi** ($\pi$) is the ratio of the circumference of a circle to its diameter.

take note

## Theorem 72 Circumference of a Circle

The circumference of a circle is $\pi$ times the diameter.

$C = \pi d$ or $C = 2\pi r$

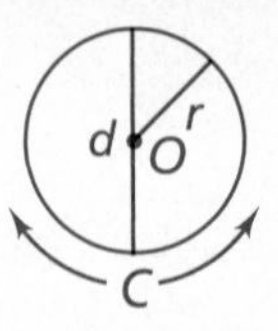


The number $\pi$ is irrational, so you cannot write it as a terminating or repeating decimal. To approximate $\pi$, you can use 3.14, $\frac{22}{7}$, or the $\pi$ key on your calculator.

Many properties of circles deal with ratios that stay the same no matter what size the circle is. This is because all circles are similar to each other. To see this, consider the circles at the right. There is a translation that maps circle $O$ so that it shares the same center with circle $P$.

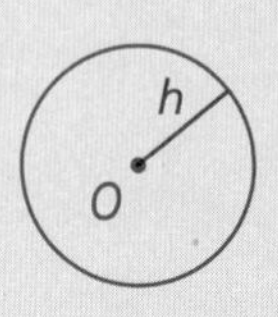


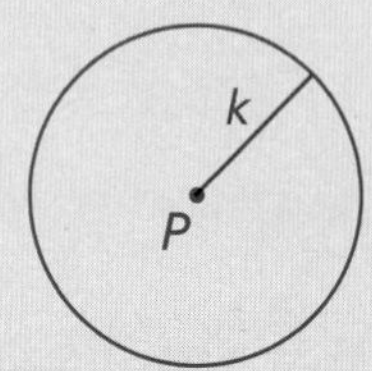


There also exists a dilation with scale factor $\frac{k}{h}$ that maps circle $O$ to circle $P$. A translation followed by a dilation is a similarity transformation. Because a similarity transformation maps circle $O$ to circle $P$, the two circles are similar.

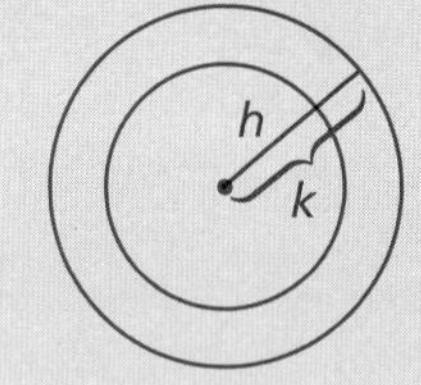


Concentric circles

Coplanar circles that have the same center are called **concentric circles**.

## Problem 3 Finding a Distance

**Got It?** **a.** A car has a circular turning radius of 16.1 ft. The distance between the two front tires is 4.7 ft. How much farther does a tire on the outside of the turn travel than a tire on the inside?

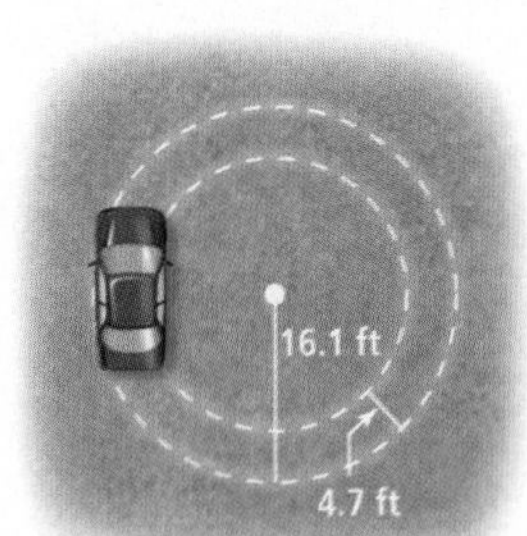


**Plan**

**What do you need to find?**

**b. Reasoning** Suppose the radius of $\odot A$ is equal to the diameter of $\odot B$. What is the ratio of the circumference of $\odot A$ to the circumference of $\odot B$? Explain.

5. Find the circumference of this circle. Leave your answer in terms of $\pi$.

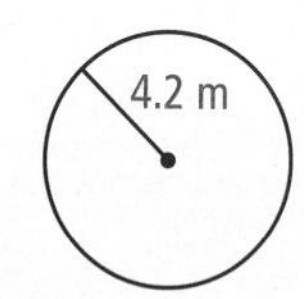


6. The wheel of a compact car has a 25-in. diameter. The wheel of a pickup truck has a 31-in. diameter. To the nearest inch, how much farther does the pickup truck wheel travel in one revolution than the compact car wheel?

The measure of an arc is in degrees, while the **arc length** is a fraction of the circumference.

Consider the arcs shown at the right. Since the circles are concentric, there is a dilation that maps $C_1$ to $C_2$. The same dilation maps the slice of the small circle to the slice of the large circle. Since corresponding lengths of similar figures are proportional,

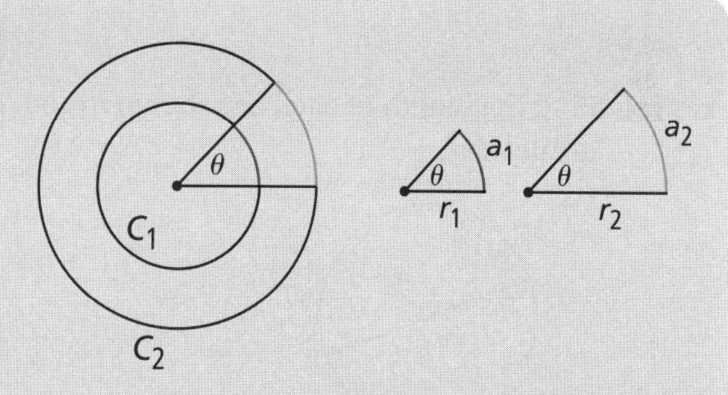


$$\frac{r_1}{r_2} = \frac{a_1}{a_2}$$

$$r_1 a_2 = r_2 a_1$$

$$a_1 = r_1 \cdot \frac{a_2}{r_2}$$

This means that the arc length $a_1$ is equal to the radius $r_1$ times some number. So for a given central angle, the length of the arc it intercepts depends only on the radius.

An arc of 60° represents $\frac{60}{360}$, or $\frac{1}{6}$, of the circle. So its arc length is $\frac{1}{6}$ of the circumference. This observation suggests the following theorem.

take note

### Theorem 73 Arc Length

The length of an arc of a circle is the product of the ratio $\frac{\text{measure of the arc}}{360}$ and the circumference of the circle.

$$\text{length of } \widehat{AB} = \frac{m\,\widehat{AB}}{360} \cdot 2\pi r$$
$$= \frac{m\,\widehat{AB}}{360} \cdot \pi d$$

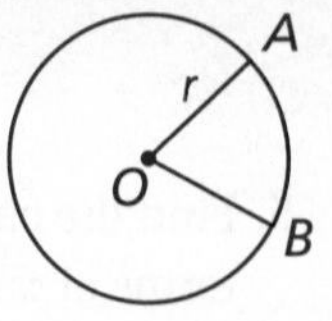

## Problem 4 Finding Arc Length

**Got It?** What is the length of a semicircle with radius 1.3 m? Leave your answer in terms of $\pi$.

**A Practice** **Find the length of each arc shown in red. Leave your answer in terms of $\pi$.**

**7.**

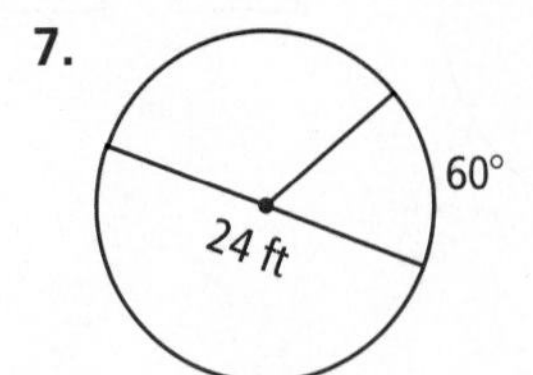


**8.**

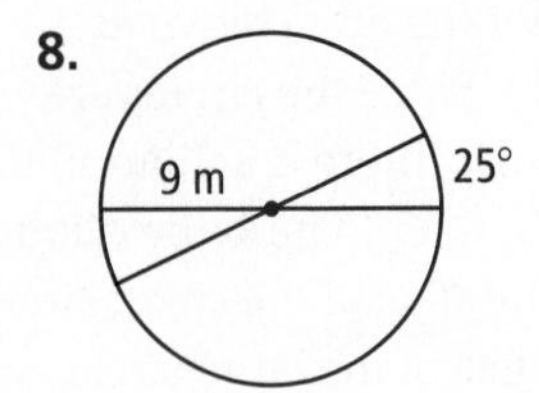

## Lesson Check

### Do you know HOW?

**Use $\odot P$ at the right to answer each question. For Exercises 13 and 14, leave your answers in terms of $\pi$.**

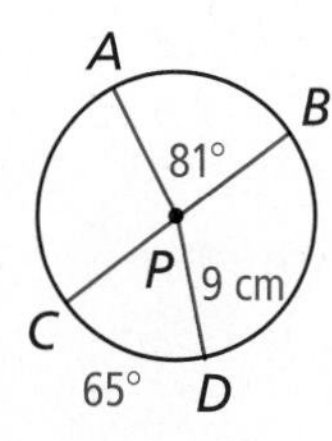


**9.** What is the name of a minor arc?

**10.** What is the name of a major arc?

**11.** What is the name of a semicircle?

**12.** What is $m\widehat{AB}$?

**13.** What is the circumference of $\odot P$?

**14.** What is the length of $\widehat{BD}$?

## Do you UNDERSTAND?

**15. Vocabulary** What is the difference between the measure of an arc and arc length? Explain.

**16. Error Analysis** Your class must find the length of $\overset{\frown}{AB}$. A classmate submits the following solution. What is the error?

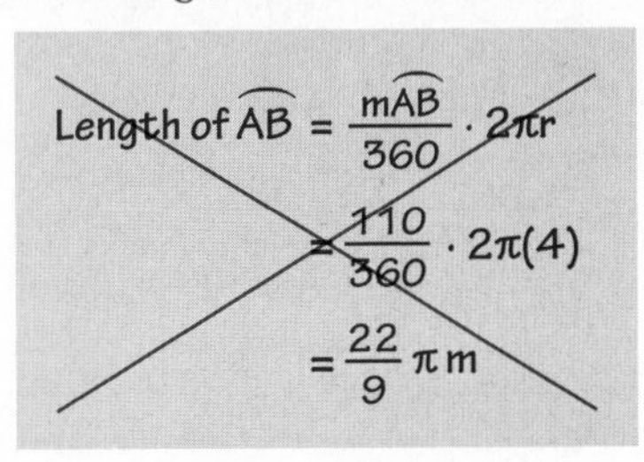


B
70°
A
C
O
4 m

## More Practice and Problem-Solving Exercises

### Apply

**17. Think About a Plan** Nina designed a semicircular arch made of wrought iron for the top of a mall entrance. The nine segments between the two concentric semicircles are each 3 ft long. What is the total length of wrought iron used to make this structure? Round your answer to the nearest foot.

- What do you know from the diagram?
- What formula should you use to find the amount of wrought iron used in the semicircular arches?

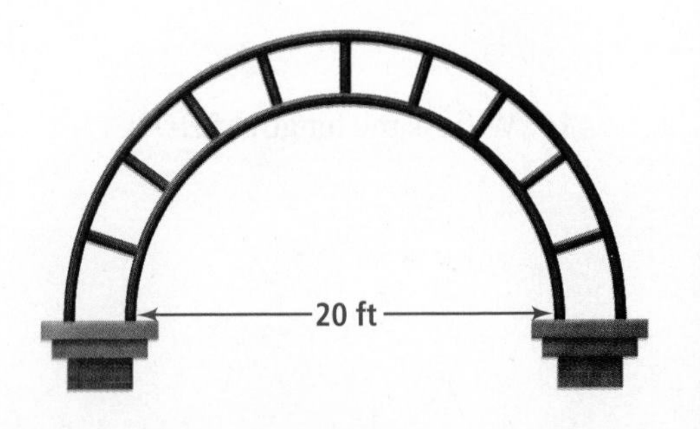

**Find each indicated measure for $\odot O$.**

**18.** $m\angle EOF$ **19.** $m\widehat{EJH}$ **20.** $m\widehat{FH}$

**21.** $m\angle FOG$ **22.** $m\widehat{JEG}$ **23.** $m\widehat{HFJ}$

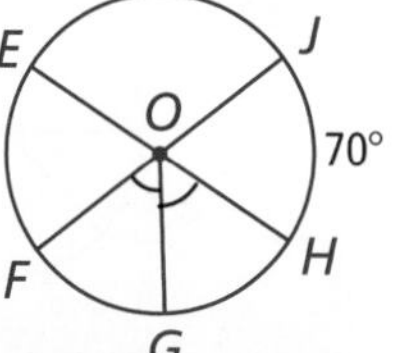


**24. Pets** A hamster wheel has a 7-in. diameter. How many feet will a hamster travel in 100 revolutions of the wheel?

STEM **25. Traffic** Five streets come together at a traffic circle, as shown at the right. The diameter of the circle traveled by a car is 200 ft. If traffic travels counterclockwise, what is the approximate distance from East St. to Neponset St.?

A 227 ft C 454 ft

B 244 ft D 488 ft

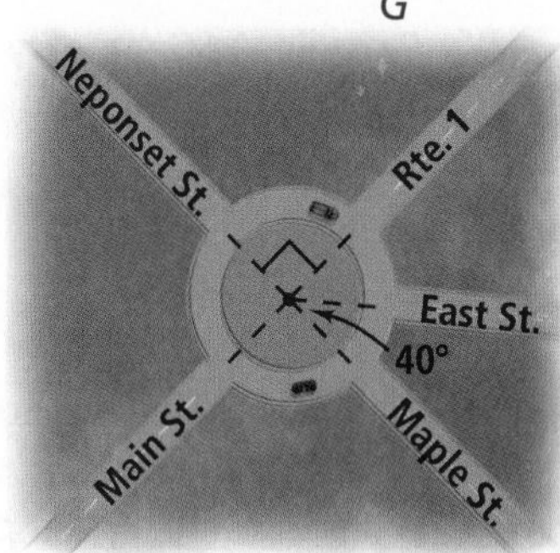


**26. Writing** Describe two ways to find the arc length of a major arc if you are given the measure of the corresponding minor arc and the radius of the circle.

**27. Time** Hands of a clock suggest an angle whose measure is continually changing. How many degrees does a minute hand move through during each time interval?

**a.** 1 min **b.** 5 min **c.** 20 min

**Algebra Find the value of each variable.**

**28.**

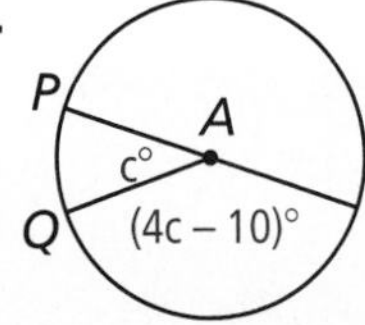


**29.**

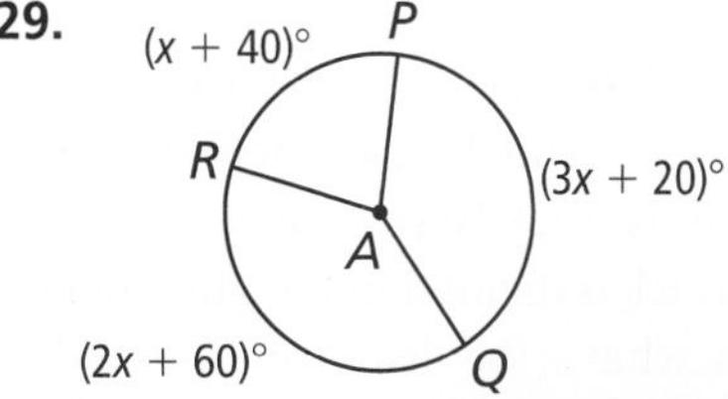


**30. Landscape Design** A landscape architect is constructing a curved path through a rectangular yard. The curved path consists of two 90° arcs. He plans to edge the two sides of the path with plastic edging. What is the total length of plastic edging he will need? Round your answer to the nearest meter.

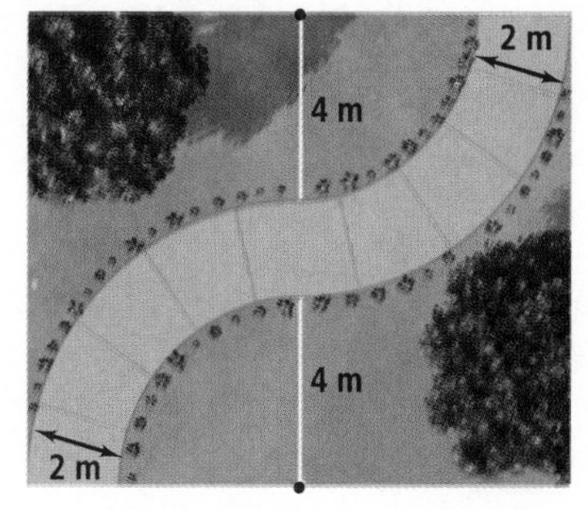


**31. Reasoning** Suppose the radius of a circle is doubled. How does this affect the circumference of the circle? Explain.

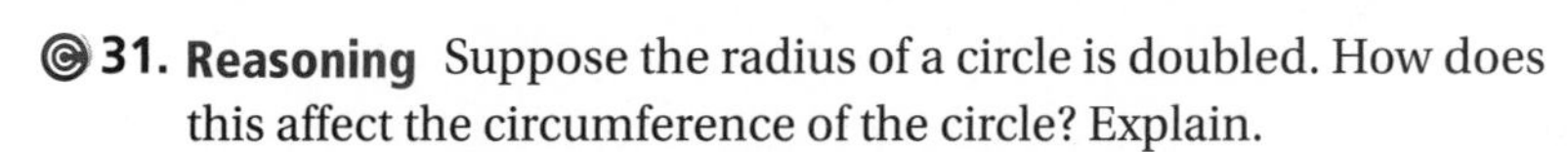

**32.** A 60° arc of $\odot A$ has the same length as a 45° arc of $\odot B$. What is the ratio of the radius of $\odot A$ to the radius of $\odot B$?

**Find the length of each arc shown in red. Leave your answer in terms of $\pi$.**

**33.**

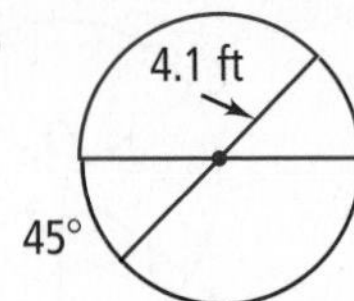


**34.**

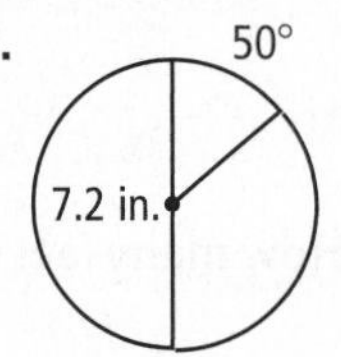


**35.**

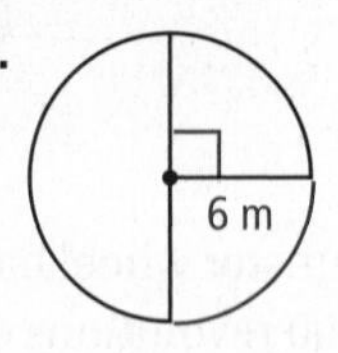


**36. Coordinate Geometry** Find the length of a semicircle with endpoints (1, 3) and (4, 7). Round your answer to the nearest tenth.

**37.** In $\odot O$, the length of $\widehat{AB}$ is $6\pi$ cm and $m\widehat{AB}$ is 120. What is the diameter of $\odot O$?

## Challenge

**38.** The diagram below shows two concentric circles. $\overline{AR} \cong \overline{RW}$. Show that the length of $\widehat{ST}$ is equal to the length of $\widehat{QR}$.

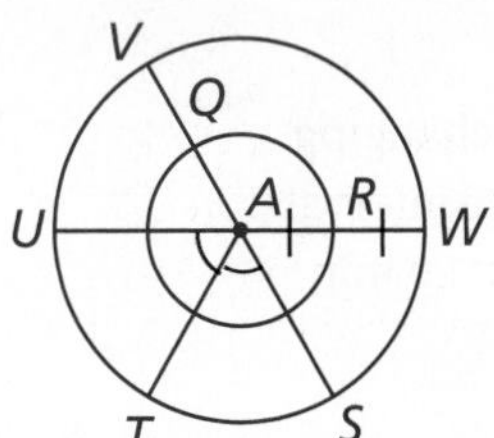


**39. Given:** $\odot P$ with $\overline{AB} \parallel \overline{PC}$

**Proof** **Prove:** $m\widehat{BC} = m\widehat{CD}$

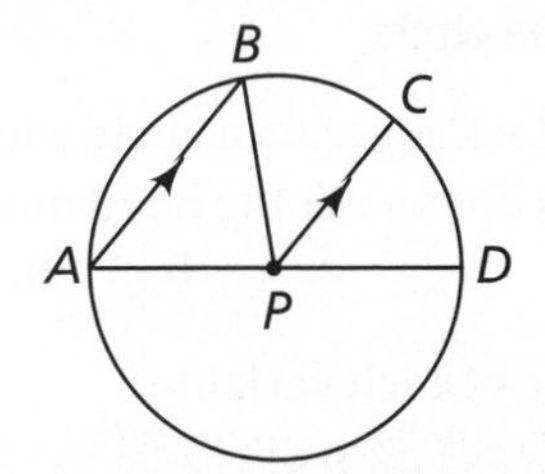


**40. Sports** An athletic field is a 100 yd-by-40 yd rectangle, with a semicircle at each of the short sides. A running track 10 yd wide surrounds the field. If the track is divided into eight lanes of equal width, what is the distance around the track along the inside edge of each lane?

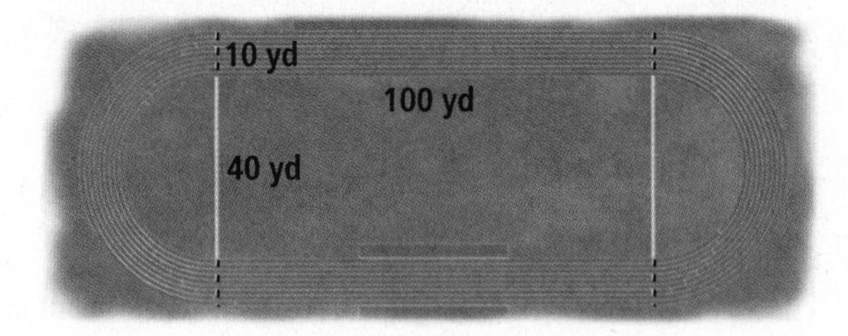

# Areas of Circles and Sectors

**G.C.5** Derive using similarity the fact that the length of the arc intercepted by an angle is proportional to the radius . . . derive the formula for the area of a sector.

**Objective** To find the areas of circles, sectors, and segments of circles

**Solve It!** Write your solution to the Solve It in the space below.

In the Solve It, you explored the area of a circle.

**Essential Understanding** You can find the area of a circle when you know its radius. You can use the area of a circle to find the area of part of a circle formed by two radii and the arc the radii form when they intersect with the circle.

take note

## Theorem 74 Area of a Circle

The area of a circle is the product of $\pi$ and the square of the radius.

$A = \pi r^2$

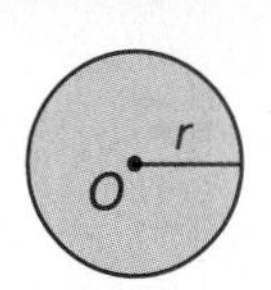

## Problem 1 Finding the Area of a Circle

**Think**

**What do you need in order to use the area formula?**

**Got It?** a. What is the area of a circular wrestling region with a 42-ft diameter?

b. **Reasoning** If the radius of a circle is halved, how does its area change? Explain.

**Practice** Find the area of the circle. Leave your answer in terms of $\pi$.

1.

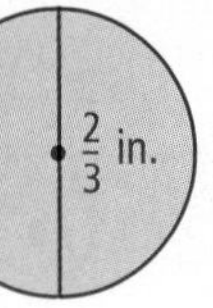


STEM 2. **Agriculture** Some farmers use a circular irrigation method. An irrigation arm acts as the radius of an irrigation circle. How much land is covered with an irrigation arm of 300 ft?

A **sector of a circle** is a region bounded by an arc of the circle and the two radii to the arc's endpoints. You name a sector using one arc endpoint, the center of the circle, and the other arc endpoint.

The area of a sector is a fractional part of the area of a circle. The area of a sector formed by a 60° arc is $\frac{60}{360}$, or $\frac{1}{6}$, of the area of the circle.

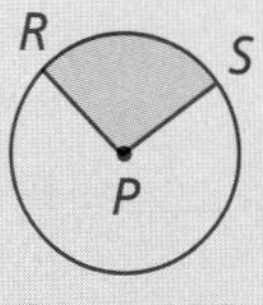

Sector *RPS*

## Theorem 75 Area of a Sector of a Circle

The area of a sector of a circle is the product of the ratio $\frac{\text{measure of the arc}}{360}$ and the area of the circle.

$$\text{Area of sector } AOB = \frac{m\overset{\frown}{AB}}{360} \cdot \pi r^2$$

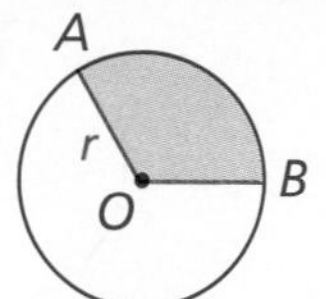


## Problem 2 Finding the Area of a Sector of a Circle

**Got It?** A circle has a radius of 4 in. What is the area of a sector bounded by a 45° minor arc? Leave your answer in terms of $\pi$.

**Think**

**What fraction of a circle's area is the area of a sector formed by a 45° arc?**

**3.** Find the area of each shaded sector of the circle. Leave your answer in terms of $\pi$.

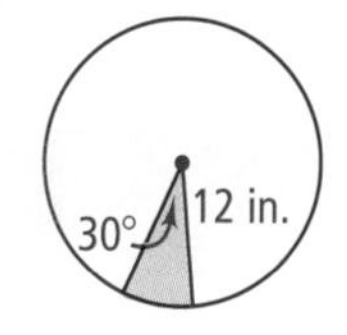


**4.** Find the area of sector *TOP* in $\odot O$ using the given information. Leave your answer in terms of $\pi$.

$d = 16$ in., $m\overset{\frown}{PT} = 135$

A part of a circle bounded by an arc and the segment joining its endpoints is a **segment of a circle**.

To find the area of a segment for a minor arc, draw radii to form a sector. The area of the segment equals the area of the sector minus the area of the triangle formed.

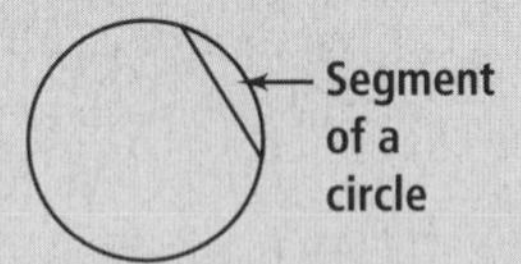


take note

## Key Concept Area of a Segment

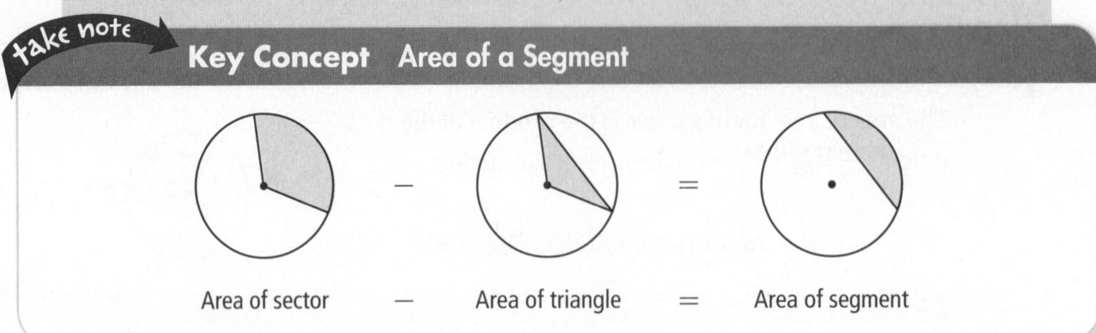

## Problem 3 Finding the Area of a Segment of a Circle

**Got It?** What is the area of the shaded segment shown at the right? Round your answer to the nearest tenth.

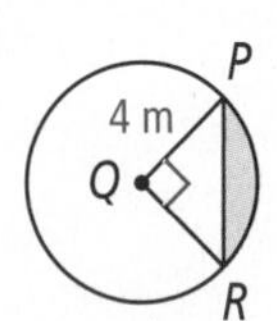


**Practice** **Find the area of each shaded segment. Round your answer to the nearest tenth.**

**5.** 120° 6 cm

**6.** 8 ft

## Lesson Check

### Do you know HOW?

**7.** What is the area of a circle with diameter 16 in.? Leave your answer in terms of $\pi$.

**Find the area of the shaded region of the circle. Leave your answer in terms of $\pi$.**

**8.**

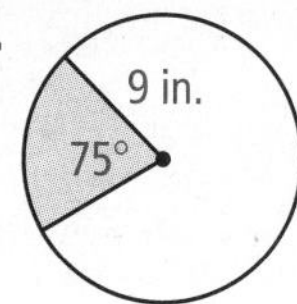


**9.**

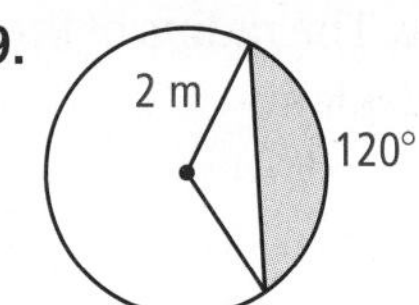


### Do you UNDERSTAND?

**10. Vocabulary** What is the difference between a sector of a circle and a segment of a circle?

**11. Reasoning** Suppose a sector of $\odot P$ has the same area as a sector of $\odot O$. Can you conclude that $\odot P$ and $\odot O$ have the same area? Explain.

**12. Error Analysis** Your class must find the area of a sector of a circle determined by a 150° arc. The radius of the circle is 6 cm. What is your classmate's error? Explain.

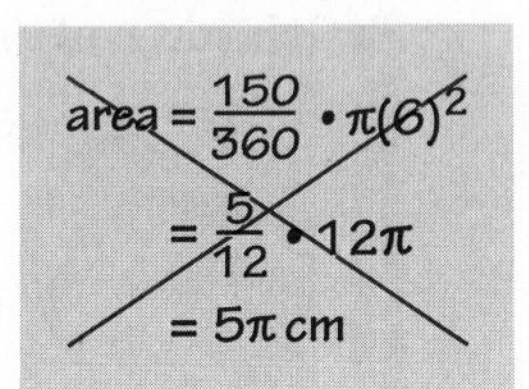


## More Practice and Problem-Solving Exercises

**Find the area of the shaded region. Leave your answer in terms of $\pi$ and in simplest radical form.**

**13.**

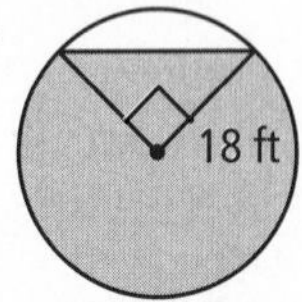


**14.**

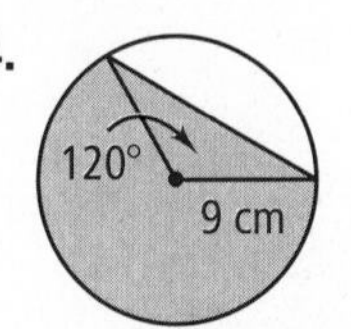


**15.**

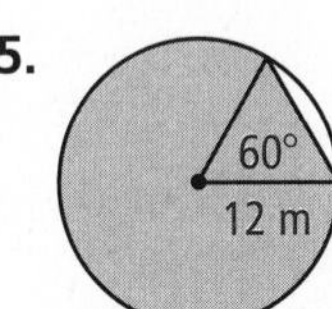


**16.**

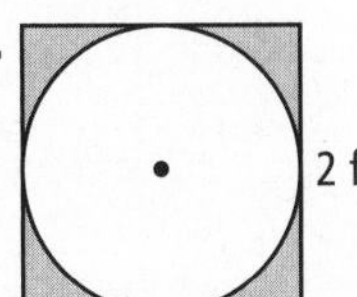


**17.**

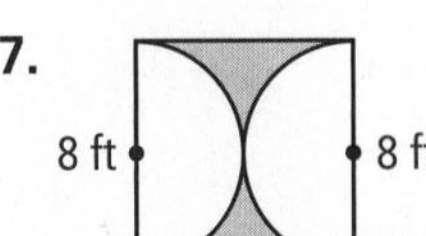


**18.** 14 in.

**19. Transportation** A town provides bus transportation to students living beyond 2 mi of the high school. What area of the town does *not* have the bus service? Round to the nearest tenth.

**20. Design** A homeowner wants to build a circular patio. If the diameter of the patio is 20 ft, what is its area to the nearest whole number?

**21. Think About a Plan** A circular mirror is 24 in. wide and has a 4-in. frame around it. What is the area of the frame?
- How can you *draw a diagram* to help solve the problem?
- What part of a circle is the width?
- Is there more than one area to consider?

STEM **22. Industrial Design** Refer to the diagram of the regular hexagonal nut. What is the area of the hexagonal face to the nearest millimeter?

4 mm
8 mm
2 mm

**23. Reasoning** $\overline{AB}$ and $\overline{CD}$ are diameters of $\odot O$. Is the area of sector $AOC$ equal to the area of sector $BOD$? Explain.

**24.** A circle with radius 12 mm is divided into 20 sectors of equal area. What is the area of one sector to the nearest tenth?

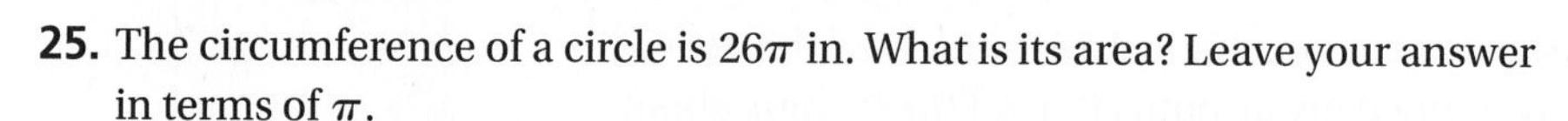

**25.** The circumference of a circle is $26\pi$ in. What is its area? Leave your answer in terms of $\pi$.

**26.** In a circle, a $90^\circ$ sector has area $36\pi$ in.$^2$. What is the radius of the circle?

**27. Open-Ended** Draw a circle and a sector so that the area of the sector is $16\pi$ cm$^2$. Give the radius of the circle and the measure of the sector's arc.

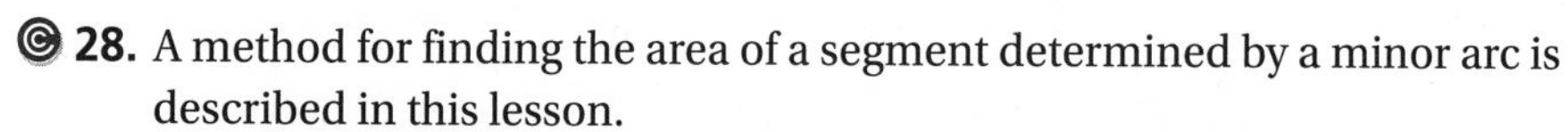

**28.** A method for finding the area of a segment determined by a minor arc is described in this lesson.

a. **Writing** Describe two ways to find the area of a segment determined by a major arc.

b. If $m\widehat{AB} = 90$ in a circle of radius 10 in., find the areas of the two segments determined by $\widehat{AB}$.

**Find the area of the shaded segment to the nearest tenth.**

**29.**

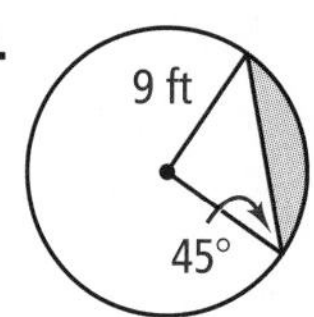


**30.**

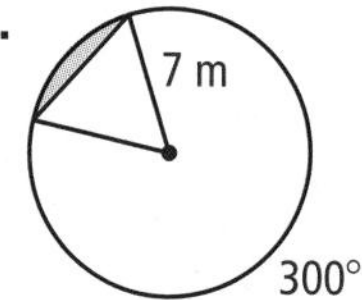


**31.**

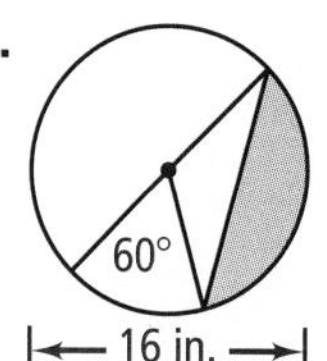


## Challenge

**Find the area of the shaded region. Leave your answer in terms of $\pi$.**

**32.**

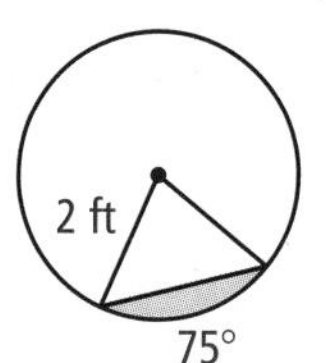


**33.**

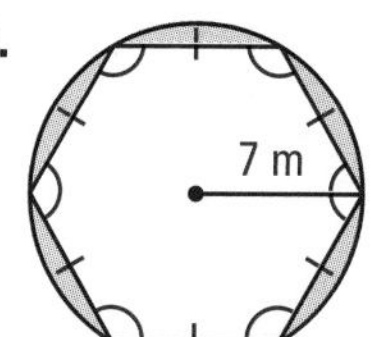


**34.**

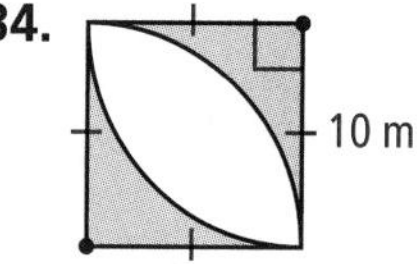

**35. Recreation** An 8 ft-by-10 ft floating dock is anchored in the middle of a pond. The bow of a canoe is tied to a corner of the dock with a 10-ft rope, as shown in the picture below.

**a.** Sketch a diagram of the region in which the bow of the canoe can travel.

**b.** What is the area of that region? Round your answer to the nearest square foot.

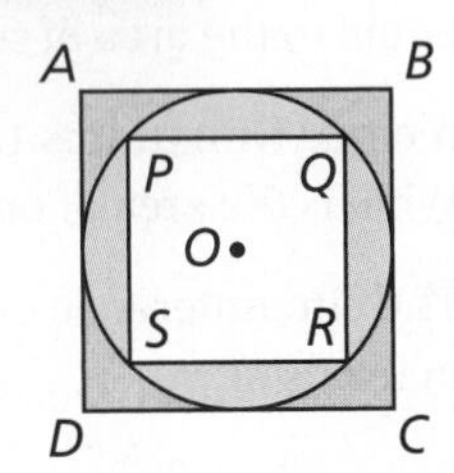


**36.** $\odot O$ at the right is inscribed in square $ABCD$ and circumscribed about square $PQRS$. Which is smaller, the blue region or the red region? Explain.

**37.** Circles $T$ and $U$ each have radius 10, and $TU = 10$. Find the area of the region that is contained inside both circles. (*Hint:* Think about where $T$ and $U$ must lie in a diagram of $\odot T$ and $\odot U$.)

ACTIVITY LAB

Use With Lesson 12-2

# Circles and Radians

G.C.5 Derive using similarity the fact that the length of the arc intercepted by an angle is proportional to the radius . . . derive the formula for the area of a sector.

Angles can be measured in degrees or *radians*. Radians are measures based on arc length.

## Activity 1

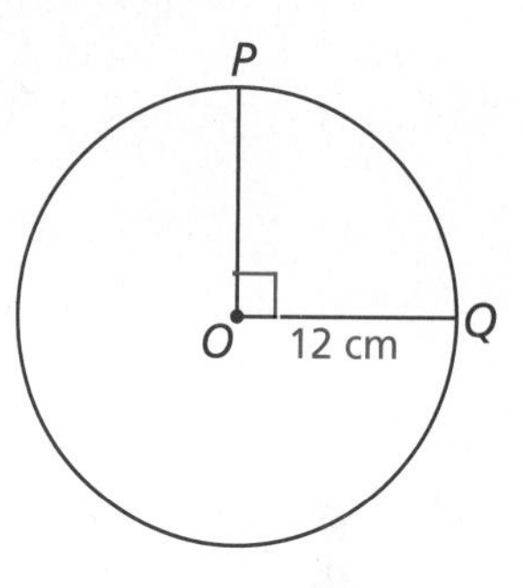


Circle $O$ has a radius of 12 cm and $m\angle POQ = 90$.

**1.** Find the length of $\widehat{PQ}$. Write your answer in terms of $\pi$.

**2.** Find the ratio of the arc length to the radius of circle $P$. This is the radian measure of $\angle POQ$.

The **radian measure** of a central angle of a circle is the ratio of the arc length of the intercepted arc to the radius of the circle.

$$\text{radian measure} = \frac{\text{arc length}}{\text{radius}}$$

One radian is equal to the measure of the central angle whose intercepted arc has a length equal to the radius of the circle.

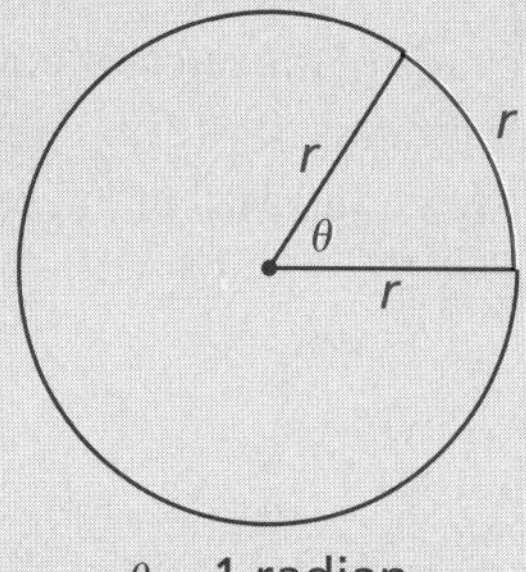


$\theta = 1$ radian

In Lesson 12-2, you learned how to find the area of the sector of a circle using proportions and the area of the circle. In Activity 2, you will derive a formula for the area of a sector when the central angle is given in radians.

## Activity 2

Consider the circle below with a central angle of $\theta$ radians and radius $r$.

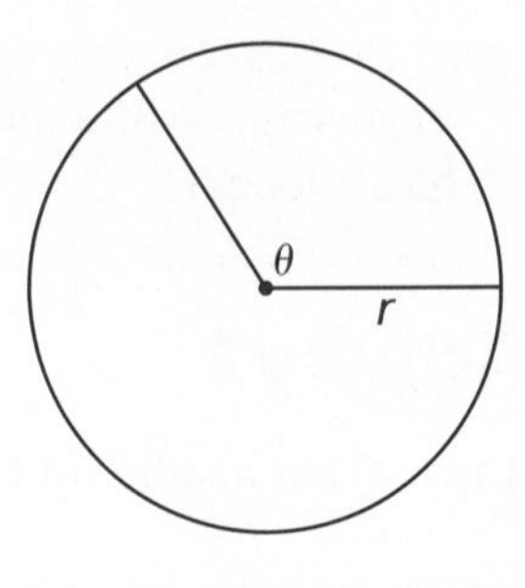


**3.** Write an expression for the area of the circle.

**4.** What is the angle measure, in radians, of a 360° central angle of the circle?

**5.** Write an expression for the ratio of $\theta$ to the radian measure of a 360° central angle.

**6.** The ratio of the area of the sector, $x$, to the area of the circle is equal to the ratio of the measure of the central angle $\theta$ to $2\pi$ radians. Write an equation that shows this proportional relationship. Then solve for $x$, the area of the sector.

## Exercises

**In Exercises 7–9, find the area of each sector with given radius and central angle. Round to the nearest tenth.**

**7.** $r = 9$ in., $m\angle\theta = 0.9$ radian

**8.** $r = 4.5$ ft, $m\angle\theta = 1.6$ radians

**9.** $r = 15$ mm, $m\angle\theta = 2$ radians

**10.** **a.** How many degrees are in $2\pi$ radians?

**b.** How many radians are in 180 degrees?

**c.** **Reasoning** How can you convert angle measures from degrees to radians? How can you convert angle measures from radians to degrees?

# 12-3 Tangent Lines

**G.C.2** Identify and describe relationships among inscribed angles, radii, and chords . . . the radius of a circle is perpendicular to the tangent where the radius intersects the circle. Also **G.C.4**

**Objective** To use properties of a tangent to a circle

**Solve It!** Write your solution to the Solve It in the space below.

In the Solve It, you drew lines that touch a circle at only one point. These lines are called tangents. This use of the word *tangent* is related to, but different from, the tangent ratio in right triangles that you studied previously.

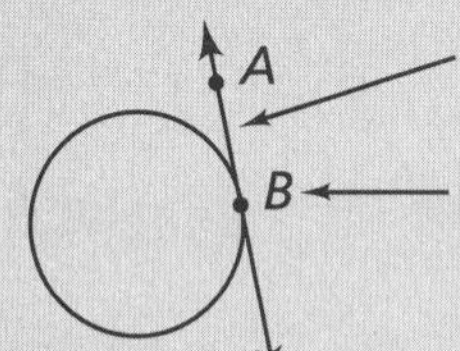


A **tangent to a circle** is a line in the plane of the circle that intersects the circle in exactly one point.

The point where a circle and a tangent intersect is the **point of tangency.**

$\overrightarrow{BA}$ is a tangent ray and $\overline{BA}$ is a tangent segment.

**Essential Understanding** A radius of a circle and the tangent that intersects the endpoint of the radius on the circle have a special relationship.

take note

## Theorem 76

| Theorem | If . . . | Then . . . |
|---|---|---|
| If a line is tangent to a circle, then the line is perpendicular to the radius at the point of tangency. | $\overleftrightarrow{AB}$ is tangent to $\odot O$ at $P$ | $\overleftrightarrow{AB} \perp \overline{OP}$ |

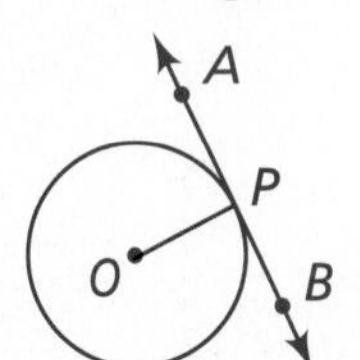

## Proof Indirect Proof of Theorem 76

**Given:** $n$ is tangent to $\odot O$ at $P$.
**Prove:** $n \perp \overline{OP}$

**Step 1** Assume that $n$ is not perpendicular to $\overline{OP}$.

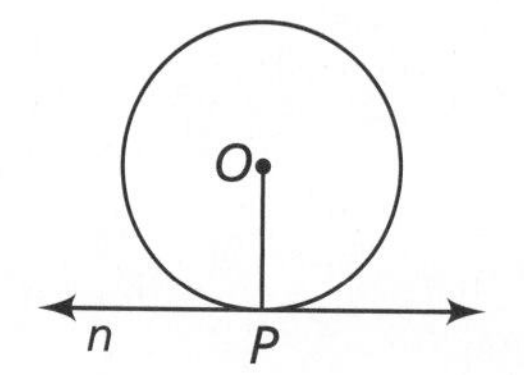


**Step 2** If line $n$ is not perpendicular to $\overline{OP}$, then, for some other point $L$ on $n$, $\overline{OL}$ must be perpendicular to $n$. Also there is a point $K$ on $n$ such that $\overline{LK} \cong \overline{LP}$ because perpendicular lines form congruent adjacent angles. $\overline{OL} = \overline{OL}$. So, $\triangle OLK \cong \triangle OLP$ by SAS.

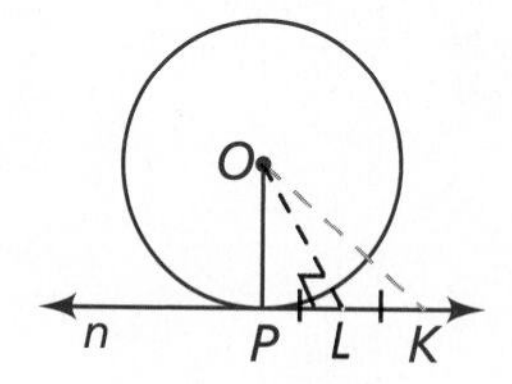


Since corresponding parts of congruent triangles are congruent, $\overline{OK} \cong \overline{OP}$. So $K$ and $P$ are both on $\odot O$ by the definition of a circle. For two points on $n$ to also be on $\odot O$ contradicts the given fact that $n$ is tangent to $\odot O$ at $P$. So the assumption that $n$ is not perpendicular to $\overline{OP}$ must be false.

**Step 3** Therefore, $n \perp \overline{OP}$ must be true.

## Problem 1 Finding Angle Measures

**Got It?** **a.** $\overline{ED}$ is tangent to $\odot O$. What is the value of $x$?

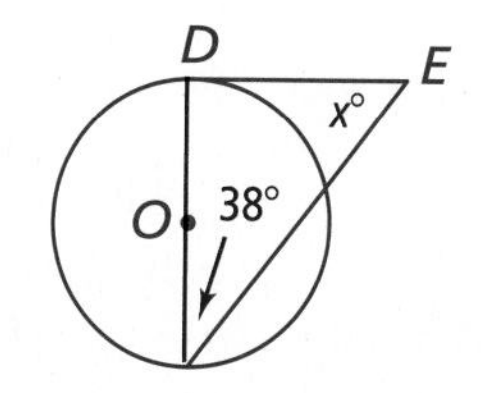


**b. Reasoning** Consider a quadrilateral like the one in Problem 1. Write a formula you could use to find the measure of any angle $x$ formed by two tangents when you know the measure of the central angle $c$ whose radii intersect the tangents.

**Practice** **Algebra** **Lines that appear to be tangent are tangent. *O* is the center of each circle. What is the value of *x*?**

**1.**

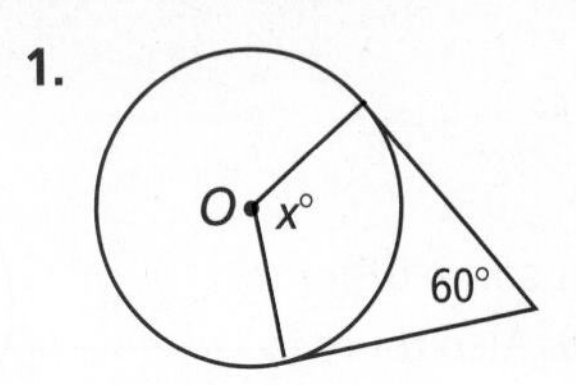


**2.**

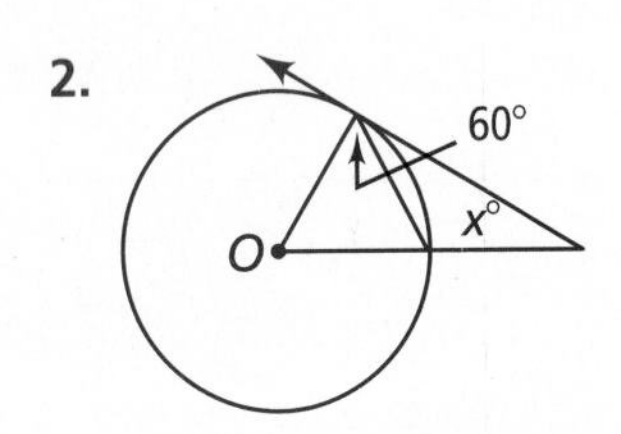

## Problem 2 Finding Distance

**Got It?** What is the distance to the horizon that a person can see on a clear day from an airplane 2 mi above Earth? Earth's radius is about 4000 mi.

**Earth Science** **The circle at the right represents Earth. The radius of Earth is about 6400 km. Find the distance $d$ to the horizon that a person can see on a clear day from each of the following heights $h$ above Earth. Round your answer to the nearest tenth of a kilometer.**

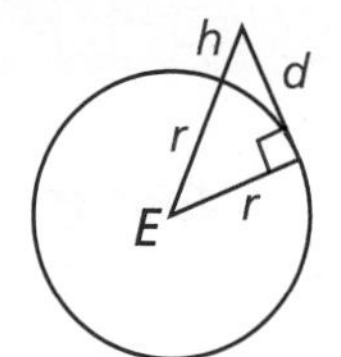


**3.** 1 km

**4.** 2500 m

Theorem 77 is the converse of Theorem 76. You can use it to prove that a line or segment is tangent to a circle. You can also use it to construct a tangent to a circle.

take note

## Theorem 77

| **Theorem** | **If . . .** | **Then . . .** |
| --- | --- | --- |
| If a line in the plane of a circle is perpendicular to a radius at its endpoint on the circle, then the line is tangent to the circle. | $\overleftrightarrow{AB} \perp \overline{OP}$ at $P$ 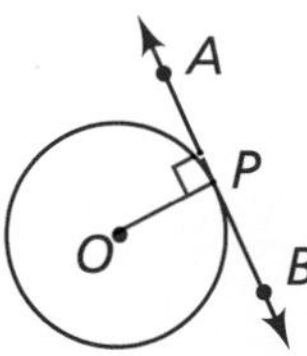  | $\overleftrightarrow{AB}$ is tangent to $\odot O$ |

*You will prove Theorem 77 in Exercise 26.*

## Problem 3 Finding a Radius

**Got It?** What is the radius of $\odot O$?

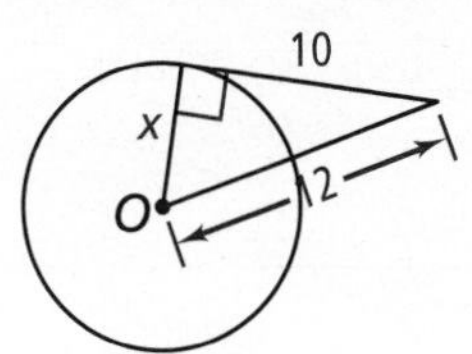


**Think**

**Why does the value *x* appear on each side of the equation?**

**A Practice** **Algebra** **In each circle, what is the value of *x*, to the nearest tenth?**

**5.**

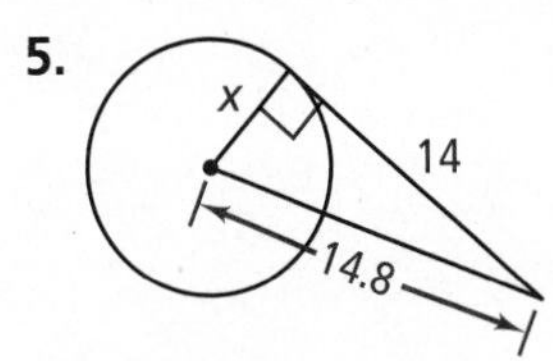


**6.**

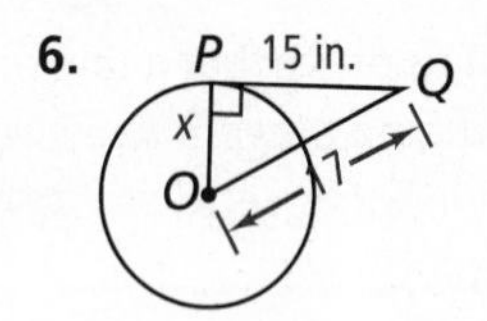

## Problem 4 Identifying a Tangent

**Got It?** Is $\overline{ML}$ tangent to $\odot N$ at $L$? Explain.

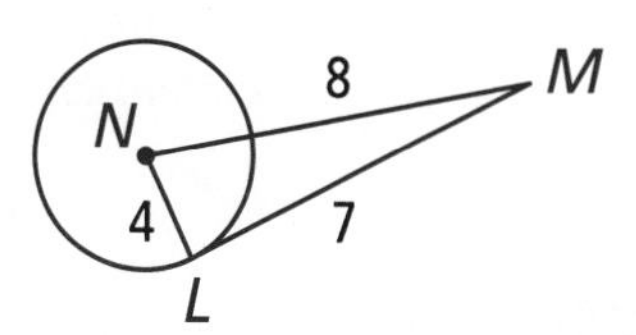


**A Practice** **Determine whether a tangent is shown in each diagram. Explain.**

**7.**

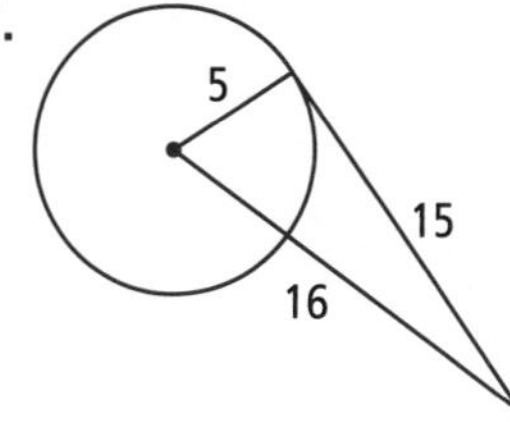


**8.**

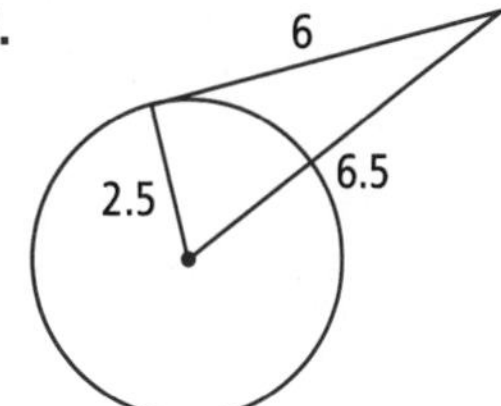


In the Solve It, you made a conjecture about the lengths of two tangents from a common endpoint outside a circle. Your conjecture may be confirmed by the following theorem.

### Take note — Theorem 78

| Theorem | If . . . | Then . . . |
| --- | --- | --- |
| If two tangent segments to a circle share a common endpoint outside the circle, then the two segments are congruent. | $\overline{BA}$ and $\overline{BC}$ are tangent to $\odot O$ | $\overline{BA} \cong \overline{BC}$ |

*You will prove Theorem 78 in Exercise 19.*

In the figure at the right, the sides of the triangle are tangent to the circle. The circle is *inscribed* in the triangle. The triangle is *circumscribed about* the circle.

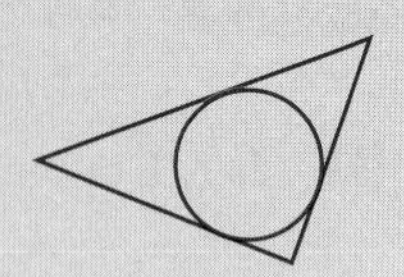

## Problem 5 Circles Inscribed in Polygons

**Got It?** $\odot O$ is inscribed in $\triangle PQR$, which has a perimeter of 88 cm. What is the length of $\overline{QY}$?

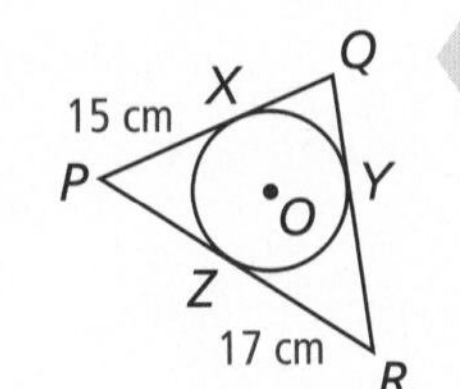


**Plan**

**How does knowing the pairs of congruent segments help?**

**Practice** **Each polygon circumscribes a circle. What is the perimeter of each polygon?**

**9.**

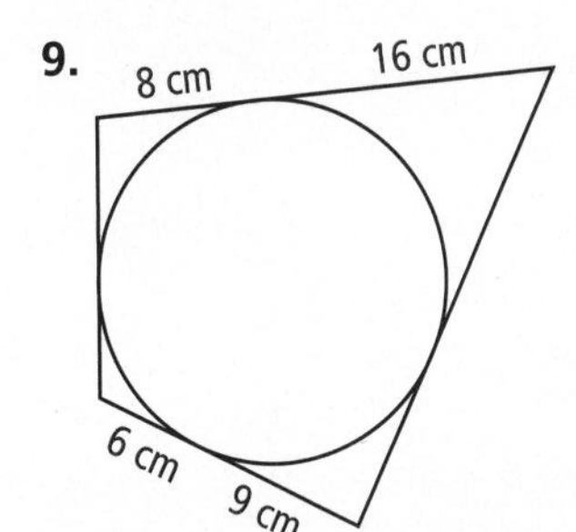


**10.**

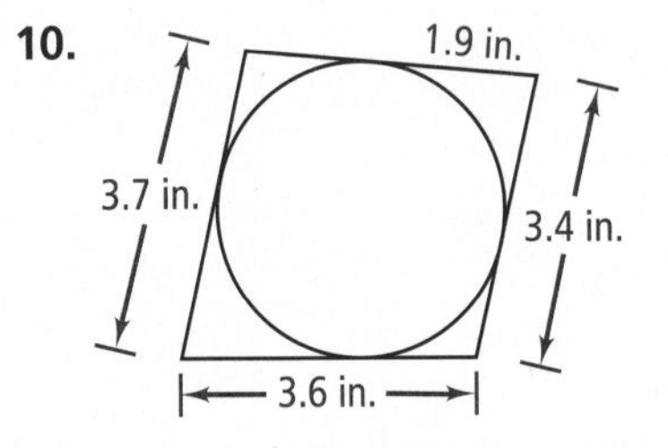

# Lesson Check

## Do you know HOW?

**Use the figure at the right for Exercises 11–13.**

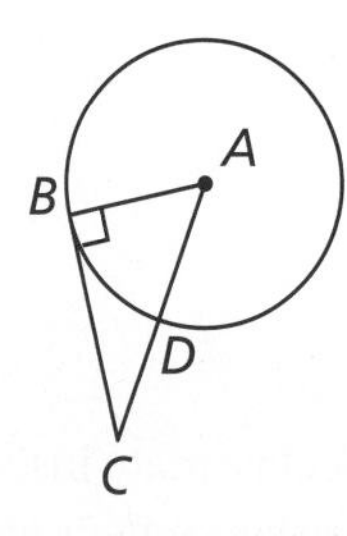


**11.** If $m\angle A = 58$, what is $m\angle ACB$?

**12.** If $AC = 10$ and $BC = 8$, what is the radius?

**13.** If $AC = 12$ and $BC = 9$, what is the radius?

## Do you UNDERSTAND?

**14. Vocabulary** How are the phrases *tangent ratio* and *tangent of a circle* used differently?

**15. Error Analysis** A classmate insists that $\overline{DF}$ is a tangent to $\odot E$. Explain how to show that your classmate is wrong.

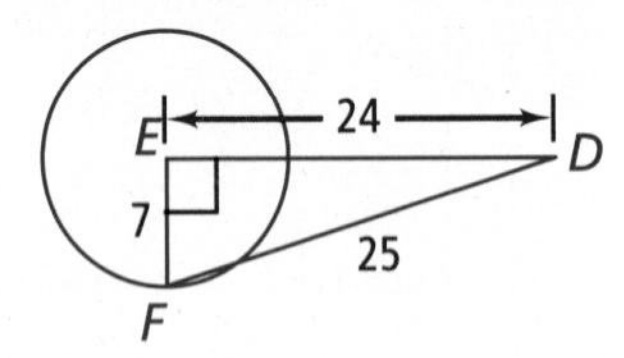


## More Practice and Problem-Solving Exercises

STEM **16. Solar Eclipse** Common tangents to two circles may be *internal* or *external*. If you draw a segment joining the centers of the circles, a common internal tangent will intersect the segment. A common external tangent will not. For this cross-sectional diagram of the sun, moon, and Earth during a solar eclipse, use the terms above to describe the types of tangents of each color.

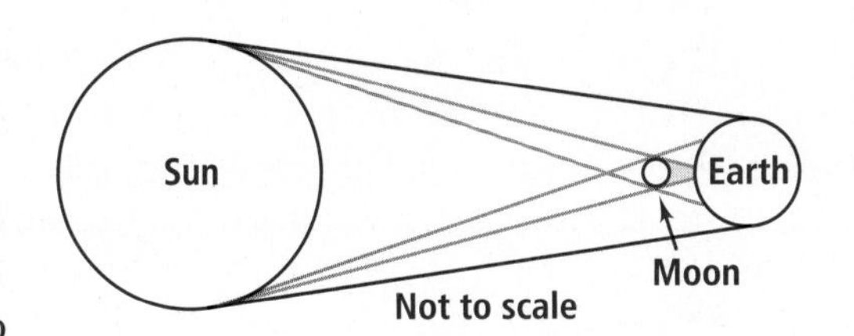


**a.** red **b.** blue **c.** orange

**d.** Which tangents show the extent on Earth's surface of total eclipse? Of partial eclipse?

**17. Reasoning** A nickel, a dime, and a quarter are touching as shown. Tangents are drawn from point *A* to both sides of each coin. What can you conclude about the four tangent segments? Explain.

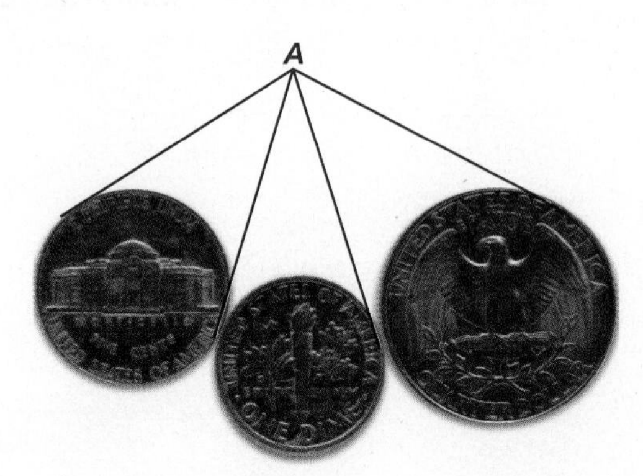

**18. Think About a Plan** Leonardo da Vinci wrote, "When each of two squares touch the same circle at four points, one is double the other." Explain why the statement is true.

- How will drawing a sketch help?
- Are both squares inside the circle?

**Proof 19.** Prove Theorem 78.

**Given:** $\overline{BA}$ and $\overline{BC}$ are tangent to $\odot O$ at $A$ and $C$, respectively.

**Prove:** $\overline{BA} \cong \overline{BC}$

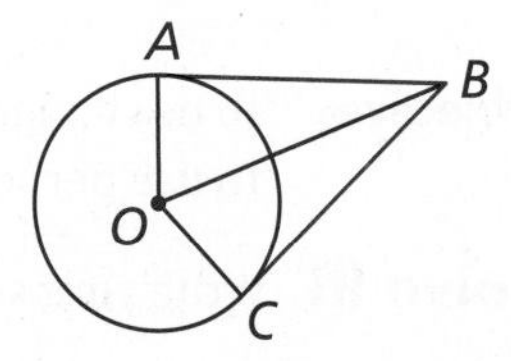


**Proof 20. Given:** $\overline{BC}$ is tangent to $\odot A$ at $D$.
$\overline{DB} \cong \overline{DC}$

**Prove:** $\overline{AB} \cong \overline{AC}$

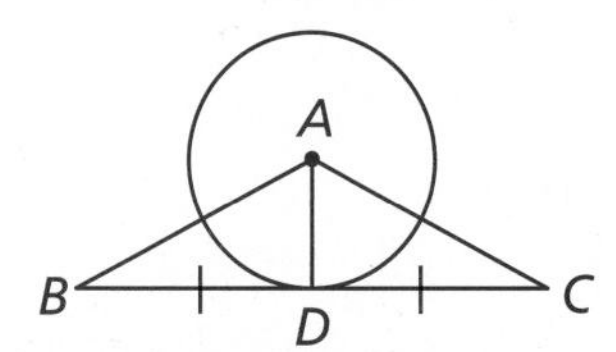


**Proof 21. Given:** $\odot A$ and $\odot B$ with common tangents $\overline{DF}$ and $\overline{CE}$

**Prove:** $\triangle GDC \sim \triangle GFE$

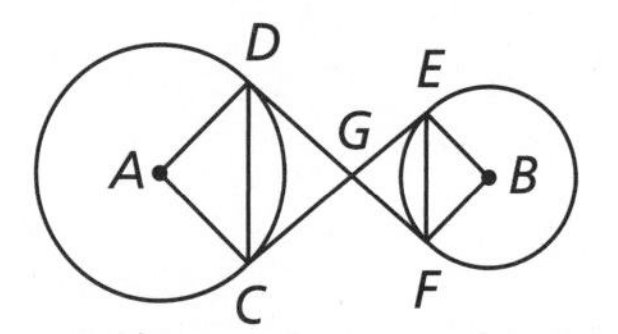


**22. a.** A belt fits snugly around the two circular pulleys. $\overline{CE}$ is an auxiliary line from $E$ to $\overline{BD}$, and $\overline{CE} \parallel \overline{BA}$. What type of quadrilateral is $ABCE$? Explain.

**b.** What is the length of $\overline{CE}$?

**c.** What is the distance between the centers of the pulleys to the nearest tenth?

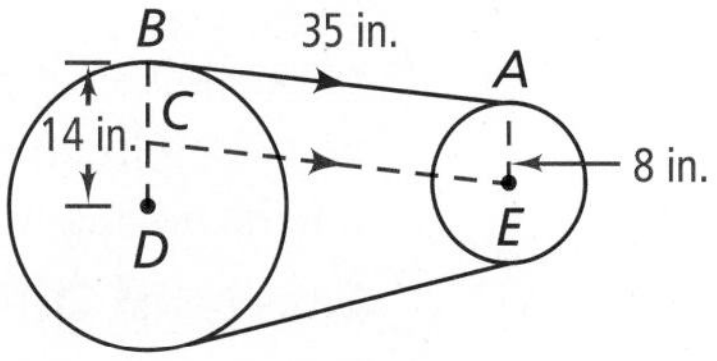

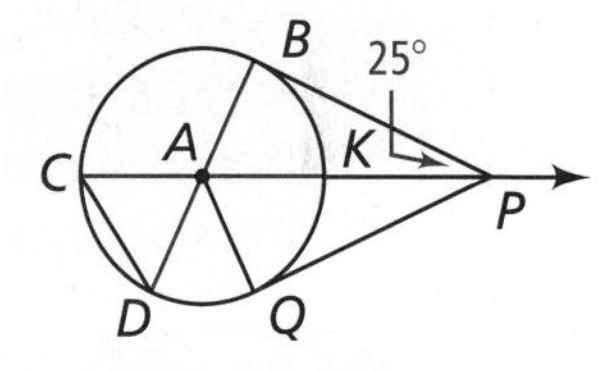


**23.** $\overline{BD}$ and $\overline{CK}$ at the right are diameters of $\odot A$. $\overline{BP}$ and $\overline{QP}$ are tangents to $\odot A$. What is $m\angle CDA$?

**24. Constructions** Draw a circle. Label the center $T$. Locate a point on the circle and label it $R$. Construct a tangent to $\odot T$ at $R$.

**25. Coordinate Geometry** Graph the equation $x^2 + y^2 = 9$. Then draw a segment from (0, 5) tangent to the circle. Find the length of the segment.

## Challenge

**Proof 26.** Write an indirect proof of Theorem 77.

**Given:** $\overleftrightarrow{AB} \perp \overline{OP}$ at $P$.

**Prove:** $\overleftrightarrow{AB}$ is tangent to $\odot O$.

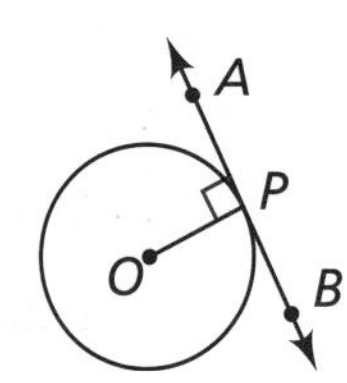


**27.** Two circles that have one point in common are *tangent circles*. Given any triangle, explain how to draw three circles that are centered at each vertex of the triangle and are tangent to each other.

# Chords and Arcs

G.C.2 Identify and describe relationships among inscribed angles, radii, and chords . . .

**Objectives** To use congruent chords, arcs, and central angles
To use perpendicular bisectors to chords

**Solve It!** Write your solution to the Solve It in the space below.

In the Solve It, you found the length of a **chord**, which is a segment whose endpoints are on a circle. The diagram shows the chord $\overline{PQ}$ and its related arc, $\widehat{PQ}$.

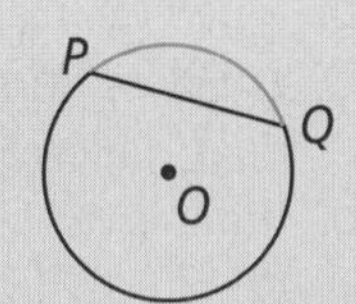


**Essential Understanding** You can use information about congruent parts of a circle (or congruent circles) to find information about other parts of the circle (or circles).

The following theorems and their converses confirm that if you know that chords, arcs, or central angles in a circle are congruent, then you know the other two parts are congruent.

## Theorem 79 and Its Converse

**Theorem**

Within a circle or in congruent circles, congruent central angles have congruent arcs.

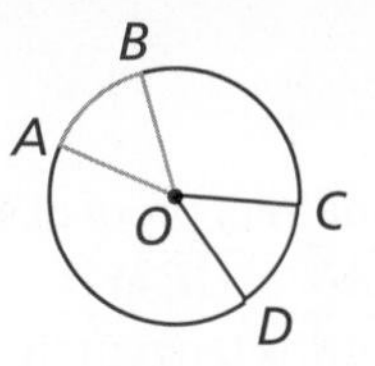


**Converse**

Within a circle or in congruent circles, congruent arcs have congruent central angles.

If $\angle AOB \cong \angle COD$, then $\widehat{AB} \cong \widehat{CD}$.
If $\widehat{AB} \cong \widehat{CD}$, then $\angle AOB \cong \angle COD$.

*You will prove Theorem 79 and its converse in Exercises 17 and 33.*

take note

## Theorem 80 and Its Converse

**Theorem**

Within a circle or in congruent circles, congruent central angles have congruent chords.

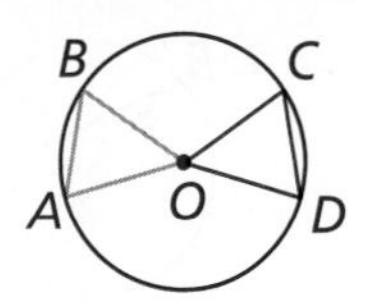


**Converse**

Within a circle or in congruent circles, congruent chords have congruent central angles.

If $\angle AOB \cong \angle COD$, then $\overline{AB} \cong \overline{CD}$.
If $\overline{AB} \cong \overline{CD}$, then $\angle AOB \cong \angle COD$.

*You will prove Theorem 80 and its converse in Exercises 18 and 34.*

## Theorem 81 and Its Converse

**Theorem**

Within a circle or in congruent circles, congruent chords have congruent arcs.

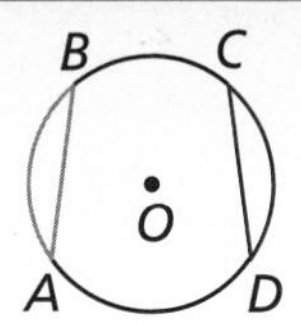


**Converse**

Within a circle or in congruent circles, congruent arcs have congruent chords.

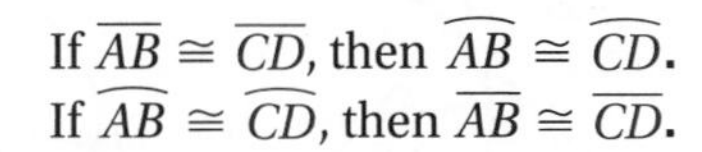
If $\overline{AB} \cong \overline{CD}$, then $\overset{\frown}{AB} \cong \overset{\frown}{CD}$.
If $\overset{\frown}{AB} \cong \overset{\frown}{CD}$, then $\overline{AB} \cong \overline{CD}$.

*You will prove Theorem 81 and its converse in Exercises 19 and 35.*

## Problem 1 Using Congruent Chords

**Got It?** **Reasoning** Use the diagram in Problem 1, shown below. Suppose you are given $\odot O \cong \odot P$ and $\angle OBC \cong \angle PDF$. How can you show $\angle O \cong \angle P$? From this, what else can you conclude?

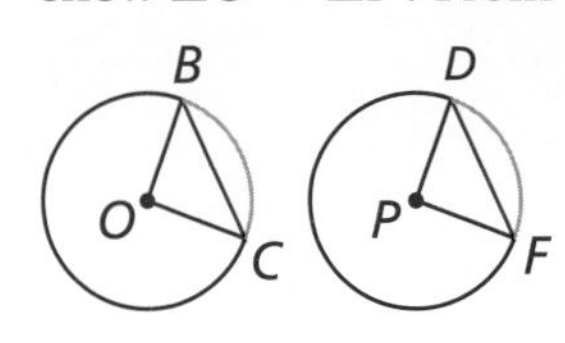

**Why is it important that the circles are congruent?**

 **Practice** **In Exercises 1 and 2, the circles are congruent. What can you conclude?**

1. 

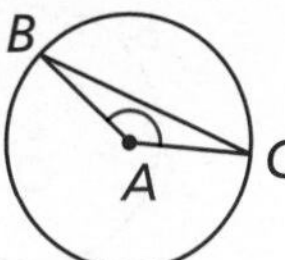


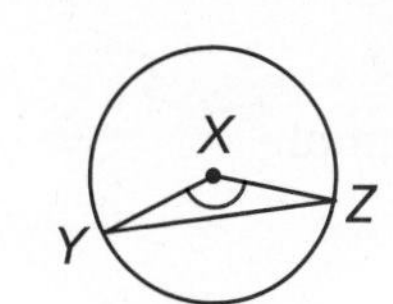


2. 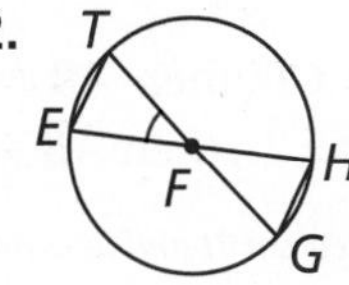


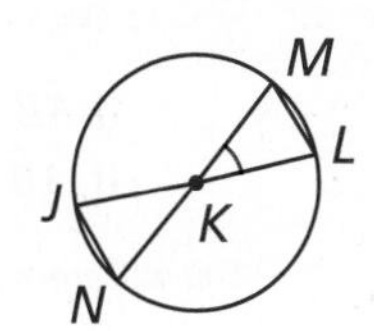


## take note — Theorem 82 and Its Converse

**Theorem**

Within a circle or in congruent circles, chords equidistant from the center or centers are congruent.

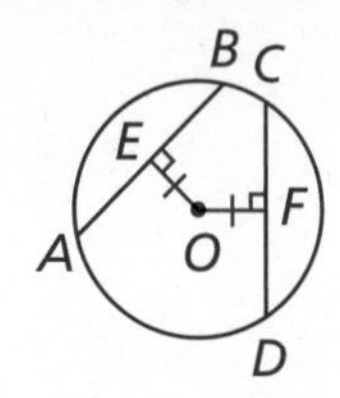


**Converse**

Within a circle or in congruent circles, congruent chords are equidistant from the center (or centers).

If $OE = OF$, then $\overline{AB} \cong \overline{CD}$.
If $\overline{AB} \cong \overline{CD}$, then $OE = OF$.

*You will prove the converse of Theorem 82 in Exercise 36.*

## Proof Proof of Theorem 82

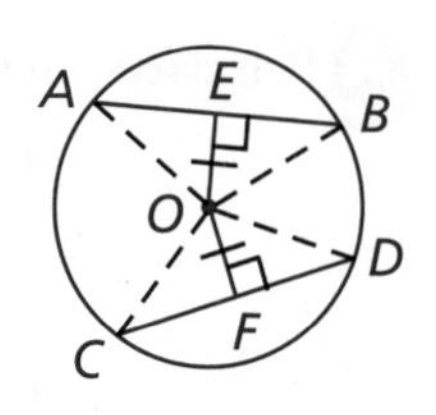


**Given:** $\odot O$, $\overline{OE} = \overline{OF}$, $\overline{OE} \perp \overline{AB}$, $\overline{OF} \perp \overline{CD}$
**Prove:** $\overline{AB} \cong \overline{CD}$

| Statements | Reasons |
|---|---|
| **1)** $\overline{OA} \cong \overline{OB} \cong \overline{OC} \cong \overline{OD}$ | **1)** Radii of a circle are congruent. |
| **2)** $\overline{OE} \cong \overline{OF}$, $\overline{OE} \perp \overline{AB}$, $\overline{OF} \perp \overline{CD}$ | **2)** Given |
| **3)** $\angle AEO$ and $\angle CFO$ are right angles. | **3)** Def. of perpendicular segments |
| **4)** $\triangle AEO \cong \triangle CFO$ | **4)** HL Theorem |
| **5)** $\angle A \cong \angle C$ | **5)** Corres. parts of $\cong$ △ are $\cong$. |
| **6)** $\angle B \cong \angle A$, $\angle C \cong \angle D$ | **6)** Isosceles Triangle Theorem |
| **7)** $\angle B \cong \angle D$ | **7)** Transitive Property of Congruence |
| **8)** $\angle AOB \cong \angle COD$ | **8)** If two ∠ of a △ are $\cong$ to two ∠ of another △, then the third ∠ are $\cong$. |
| **9)** $\overline{AB} \cong \overline{CD}$ | **9)** $\cong$ central angles have $\cong$ chords. |

## Problem 2 Finding the Length of a Chord

**Got It?** What is the value of $x$? Justify your answer.

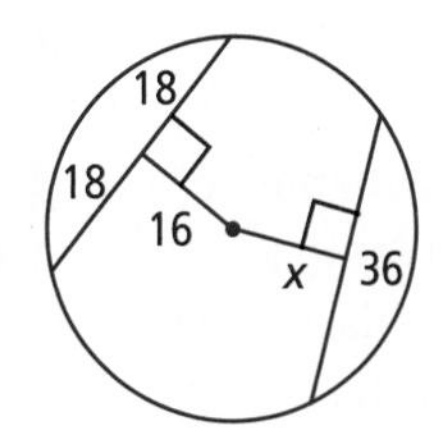


**Plan**
**What information can you gather from the chords?**

**Practice** Find the value of $x$.

**3.**

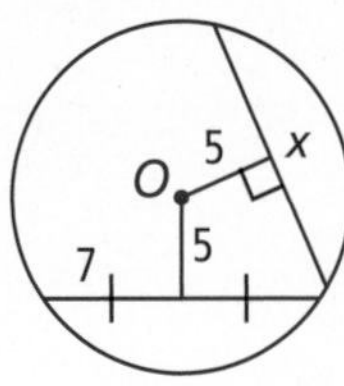


**4.**

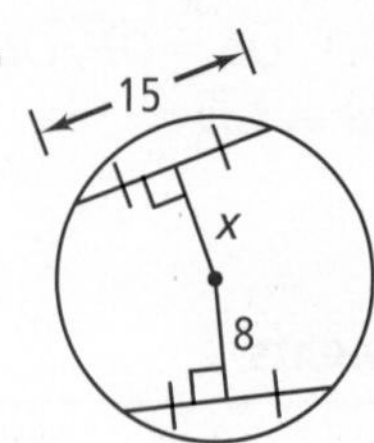


The Converse of the Perpendicular Bisector Theorem from Theorem 26 has special applications to a circle and its diameters, chords, and arcs.

take note

## Theorem 83

| Theorem | If . . . | Then . . . |
|---|---|---|
| In a circle, if a diameter is perpendicular to a chord, then it bisects the chord and its arc. | $\overline{AB}$ is a diameter and $\overline{AB} \perp \overline{CD}$ | $\overline{CE} \cong \overline{ED}$ and $\overset{\frown}{CA} \cong \overset{\frown}{AD}$ |

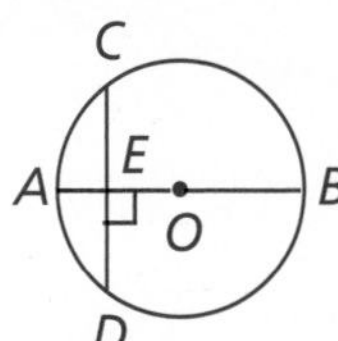


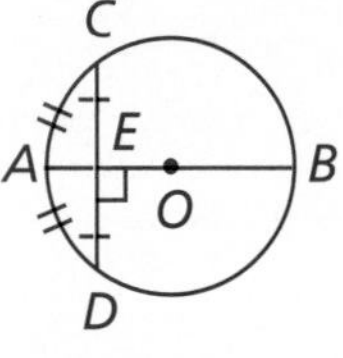


*You will prove Theorem 83 in Exercise 20.*

## Theorem 84

| Theorem | If . . . | Then . . . |
|---|---|---|
| In a circle, if a diameter bisects a chord (that is not a diameter), then it is perpendicular to the chord. | $\overline{AB}$ is a diameter and $\overline{CE} \cong \overline{ED}$ | $\overline{AB} \perp \overline{CD}$ |

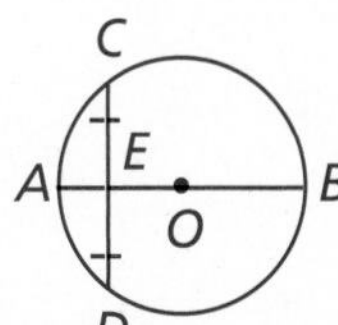


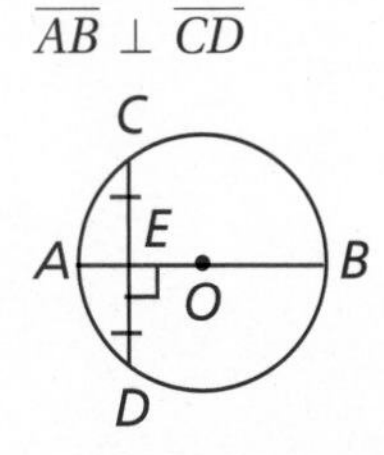

take note

## Theorem 85

| Theorem | If . . . | Then . . . |
|---|---|---|
| In a circle, the perpendicular bisector of a chord contains the center of the circle. | $\overline{AB}$ is the perpendicular bisector of chord $\overline{CD}$ | $\overline{AB}$ contains the center of $\odot O$ |

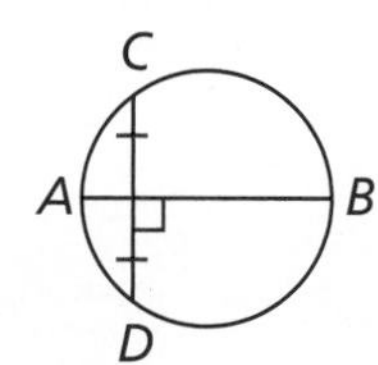


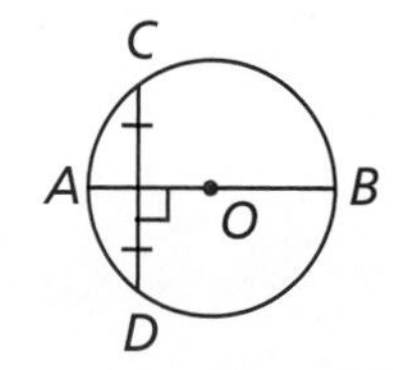


*You will prove Theorem 85 in Exercise 31.*

### Proof Proof of Theorem 84

**Given:** $\odot O$ with diameter $\overline{AB}$ bisecting $\overline{CD}$ at $E$
**Prove:** $\overline{AB} \perp \overline{CD}$

**Proof:** $OC = OD$ because the radii of a circle are congruent. $CE = ED$ by the definition of *bisect*. Thus, $O$ and $E$ are both equidistant from $C$ and $D$. By the Converse of the Perpendicular Bisector Theorem, both $O$ and $E$ are on the perpendicular bisector of $\overline{CD}$. Two points determine one line or segment, so $\overline{OE}$ is the perpendicular bisector of $\overline{CD}$. Since $\overline{OE}$ is part of $\overline{AB}$, $\overline{AB} \perp \overline{CD}$.

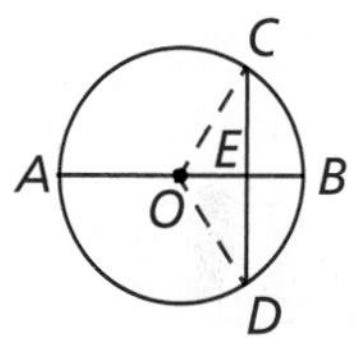


ONLINE PROBLEMS

## Problem 3 Using Diameters and Chords

**Got It?** Trace a coin. What is its radius?

5. In the diagram at the right, $\overline{GH}$ and $\overline{KM}$ are perpendicular bisectors of the chords they intersect. What can you conclude about the center of the circle? Justify your answer.

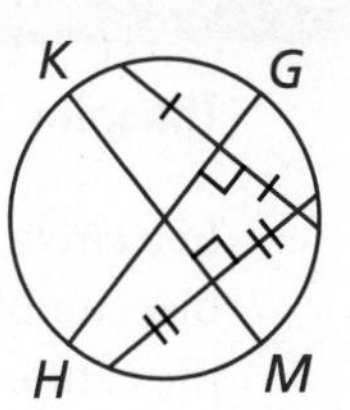


6. In $\odot O$, $\overline{AB}$ is a diameter of the circle and $\overline{AB} \perp \overline{CD}$. What conclusions can you make?

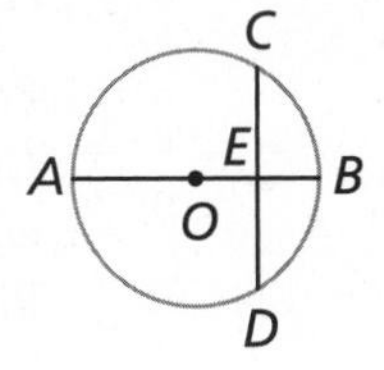


## Problem 4 Finding Measures in a Circle

**Got It? Reasoning** In part (B) of Problem 4, how does the auxiliary $\overline{BA}$ make it simpler to solve for $y$?

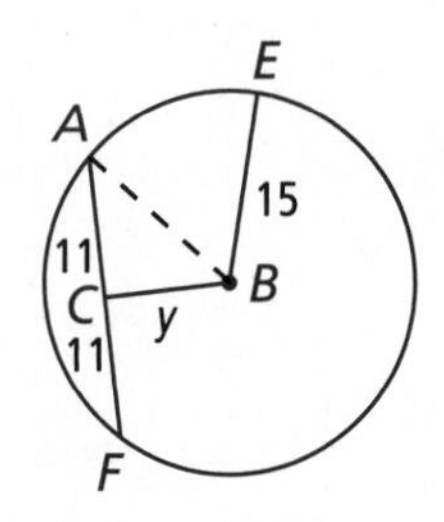

**Practice** **Algebra** Find the value of $x$ to the nearest tenth.

7. 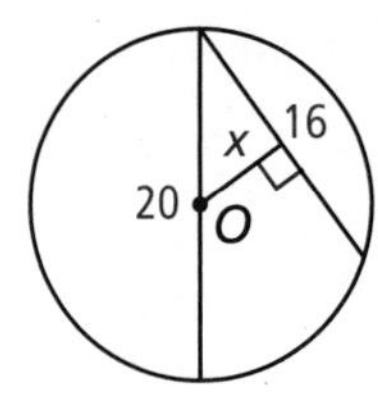


8. 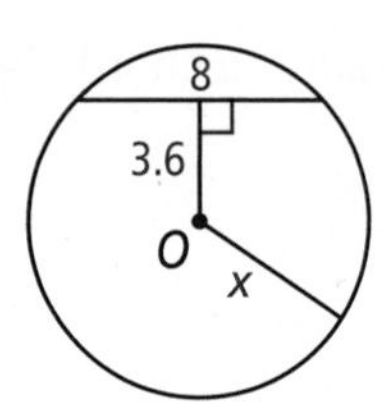

## Lesson Check

### Do you know HOW?

**In $\odot O$, $m\overset{\frown}{CD} = 50$ and $\overline{CA} \cong \overline{BD}$.**

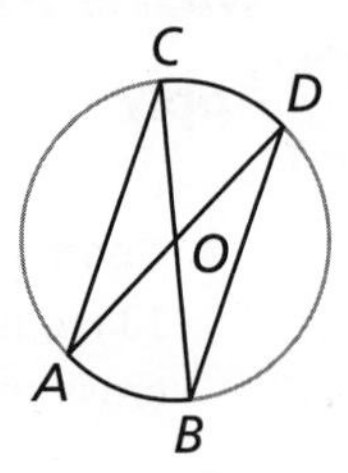


**9.** What is $m\overset{\frown}{AB}$? How do you know?

**10.** What is true of $\overset{\frown}{CA}$ and $\overset{\frown}{BD}$? Why?

**11.** Since $CA = BD$, what do you know about the distance of $\overline{CA}$ and $\overline{BD}$ from the center of $\odot O$?

## Do you UNDERSTAND?

**12. Vocabulary** Is a radius a chord? Is a diameter a chord? Explain your answers.

**13. Error Analysis** What is the error in the diagram?

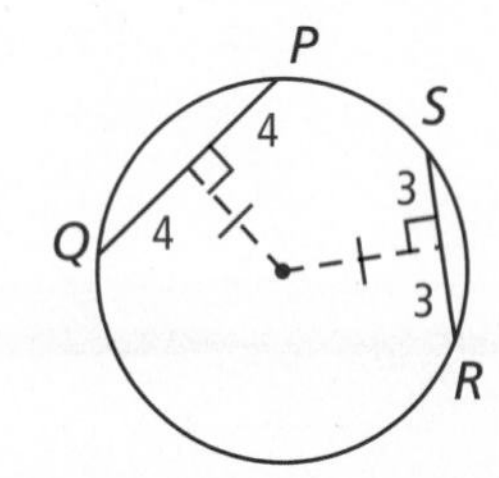


## More Practice and Problem-Solving Exercises

### B Apply

**14. Geometry in 3 Dimensions** In the figure at the right, sphere $O$ with radius 13 cm is intersected by a plane 5 cm from center $O$. Find the radius of the cross section $\odot A$.

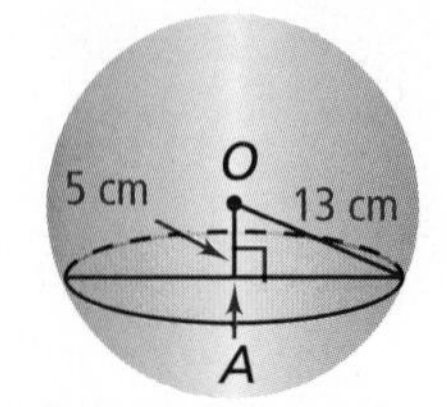


**15. Geometry in 3 Dimensions** A plane intersects a sphere that has radius 10 in., forming the cross section $\odot B$ with radius 8 in. How far is the plane from the center of the sphere?

**16. Think About a Plan** Two concentric circles have radii of 4 cm and 8 cm. A segment tangent to the smaller circle is a chord of the larger circle. What is the length of the segment to the nearest tenth?

- How will you start the diagram?
- Where is the best place to position the radius of each circle?

Proof **17.** Prove Theorem 79.

**Given:** $\odot O$ with $\angle AOB \cong \angle COD$
**Prove:** $\overset{\frown}{AB} \cong \overset{\frown}{CD}$

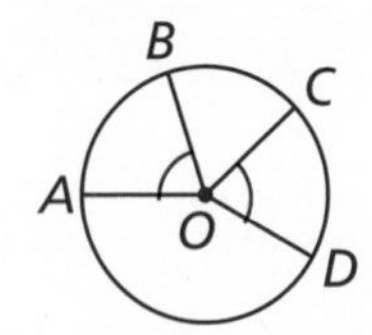


Proof **18.** Prove Theorem 80.

**Given:** $\odot O$ with $\angle AOB \cong \angle COD$
**Prove:** $\overline{AB} \cong \overline{CD}$

Proof **19.** Prove Theorem 81.

**Given:** $\odot O$ with $\overline{AB} \cong \overline{CD}$
**Prove:** $\overset{\frown}{AB} \cong \overset{\frown}{CD}$

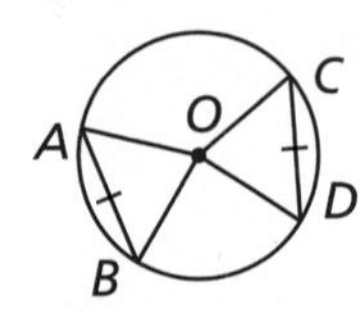


Proof **20.** Prove Theorem 83.

**Given:** $\odot O$ with diameter $\overline{ED} \perp \overline{AB}$ at $C$
**Prove:** $\overset{\frown}{AC} \cong \overset{\frown}{BC}$, $\overset{\frown}{AD} \cong \overset{\frown}{BD}$

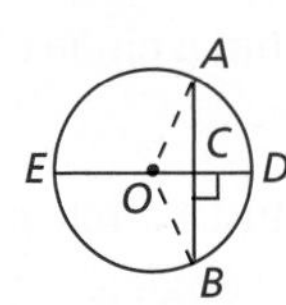


**$\odot A$ and $\odot B$ are congruent. $\overline{CD}$ is a chord of both circles.**

**21.** If $AB = 8$ in. and $CD = 6$ in., how long is a radius?

**22.** If $AB = 24$ cm and a radius $= 13$ cm, how long is $\overline{CD}$?

**23.** If a radius $= 13$ ft and $CD = 24$ ft, how long is $\overline{AB}$?

**24. Construction** Use Theorem 80 to construct a regular octagon.

**25.** In the diagram at the right, the endpoints of the chord are the points where the line $x = 2$ intersects the circle $x^2 + y^2 = 25$. What is the length of the chord? Round your answer to the nearest tenth.

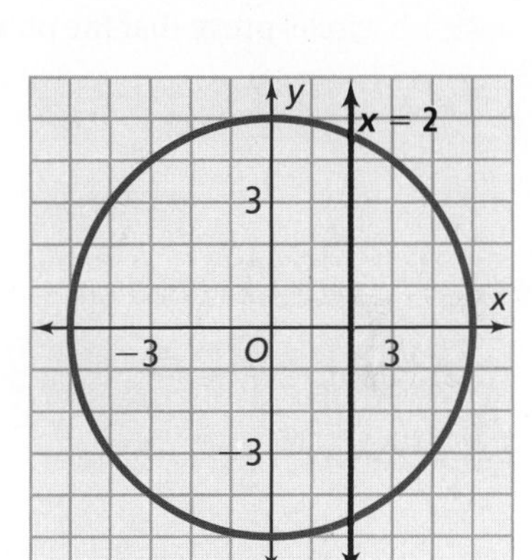


**26. Construction** Use a circular object such as a can or a saucer to draw a circle. Construct the center of the circle.

**27. Writing** Theorems 79 and 80 both begin with the phrase "within a circle or in congruent circles." Explain why the word *congruent* is essential for both theorems.

**Find $m\overset{\frown}{AB}$. (*Hint:* You will need to use trigonometry in Exercise 30.)**

**28.**

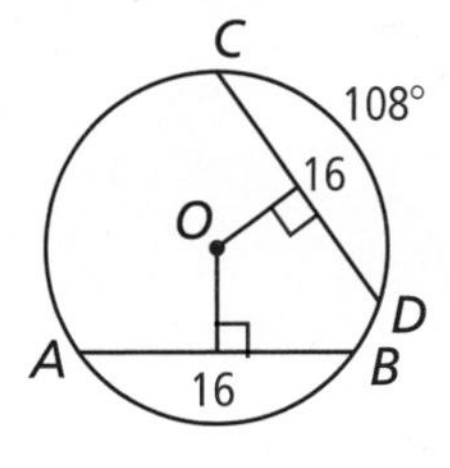


**29.**

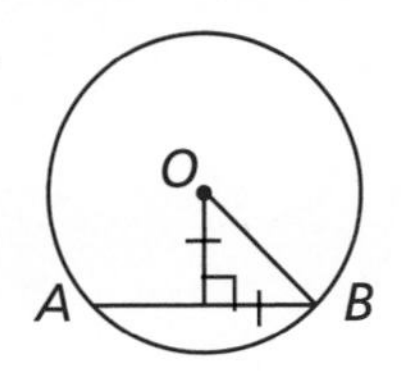


**30.**

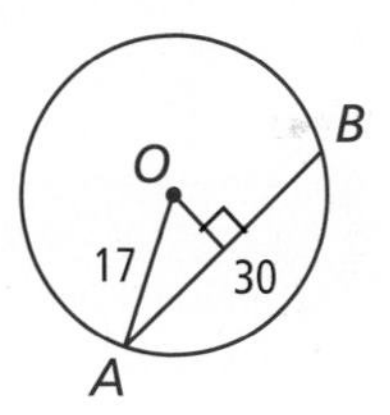


Proof **31.** Prove Theorem 85.

**Given:** $\ell$ is the $\perp$ bisector of $\overline{WY}$.
**Prove:** $\ell$ contains the center of $\odot X$.

Proof **32. Given:** $\odot A$ with $\overline{CE} \perp \overline{BD}$
**Prove:** $\overset{\frown}{BC} \cong \overset{\frown}{DC}$

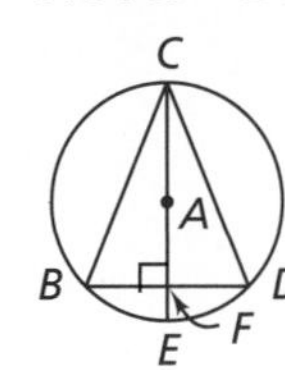

Proof Prove each of the following.

**33.** Converse of Theorem 79: Within a circle or in congruent circles, congruent arcs have congruent central angles.

**34.** Converse of Theorem 80: Within a circle or in congruent circles, congruent chords have congruent central angles.

**35.** Converse of Theorem 81: Within a circle or in congruent circles, congruent arcs have congruent chords.

**36.** Converse of Theorem 82: Within a circle or congruent circles, congruent chords are equidistant from the center (or centers).

Proof **37.** If two circles are concentric and a chord of the larger circle is tangent to the smaller circle, prove that the point of tangency is the midpoint of the chord.

# 12-5 Inscribed Angles

**G.C.2** Identify and describe relationships among inscribed angles, radii, and chords . . . Also **G.C.3, G.C.4**

**Objectives** To find the measure of an inscribed angle
To find the measure of an angle formed by a tangent and a chord

**Solve It!** Write your solution to the Solve It in the space below.

An angle whose vertex is on the circle and whose sides are chords of the circle is an **inscribed angle**. An arc with endpoints on the sides of an inscribed angle, and its other points in the interior of the angle, is an **intercepted arc**. In the diagram, inscribed $\angle C$ intercepts $\overset{\frown}{AB}$.

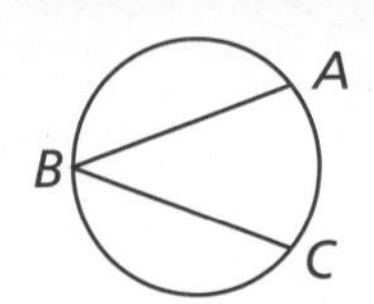


**Essential Understanding** Angles formed by intersecting lines have a special relationship to the arcs the intersecting lines intercept. In this lesson, you will study arcs formed by inscribed angles.

take note

### Theorem 86 Inscribed Angle Theorem

The measure of an inscribed angle is half the measure of its intercepted arc.

$$m\angle B = \frac{1}{2}m\overset{\frown}{AC}$$

To prove Theorem 86, there are three cases to consider.

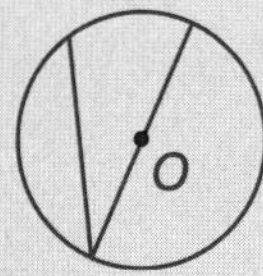


I: The center is on a side of the angle.

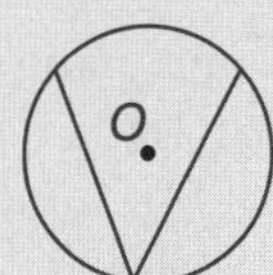


II: The center is inside the angle.

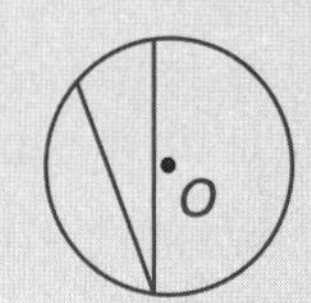


III: The center is outside the angle.

The following is a proof of Case I. You will prove Case II and Case III in Exercises 19 and 20.

## Proof of Theorem 86, Case I

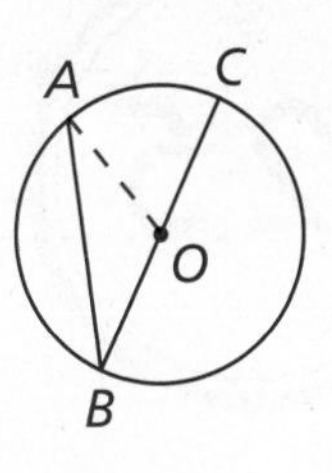


**Given:** $\odot O$ with inscribed $\angle B$ and diameter $\overline{BC}$

**Prove:** $m\angle B = \frac{1}{2} m\widehat{AC}$

Draw radius $\overline{OA}$ to form isosceles $\triangle AOB$ with $OA = OB$ and, hence, $m\angle A = m\angle B$ (Isosceles Triangle Theorem).

| | |
|---|---|
| $m\angle AOC = m\angle A + m\angle B$ | Triangle Exterior Angle Theorem |
| $m\widehat{AC} = m\angle AOC$ | Definition of measure of an arc |
| $m\widehat{AC} = m\angle A + m\angle B$ | Substitute. |
| $m\widehat{AC} = 2m\angle B$ | Substitute and simplify. |
| $\frac{1}{2} m\widehat{AC} = m\angle B$ | Divide each side by 2. |

## Problem 1 Using the Inscribed Angle Theorem

**Got It?** **a.** In $\odot O$, what is $m\angle A$?

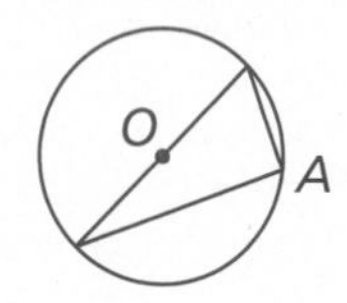


**b.** What are $m\angle A$, $m\angle B$, $m\angle C$, and $m\angle D$?

**Plan**
**What is the intercepted arc of each angle?**

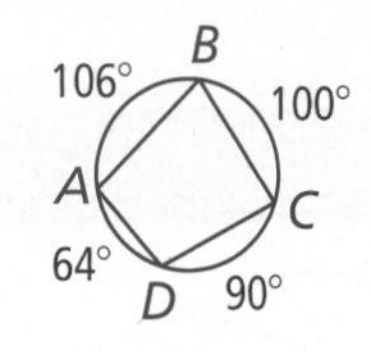


**c.** What do you notice about the sums of the measures of the opposite angles in the quadrilateral in part (b)?

**Practice** **Find the value of each variable. For each circle, the dot represents the center.**

**1.**

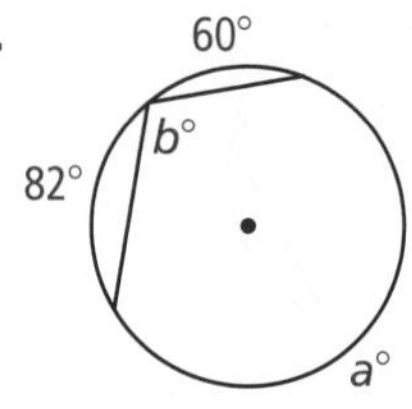


**2.**

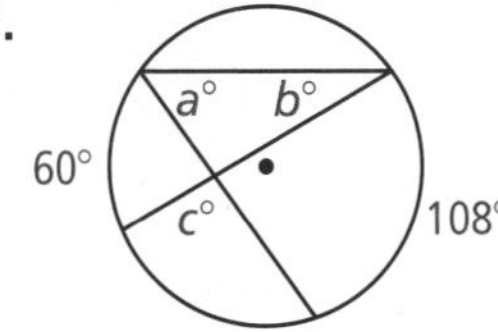


You will use three corollaries to the Inscribed Angle Theorem to find measures of angles in circles. The first corollary may confirm an observation you made in the Solve It.

take note

## Corollaries to Theorem 86 The Inscribed Angle Theorem

### Corollary 1

Two inscribed angles that intercept the same arc are congruent.

### Corollary 2

An angle inscribed in a semicircle is a right angle.

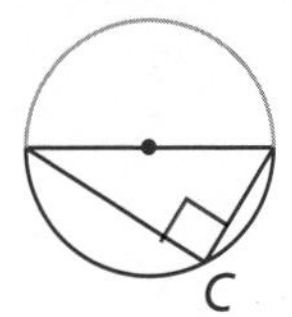


### Corollary 3

The opposite angles of a quadrilateral inscribed in a circle are supplementary.

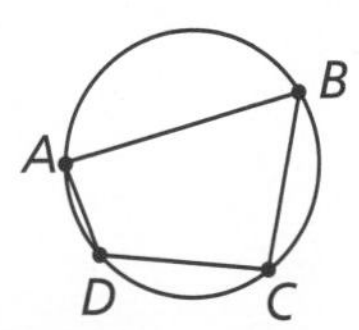


*You will prove these corollaries in Exercises 24–26.*

## Problem 2 Using Corollaries to Find Angle Measures

**Got It?** In the diagram at the right, what is the measure of each numbered angle?

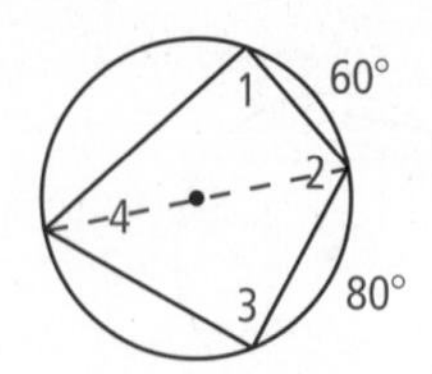


**Think**

**What does the auxiliary line represent in the diagram?**

**A Practice** **Find the value of each variable. For each circle, the dot represents the center.**

**3.**

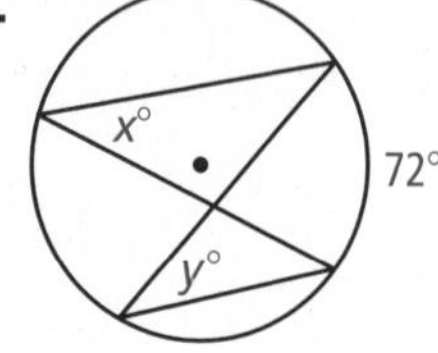


**4.**

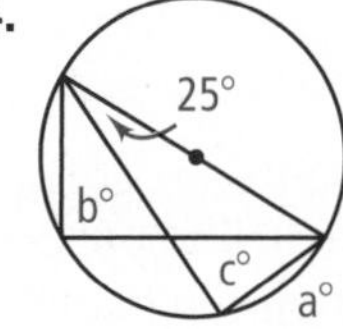


The following diagram shows point $A$ moving along the circle until a tangent is formed. From the Inscribed Angle Theorem, you know that in the first three diagrams $m\angle A$ is $\frac{1}{2}m\widehat{BC}$. As the last diagram suggests, this is also true when $A$ and $C$ coincide.

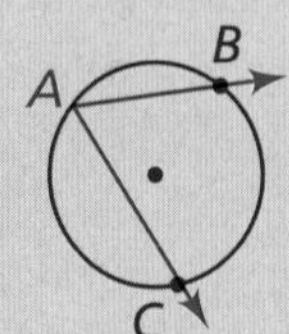


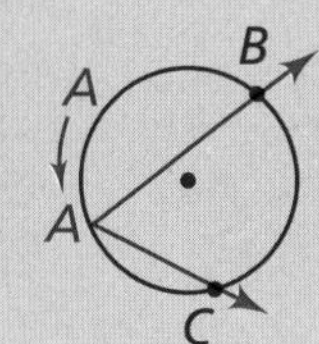


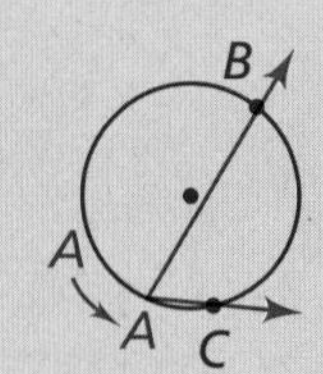


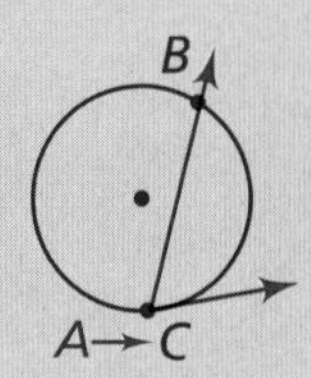

take note

## Theorem 87

The measure of an angle formed by a tangent and a chord is half the measure of the intercepted arc.

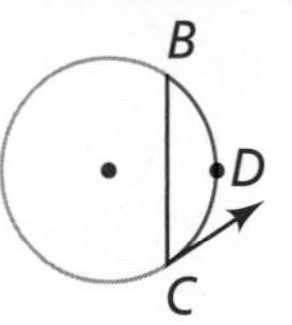

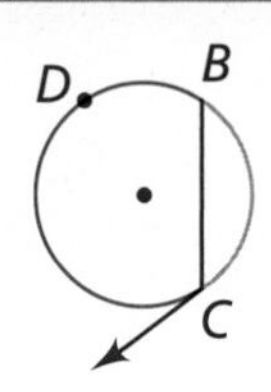


$m\angle C = \frac{1}{2}m\widehat{BDC}$

*You will prove Theorem 87 in Exercise 27.*

## Problem 3 Using Arc Measure

**Got It?** **a.** In the diagram at the right, $\overline{KJ}$ is tangent to $\odot O$. What are the values of $x$ and $y$?

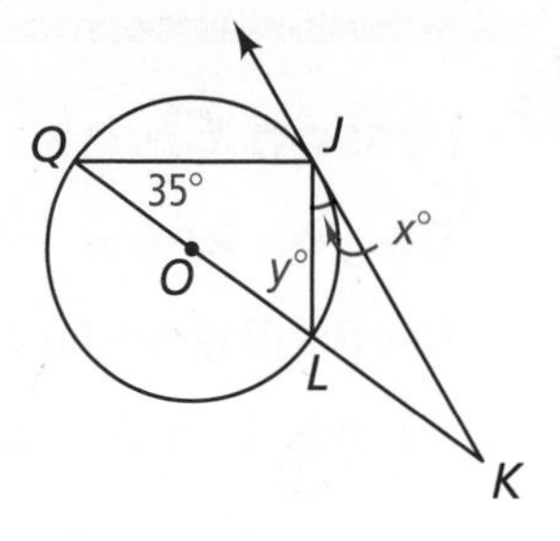


**b. Reasoning** In part (a), an inscribed angle ($\angle Q$) and an angle formed by a tangent and chord ($\angle KJL$) intercept the same arc. What is always true of these angles? Explain.

**Practice** **In Exercises 5 and 6, find the value of each variable. Lines that appear to be tangent are tangent.**

**5.**

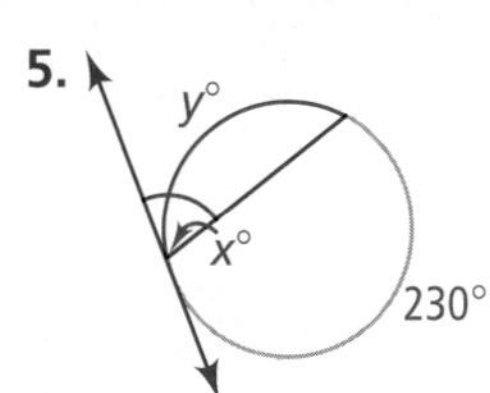

6. 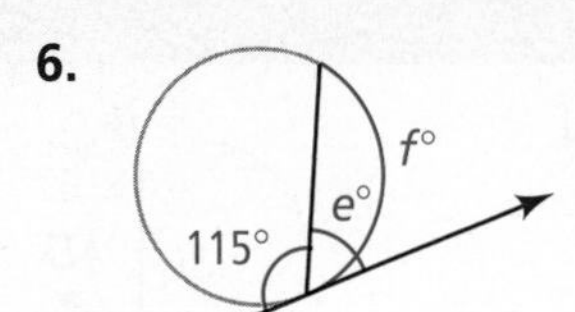

## Lesson Check

### Do you know HOW?

**Use the diagram for Exercises 7–9.**

**7.** Which arc does $\angle A$ intercept?

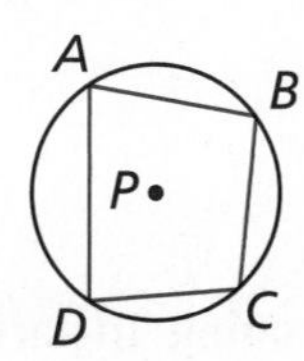


**8.** Which angle intercepts $\overparen{ABC}$?

**9.** Which angles of quadrilateral *ABCD* are supplementary?

## Do you UNDERSTAND?

**10. Vocabulary** What is the relationship between an inscribed angle and its intercepted arc?

**11. Error Analysis** A classmate says that $m\angle A = 90$. What is your classmate's error?

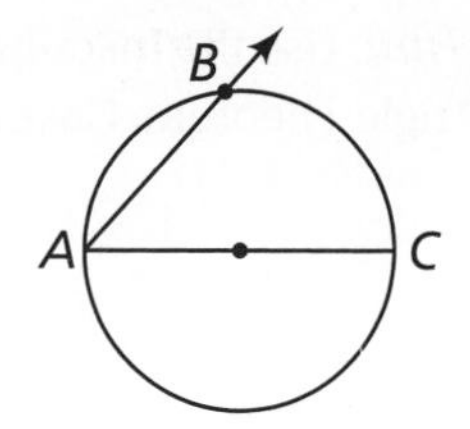


## More Practice and Problem-Solving Exercises

### B Apply

**12. Writing** A parallelogram inscribed in a circle must be what kind of parallelogram? Explain.

**Find each indicated measure for $\odot O$.**

**13.** **a.** $m\widehat{BC}$
**b.** $m\angle B$
**c.** $m\angle C$
**d.** $m\widehat{AB}$

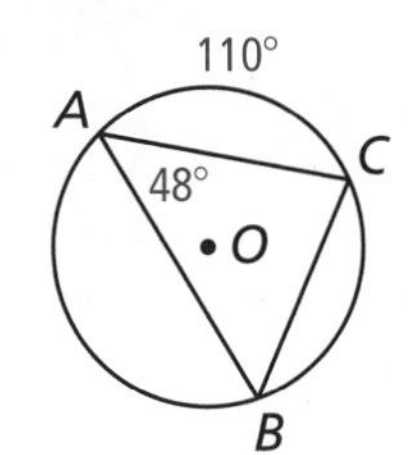


**14.** **a.** $m\angle A$
**b.** $m\widehat{CE}$
**c.** $m\angle C$
**d.** $m\angle D$
**e.** $m\angle ABE$

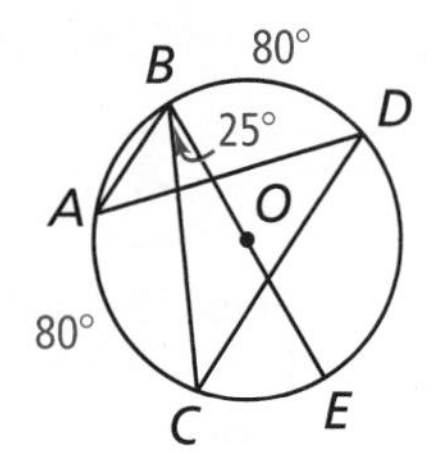


**15. Think About a Plan** What kind of trapezoid can be inscribed in a circle? Justify your response.

- Draw several diagrams to make a conjecture.
- How can parallel lines help?

**Find the value of each variable. For each circle, the dot represents the center.**

**16.**

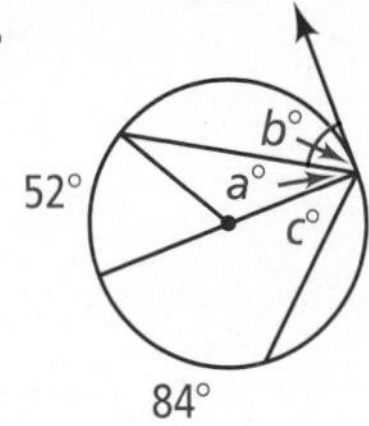


**17.**

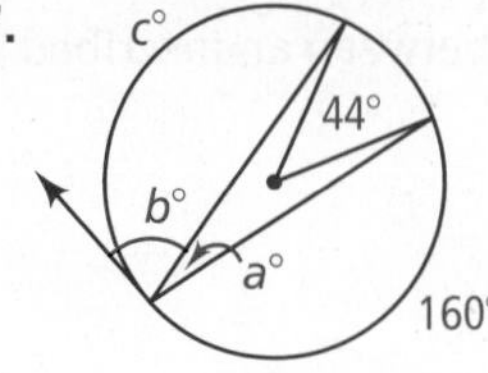


**18.**

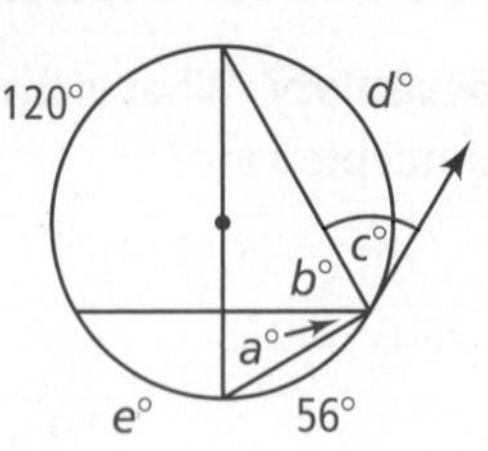


**Write a proof for Exercises 19 and 20.**

Proof **19.** Inscribed Angle Theorem, Case II

**Given:** $\odot O$ with inscribed $\angle ABC$

**Prove:** $m\angle ABC = \frac{1}{2} m\overset{\frown}{AC}$

(*Hint:* Use the Inscribed Angle Theorem, Case I.)

Proof **20.** Inscribed Angle Theorem, Case III

**Given:** $\odot S$ with inscribed $\angle PQR$

**Prove:** $m\angle PQR = \frac{1}{2} m\overset{\frown}{PR}$

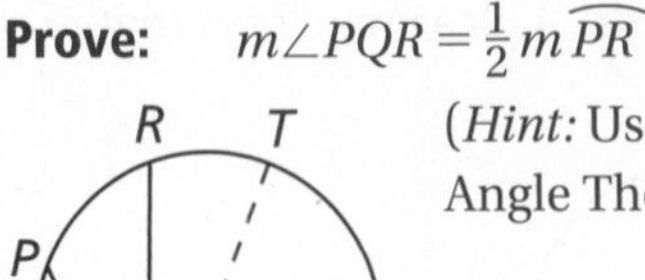


(*Hint:* Use the Inscribed Angle Theorem, Case I.)

**21. Television** The director of a telecast wants the option of showing the same scene from three different views.

**a.** Explain why cameras in the positions shown in the diagram will transmit the same scene.

**b. Reasoning** Will the scenes look the same when the director views them on the control room monitors? Explain.

**22. Reasoning** Can a rhombus that is not a square be inscribed in a circle? Justify your answer.

**23. Constructions** The diagrams below show the construction of a tangent to a circle from a point outside the circle. Explain why $\overleftrightarrow{BC}$ must be tangent to $\odot A$. (*Hint:* Copy the third diagram and draw $\overline{AC}$.)

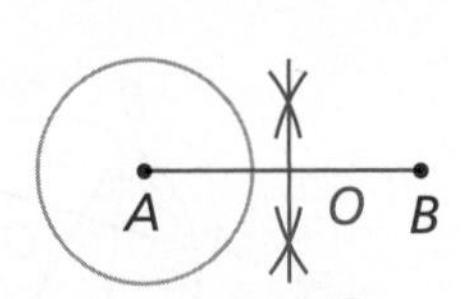


**Given:** $\odot A$ and point $B$ Construct the midpoint of $\overline{AB}$. Label the point $O$.

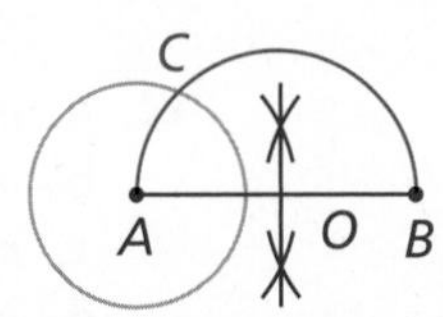


Construct a semicircle with radius $OA$ and center $O$. Label its intersection with $\odot A$ as $C$.

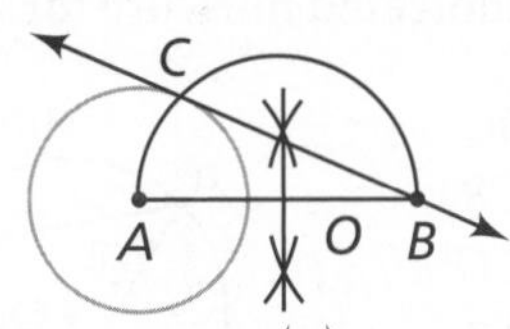


Draw $\overleftrightarrow{BC}$.

**Write a proof for Exercises 24–27.**

Proof **24.** Inscribed Angle Theorem, Corollary 1

**Given:** $\odot O$, $\angle A$ intercepts $\overset{\frown}{BC}$, $\angle D$ intercepts $\overset{\frown}{BC}$.

**Prove:** $\angle A \cong \angle D$

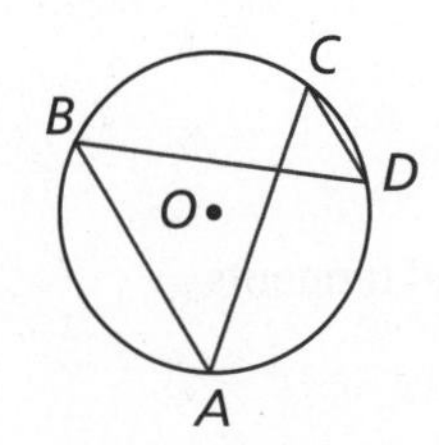


Proof **25.** Inscribed Angle Theorem, Corollary 2

**Given:** $\odot O$ with $\angle CAB$ inscribed in a semicircle

**Prove:** $\angle CAB$ is a right angle.

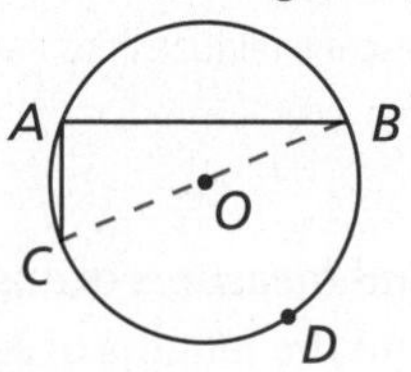


Proof **26.** Inscribed Angle Theorem, Corollary 3

**Given:** Quadrilateral $ABCD$ inscribed in $\odot O$

**Prove:** $\angle A$ and $\angle C$ are supplementary. $\angle B$ and $\angle D$ are supplementary.

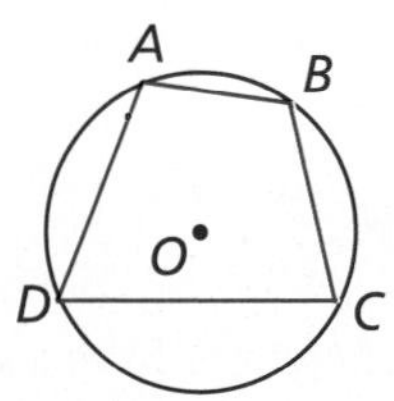


Proof **27.** Theorem 87

**Given:** $\overline{GH}$ and tangent $\ell$ intersecting $\odot E$ at $H$

**Prove:** $m\angle GHI = \frac{1}{2} m\overset{\frown}{GFH}$

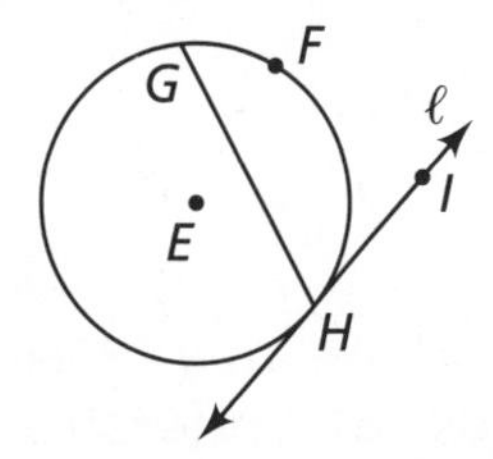


## Challenge

**Reasoning Is the statement *true* or *false*? If it is true, give a convincing argument. If it is false, give a counterexample.**

**28.** If two angles inscribed in a circle are congruent, then they intercept the same arc.

**29.** If an inscribed angle is a right angle, then it is inscribed in a semicircle.

Proof **30.** Prove that if two arcs of a circle are included between parallel chords, then the arcs are congruent.

**31. Constructions** Draw two segments. Label their lengths $x$ and $y$. Construct the geometric mean of $x$ and $y$. (*Hint:* Recall a theorem about a geometric mean.)

# 12-6 Angle Measures and Segment Lengths

G.C.2 Identify and describe relationships among inscribed angles, radii, and chords . . .

**Objectives** To find measures of angles formed by chords, secants, and tangents
To find the lengths of segments associated with circles

**Solve It!** Write your solution to the Solve It in the space below.

**Essential Understanding** Angles formed by intersecting lines have a special relationship to the related arcs formed when the lines intersect a circle. In this lesson, you will study angles and arcs formed by lines intersecting either within a circle or outside a circle.

take note

### Theorem 88

The measure of an angle formed by two lines that intersect inside a circle is half the sum of the measures of the intercepted arcs.

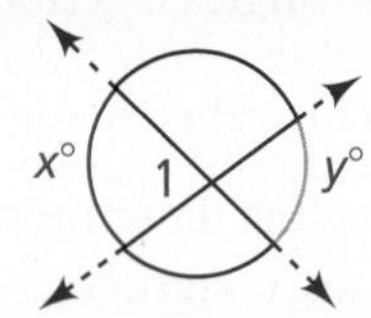


$$m\angle 1 = \frac{1}{2}(x + y)$$

### Theorem 89

The measure of an angle formed by two lines that intersect outside a circle is half the difference of the measures of the intercepted arcs.

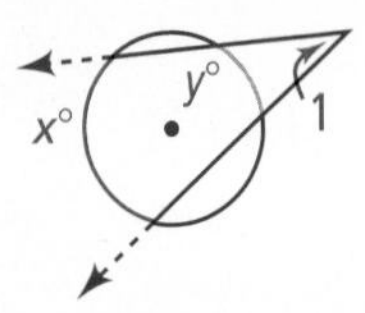


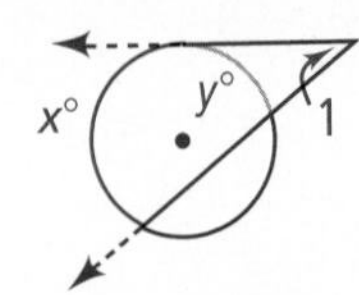


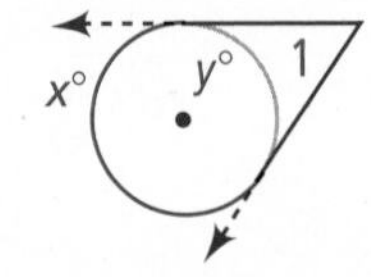


$$m\angle 1 = \frac{1}{2}(x - y)$$

*You will prove Theorem 89 In Exercises 28 and 29.*

In Theorem 88, the lines from a point outside the circle going through the circle are called secants. A **secant** is a line that intersects a circle at two points. $\overleftrightarrow{AB}$ is a secant, $\overrightarrow{AB}$ is a secant ray, and $\overline{AB}$ is a secant segment. A chord is part of a secant.

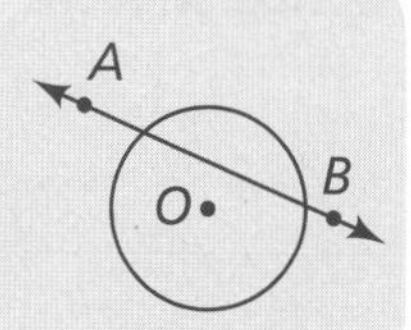


## Proof Proof of Theorem 88

**Given:** $\odot O$ with intersecting chords $\overline{AC}$ and $\overline{BD}$

**Prove:** $m\angle 1 = \frac{1}{2}(m\widehat{AB} + m\widehat{CD})$

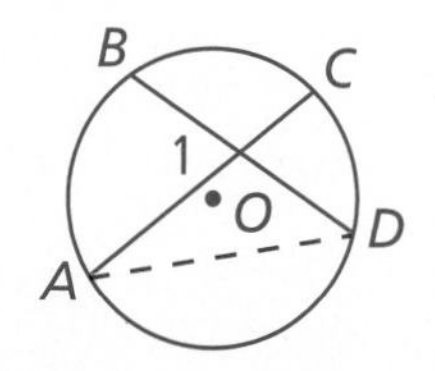


Begin by drawing auxiliary $\overline{AD}$ as shown in the diagram.

$m\angle BDA = \frac{1}{2}m\widehat{AB}$, and $m\angle CAD = \frac{1}{2}m\widehat{CD}$

Inscribed Angle Theorem

$m\angle 1 = m\angle BDA + m\angle CAD$

△ Exterior Angle Theorem

$m\angle 1 = \frac{1}{2}m\widehat{AB} + \frac{1}{2}m\widehat{CD}$

Substitute.

$m\angle 1 = \frac{1}{2}(m\widehat{AB} + m\widehat{CD})$

Distributive Property

## ONLINE PROBLEMS Problem 1 Finding Angle Measures

**Got It?** What is the value of each variable?

**a.**

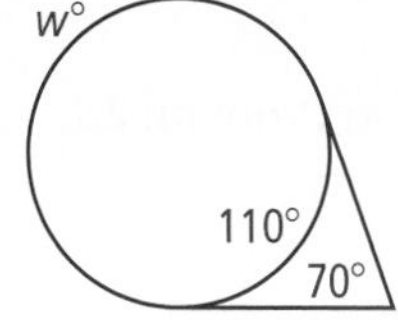


**b.**

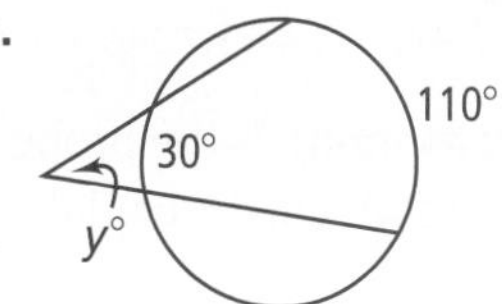


**c.**

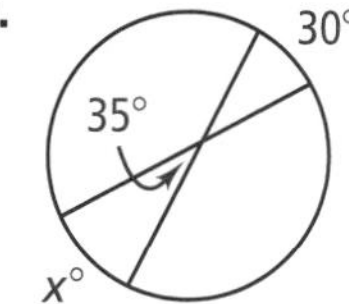

**Practice** **Algebra** Find the value of each variable.

1. 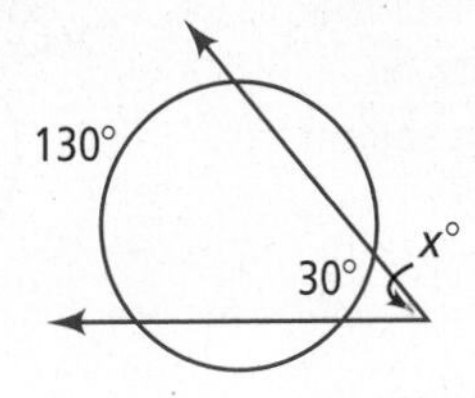


2. 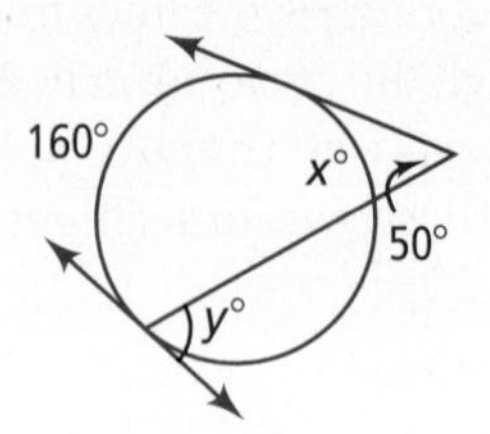

## Problem 2 Finding an Arc Measure

**Think**

**How can you represent the measures of the arcs?**

**Got It?** **a.** A departing space probe sends back a picture of Earth as it crosses Earth's equator. The angle formed by the two tangents to the equator is 20°. What is the measure of the arc of the equator that is visible to the space probe?

**b. Reasoning** Is the probe or the geostationary satellite in Problem 2 closer to Earth? Explain.

**Practice** **3. Algebra** Find the value of each variable.

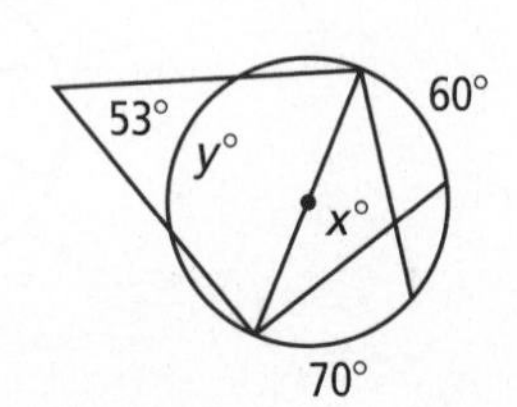

**4. Photography** You focus your camera on a circular fountain. Your camera is at the vertex of the angle formed by tangents to the fountain. You estimate that this angle is 40°. What is the measure of the arc of the circular basin of the fountain that will be in the photograph?

**Essential Understanding** There is a special relationship between two intersecting chords, two intersecting secants, or a secant that intersects a tangent. This relationship allows you to find the lengths of unknown segments.

From a given point $P$, you can draw two segments to a circle along infinitely many lines. For example, $\overline{PA_1}$ and $\overline{PB_1}$ lie along one such line. Theorem 90 states the surprising result that no matter which line you use, the product of the lengths $PA \cdot PB$ remains constant.

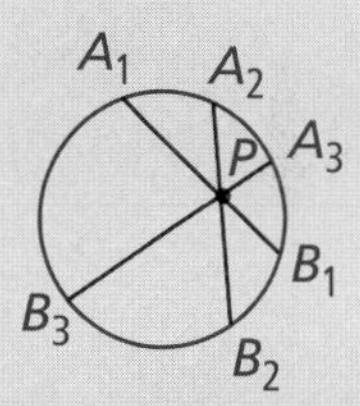


take note

## Theorem 90

For a given point and circle, the product of the lengths of the two segments from the point to the circle is constant along any line through the point and circle.

I.

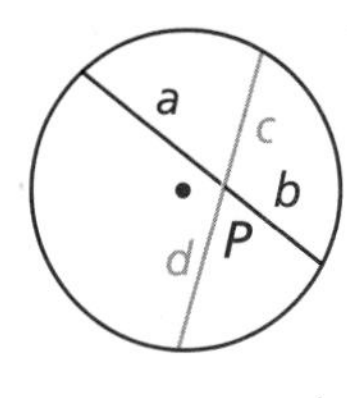


$a \cdot b = c \cdot d$

II.

x w P y z

$(w + x)w = (y + z)y$

III.

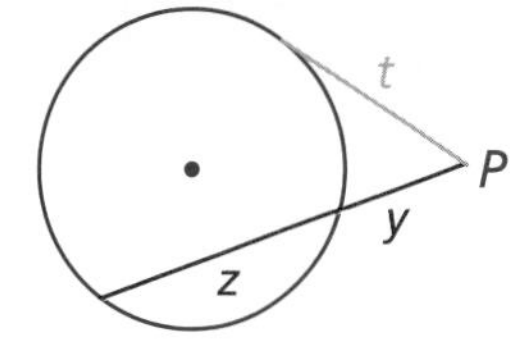


$(y + z)y = t^2$

As you use Theorem 90, remember the following.

- **Case I:** The products of the chord segments are equal.
- **Case II:** The products of the secants and their outer segments are equal.
- **Case III:** The product of a secant and its outer segment equals the square of the tangent.

Here is a proof for Case I. You will prove Case II and Case III in Exercises 30 and 31.

## Proof Proof of Theorem 90, Case I

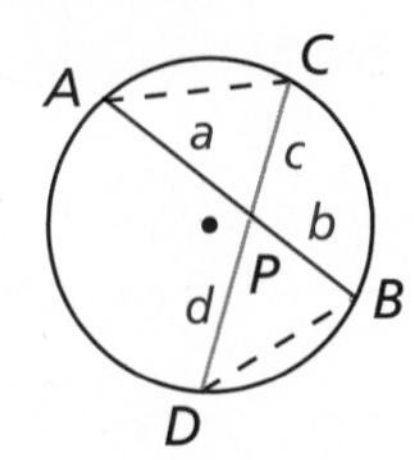


**Given:** A circle with chords $\overline{AB}$ and $\overline{CD}$ intersecting at $P$

**Prove:** $a \cdot b = c \cdot d$

Draw $\overline{AC}$ and $\overline{BD}$. $\angle A \cong \angle D$ and $\angle C \cong \angle B$ because each pair intercepts the same arc, and angles that intercept the same arc are congruent. $\triangle APC \sim \triangle DPB$ by the Angle-Angle Similarity Postulate. The lengths of corresponding sides of similar triangles are proportional, so $\frac{a}{d} = \frac{c}{b}$. Therefore, $a \cdot b = c \cdot d$.

## Problem 3 Finding Segment Lengths

**Plan**

**How can you identify the segments needed to use Theorem 90?**

**Got It?** What is the value of the variable to the nearest tenth?

**a.**

**b.**

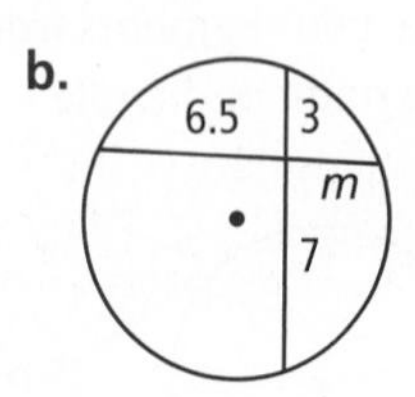

**Practice** **Algebra** **Find the value of each variable using the given chord, secant, and tangent lengths. If the answer is not a whole number, round to the nearest tenth.**

**5.**

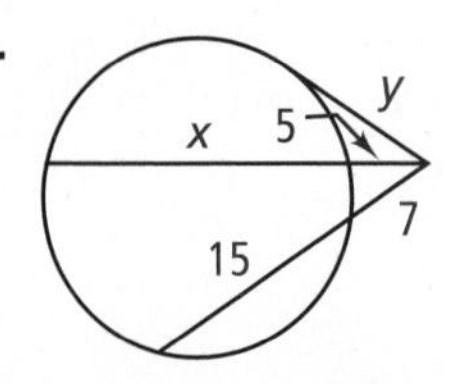


**6.**

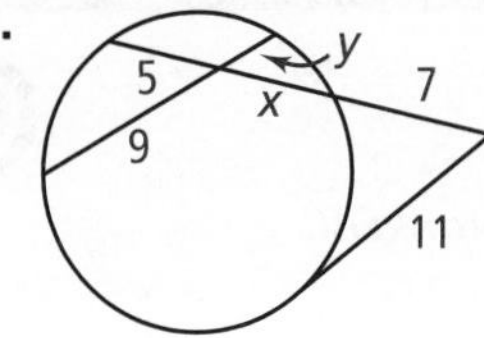

## Lesson Check

### Do you know HOW?

**7.** What is the value of $x$?

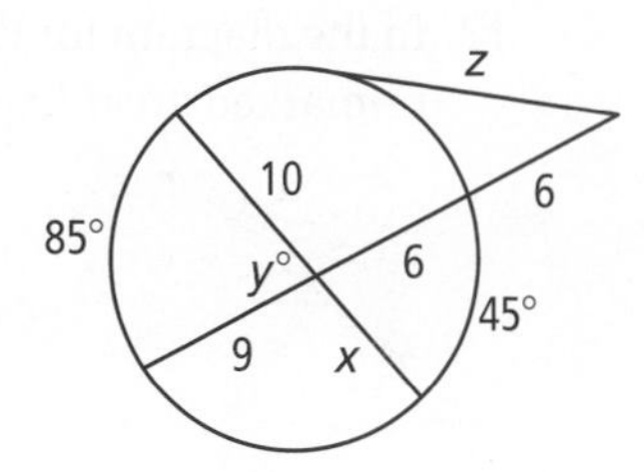


**8.** What is the value of $y$?

**9.** What is the value of $z$, to the nearest tenth?

**10.** The measure of the angle formed by two tangents to a circle is 80. What are the measures of the intercepted arcs?

## Do you UNDERSTAND?

**11. Vocabulary** Describe the difference between a *secant* and a *tangent*.

**12.** In the diagram for Exercises 7–9, is it possible to find the measures of the unmarked arcs? Explain.

**13. Error Analysis** To find the value of $x$, a student wrote the equation $(7.5)6 = x^2$. What error did the student make?

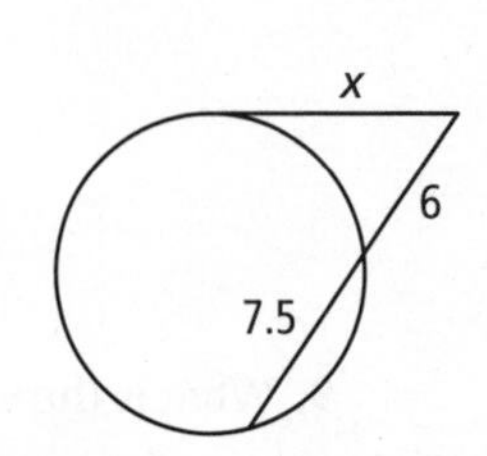

# More Practice and Problem-Solving Exercises

## B Apply

**Algebra** $\overline{CA}$ and $\overline{CB}$ are tangents to $\odot O$. Write an expression for each arc or angle in terms of the given variable.

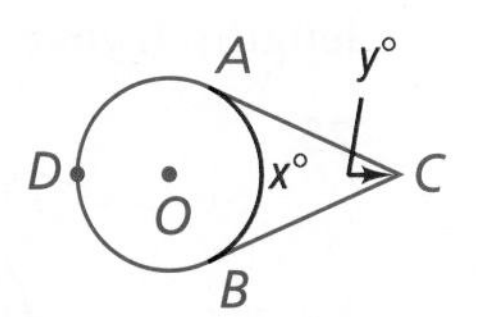


**14.** $m\widehat{ADB}$ using $x$ **15.** $m\angle C$ using $x$ **16.** $m\widehat{AB}$ using $y$

**Find the diameter of $\odot O$. A line that appears to be tangent is tangent. If your answer is not a whole number, round it to the nearest tenth.**

**17.**

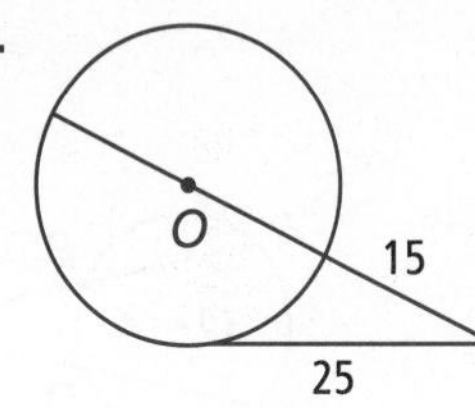


**18.**

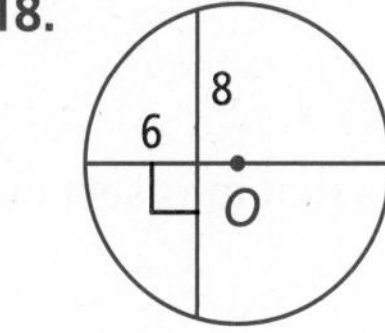


**19.**

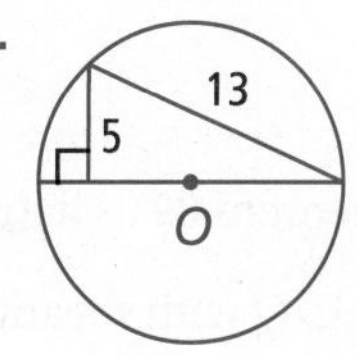


**20.** A circle is inscribed in a quadrilateral whose four angles have measures 85, 76, 94, and 105. Find the measures of the four arcs between consecutive points of tangency.

**STEM 21. Engineering** The basis for the design of the Wankel rotary engine is an equilateral triangle. Each side of the triangle is a chord to an arc of a circle. The opposite vertex of the triangle is the center of the circle that forms the arc. In the diagram below, each side of the equilateral triangle is 8 in. long.

Wankel engine

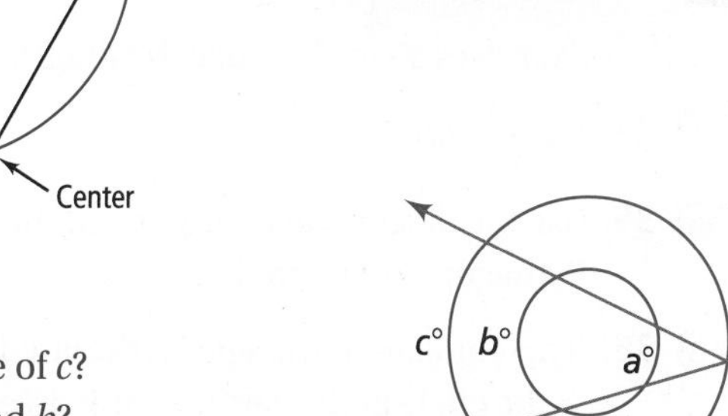

**a.** Use what you know about equilateral triangles and find the value of $x$.

**b. Reasoning** Copy the diagram and complete the circle with the given center. Then use Theorem 90 to find the value of $x$. Show that your answers to parts (a) and (b) are equal.

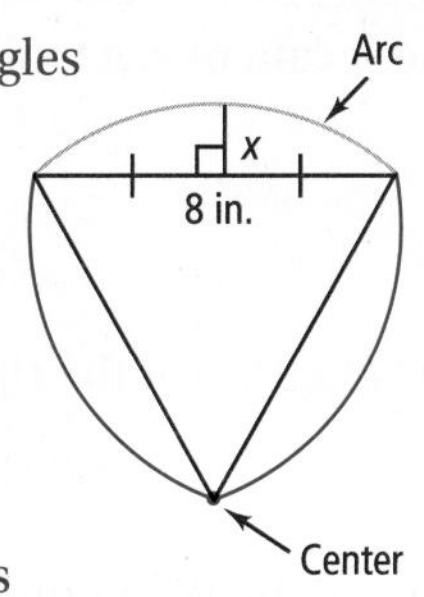


**22. Think About a Plan** In the diagram, the circles are concentric. What is a formula you could use to find the value of $c$ in terms of $a$ and $b$?

- How can you use the inscribed angle to find the value of $c$?
- What is the relationship of the inscribed angle to $a$ and $b$?

c° b° a°

**23.** $\triangle PQR$ is inscribed in a circle with $m\angle P = 70$, $m\angle Q = 50$, and $m\angle R = 60$. What are the measures of $\widehat{PQ}$, $\widehat{QR}$, and $\widehat{PR}$?

**24. Reasoning** Use the diagram at the right. If you know the values of $x$ and $y$, how can you find the measure of each numbered angle?

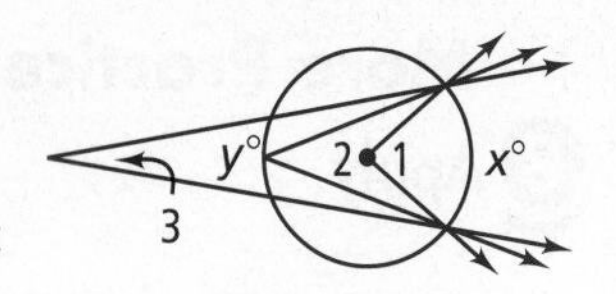


**Algebra Find the values of $x$ and $y$ using the given chord, secant, and tangent lengths. If your answer is not a whole number, round it to the nearest tenth.**

**25.**

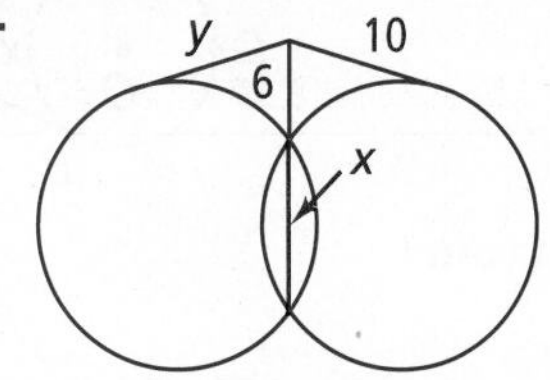


**26.**

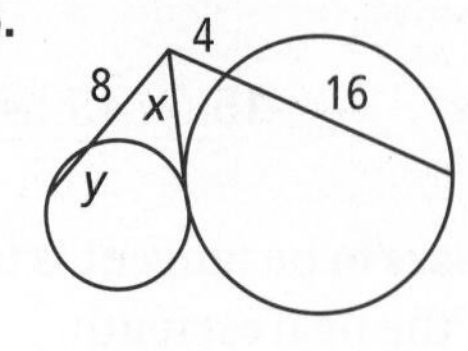


**27.**

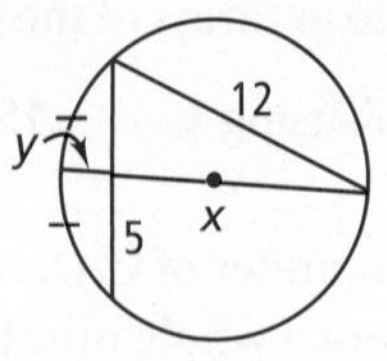


**Proof 28.** Prove Theorem 89 as it applies to two secants that intersect outside a circle.

**Given:** $\odot O$ with secants $\overline{CA}$ and $\overline{CE}$

**Prove:** $m\angle ACE = \frac{1}{2}(m\widehat{AE} - m\widehat{BD})$

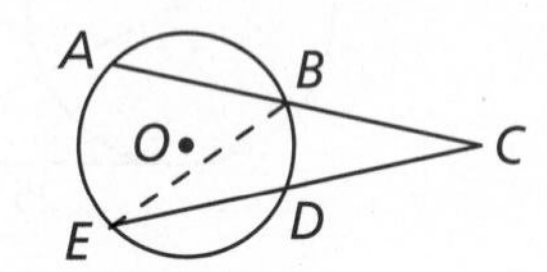


**Proof 29.** Prove the other two cases of Theorem 89. (See Exercise 28.)

**For Exercises 30 and 31, write proofs that use similar triangles.**

**Proof 30.** Prove Theorem 90, Case II.

**Proof 31.** Prove Theorem 90, Case III.

**32.** The diagram at the right shows a *unit circle,* a circle with radius 1.

**a.** What triangle is similar to $\triangle ABE$?

**b.** Describe the connection between the ratio for the tangent of $\angle A$ and the segment that is tangent to $\odot A$.

**c.** The secant ratio is $\frac{\text{hypotenuse}}{\text{length of leg adjacent to an angle}}$. Describe the connection between the ratio for the secant of $\angle A$ and the segment that is the secant in the unit circle.

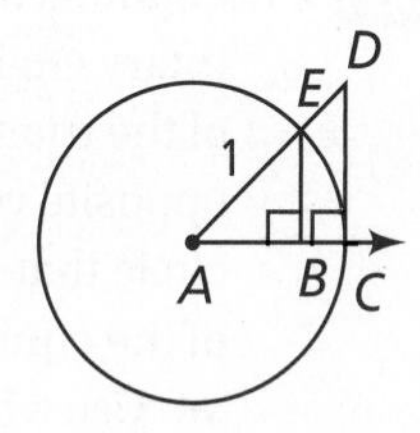

## Challenge

**For Exercises 33 and 34, use the diagram at the right. Prove each statement.**

**Proof 33.** $m\angle 1 + m\widehat{PQ} = 180$

**Proof 34.** $m\angle 1 + m\angle 2 = m\widehat{QR}$

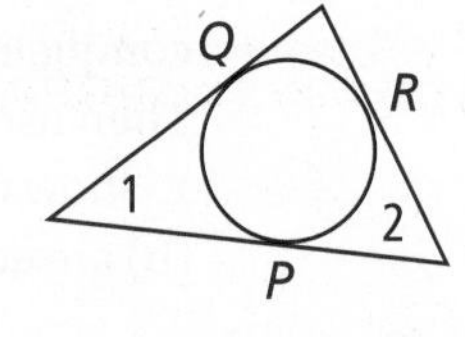


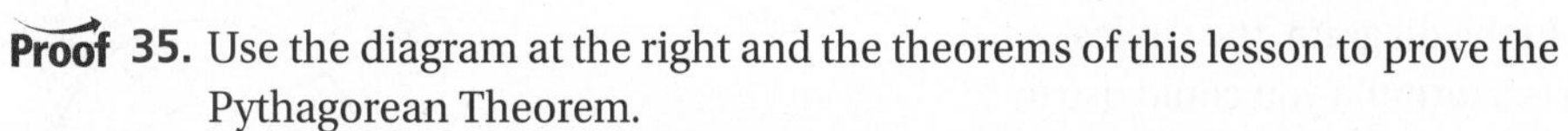

**Proof 35.** Use the diagram at the right and the theorems of this lesson to prove the Pythagorean Theorem.

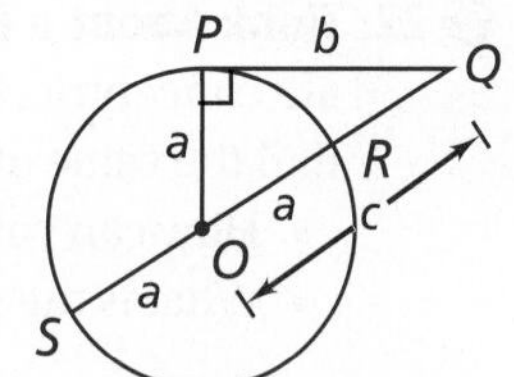


**Proof 36.** If an equilateral triangle is inscribed in a circle, prove that the tangents to the circle at the vertices form an equilateral triangle.

# 12 Chapter Review

## 12-1 Circles and Arcs

### Quick Review

A **circle** is the set of all points in a plane equidistant from a point called the **center**. The **circumference** of a circle is $C = \pi d$ or $C = 2\pi r$. **Arc length** is a fraction of a circle's circumference. The length of $\widehat{AB} = \frac{m\widehat{AB}}{360} \cdot 2\pi r$.

Semicircle, Minor arc, Diameter, Radius, Central angle. $\widehat{ACB}$ is a major arc.

### Example

**A circle has a radius of 5 cm. What is the length of an arc measuring 80°?**

length of $\widehat{AB} = \frac{m\widehat{AB}}{360} \cdot 2\pi r$ Use the arc length formula.

$= \frac{80}{360} \cdot 2\pi(5)$ Substitute.

$= \frac{20}{9}\pi$ Simplify.

The length of the arc is $\frac{20}{9}\pi$ cm.

### Exercises

**Find each measure.**

1. $m\angle APD$
2. $m\widehat{AC}$
3. $m\widehat{ABD}$
4. $m\angle CPA$

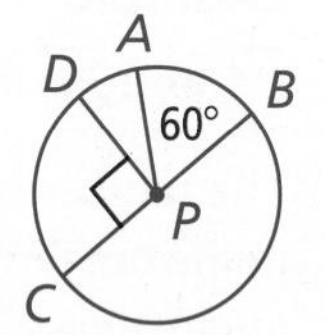


**Find the length of each arc shown in red. Leave your answer in terms of $\pi$.**

5. 110° 4 in.

6.

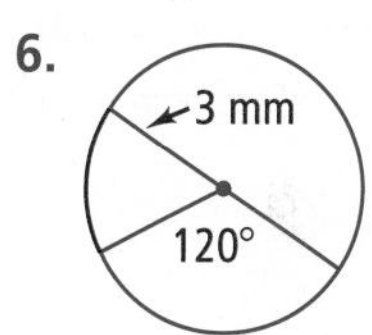


7.

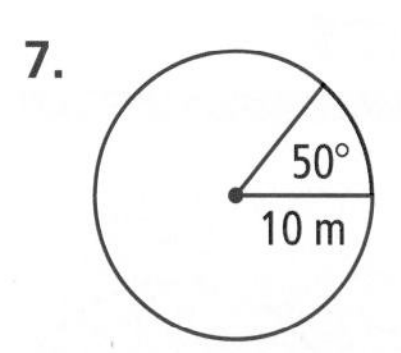


8.

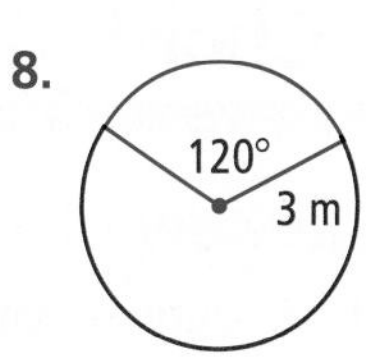


## 12-2 Areas of Circles and Sectors

### Quick Review

The area of a circle is $A = \pi r^2$. A **sector of a circle** is a region bounded by two radii and their intercepted arc. The area of sector $APB = \frac{m\widehat{AB}}{360} \cdot \pi r^2$.

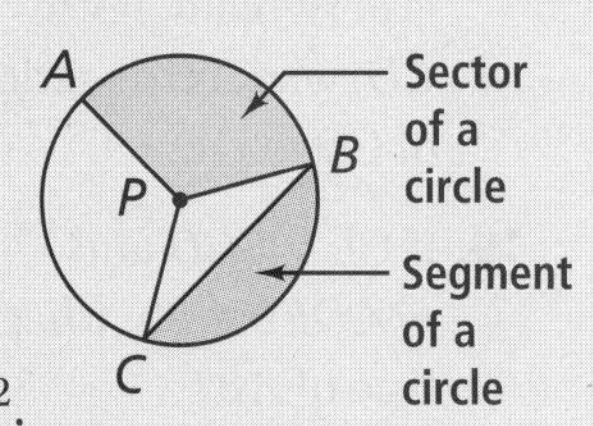


A **segment of a circle** is the part bounded by an arc and the segment joining its endpoints.

### Example

**What is the area of the shaded region?**

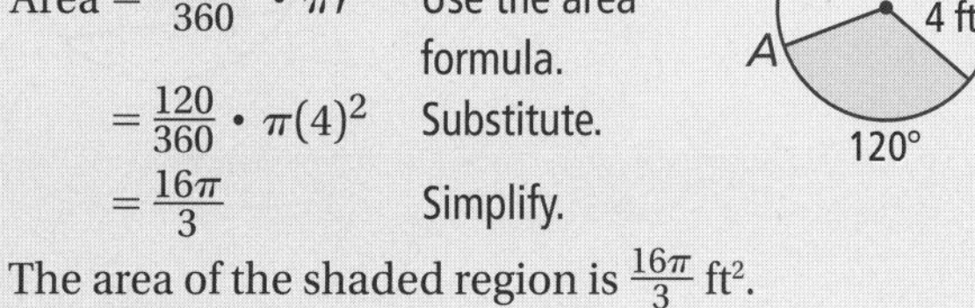

Area $= \frac{m\widehat{AB}}{360} \cdot \pi r^2$ Use the area formula.

$= \frac{120}{360} \cdot \pi(4)^2$ Substitute.

$= \frac{16\pi}{3}$ Simplify.

The area of the shaded region is $\frac{16\pi}{3}$ ft².

A, B, 4 ft, 120°

### Exercises

**What is the area of each circle? Leave your answer in terms of $\pi$.**

9.

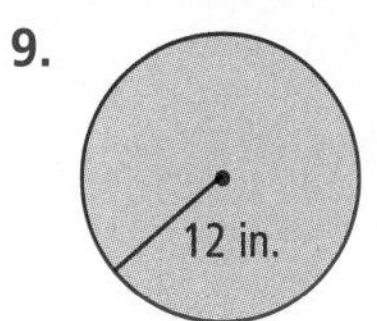


10.

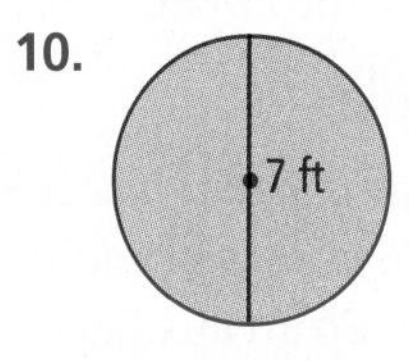


**Find the area of each shaded region. Round your answer to the nearest tenth.**

11.

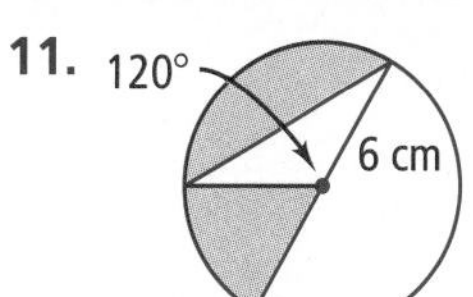


12.

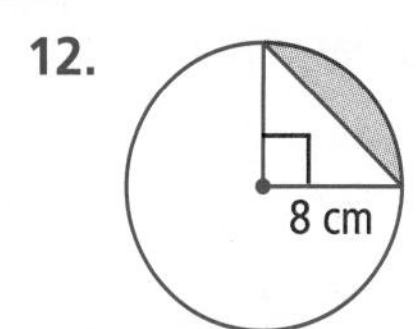


13. A circle has a radius of 20 cm. What is the area of the smaller segment of the circle formed by a 60° arc? Round to the nearest tenth.

## 12-3 Tangent Lines

### Quick Review

A **tangent** to a circle is a line that intersects the circle at exactly one point. The radius to that point is perpendicular to the tangent. From any point outside a circle, you can draw two segments tangent to a circle. Those segments are congruent.

### Example

**$\overrightarrow{PA}$ and $\overrightarrow{PB}$ are tangents. Find $x$.**

The radii are perpendicular to the tangents. Add the angle measures of the quadrilateral:

$$x + 90 + 90 + 40 = 360$$
$$x + 220 = 360$$
$$x = 140$$

### Exercises

**Use $\odot O$ for Exercises 14–16.**

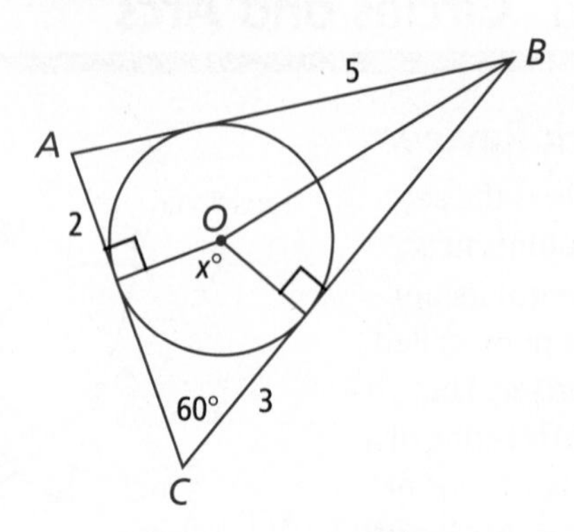


**14.** What is the perimeter of $\triangle ABC$?

**15.** $OB = \sqrt{28}$. What is the radius?

**16.** What is the value of $x$?

## 12-4 Chords and Arcs

### Quick Review

A **chord** is a segment whose endpoints are on a circle. Congruent chords are equidistant from the center. A diameter that bisects a chord that is not a diameter is perpendicular to the chord. The perpendicular bisector of a chord contains the center of the circle.

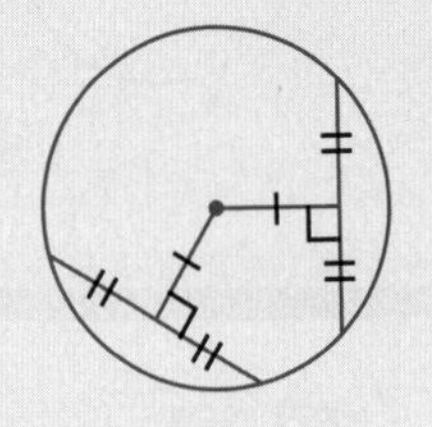

### Example

Since the chord is bisected, $m\angle ACB = 90$. The radius is 13 units. So an auxiliary segment from $A$ to $B$ is 13 units. Use the Pythagorean Theorem.

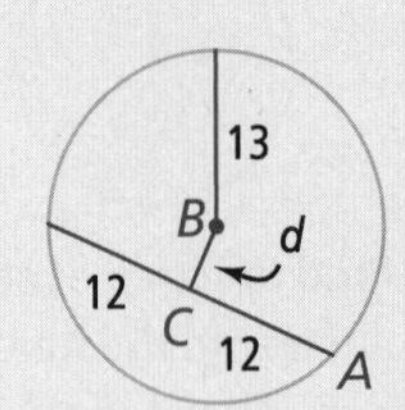


$$d^2 + 12^2 = 13^2$$
$$d^2 = 25$$
$$d = 5$$

### Exercises

**Use the figure below for Exercises 17–19.**

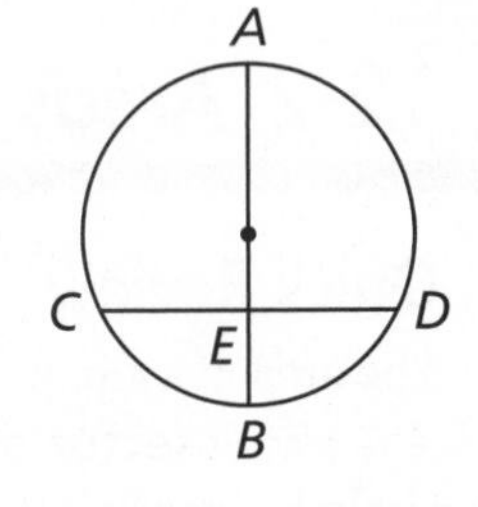


**17.** If $\overline{AB}$ is a diameter and $CE = ED$, then $m\angle AEC = \underline{\quad ? \quad}$.

**18.** If $\overline{AB}$ is a diameter and is at right angles to $\overline{CD}$, what is the ratio of $CD$ to $DE$?

**19.** If $CE = \frac{1}{2}CD$ and $m\angle DEB = 90$, what is true of $\overline{AB}$?

**Use the circle below for Exercises 20 and 21.**

**20.** What is the value of $x$?

**21.** What is the value of $y$?

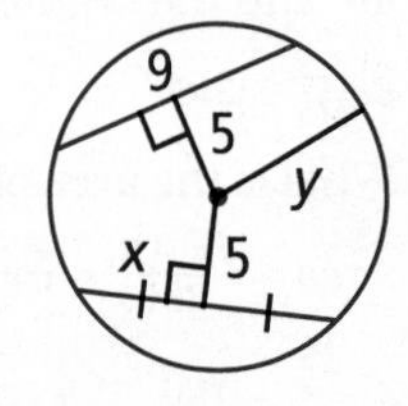

# 12-5 Inscribed Angles

## Quick Review

An **inscribed angle** has its vertex on a circle and its sides are chords. An **intercepted arc** has its endpoints on the sides of an inscribed angle, and its other points in the interior of the angle. The measure of an inscribed angle is half the measure of its intercepted arc.

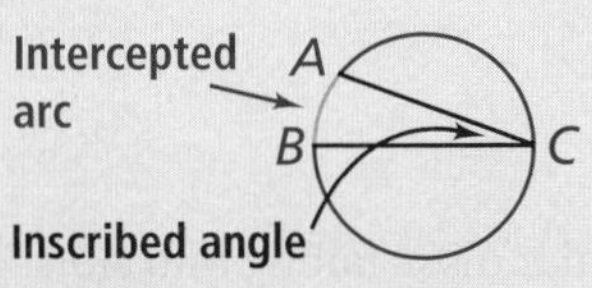


## Example

**What is $m\widehat{PS}$? What is $m\angle R$?**

The $m\angle Q = 60$ is half of $m$, so $m\widehat{PS} = 120$. $\angle R$ intercepts the same arc as $\angle Q$, so $m\angle R = 60$.

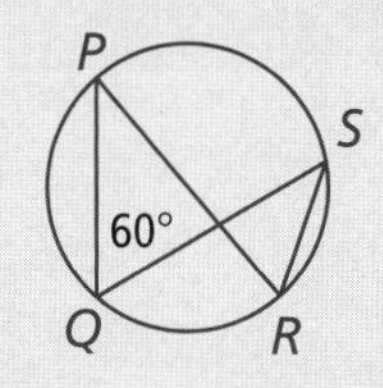


## Exercises

**Find the value of each variable. Line $\ell$ is a tangent.**

**22.**

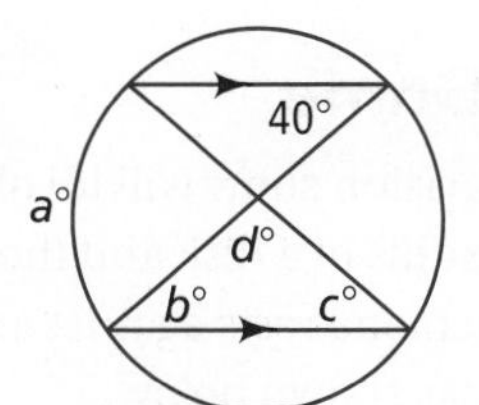


**23.**

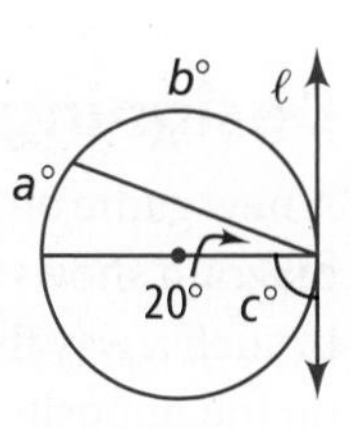


**24.**

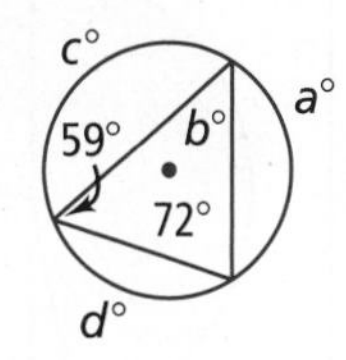


**25.**

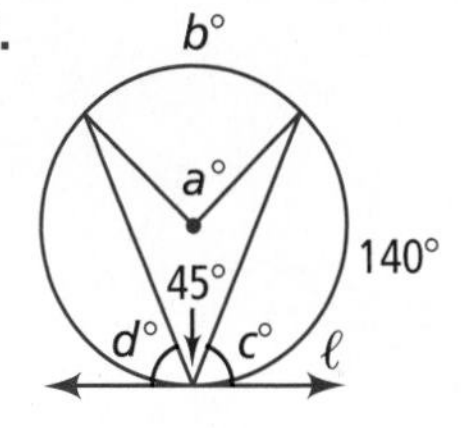


# 12-6 Angle Measures and Segment Lengths

## Quick Review

A **secant** is a line that intersects a circle at two points. The following relationships are true:

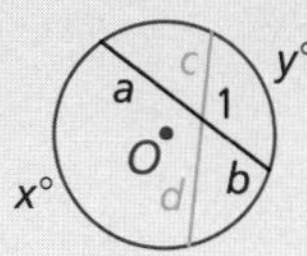


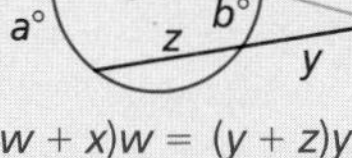


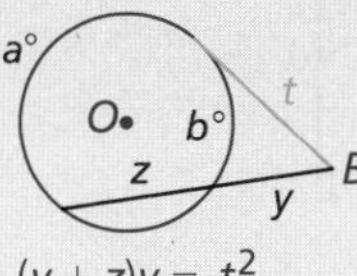


$a \cdot b = c \cdot d$

$m\angle 1 = \frac{1}{2}(x + y)$

$(w + x)w = (y + z)y$

$m\angle B = \frac{1}{2}(a - b)$

$(y + z)y = t^2$

$m\angle B = \frac{1}{2}(a - b)$

## Example

**What is the value of $x$?**

$(x + 10)10 = (19 + 9)9$

$10x + 100 = 252$

$x = 15.2$

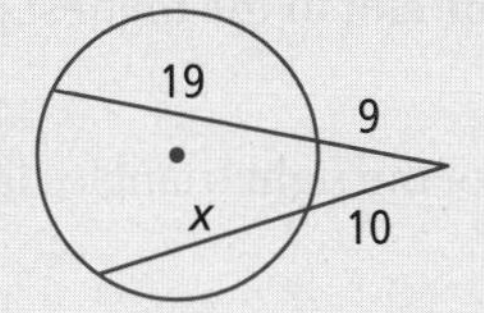


## Exercises

**Find the value of each variable.**

**26.**

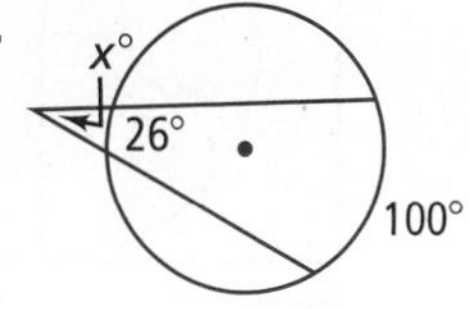


**27.**

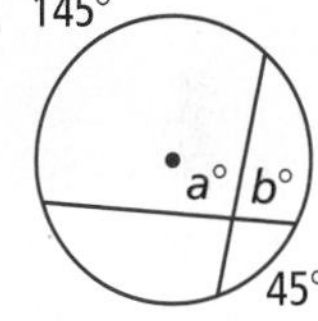


**28.**

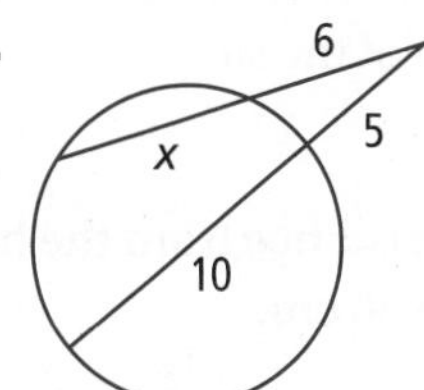


**29.**

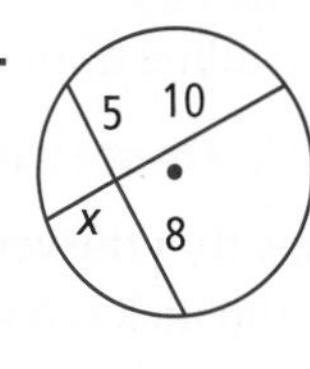

# Pull It All Together

## Designing a Game

A new game on a television show will involve flat circular disks falling into slots. The diagram shows the radius of a disk and the dimensions of a slot. The disks always fall in such a way that each one rests against a side of the slot, first on one side and then on the opposite side, as shown below.

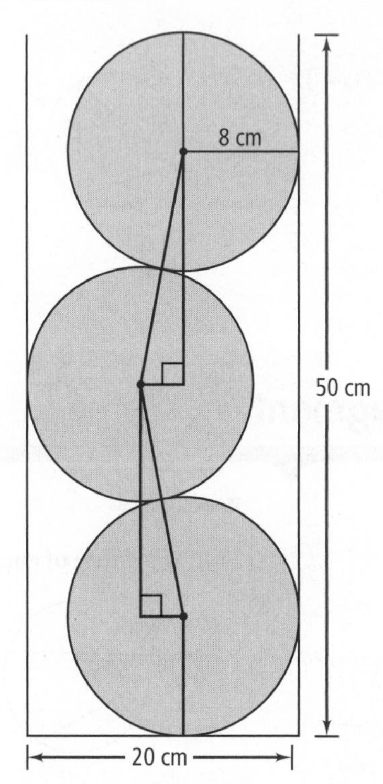


The game designer must verify that three disks will fit into a slot, without the top disk protruding from the top of the slot.

### Task Description

**Show that the vertical distance from the bottom of the slot to the highest point on the top disk is less than 50 cm.**

- How would knowing the length of the longer leg of the right triangles in the diagram help you solve the problem?
- What are the lengths of the hypotenuse and shorter leg of the right triangles? How can you use these measurements to find the length of the longer leg?

# Postulates and Theorems

## Postulates

### Postulate 1
Through any two points there is exactly one line.

### Postulate 2
If two distinct lines intersect, then they intersect in exactly one point.

### Postulate 3
If two distinct planes intersect, then they intersect in exactly one line.

### Postulate 4
Through any three noncollinear points there is exactly one plane.

### Postulate 5
**Ruler Postulate**
Every point on a line can be paired with a real number. This makes a one-to-one correspondence between the points on the line and the real numbers.

### Postulate 6
**Segment Addition Postulate**
If three points $A$, $B$, and $C$ are collinear and $B$ is between $A$ and $C$, then $AB + BC = AC$.

### Postulate 7
**Protractor Postulate**
Consider $\overrightarrow{OB}$ and a point $A$ on one side of $\overrightarrow{OB}$. Every ray of the form $\overrightarrow{OA}$ can be paired one to one with a real number from 0 to 180.

### Postulate 8
**Angle Addition Postulate**
If point $B$ is in the interior of $\angle AOC$, then $m\angle AOB + m\angle BOC = m\angle AOC$.

### Postulate 9
**Linear Pair Postulate**
If two angles form a linear pair, then they are supplementary.

### Postulate 10
**Area Addition Postulate**
The area of a region is the sum of the area of its nonoverlapping parts.

### Postulate 11
**Same-Side Interior Angles Postulate**
If a transversal intersects two parallel lines, then same-side interior angles are supplementary.

### Postulate 12
**Parallel Postulate**
Through a point not on a line, there is one and only one line parallel to the given line.

### Postulate 13
**Perpendicular Postulate**
Through a point not on a line, there is one and only one line perpendicular to the given line.

### Postulate 14
**Side-Side-Side (SSS) Postulate**
If three sides of one triangle are congruent to the three sides of another triangle, then the two triangles are congruent.

### Postulate 15
**Side-Angle-Side (SAS) Postulate**
If two sides and the included angle of one triangle are congruent to two sides and the included angle of another triangles, then the two triangles are congruent.

### Postulate 16
**Angle-Side-Angle (ASA) Postulate**
If two angles and the included side of one triangle are congruent to two angles and the included side of another triangle, then the two triangles are congruent.

## Theorems

### Theorem 1
**Vertical Angles Theorem**
Vertical angles are congruent.

### Theorem 2
**Congruent Supplements Theorem**
If two angles are supplements of the same angle (or of two congruent angles), then the two angles are congruent.

### Theorem 3
**Congruent Complements Theorem**
If two angles are complements of the same angle (or of two congruent angles), then the two angles are congruent.

### Theorem 4
All right angles are congruent.

### Theorem 5
If two angles are congruent and supplementary, then each is a right angle.

### Theorem 6
**Alternate Interior Angles Theorem**
If a transversal intersects two parallel lines, the alternate interior angles are congruent.

### Theorem 7
**Corresponding Angles Theorem**
If a transversal intersects two parallel lines, then corresponding angles are congruent.

### Theorem 8
**Alternate Exterior Angles Theorem**
If a transversal intersects two parallel lines, then alternate exterior angles are congruent.

### Theorem 9
**Converse of the Corresponding Angles Theorem**
If two lines and a transversal form corresponding angles that are congruent, then the two lines are parallel.

### Theorem 10
**Converse of the Alternate Interior Angles Theorem**
If two lines and a transversal form alternate interior angles that are congruent, then the two lines are parallel.

### Theorem 11
**Converse of the Same-Side Interior Angles Postulate**
If two lines and a transversal form same-side interior angles that are congruent, then the two lines are parallel.

### Theorem 12
**Converse of the Alternate Exterior Angles Theorem**
If two lines and a transversal form alternate exterior angles that are congruent, then the two lines are parallel.

### Theorem 13
If two lines are parallel to the same line, then they are parallel to each other.

### Theorem 14
In a plane, if two lines are perpendicular to the same line, then they are parallel to each other.

### Theorem 15
**Perpendicular Transversal Theorem**
In a plane, if a line is perpendicular to one of two parallel lines, then it is perpendicular to the other.

### Theorem 16
**Triangle Angle-Sum Theorem**
The sum of the measures of the angles of a triangle is 180.

### Theorem 17
**Triangle Exterior Angle Theorem**
The measure of each exterior angle of a triangle equals the sum of the measure of its two remote interior angles.

**Corollary**
The measure of an exterior angle of a triangle is greater than the measure of each of its remote interior angles.

### Theorem 18
**Third Angles Theorem**
If two angles of one triangle are congruent to two angles of another triangle, than the third angles are congruent.

### Theorem 19
**Angle-Angle-Side (AAS) Theorem**
If two angles and a nonincluded side of one triangle are congruent to two angles and a nonincluded side of another triangle, then the two triangles are congruent.

### Theorem 20
**Isosceles Triangle Theorem**
If two sides of a triangle are congruent, then the angles opposite those sides are congruent.

**Corollary**
If a triangle is equilateral, then the triangle is equiangular.

### Theorem 21
**Converse of the Isosceles Triangle Theorem**
If two angles of a triangle are congruent, then the sides opposite the angles are congruent.

**Corollary**
If a triangle is equiangular, then it is equilateral.

### Theorem 22
If a line bisects the vertex angle of an isosceles triangle, then the line is also the perpendicular bisector of the base.

### Theorem 23
**Hypotenuse-Leg (HL) Theorem**
If the hypotenuse and a leg of one right triangle are congruent to the hypotenuse and a leg of another right triangle, then the triangles are congruent.

### Theorem 24
**Triangle Midsegment Theorem**
If a line segment joins the midpoints of two sides of a triangle, then the segment is parallel to the third side and is half as long.

### Theorem 25
**Perpendicular Bisector Theorem**
If a point is on the perpendicular bisector of a line segment, then it is equidistant from the endpoints of the segment.

### Theorem 26
**Converse of the Perpendicular Bisector Theorem**
If a point is equidistant from the endpoints of a line segment, then it is on the perpendicular bisector of the segment.

### Theorem 27
**Angle Bisector Theorem**
If a point is on the bisector of an angle, then the point is equidistant from the sides of the angle.

### Theorem 28
**Converse of the Angle Bisector Theorem**
If a point in the interior of an angle is equidistant from the sides of the angle, then the point is on the angle bisector

### Theorem 29
**Concurrency of Perpendicular Bisectors Theorem**
The perpendicular bisectors of the sides of a triangle are concurrent at a point equidistant from the vertices.

### Theorem 30
**Concurrency of Angle Bisectors Theorem**
The bisectors of the angles of a triangle are concurrent at a point equidistant from the sides of the triangle.

### Theorem 31
**Concurrency of Medians Theorem**
The medians of a triangle are concurrent at a point that is two-thirds the distance from each vertex to the midpoint of the opposite side.

### Theorem 32
**Concurrency of Altitudes Theorem**
The lines that contain the altitudes of a triangle are concurrent.

### Theorem 33
If two sides of a triangle are not congruent, then the larger angle lies opposite the longer side.

### Theorem 34
If two angles of a triangle are not congruent, then the longer side lies opposite the larger angle.

### Theorem 35
**Triangle Inequality Theorem**
The sum of the lengths of any two sides of a triangle is greater than the length of the third side.

### Theorem 36
**The Hinge Theorem (SAS Inequality Theorem)**
If two sides of one triangle are congruent to two sides of another triangle and the included angles are not congruent, then the longer third side is opposite the larger included angle.

### Theorem 37
**Converse of the Hinge Theorem (SSS Inequality)**
If two sides of one triangle are congruent to two sides of another triangle and the third sides are not congruent, then the larger included angle is opposite the longer third side.

### Theorem 38
**Polygon Angle-Sum Theorem**
The sum of the measures of the angles of an $n$-gon is $(n - 2)180$.

**Corollary**
The measure of each angle of a regular $n$-gon is $\frac{(n-2)180}{n}$.

### Theorem 39
The sum of the measures of the exterior angles of a polygon, one at each vertex, is 360.

### Theorem 40
If a quadrilateral is a parallelogram, then its opposite sides are congruent.

### Theorem 41
If a quadrilateral is a parallelogram, then its consecutive angles are supplementary.

### Theorem 42
If a quadrilateral is a parallelogram, then its opposite angles are congruent.

### Theorem 43
If a quadrilateral is a parallelogram, then its diagonals bisect each other.

### Theorem 44
If three (or more) parallel lines cut off congruent segments on one transversal, then they cut off congruent segments on every transversal.

### Theorem 45
If both pairs of opposite sides of a quadrilateral are congruent, then the quadrilateral is a parallelogram.

### Theorem 46
If an angle of a quadrilateral is supplementary to both of its consecutive angles, then the quadrilateral is a parallelogram.

### Theorem 47
If both pairs of opposite angles of a quadrilateral are congruent, then the quadrilateral is a parallelogram.

### Theorem 48
If the diagonals of a quadrilateral bisect each other, then the quadrilateral is a parallelogram.

### Theorem 49
If one pair of opposite sides of a quadrilateral is both congruent and parallel, then the quadrilateral is a parallelogram.

### Theorem 50
If a parallelogram is a rhombus, then its diagonals are perpendicular.

### Theorem 51
If a parallelogram is a rhombus, then each diagonal bisects a pair of opposite angles.

### Theorem 52
If a parallelogram is a rectangle, then its diagonals are congruent.

### Theorem 53
If the diagonals of a parallelogram are perpendicular, then the parallelogram is a rhombus.

### Theorem 54
If one diagonal of a parallelogram bisects a pair of opposite angles, then the parallelogram is a rhombus.

### Theorem 55
If the diagonals of a parallelogram are congruent, then the parallelogram is a rectangle.

### Theorem 56
If a quadrilateral is an isosceles trapezoid, then each pair of base angles is congruent.

### Theorem 57
If a quadrilateral is an isosceles trapezoid, then its diagonals are congruent.

### Theorem 58
**Trapezoid Midsegment Theorem**
If a quadrilateral is a trapezoid, then

(1) the midsegment is parallel to the bases,and

(2) the length of the midsegment is half the sum of the lengths of the bases.

### Theorem 59
If a quadrilateral is a kite, then its diagonals are perpendicular.

### Theorem 60
**Side-Angle-Side Similarity (SAS ~) Theorem**
If an angle of one triangle is congruent to an angle of a second triangle, and the sides that include the two angles are proportional, then the triangles are similar.

### Theorem 61
**Side-Side-Side Similarity (SSS ~) Theorem**
If the corresponding sides of two triangles are proportional, then the triangles are similar.

### Theorem 62
The altitude to the hypotenuse of a right triangle divides the triangle into two triangles that are similar to the original triangle and to each other.

**Corollary 1**
The length of the altitude to the hypotenuse of a right triangle is the geometric mean of the lengths of the segments of the hypotenuse.

**Corollary 2**
The altitude to the hypotenuse of a right triangle separates the hypotenuse so that the length of each leg of the triangle is the geometric mean of the length of the hypotenuse and the length of the segment of the hypotenuse adjacent to the leg.

### Theorem 63
**Side-Splitter Theorem**
If a line is parallel to one side of a triangle and intersects the other two sides, then it divides those sides proportionally.

**Converse**
If a line divides two sides of a triangle proportionally, then it is parallel to the third side.

**Corollary**
If three parallel lines intersect two transversals, then the segments intercepted on the transversals are proportional.

### Theorem 64
**Triangle-Angle-Bisector Theorem**
If a ray bisects an angle of a triangle, then it divides the opposite side into two segments that are proportional to the other two sides of the triangle.

### Theorem 65
**Pythagorean Theorem**
If a triangle is a right triangle, then the sum of the squares of the lengths of the legs is equal to the square of the length of the hypotenuse.

## Theorem 66

**Converse of the Pythagorean Theorem**

If the sum of the squares of the lengths of two sides of a triangle is equal to the square of the length of the third side, then the triangle is a right triangle.

## Theorem 67

If the square of the length of the longest side of a triangle is greater than the sum of the squares of the lengths of the other two sides, then the triangle is obtuse.

## Theorem 68

If the square of the length of the longest side of a triangle is less than the sum of the squares of the lengths of the other two sides, then the triangle is acute.

## Theorem 69

**45°-45°-90° Triangle Theorem**

In a 45°-45°-90° triangle, both legs are congruent and the length of the hypotenuse is $\sqrt{2}$ times the length of a leg.

## Theorem 70

**30°-60°-90° Triangle Theorem**

In a 30°-60°-90° triangle, the length of the hypotenuse is twice the length of the shorter leg. The length of the longer leg is $\sqrt{3}$ times the length of the shorter leg.

hypotenuse = 2 • shorter leg longer leg 5 $\sqrt{3}$ • shorter leg.

## Theorem 71

**Area of a Regular Polygon**

The area of a regular polygon is half the product of the apothem and the perimeter.

## Theorem 72

**Circumference of a Circle**

The circumference of a circle is $\pi$ times the diameter.

$C = \pi d$ or $C = 2\pi r$

## Theorem 73

**Arc Length**

The length of an arc of a circle is the product of the ratio $\frac{\text{measure of the arc}}{360}$ and the circumference of the circle.

length of $\widehat{AB} = \frac{m\widehat{AB}}{360} \cdot 2\pi r$ or

length of $\widehat{AB} = \frac{m\widehat{AB}}{360} \cdot \pi d$

## Theorem 74

**Area of a Circle**

The area of a circle is the product of $\pi$ and the square of the radius.

$A = \pi r^2$

## Theorem 75

**Area of a Sector of a Circle**

The area of a sector of a circle is the product of the ratio $\frac{\text{measure of the arc}}{360}$ and the area of the circle.

Area of sector $AOB = \frac{m\widehat{AB}}{360} \cdot \pi r^2$

## Theorem 76

If a line is tangent to a circle, then the line is perpendicular to the radius at the point of tangency.

## Theorem 77

If a line in the plane of a circle is perpendicular to a radius at its endpoint on the circle, then the line is tangent to the circle.

## Theorem 78

If two segments are tangent to a circle from a point outside the circle, then the two segments are congruent.

## Theorem 79

Within a circle or in congruent circles, congruent central angles have congruent arcs.

**Converse**

Within a circle or in congruent circles, congruent arcs have congruent central angles.

## Theorem 80

Within a circle or in congruent circles, congruent central angles have congruent chords.

**Converse**

Within a circle or in congruent circles, congruent chords have congruent central angles.

## Theorem 81

Within a circle or in congruent circles, congruent chords have congruent arcs.

**Converse**

Within a circle or in congruent circles, congruent arcs have congruent chords.

## Theorem 82

Within a circle or in congruent circles, chords equidistant from the center (or centers) are congruent.

**Converse**

Within a circle or in congruent circles, congruent chords are equidistant from the center (or centers).

## Theorem 83

In a circle, if a diameter is perpendicular to a chord, it bisects the chord and its arc.

Postulates • Theorems

### Theorem 84
In a circle, if a diameter bisects a chord (that is not a diameter), it is perpendicular to the chord.

### Theorem 85
In a circle, the perpendicular bisector of a chord contains the center of the circle.

### Theorem 86
**Inscribed Angle Theorem**
The measure of an inscribed angle is half the measure of its intercepted arc.

**Corollary 1**
Two inscribed angles that intercept the same arc are congruent.

**Corollary 2**
An angle inscribed in a semicircle is a right angle.

**Corollary 3**
The opposite angles of a quadrilateral inscribed in a circle are supplementary.

### Theorem 87
The measure of an angle formed by a tangent and a chord is half the measure of the intercepted arc.

### Theorem 88
The measure of an angle formed by two lines that intersect inside a circle is half the sum of the measures of the intercepted arcs.

### Theorem 89
The measure of an angle formed by two lines that intersect outside a circle is half the difference of the measures of the intercepted arcs.

### Theorem 90
For a given point and circle, the product of the lengths of the two segments from the point to the circle is constant along any line through the point and circle.

### Theorem 91
**Lateral and Surface Areas of a Prism**
The lateral area of a right prism is the product of the perimeter of the base and the height of the prism.

$L.A. = ph$

The surface area of a right prism is the sum of the lateral area and the areas of the two bases.

$S.A. = L.A. + 2B$

### Theorem 92
**Lateral and Surface Areas of a Cylinder**
The lateral area of a right cylinder is the product of the circumference of the base and the height of the cylinder.

$L.A. = 2\pi rh$, or $L.A. = \pi dh$

The surface area of a right cylinder is the sum of the lateral area and areas of the two bases.

$S.A. = L.A. + 2B$, or $S.A. = \pi rh + 2\pi r^2$

### Theorem 93
**Lateral and Surface Areas of a Pyramid**
The lateral area of a regular pyramid is half the product of the perimeter $p$ of the base and the slant height $\ell$ of the pyramid.

$L.A. = \frac{1}{2}p\ell$

The surface area of a regular pyramid is the sum of the lateral area and the area $B$ of the base.

$S.A. = L.A. + B$

### Theorem 94
**Lateral and Surface Areas of a Cone**
The lateral area of a right cone is half the product of the circumference of the base and the slant height of the cone.

$L.A. = \frac{1}{2} \cdot 2\pi r\ell$ or $L.A. = \pi r\ell$

The surface area of a right cone is the sum of the lateral area and the area of the base.

$S.A. = L.A. + B$

### Theorem 95
**Cavalieri's Principle**
If two space figures have the same height and the same cross-sectional area at every level, then they have the same volume.

### Theorem 96
**Volume of a Prism**
The volume of a prism is the product of the area of the base and the height of the prism.

$V = Bh$

### Theorem 97
**Volume of a Cylinder**
The volume of a cylinder is the product of the area of the base and the height of the cylinder.

$V = Bh$, or $V = \pi r^2 h$

### Theorem 98
**Volume of a Pyramid**
The volume of a pyramid is one third the product of the area of the base and the height of the pyramid.

$V = \frac{1}{3}Bh$

### Theorem 99
**Volume of a Cone**
The volume of a cone is one third the product of the area of the base and the height of the cone.
$V = \frac{1}{3}Bh$ or $V = \frac{1}{3}\pi r^2 h$

### Theorem 100
**Surface Area of a Sphere**
The surface area of a sphere is four times the product of $\pi$ and the square of the radius of the sphere.
$V = 4\pi r^2$

### Theorem 101
**Volume of a Sphere**
The volume of a sphere is four thirds the product of $\pi$ and the cube of the radius of the sphere.
$V = \frac{4}{3}\pi r^3$

### Theorem 102
**Factor Theorem**
The expression $x - a$ is a factor of a polynomial if and only if the value of $a$ is a zero of the related polynomial function.

### Theorem 103
**Remainder Theorem**
If you divide a polynomial $P(x)$ of degree $n \geq 1$ by $x - a$, then the remainder is $P(a)$.

### Theorem 104
**Rational Root Theorem**
Let $P(x)$ be a polynomial of degree $n$ with leading coefficient $a_n$ and constant term $a_0$. Then the possible real roots of $P(x)$ are of the form $\frac{p}{q}$ where $p$ is an integer factor of $a_n$ and $q$ is an integer factor of $a_0$.

### Theorem 105
**Conjugate Root Theorem**
If $P(x)$ is a polynomial with rational coefficients, then the irrational roots of $P(x) = 0$ occur in conjugate pairs.

If $P(x)$ is a polynomial with real coefficients, then the complex roots of $P(x) = 0$ occur in conjugate pairs.

### Theorem 106
**Descartes's Rule of Signs**
Let $P(x)$ be a polynomial with real coefficients written in standard form.

- The number of real roots of $P(x) = 0$ is either equal to the number of sign changes between consecutive coefficients of $P(x)$ or is less than that by an even number.
- The number of negative real roots of $P(x) = 0$ is either equal to the number of sign changes between consecutive coefficients of $P(-x)$ or is less than that by an even number.

In both cases, count multiple roots according to their multiplicity.

### Theorem 107
**Fundamental Theorem of Algebra**
If $P(x)$ is a polynomial of degree $n \geq 1$, then $P(x) = 0$ has exactly $n$ roots, including multiple and complex roots.

### Theorem 108
**Binomial Theorem**
For every positive integer $n$,
$(a + b)^n = P_0a^n + P_1a^{n-1}b + P_2a^{n-2}b^2 + \ldots +$ $P_{n-1}ab^{n-1} + P_nb_n$ where $P_0, P_1, \ldots, P_n$ are the numbers in the $n$th row of Pascal's Triangle.

### Theorem 109
**Law of Sines**
$\frac{\sin A}{a} = \frac{\sin B}{b} = \frac{\sin C}{c}$

### Theorem 110
**Law of Cosines**
$a^2 = b^2 + c^2 - 2bc \cos A$
$b^2 = a^2 + c^2 - 2ac \cos B$
$c^2 = a^2 + b^2 - 2ab \cos C$

### Theorem 111
**Perimeters and Areas of Similar Figures**
If the scale factor of two similar solids figures is $\frac{a}{b}$, then

- the ratio of their perimeters is $\frac{a}{b}$, and
- the ratio of their areas is $\frac{a^2}{b^2}$.

### Theorem 112
**Areas and Volumes of Similar Solids**
If the scale factor of two similar solids is $\frac{a}{b}$, then

- the ratio of their corresponding areas is $\frac{a^2}{b^2}$, and
- the ratio of their volumes is $\frac{a^3}{b^3}$.

# *Visual* **Glossary**

## English | Spanish

### A

**Absolute value function (p. 91)** A function of the form $f(x) = |mx + b| + c$, where $m \neq 0$, is an absolute value function.

**Función de valor absoluto (p. 91)** Una función de la forma $f(x) = |mx + b| + c$, donde $m \neq 0$, es una función de valor absoluto.

**Example** $f(x) = |3x - 2| + 3$
$f(x) = |2x|$

---

**Adjacent arcs (p. 856)** Adjacent arcs are on the same circle and have exactly one point in common.

**Arcos adyacentes (p. 856)** Los arcos adyacentes están en el mismo círculo y tienen exactamente un punto en común.

**Example**

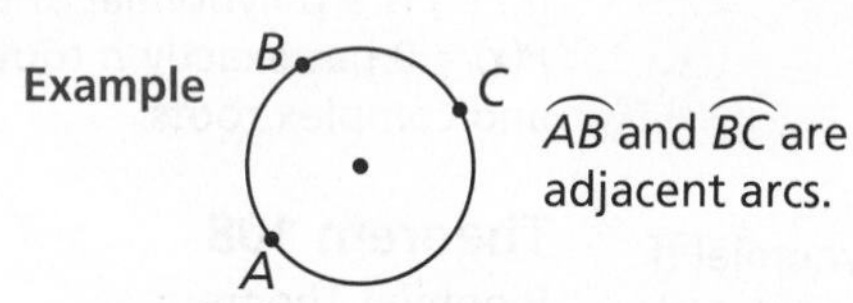


$\overset{\frown}{AB}$ and $\overset{\frown}{BC}$ are adjacent arcs.

---

**Altitude** *See* **parallelogram; trapezoid.**

**Altura** *Ver* **parallelogram; trapezoid.**

---

**Amplitude (p. 576)** The amplitude of a periodic function is half the difference between the maximum and minimum values of the function.

**Amplitud (p. 576)** La amplitud de una función periódica es la mitad de la diferencia entre los valores máximo y mínimo de la función.

**Example** The maximum and minimum values of $y = 4 \sin x$ are 4 and $-4$, respectively. amplitude $= \frac{4 - (-4)}{2} = 4$

---

**Angle bisector (p. 737)** An angle bisector is a ray that divides an angle into two congruent angles.

**Bisectriz de un ángulo (p. 737)** La bisectriz de un ángulo es una semirrecta que divide al ángulo en dos ángulos congruentes.

**Example**

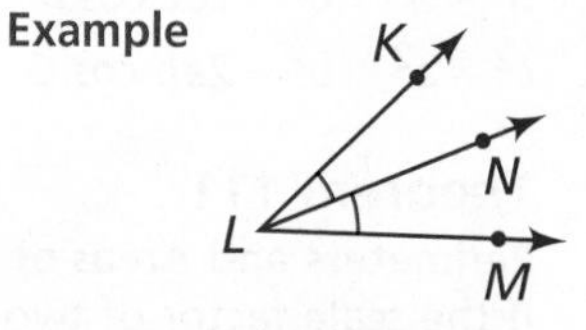


$\overrightarrow{LN}$ bisects $\angle KLM$.
$\angle KLN \cong \angle NLM$.

---

**Arc length (p. 859)** The length of an arc of a circle is the product of the ratio $\frac{\text{measure of the arc}}{360}$ and the circumference of the circle.

**Longitud de un arco (p. 859)** La longitud del arco de un círculo es el producto del cociente $\frac{\text{medida del arco}}{360}$ por la circunferencia del círculo.

**Example**

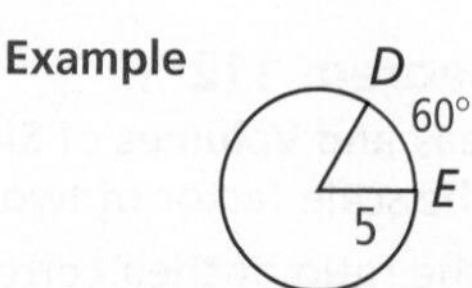


Length of $\overset{\frown}{DE} = \frac{60}{360} \cdot 2\pi(5) = \frac{5\pi}{3}$

# English

# Spanish

**Area (p. 809)** The area of a plane figure is the number of square units enclosed by the figure.

**Área (p. 809)** El área de una figura plana es la cantidad de unidades cuadradas que contiene la figura.

**Example** 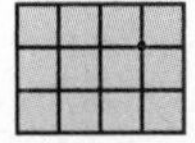 The area of the rectangle is 12 square units, or 12 units$^2$.

**Arithmetic mean (p. 698)** The arithmetic mean, or average, of two numbers is their sum divided by two.

**Media aritmética (p. 698)** La media aritmética, o promedio, de dos números es su suma dividida por dos.

**Example** The arithmetic mean of 12 and 15 is $\frac{12 + 15}{2} = 13.5$

**Arithmetic sequence (p. 696)** An arithmetic sequence is a sequence with a constant difference between consecutive terms.

**Secuencia aritmética (p. 696)** Una secuencia aritmética es una secuencia de números en la que la diferencia entre dos números consecutivos es constante.

**Example** The arithmetic sequence 1, 5, 9, 13, . . . has a common difference of 4.

**Arithmetic series (p. 711)** An arithmetic series is a series whose terms form an arithmetic sequence.

**Serie aritmética (p. 711)** Una serie aritmética es una serie cuyos términos forman una progresión aritmética.

**Example** $1 + 5 + 9 + 13 + 17 + 21$ is an arithmetic series with six terms.

**Asymptote (p. 376)** An asymptote is a line that a graph approaches as $x$ or $y$ increases in absolute value.

**Asíntota (p. 376)** Una asíntota es una recta a la cual se acerca una gráfica a medida que $x$ o $y$ aumentan de valor absoluto.

**Example** The function $y = \frac{x+2}{x-2}$ has $x = 2$ as a vertical asymptote and $y = 1$ as a horizontal asymptote.

**Axis of symmetry (pp. 91, 151)** The axis of symmetry is the line that divides a figure into two parts that are mirror images.

**Eje de simetría (pp. 91, 151)** El eje de simetría es la recta que divide una figura en dos partes que son imágenes una de la otra.

**Example**

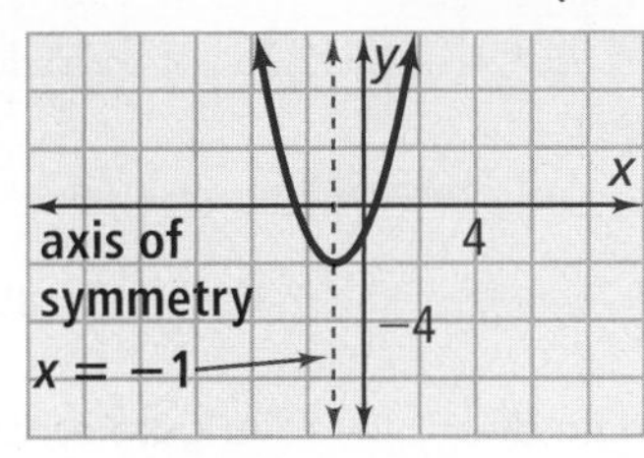


$y = x^2 + 2x - 1$

Visual **Glossary**

| English | Spanish |
|---|---|

## B

**Base(s)** *See* **parallelogram; trapezoid; triangle.**

**Base(s)** *Ver* **parallelogram; trapezoid; triangle.**

**Bias (p. 23)** A bias is a systematic error introduced by the sampling method.

**Sesgo (p. 23)** El sesgo es un error sistemático introducido por medio del método de muestreo.

**Bimodal (p. 4)** A bimodal data set has two modes.

**Bimodal (p. 4)** Un conjunto bimodal de datos tiene dos modas.

**Example** {1, 2, 3, 3, 4, 5, 6, 6} mode = 3 and 6

**Bisect (p. 737)** *See* **Angle bisector; Segment bisector.**

**Bisecar (p. 737)** *Ver* **Angle bisector; Segment bisector.**

**Boundary (p. 102)** A boundary of the graph of a linear inequality is a line in the coordinate plane. It separates the solutions of the inequality from the nonsolutions. Points of the line itself may or may not be solutions.

**Límite (p. 102)** Un límite de la gráfica de una desigualdad lineal es una línea en el plano de coordenadas. Ésta separa las soluciones de la desigualdad de las no soluciones. Las soluciones pueden ser o no puntos de la línea.

**Box-and-whisker plot (p. 6)** A box-and-whisker plot is a method of displaying data that uses quartiles to form the center box and the maximum and minimum values to form the whiskers.

**Gráfica de cajas (p. 6)** Una gráfica de cajas es un método para mostrar datos que utiliza cuartiles para formar una casilla central y los valores máximos y mínimos para formar los conectores.

**Example**

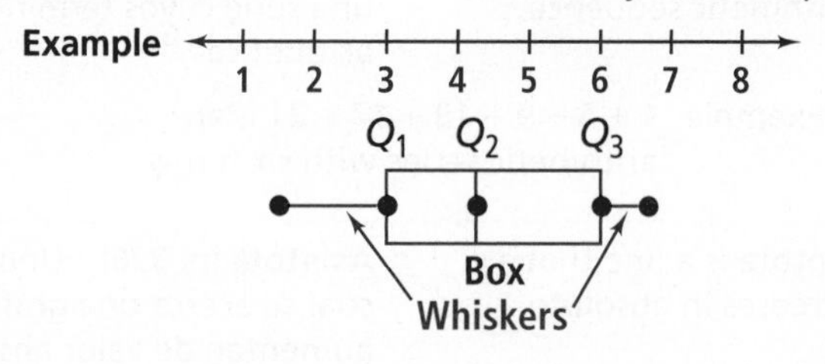


**Branch (p. 377)** Each piece of a discontinuous graph is called a branch.

**Rama (p. 377)** Cada segmento de una gráfica discontinua se llama rama.

**Example**

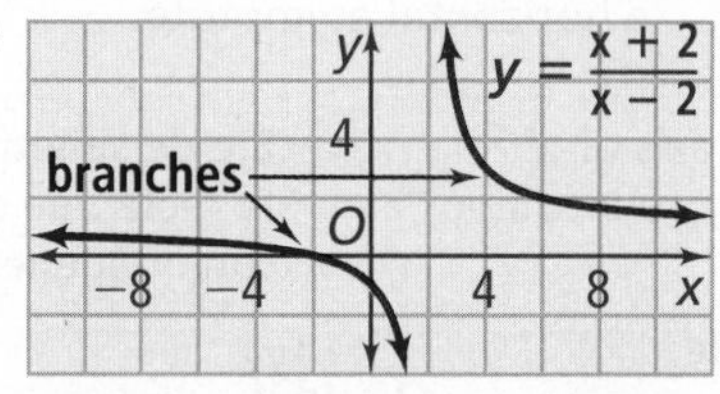


## C

**Center (p. 855)** *See* **circle**

**Centro (p. 855)** *Ver* **circle**

**Central angle (p. 589, 855)** A central angle of a circle is an angle whose vertex is at the center of a circle.

**Ángulo central (p. 589, 855)** El ángulo central de un círculo es un ángulo cuyo vértice está situado en el centro del círculo.

**Example**

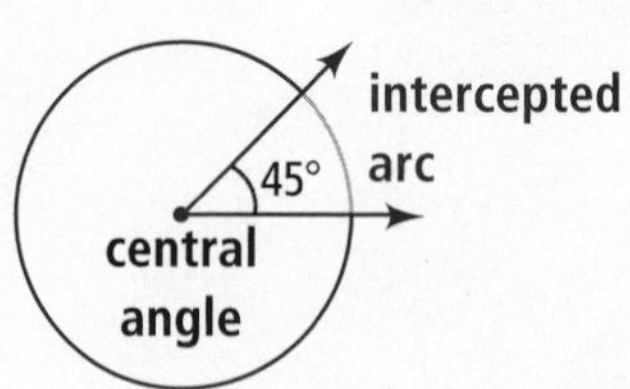

## English

## Spanish

**Change of Base Formula (p. 537)** $\log_b M = \frac{\log_c M}{\log_c b}$, where $M$, $b$, and $c$ are positive numbers, and $b \neq 1$ and $c \neq 1$.

**Fórmula de cambio de base (p. 537)** $\log_b M = \frac{\log_c M}{\log_c b}$, donde $M$, $b$ y $c$ son números positivos y $b \neq 1$ y $c \neq 1$.

**Example** $\log_3 8 = \frac{\log 8}{\log 3} \approx 1.8928$

---

**Chord (p. 886)** A chord of a circle is a segment whose endpoints are on the circle.

**Cuerda (p. 886)** Una cuerda de un círculo es un segmento cuyos extremos son dos puntos del círculo.

**Example**

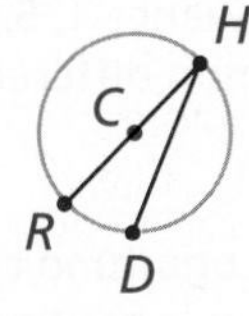


$\overline{HD}$ and $\overline{HR}$ are chords of $\odot C$.

---

**Circle (p. 855)** A circle is the set of all points in a plane that are a given distance, the *radius*, from a given point, the *center*. The standard form for an equation of a circle with center $(h, k)$ and radius $r$ is $(x - h)^2 + (y - k)^2 = r^2$.

**Círculo (p. 855)** Un círculo es el conjunto de todos los puntos de un plano situados a una distancia dada, el *radio*, de un punto dado, el *centro*. La fórmula normal de la ecuación de un círculo con centro $(h, k)$ y radio $r$ es $(x - h)^2 + (y - k)^2 = r^2$.

**Example**

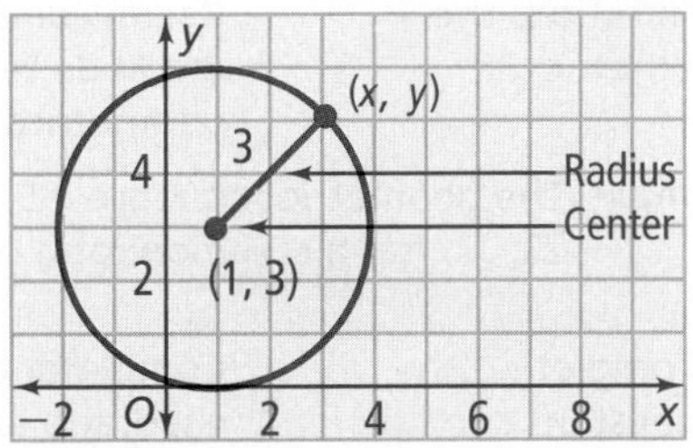


The equation of the circle whose center is (1, 3) and whose radius is 3 is $(x - 1)^2 + (y - 3)^2 = 9$.

---

**Circumference (p. 858)** The circumference of a circle is the distance around the circle. Given the radius $r$ of a circle, you can find its circumference $C$ by using the formula $C = 2\pi r$.

**Circunferencia (p. 858)** La circunferencia de un círculo es la distancia alrededor del círculo. Dado el radio $r$ de un círculo, se puede hallar la circunferencia $C$ usando la fórmula $C = 2\pi r$.

**Example**

$$C = 2\pi r = 2\pi(4) = 8\pi$$

Circumference is the distance around the circle.

---

**Circumscribed circle (p. 740)** A circle is circumscribed about a polygon if the vertices of the polygon are on the circle.

**Círculo circunscrito (p. 740)** Un círculo está circunscrito a un polígono si los vértices del polígono están en el círculo.

**Example**

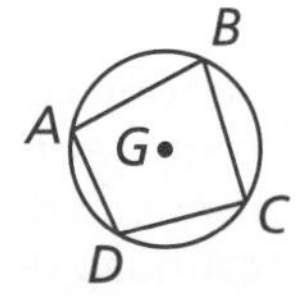


$\odot G$ is circumscribed about *ABCD*.

## English | Spanish

**Combined variation (p. 367)** A combined variation is a relation in which one variable varies with respect to each of two or more variables.

**Variación combinada (p. 367)** Una variación combinada es una relación en la que una variable varía con respecto a cada una de dos o más variables.

**Example** $y = kx^2\sqrt{z}$
$z = \frac{kx}{y}$

---

**Common difference (p. 696)** A common difference is the difference between consecutive terms of an arithmetic sequence.

**Diferencia común (p. 696)** La diferencia común es la diferencia entre los términos consecutivos de una progresión aritmética.

**Example** The arithmetic sequence 1, 5, 9, 13, . . . has a common difference of 4.

---

**Common logarithm (p. 527)** A common logarithm is a logarithm that uses base 10. You can write the common logarithm $\log_{10} y$ as $\log y$.

**Logaritmo común (p. 527)** El logaritmo común es un logaritmo de base 10. El logaritmo común $\log_{10} y$ se expresa como $\log y$.

**Example** $\log 1 = 0$
$\log 10 = 1$
$\log 50 = 1.698970004\ldots$

---

**Common ratio (p. 703)** A common ratio is the ratio of consecutive terms of a geometric sequence.

**Razón común (p. 703)** Una razón común es la razón de términos consecutivos en una secuencia geométrica.

**Example** The geometric sequence 2.5, 5, 10, 20, . . . has a common ratio of 2.

---

**Completing the square (p. 187)** Completing the square is the process of finding a constant $c$ to add to $x^2 + bx$ so that $x^2 + bx + c$ is the square of a binomial.

**Completar el cuadrado (p. 187)** Completar un cuadrado es el proceso mediante el cual se halla una constante $c$ que se le pueda sumar a $x^2 + bx$, de manera que $x^2 + bx + c$ sea el cuadrado de un binomio.

**Example** $x^2 - 12x + ■$
$x^2 - 12x + \left(\frac{-12}{2}\right)^2$
$x^2 - 12x + 36$

---

**Complex fraction (p. 351)** A complex fraction is a rational expression that has a fraction in its numerator or denominator, or in both its numerator and denominator.

**Fracción compleja (p. 351)** Una fracción compleja es una expresión racional en la que el numerador, el denominador o ambos son una fracción.

**Example** $\frac{\frac{2}{1}}{5}$, $\frac{\frac{2}{7}}{\frac{3}{2}}$

---

**Composite function (p. 469)** A composite function is a combination of two functions such that the output from the first function becomes the input for the second function.

**Función compuesta (p. 469)** Una función compuesta es la combinación de dos funciones. La cantidad de salida de la primera función es la cantidad de entrada de la segunda función.

**Example** $f(x) = 2x + 1$, $g(x) = x^2 - 1$
$(g \circ f)(5) = g(f(5)) = g(2(5) + 1)$
$= g(11)$
$= 11^2 - 1 = 120$

## English | Spanish

**Compound inequality (p. 67)** You can join two inequalities with the word *and* or the word *or* to form a compound inequality.

**Desigualdad compuesta (p. 67)** Puedes unir dos desigualdades por medio de la palabra *y* o la palabra *o* para formar una desigualdad compuesta.

**Example** $-1 < x$ and $x \leq 3$
$x < -1$ or $x \geq 3$

**Concentric circles (p. 858)** Concentric circles lie in the same plane and have the same center.

**Círculos concéntricos (p. 470)** Los círculos concéntricos están en el mismo plano y tienen el mismo centro

**Example**

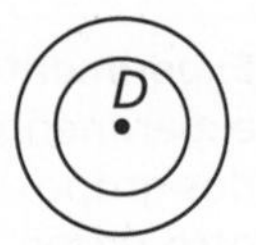


The two circles both have center $D$ and are therefore concentric.

**Confidence interval (p. 42)** Based on the mean of a sample or a sample proportion, the confidence interval indicates the interval in which the population mean or population proportion is likely to lie for a given confidence level.

**Intervalo de confianza (p. 42)** El intervalo de confianza se basa en la media de una muestra o en la proporción de una muestra, e indica el intervalo en el que probablemente se encuentra dicha media o proporción de la población para un nivel de confianza dado.

**Example** For an elementary history book, a sample of 30 trials indicates that the mean number of words in a sentence is 12.7. The margin of error at a 95% confidence level is 1.5 words per sentence. The mean number of words $\mu$ in all of the sentences in the book at a 95% confidence level is $12.7 - 1.5 \leq \mu \leq 12.7 + 1.5$.

**Congruent circles (p. 855)** Congruent circles are circles whose radii are congruent.

**Círculos congruentes (p. 855)** Los círculos congruentes son círculos cuyos radios son congruentes.

**Example**

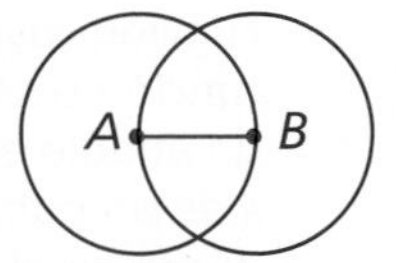


$\odot A$ and $\odot B$ have the same radius, so $\odot A \cong \odot B$.

**Constant of proportionality (p. 325)** If $y = ax^b$ describes $y$ as a power function of $x$, then $y$ varies directly with, or is proportional to, the $b$th power of $x$. The constant $a$ is the constant of proportionality.

**Constante de proporcionalidad (p. 325)** Si $y = ax^b$ describe a $y$ como una potencia de la función de $x$, entonces $y$ varía directamente con, o es proporcional a, la $b$ma potencia de $x$. La constante $a$ es la constante de proporcionalidad.

**Continuous graph (p. 386)** A graph is continuous if it has no jumps, breaks, or holes.

**Gráfica continua (p. 386)** Una gráfica es continua si no tiene saltos, interrupciones o huecos.

**Continuous probability distribution (p. 34)** A continuous probability distribution has as its events any of the infinitely many values in an interval of real numbers.

**Distribución de probabilidad continua (p. 34)** Una distribución de probabilidad continua tiene como sucesos a cualquiera del número infinito de valores en un intervalo de números reales.

| English | Spanish |
|---|---|

**Continuously compounded interest (p. 520)** When interest is compounded continuously on principal $P$, the value $A$ of an account is $A = Pe^{rt}$.

**Interés compuesto continuo (p. 520)** En un sistema donde el interés es compuesto continuamente sobre el capital $P$, el valor de $A$ de una cuenta es $A = Pe^{rt}$.

**Example** Suppose that $P = \$1200$, $r = 0.05$, and $t = 3$.
Then $A = 1200e^{0.05 \cdot 3}$
$= 1200(2.718\ldots)^{0.15}$
$\approx 1394.20$

**Controlled experiment (p. 24)** In a controlled experiment, you divide the sample into two groups. You impose a treatment on one group but not the other "control" group. Then you compare the effect on the treated group to the control group.

**Experimento controlado (p. 24)** En un experimento controlado, se divide la muestra en dos grupos. Uno de los grupos se manipula y el otro grupo "controlado" se mantiene en su estado original. Luego se comparan el estado del grupo manipulado y el estado del grupo controlado.

**Convenience sample (p. 22)** In a convenience sample you select any members of the population who are conveniently and readily available.

**Muestra de conveniencia (p. 22)** En una muestra de conveniencia se selecciona a cualquier miembro de la población que está convenientemente disponible.

**Converge (p. 725)** An infinite series $a_1 + a_2 + \ldots + a_n + \ldots$ converges if the sum $a_1 + a_2 + \ldots + a_n$ get closer and closer to a real number as $n$ increases.

**Convergir (p. 725)** Una serie infinita $a_1 + a_2 + \ldots + a_n + \ldots$ es convergente si la suma $a_1 + a_2 + \ldots + a_n$ se aproxima cada vez más a un número real a medida que el valor de $n$ incrementa.

**Example** $1 + \frac{1}{2} + \frac{1}{4} + \frac{1}{8} + \ldots$ converges.

**Cosecant function (p. 641)** The cosecant (csc) function is the reciprocal of the sine function. For all real numbers $\theta$ except those that make $\sin \theta = 0$, $\csc \theta = \frac{1}{\sin \theta}$.

**Función cosecante (p. 641)** La función cosecante (csc) se define como el recíproco de la función seno. Para todos los números reales $\theta$, excepto aquéllos para los que $\sin \theta = 0$, $\csc \theta = \frac{1}{\sin \theta}$.

**Example** If $\sin \theta = \frac{5}{13}$, then $\csc \theta = \frac{13}{5}$.

**Cosine function, Cosine of $\theta$ (pp. 584, 610)** The cosine function, $y = \cos \theta$, matches the measure $\theta$ of an angle in standard position with the $x$-coordinate of a point on the unit circle. This point is where the terminal side of the angle intersects the unit circle. The $x$-coordinate is the cosine of $\theta$.

**Función coseno, Coseno de $\theta$ (pp. 584, 610)** La función coseno, $y = \cos \theta$, empareja la medida $\theta$ de un ángulo en posición estándar con la coordenada $x$ de un punto en el círculo unitario. Este es el punto en el que el lado terminal del ángulo interseca al círculo unitario. La coordenada $x$ es el coseno de $\theta$.

**Example**

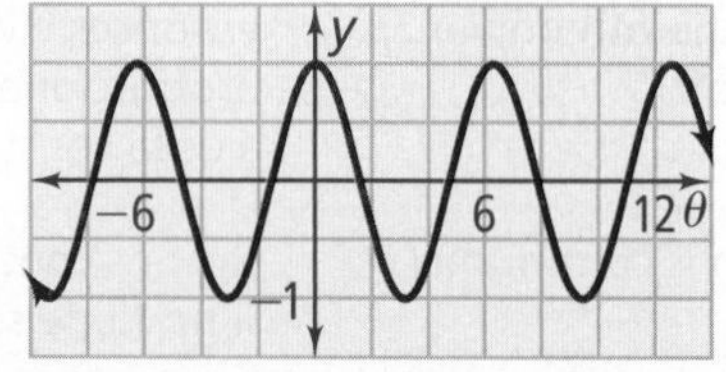


1 y P(cos θ, sin θ)
−1 O 1 x
θ
−1

**Cotangent function (p. 641)** The cotangent (cot) function is the reciprocal of the tangent function. For all real numbers $\theta$ except those that make $\tan \theta = 0$, $\cot \theta = \frac{1}{\tan \theta}$.

**Función cotangente (p. 641)** La función cotangente (cot) es el recíproco de la función tangente. Para todos los números reales $\theta$, excepto aquéllos para los que $\tan \theta = 0$, $\cot \theta = \frac{1}{\tan \theta}$.

**Example** If $\tan \theta = \frac{5}{12}$, then $\cot \theta = \frac{12}{5}$.

# English

# Spanish

**Coterminal angle (p. 583)** Two angles in standard position are coterminal if they have the same terminal side.

**Ángulo coterminal (p. 582)** Dos ángulos que están en posición normal son coterminales si tienen el mismo lado terminal.

**Example**

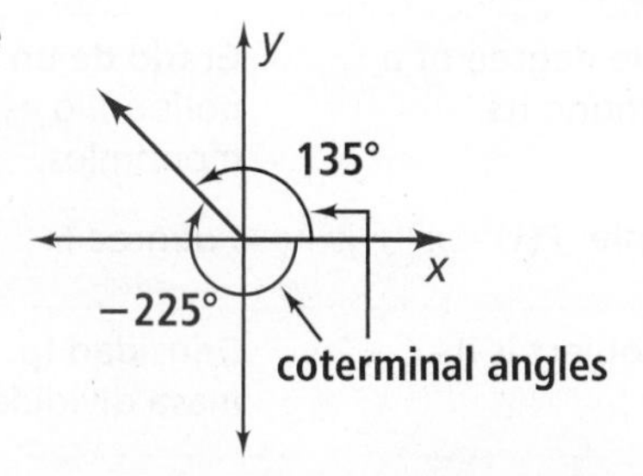


Angles that have measures 135° and −225° are coterminal.

**Cross section (p. 778)** A cross section is the intersection of a solid and a plane.

**Sección de corte (p. 778)** Una sección de corte es la intersección de un plano y un cuerpo geométrico.

**Example**

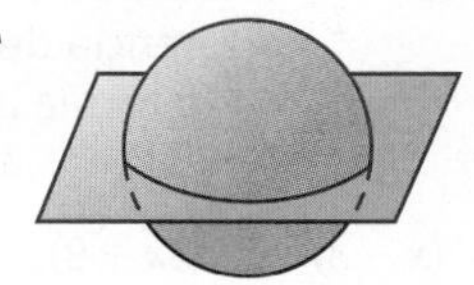

The cross section is a circle.

**Cumulative frequency (p. 31)** When you can assign numerical values to events, cumulative frequency is the number of times events with values that are less than or equal to a given value occur.

**Frequencia acumulativa (p. 31)** Cuando se puede asignar valores numéricos a los eventos, la frecuencia acumulativa es el número de veces que occuren los eventos con valores que son menores que o igual a un valor dado.

**Cumulative probability (p. 31)** When you can assign numerical values to events, cumulative probability is the probability that an event with a value less than or equal to a given value occurs.

**Probabilidad acumulativa (p. 31)** Cuando se puede asignar valores numéricos a los eventos, la probabilidad acumulativa es la probabilidad de que un evento con un valor que es menor que o igual a un valor dado ocurra.

**Cycle (p. 573)** A cycle of a periodic function is an interval of *x*-values over which the function provides one complete pattern of *y*-values.

**Ciclo (p. 573)** El ciclo de una función periódica es un intervalo de valores de *x* de los cuales la función produce un patrón completo de valores de *y*.

**Example**

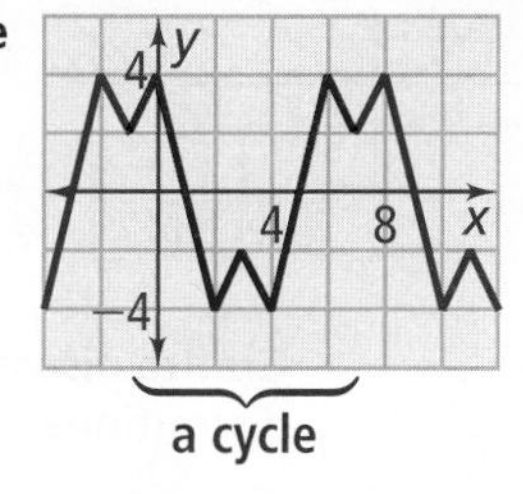


## D

**Decay factor (p. 508)** In an exponential function of the form $y = ab^x$, $b$ is the decay factor if $0 < b < 1$.

**Factor de decremento (p. 508)** En una función exponencial de la forma $y = ab^x$, $b$ es el factor de decremento si, $0 < b < 1$.

**Example** In the equation $y = 0.3^x$, 0.7 is the decay factor.

## English | Spanish

**Degree of a monomial (p. 239)** The degree of a monomial in one variable is the exponent of the variable.

**Grado de un monomio (p. 239)** El grado de un monomio en una variable es el exponente de la variable.

**Degree of a polynomial (p. 239)** The degree of a polynomial is the greatest degree among its monomial terms.

**Grado de un polinomio (p. 239)** El grado de un polinomio es el grado mayor entre los términos de monomios.

**Example** $P(x) = x^6 + 2x^3 - 3$ degree 6

**Density (p. 747)** The density of an object is its mass divided by its volume.

**Densidad (p. 747)** La densidad de un objeto es su masa dividida por su volumen.

**Diameter of a circle (p. 855)** A diameter of a circle is a segment that contains the center of the circle and whose endpoints are on the circle. The term *diameter* can also mean the length of this segment.

**Diámetro de un circulo (p. 855)** Un diámetro de un círculo es un segmento que contiene el centro del ciírculo y cuyos extremos estan en el círculo. El término *diámetro* tambien puedi referirse a la longitud de este segmento.

**Difference of cubes (p. 266)** A difference of cubes is an expression of the form $a^3 - b^3$. It can be factored as $(a - b)(a^2 + ab + b^2)$.

**Diferencia de dos cuadrados (p. 266)** La diferencia de dos cuadrados es una expresión de la forma $a^3 - b^3$. Sepuede factorizar como $(a - b)(a^2 + ab + b^2)$.

**Example** $x^3 - 27 = (x - 3)(x^2 + 3x + 9)$

**Difference of two squares (p. 173)** A difference of two squares is an expression of the form $a^2 - b^2$. It can be factored as $(a + b)(a - b)$.

**Diferencia de dos cubos (p. 173)** La diferencia de dos cubos es una expresión de la forma $a^2 - b^2$. Se puede factorizar como $(a + b)(a - b)$.

**Example** $25a^2 - 4 = (5a + 2)(5a - 2)$

$m^6 - 1 = (m^3 + 1)(m^3 - 1)$

**Directrix (p. 212)** The directrix of a parabola is the fixed line used to define a parabola. Each point of the parabola is the same distance from the focus and the directrix.

**Directriz (p. 212)** La directriz de una parábola es la recta fija con que se define una parábola. Cada punto de la parábola está a la misma distancia del foco y de la directriz.

**Example**

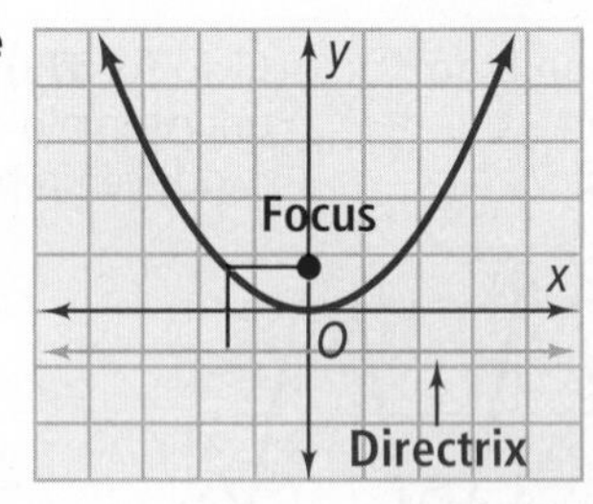


**Discontinuous graph (p. 386)** A graph is discontinuous if it has a jump, break, or hole.

**Gráfica discontinua (p. 386)** Una gráfica es discontinua si tiene un salto, interrupción o hueco.

**Discrete probability distribution (p. 34)** A discrete probability distribution has a finite number of possible events.

**Distribución de probabilidad discreta (p. 34)** Una distribución de probabilidad discreta tiene un número finito de sucesos posibles.

# English

# Spanish

**Discriminant (p. 196)** The discriminant of a quadratic equation in the form $ax^2 + bx + c = 0$ is the value of the expression $b^2 - 4ac$.

**Discriminante (p. 196)** El discriminante de una ecuación cuadrática en la forma $ax^2 + bx + c = 0$ es el valor de la expresión $b^2 - 4ac$.

**Example** $3x^2 - 6x + 1$
discriminant $= (-6)^2 - 4(3)(1)$
$= 36 - 12 = 24$

**Diverge (p. 725)** An infinite series diverges if it does not converge.

**Divergir (p. 725)** Una serie infinita es divergente si no es convergente.

**Example** $1 + 2 + 4 + 8 + \ldots$ diverges.

## E

**Edge (p. 774)** *See* **polyhedron.**

**Arista (p. 774)** *Ver* **polyhedron.**

**End behavior (p. 241)** End behavior of the graph of a function describes the directions of the graph as you move to the left and to the right, away from the origin.

**Comportamiento extremo (p. 241)** El comportamiento extremo de la gráfica de una función describe las direcciones de la gráfica al moverse a la izquierda y a la derecha, apartándose del origen.

**Equivalent systems (p. 113)** Equivalent systems are systems that have the same solution(s).

**Sistemas equivalentes (p. 113)** Sistemas equivalentes son sistemas que tienen la misma solución o las mismas soluciones.

**Even function (p. 248)** A function $f$ is an even function if and only if $f(-x) = f(x)$ for all values of $x$ in its domain.

**Función par (p. 248)** Una función $f$ es una función par si y solo si $f(-x) = f(x)$ para todos los valores de $x$ en su dominio.

**Example** $f(x) = x^2 + |x|$ is an even function because $f(-x) = (-x)^2 + |-x|$
$= x^2 + |x| = f(x)$

**Excluded value (p. 339)** A value of $x$ for which a rational expression $f(x)$ is undefined.

**Valor excluido (p. 339)** Valor de $x$ para el cual una expresión racional es indefinida.

**Explicit formula (p. 687)** An explicit formula expresses the $n$th term of a sequence in terms of $n$.

**Fórmula explícita (p. 687)** Una fórmula explícita expresa el $n$-ésimo término de una progresión en función de $n$.

**Example** Let $a_n = 2n + 5$ for positive integers $n$.
If $n = 7$, then $a_7 = 2(7) + 5 = 19$.

**Exponential decay (p. 506)** Exponential decay is modeled by a function of the form $y = ab^x$ with $0 < b < 1$.

**Decaimiento exponencial (p. 506)** El decaimiento exponencial se expresa con una función $y = ab^x$ donde $0 < b < 1$.

**Exponential equation (p. 542)** An exponential equation contains the form $b^{cx}$, with the exponent including a variable.

**Ecuación exponencial (p. 542)** Una ecuación exponencial tiene la forma $b^{cx}$, y su exponente incluye una variable.

**Example**

$$\begin{aligned} 5^{2x} &= 270 \\ \log 5^{2x} &= \log 270 \\ 2x \log 5 &= \log 270 \\ 2x &= \frac{\log 270}{\log 5} \\ 2x &\approx 3.4785 \\ x &\approx 1.7392 \end{aligned}$$

## English | Spanish

**Exponential function (p. 505)** The general form of an exponential function is $y = ab^x$, where $x$ is a real number, $a \neq 0$, $b > 0$, and $b \neq 1$. When $b > 1$, the function models exponential growth with growth factor $b$. When $0 < b < 1$, the function models exponential decay with decay factor $b$.

**Función exponencial (p. 505)** La forma general de una función exponencial es $y = ab^x$, donde $x$ es un número real, $a \neq 0$, $b > 0$ y $b \neq 1$. Cuando $b > 1$, la función representa un incremento exponencial con factor de incremento $b$. Cuando $0 < b < 1$, la función representa el decremento exponencial con factor de decremento $b$.

**Example**

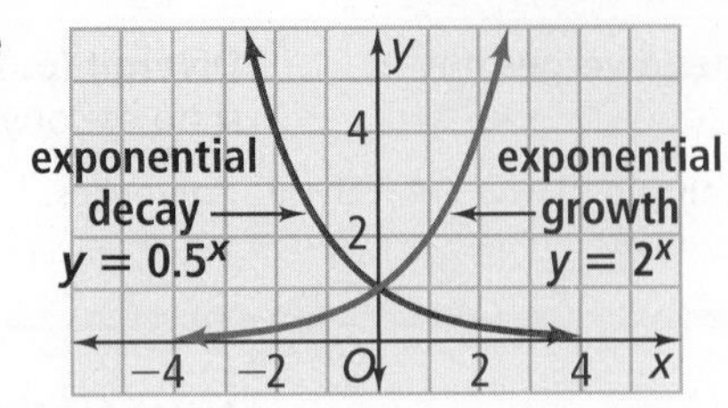


**Exponential growth (p. 506)** Exponential growth is modeled by a function of the form $y = ab^x$ with $b > 1$.

**Crecimiento exponencial (p. 506)** El crecimiento exponencial se expresa con una función de la forma $y = ab^x$ donde $b > 1$.

### F

**Face (p. 774)** *See* **polyhedron.**

**Cara (p. 774)** *Ver* **polyhedron.**

**Factoring (p. 169)** Factoring is rewriting an expression as the product of its factors.

**Descomposición factorial (p. 169)** Descomponer en factores es el proceso de escribir de nuevo una expresión como el producto de sus factores.

**Example** expanded form $x^2 + x - 56$ factored form $(x + 8)(x - 7)$

**Finite Series (p. 711)** A finite series is a series with a finite number of terms.

**Serie finite (p. 711)** Una serie finita es una serie con un número finito de términos.

**Focal length (p. 212)** The focal length of a parabola is the distance between the vertex and the focus.

**Distancia focal (p. 212)** La distancia focal de una parábola es la distancia entre el vértice y el foco.

**Focus (plural: foci) of a parabola (p. 212)** A parabola is the set of all points in a plane that are the same distance from a fixed line and a fixed point not on the line. The fixed point is the focus of the parabola.

**Foco de una parabola (p. 212)** Una parábola es el conjunto de todos los puntos en un plano con la misma distancia desde una línea fija y un punto fijo que no permanece en la línea. El punto fijo es el foco de la parábola.

### G

**Geometric mean (p. 707)** The geometric mean of any two positive numbers is the positive square root of the product of the two numbers.

**Media geométrica (p. 707)** La media geométrica de dos números positivos es la raíz cuadrada positiva del producto de los dos números.

**Example** The Geometric mean of 12 and 18
$\sqrt{12 \cdot 18} \approx 14.6969.$

| English | Spanish |
| --- | --- |
| **Geometric probability (p. 765)** Geometric probability is a probability that uses a geometric model in which points represent outcomes. | **Probabilidad geométrica (p. 765)** La probabilidad geométrica es una probabilidad que utiliza un modelo geométrico donde se usan puntos para representar resultados. |

**Example** 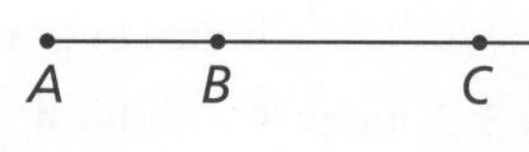

$P(H \text{ on } \overline{BC}) = \frac{BC}{AD}$

| English | Spanish |
| --- | --- |
| **Geometric sequence (p. 703)** A geometric sequence is a sequence with a constant ratio between consecutive terms. | **Secuencia geométrica (p. 703)** Una secuencia geométrica es una secuencia con una razón constante entre términos consecutivos. |

**Example** The geometric sequence 2.5, 5, 10, 20, 40 . . . , has a common ratio of 2.

| English | Spanish |
| --- | --- |
| **Geometric series (p. 723)** A geometric series is the sum of the terms in a geometric sequence. | **Serie geométrica (p. 723)** Una serie geométrica es la suma de términos en una progresión geométrica. |

**Example** One geometric series with five terms is $2.5 + 5 + 10 + 20 + 40$.

| English | Spanish |
| --- | --- |
| **Greatest common factor (p. 171)** The greatest common factor (GCF) of an expression is the common factor of each term of the expression that has the greatest coefficient and the greatest exponent. | **Máximo factor común (p. 171)** El máximo factor común de una expresión es el factor común de cada término de la expresión que tiene el mayor coeficiente y el mayor exponente. |

**Example** The GCF of $4x^2 + 20x - 12$ is 4.

| English | Spanish |
| --- | --- |
| **Greatest integer function (p. 99)** The greatest integer function corresponds each input $x$ to the greatest integer less than or equal to $x$. | **Función del entero mayor (p. 99)** La función del entero mayor relaciona cada entrada $x$ con el entero mayor que es menor oigual a $x$. |
| **Growth factor (p. 508)** In an exponential function of the form $y = ab^x$, $b$ is the growth factor if $b > 1$. | **Factor de incremento (p. 508)** En una función exponencial de la forma $y = ab^x$, $b$ es el factor de incremento si $b > 1$. |

**Example** In the exponential equation $y = 2^x$, 2 is the growth factor.

## H

| English | Spanish |
| --- | --- |
| **Half-plane (p. 102)** A half-plane is the set of points in a coordinate plane that are on one side of the boundary of the graph of a linear inequality. | **Semiplano (p. 102)** Un semiplano es el conjunto de puntos de un plano de coordenadas que están a un lado del límite de la gráfica de desigualdad lineal. |
| **Height** *See* **parallelogram; trapezoid; triangle.** | **Altura** *Ver* **parallelogram; trapezoid.** |

## English | Spanish

### I

**Identity (p. 58)** An equation that is true for every value of the variable is an identity.

**Identidad (p. 58)** Una ecuación que es verdadera para cada valor de la variable es una identidad.

**Index (p. 426)** With a radical sign, the index indicates the degree of the root.

**Índice (p. 426)** Con un signo de radical, el índice indica el grado de la raíz.

**Example** index 2 index 3 index 4

$\sqrt{16}$ $\sqrt[3]{16}$ $\sqrt[4]{16}$

**Infinite series (p. 711)** An infinite series is a series with infinitely many terms.

**Serie infinita (p. 711)** Una serie infinita es una serie con un número infinito de términos.

**Inscribed angle (p. 897)** An angle is inscribed in a circle if the vertex of the angle is on the circle and the sides of the angle are chords of the circle.

**Ángulo inscrito (p. 897)** Un ángulo está inscrito en un círculo si el vértice del ángulo está en el círculo y los lados del ángulo son cuerdas del círculo.

**Example**

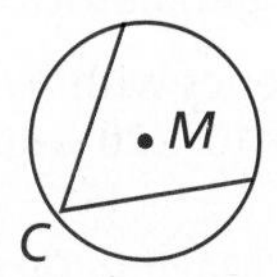


$\angle C$ is inscribed in $\odot M$.

**Inscribed polygon (p. 742)** A polygon is inscribed in a circle if the vertices of the polygon are on the circle.

**Polígono inscrito (p. 742)** Un polígono está inscrito en un círculo si los vertices del polígono están en el círculo.

**Example**

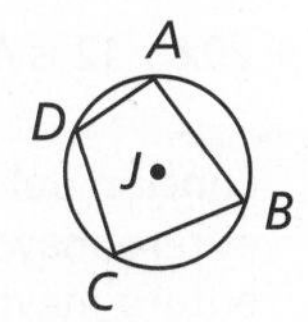


*ABCD* is inscribed in $\odot J$.

**Intercepted arc (p. 897)** An intercepted arc is an arc of a circle having endpoints on the sides of an inscribed angle, and its other points in the interior of the angle.

**Arco interceptor (p. 897)** Un arco interceptor es un arco de un círculo cuyos extremos están en los lados de un ángulo inscrito y los punto restantes están en el interior del ángulo.

**Example**

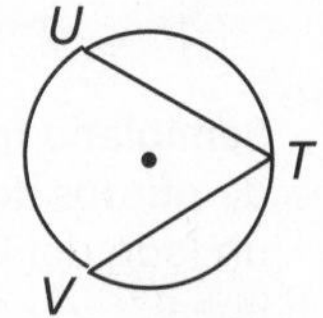


$\overset{\frown}{UV}$ is the intercepted arc of inscribed $\angle T$.

**Initial side (p. 581)** When an angle is in standard position, the initial side of the angle is given to be on the positive *x*-axis. The other ray is the terminal side of the angle.

**Lado inicial (p. 581)** Cuando un ángulo está en posición normal, el lado inicial del ángulo se ubica en el eje positivo de las *x*. El otro rayo, o semirrecta, forma el lado terminal del ángulo.

**Example**

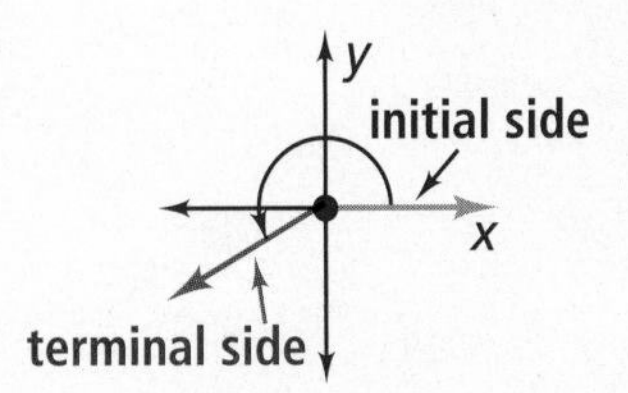

## English | Spanish

**Intercepted arc (p. 589)** An intercepted arc is the portion of a circle whose endpoints are on the sides of a central angle of the circle and whose remaining points lie in the interior of the angle.

**Arco interceptado (p. 589)** Un arco interceptado es la porción de un círculo cuyos extremos quedan sobre los lados de un ángulo central del círculo y cuyos puntos restantes quedan en el interior del ángulo.

**Example**

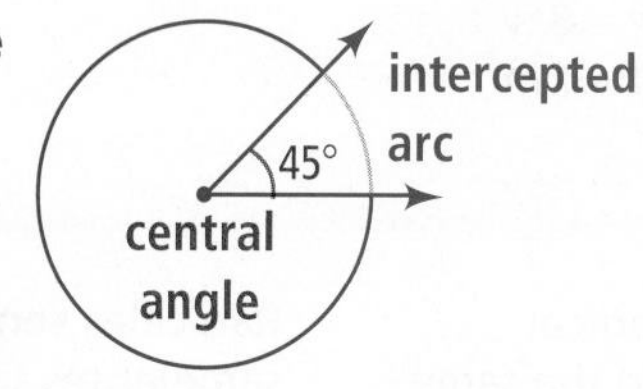


**Interquartile range (p. 5)** The interquartile range of a set of data is the difference between the third and first quartiles.

**Intervalo intercuartil (p. 5)** El rango intercuartil de un conjunto de datos es la diferencia entre el tercero y el primer cuartiles.

**Example** The first and third quartiles of the data set {2, 3, 4, 5, 5, 6, 7, 7} are 3.5 and 6.5. The interquartile range is $6.5 - 3.5 = 3$.

**Inverse function (p. 477)** If function *f* pairs a value *b* with *a* then its inverse, denoted $f^{-1}$, pairs the value *a* with *b*. If $f^{-1}$ is also a function, then *f* and $f^{-1}$ are inverse functions.

**Funcion inversa (p. 477)** Si la función *f* empareja un valor *b* con *a*, entonces su inversa, cuya notación es $f^{-1}$, empareja el valor *a* con *b*. Si $f^{-1}$ también es una función, entonces *f* y $f^{-1}$ son funciones inversas.

**Example** If $f(x) = x + 3$, then $f^{-1}(x) = x - 3$.

**Inverse operations (p. 56)** Inverse operations are operations that undo each other.

**Operaciones inversas (p. 56)** Operaciones inversas son operaciones que se cancelan mutuamente.

**Inverse relation (p. 477)** If a relation pairs element *a* of its domain with element *b* of its range, the inverse relation "undoes" the relation and pairs *b* with *a*. If (*a*, *b*) is an ordered pair of a relation, then (*b*, *a*) is an ordered pair of its inverse.

**Relación inversa (p. 477)** Si una relación empareja el elemento *a* de su dominio con el elemento *b* de su rango, la relación inversa "deshace" la relación y empareja *b* con *a*. Si (*a*, *b*) es un par ordenado de una relación, entonces (*b*, *a*) es un par ordenado de su inversa.

**Inverse variation (p. 363)** An inverse variation is a relation represented by an equation of the form $xy = k$, $y = \frac{x}{k}$, or $x = \frac{y}{k}$, where $k \neq 0$.

**Variación inversa (p. 363)** Una variación inversa es una relación representada por la ecuación $xy = k$, $y = \frac{x}{k}$, ó $x = \frac{y}{k}$. donde $k \neq 0$.

**Example**

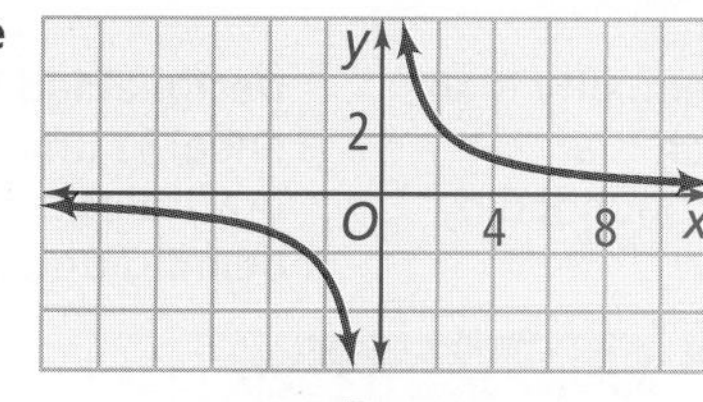


$xy = 5$, or $y = \frac{5}{x}$

# English

# Spanish

## J

**Joint variation (p. 367)** A joint variation is a relation in which one variable varies directly with respect to each of two or more variables.

**Variación conjunta (p. 367)** Una variación conjunta es una relación en la cual el valor de una variable varía directamente con respecto a cada una de dos o más variables.

**Example** $z = 8xy$
$T = kPV$

## L

**Like radicals (p. 440)** Like radicals are radical expressions that have the same index and the same radicand.

**Radicales semejantes (p. 440)** Los radicales semejantes son expresiones radicales que tienen el mismo índice y el mismo radicando.

**Example** $4\sqrt[3]{7}$ and $\sqrt[3]{7}$ are like radicals.

**Limits (p. 714)** Limits in summation notation are the least and greatest integer values of the index $n$.

**Límites (p. 714)** Los límites en notación de sumatoria son el menor y el mayor valor del índice $n$ en números enteros.

**Example**

$$\sum_{n=1}^{3} (3n + 5)$$

limits (pointing to 3 and $n = 1$)

**Linear equation (p. 75)** A linear equation in two variables is an equation that can be written in the form $ax + by = c$. *See also* **Standard form of a linear equation.**

**Ecuación lineal (p. 75)** Una ecuación lineal de dos variables es una ecuación que se puede escribir de la forma $ax + by = c$. *Ver también* **Standard form of a linear equation.**

**Example** $y = 2x + 1$ can be written as $-2x + y = 1$.

**Linear function (p. 75)** A function whose graph is a line is a linear function. You can represent a linear function with a linear equation.

**Función lineal (p. 75)** Una función cuya gráfica es una recta es una función lineal. La función lineal se representa con una ecuación lineal.

**Example**

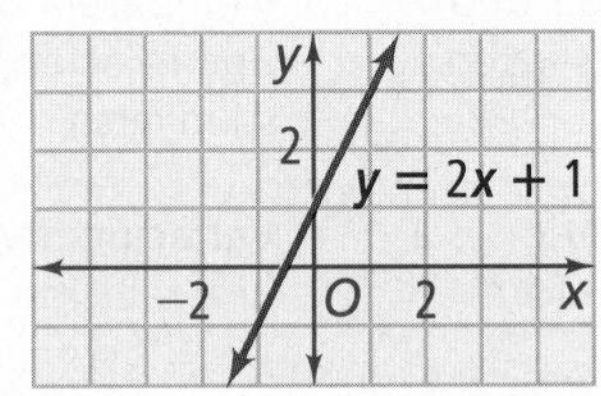


**Linear inequality (p. 102)** A linear inequality is an inequality in two variables whose graph is a region of the coordinate plane that is bounded by a line.

**Desigualdad lineal (p. 102)** Una desigualdad lineal es una desigualdad de dos variables cuya gráfica es una región del plano de coordenadas delimitado por una recta.

**Example**

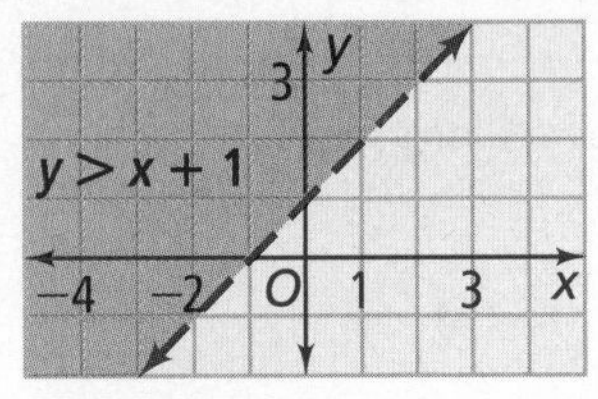

| English | Spanish |
|---|---|

**Literal equation (p. 59)** A literal equation is an equation that uses more than one letter as a variable.

**Ecuación literal (p. 59)** Una ecuación literal es una ecuación en la cual más de una letra expresa una variable.

**Locus (p. 794)** A locus is a set of points, all of which meet a stated condition.

**Lugar geométrico (p. 794)** Un lugar geométrico es un conjunto de puntos que cumplen una condición dada.

**Example**

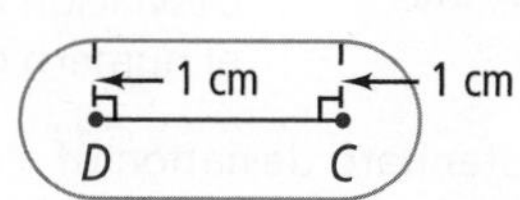


The points in blue are the locus of points in a plane 1 cm from $\overline{DC}$.

**Logarithm (p. 525)** The logarithm base $b$ of a positive number $x$ is defined as follows: $\log_b x = y$, if and only if $x = b^y$.

**Logaritmo (p. 525)** La base del logaritmo $b$ de un número positivo $x$ se define como $\log_b x = y$, si y sólo si $x = b^y$.

**Example** $\log_2 8 = 3$

$\log_{10} 100 = \log 100 = 2$

$\log_5 5^7 = 7$

**Logarithmic equation (p. 546)** A logarithmic equation is an equation that includes a logarithm involving a variable.

**Ecuación logarítmica (p. 546)** Una ecuación logarítmica es una ecuación que incluye un logaritmo con una variable.

**Example** $\log_3 x = 4$

**Logarithmic function (p. 528)** A logarithmic function is the inverse of an exponential function.

**Función logarítmica (p. 528)** Una función logarítmica es la inversa de una función exponencial.

**Example**

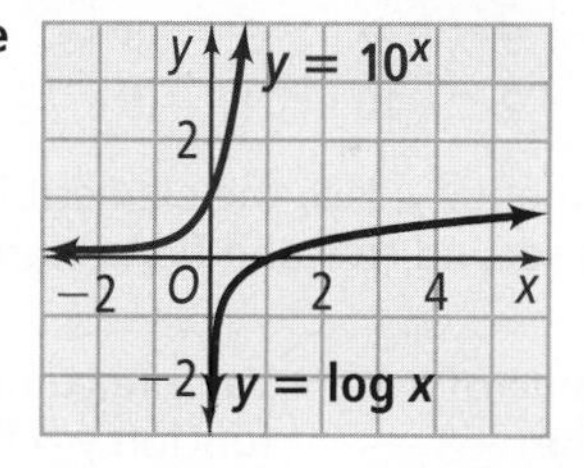


**Logarithmic scale (p. 527)** A logarithmic scale is a scale that uses the logarithm of a quantity instead of the quantity itself.

**Escala logarítmica (p. 527)** Una escala logarítmica es una escala que usa el logaritmo de una cantidaden vez de la cantidad misma.

## M

**Major arc (p. 855)** A major arc of a circle is an arc that is larger than a semicircle.

**Arco mayor (p. 855)** Un arco mayor de un círculo es cualquier arco más grande que un semicírculo.

**Example**

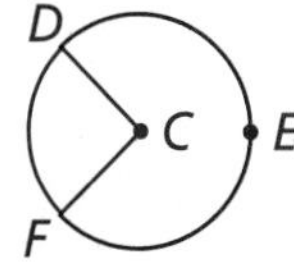


$\overset{\frown}{DEF}$ is a major arc of $\odot C$.

## English

## Spanish

**Margin of error (p. 42)** The distance from the sample mean or sample proportion that is used to create a confidence interval for the population mean or the population proportion. For a 95% confidence level, $ME = 1.96 \cdot \frac{s}{\sqrt{n}}$, where $ME$ is the margin of error, $s$ is the standard deviation of the sample data, and $n$ is the number of values in the sample.

**Margen de error (p. 42)** La distancia desde la media de una muestra o desde la proporción de una muestra que se usa para crear el intervalo de confianza para la media o proporción de una población. Para un nivel de confianza de 95%, $ME = 1.96 \cdot \frac{s}{\sqrt{n}}$, siendo $ME$ el margen de error, $s$ la desviación estándar de los datos de la muestra, y $n$ el número de valores en la muestra.

**Example** The standard deviation of a sample is 5.0 and the number of trials is 30. The margin of error at a 95% confidence level is $ME = 1.96 \cdot \frac{50}{\sqrt{30}} \approx 1.79$.

---

**Matrix (p. 135)** A matrix is a rectangular array of numbers written within brackets.

**Matriz (p. 135)** Una matriz es un conjunto de números encerrados en corchetes y dispuestos en forma de rectángulo.

**Example**

$$A = \begin{bmatrix} 1 & -2 & 0 & 10 \\ 9 & 7 & -3 & 8 \\ 2 & -10 & 1 & -6 \end{bmatrix}$$

The number 2 is the element in the third row and first column. $A$ is a $3 \times 4$ matrix.

---

**Matrix element (p. 135)** Every item listed in a matrix is an element of the matrix. An element is identified by its position in the matrix.

**Elemento matricial (p. 135)** Cada cifra de una matriz es un elemento de la matriz. El elemento se identifica según la posición que ocupa en la matriz.

**Example**

$$A = \begin{bmatrix} 1 & -2 & 0 & 10 \\ 9 & 7 & -3 & 8 \\ 2 & -10 & 1 & -6 \end{bmatrix}$$

Element $a_{21}$ is 9, the element in the second row and first column.

---

**Maximum value (p. 153)** The maximum value of a function $y = f(x)$ is the greatest $y$-value of the function. It is the $y$-coordinate of the highest point on the graph of $f$.

**Valor máximo (p. 153)** El valor máximo de una función $y = f(x)$ es el valor más alto de y de la función. Es la coordenada $y$ del punto más alto de la gráfica de $f$.

---

**Mean (p. 3)** The sum of the data values divided by the number of data values is the mean. *See also* **Arithmetic mean.**

**Media (p. 3)** La suma de los valores de datos dividida por el número de valores de datos sumados es la media. *Ver también* **Arithmetic mean.**

**Example** {1, 2, 3, 3, 6, 6}

$$\text{mean} = \frac{1+2+3+3+6+6}{6} = \frac{21}{6} = 3.5$$

## English

## Spanish

**Measures of central tendency (p. 3)** The mean, the median, and the mode are each central values that help describe a set of data. They are called measures of central tendency.

**Medidas de tendencia central (p. 3)** La media, la mediana y la moda son los valores centrales que facilitan la descripción de un conjunto de datos. A estos valores se les llama medidas de tendencia central.

**Example** {1, 2, 3, 3, 4, 5, 6, 6}
mean = 3.75
median = 3.5
modes = 3 and 6

**Measure of variation (p. 15)** Measures of variation, such as the range, the interquartile range, and the standard deviation, describe how the data in a data set are spread out.

**Medida de dispersión (p. 15)** Las medidas de dispersión, tal como el rango, el intervalo intercuartil y la desviación típica, describen cómo se dispersan los datos en un conjunto de datos.

**Median (p. 3)** The median is the middle value in a data set. If the data set contains an even number of values, the median is the mean of the two middle values.

**Mediana (p. 3)** La mediana es el valor situado en el medio en un conjunto de datos. Si el conjunto de datos contiene un número par de valores, la mediana es la media de los dos valores del medio.

**Example** {1, 2, 3, 3, 4, 5, 6, 6}
median $= \frac{3+4}{2} = \frac{7}{2} = 3.5$

**Midline (p. 576)** The horizontal line through the average of the maximum and minimum values.

**Línea media (p. 576)** La recta horizontal que pasa a través de la meda de los valores máximos y mínimos.

**Example**

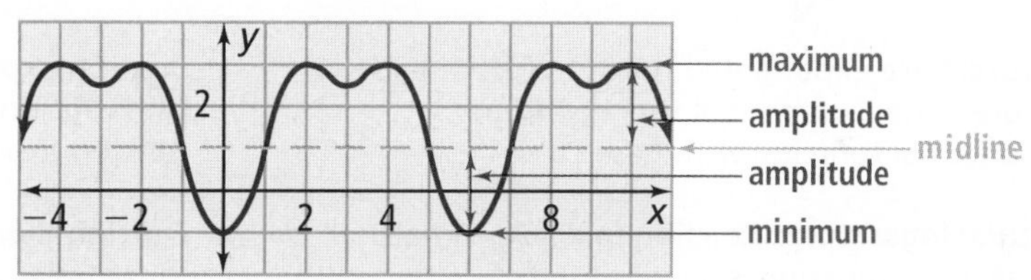


**Minimum value (p. 153)** The minimum value of a function $y = f(x)$ is the least $y$-value of the function. It is the $y$-coordinate of the lowest point on the graph of $f$.

**Valor mínimo (p. 153)** El valor mínimo de una función $y = f(x)$ es el valor más bajo de $y$ de la función. Es la coordenada $y$ del punto más bajo de la gráfica de $f$.

**Minor arc (p. 855)** A minor arc is an arc that is smaller than a semicircle.

**Arco menor (p. 855)** Un arco menor de un círculo es un arco más corto que un semicírculo.

**Example**

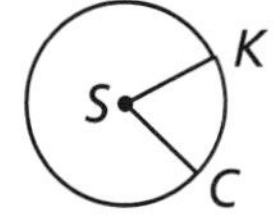


$\overset{\frown}{KC}$ is a minor arc of $\odot S$.

**Mode (p. 3)** The mode is the most frequently occurring value (or values) in a set of data.

**Moda (p. 3)** La moda es el valor o valores que ocurren con mayor frecuencia en un conjunto de datos.

**Example** {1, 2, 3, 3, 4, 5, 6, 6}
The modes are 3 and 6.

## English / Spanish

**Monomial (p. 239)** A monomial is either a real number, a variable, or a product of real numbers and variables with whole number exponents.

**Monomio (p. 239)** Un monomio es un número real, una variable o un producto de números reales y variables cuyos exponentes son números enteros.

**Example** $1, x, 2z, 4ab^2$

---

**Multiple zero (p. 259)** If a linear factor is repeated in the complete factored form of a polynomial, the zero related to that factor is a multiple zero.

**Cero múltiplo (p. 259)** Si un factor lineal se repite en la forma factorizada completa de un polinomio, el cero relacionado con ese factor es un cero múltiplo.

**Example** The zeros of the function $P(x) = 2x(x - 3)^2(x + 1)$ are 0, 3, and $-1$. Since $(x - 3)$ occurs twice as a factor, 3 is a multiple zero.

---

**Multiplicity (p. 259)** The multiplicity of a zero of a polynomial function is the number of times the related linear factor is repeated in the factored form of the polynomial.

**Multiplicidad (p. 259)** La multiplicidad de un cero de una función polinomial es el número de veces que el factor lineal relacionado se repite en la forma factorizada del polinomio.

**Example** The zeros of the function $P(x) = 2x(x - 3)^2(x + 1)$ are 0, 3, and $-1$. Since $(x - 3)$ occurs twice as a factor, the zero 3 has multiplicity 2.

## N

**Natural base exponential function (p. 519)** A natural base exponential function is an exponential function with base e.

**Función exponencial con base natural (p. 519)** Una función exponencial con base natural es una función exponencial con base e.

---

**Natural logarithmic function (p. 553)** A natural logarithmic function is a logarithmic function with base e. The natural logarithmic function, $y = \ln x$, is $y = \log_e x$. It is the inverse of $y = e^x$.

**Función logarítmica natural (p. 553)** Una función logarítmica natural es una función logarítmica con base e. La función logarítmica natural, $y = \ln x$, es $y = \log_e x$. Ésta es la función inversa de $y = e^x$.

**Example**

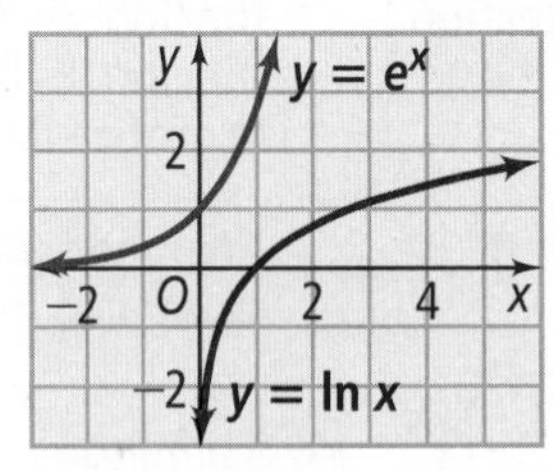


$\ln e^3 = 3$
$\ln 10 \approx 2.3026$
$\ln 36 \approx 3.5835$

---

**Non-removable discontinuity (p. 386)** A non-removable discontinuity is a point of discontinuity that is not removable. It represents a break in the graph of *f* where you cannot redefine *f* to make the graph continuous.

**Discontinuidad irremovible (p. 386)** Una discontinuidad irremovible es un punto de discontinuidad que no se puede remover. Representa una interrupción en la gráfica *f* donde no se puede redefinir *f* para volverla una gráfica continua.

## English

## Spanish

**Normal distribution (p. 34)** A normal distribution shows data that vary randomly from the mean in the pattern of a bell-shaped curve.

**Distribución normal (p. 34)** Una distribución normal muestra, con una curva en forma de campana, datos que varían alcatoriamento respecto de la media.

**Example**

**Distribution of Test Scores**

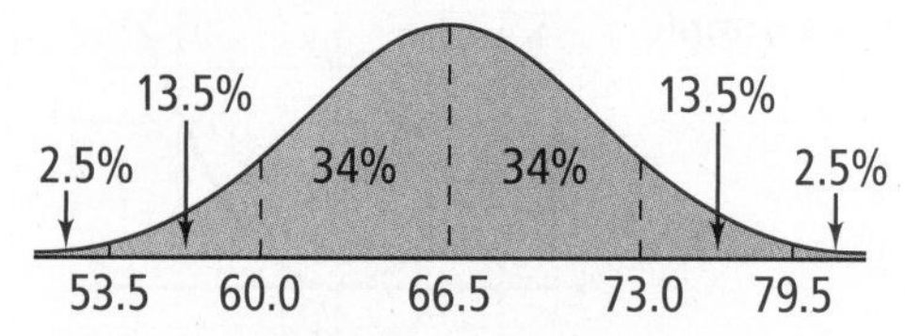


In a class of 200 students, the scores on a test were normally distributed. The mean score was 66.5 and the standard deviation was 6.5. The number of students who scored greater than 73 was about 13.5% + 2.5% of those who took the test.
16% of 200 = 32
About 32 students scored 73 or higher on the test.

***n*th root (p. 425)** For any real numbers $a$ and $b$, and any positive integer $n$, if $a^n = b$, then $a$ is an $n$th root of $b$.

**raíz *n*-ésima (p. 425)** Para todos los números reales $a$ y $b$, y todo número entero positivo $n$, si $a^n = b$, entonces $a$ es la $n$-ésima raíz de $b$.

**Example** $\sqrt[5]{32} = 2$ because $2^5 = 32$.
$\sqrt[4]{81} = 3$ because $3^4 = 81$.

## O

**Observational study (p. 24)** In an observational study, you measure or observe members of a sample in such a way that they are not affected by the study.

**Estudio de observación (p. 24)** En un estudio de observación, se miden u observan a los miembros de una muestra de tal manera que no les afecte el estudio.

**Odd function (p. 248)** A function $f$ is an odd function if and only if $f(-x) = -f(x)$ for all values of $x$ in its domain.

**Función impar (p. 248)** Una función $f$ es una función impar si y solo si $f(-x) = -f(x)$ para todos los valores de $x$ en su dominio.

**Example** The function $f(x) = x^3 + 2x$ is odd because $f(-x) = (-x)^3 + 2(-x)$
$= -x^3 - 2x = -f(x)$

**Outlier (p. 5)** An outlier is a value substantially different from the rest of the data in a set.

**Valor extremo (p. 5)** Un valor extremo es un valor considerablemente diferente al resto de los datos de un conjunto.

**Example** The outlier in the data set {56, 64, 73, 59, 98, 65, 59} is 98.

| English | Spanish |
| --- | --- |

## P

**Parabola (p. 151)** A parabola is the graph of a quadratic function. It is the set of all points $P$ in a plane that are the same distance from a fixed point $F$, the focus, as they are from a line $d$, the directrix.

**Parábola (p. 151)** La parábola es la gráfica de una función cuadrática. Es el conjunto de todos los puntos $P$ situados en un plano a la misma distancia de un punto fijo $F$, o foco, y de la recta $d$, o directriz.

**Example**

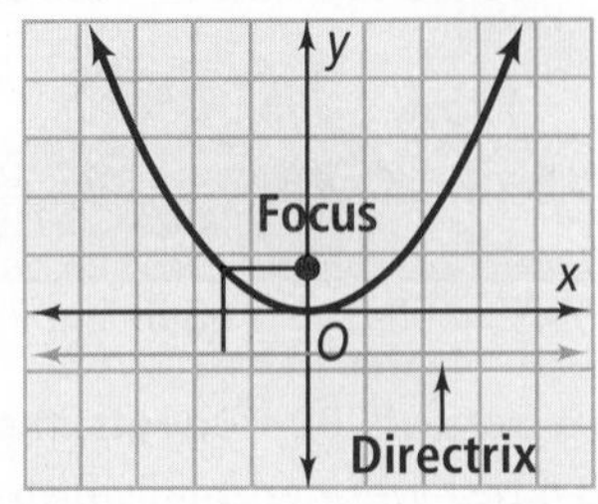


**Parallelogram (p. 823)** A parallelogram is a quadrilateral with two pairs of parallel sides. You can choose any side to be the *base*. An *altitude* is any segment perpendicular to the line containing the base drawn from the side opposite the base. The *height* is the length of an altitude.

**Paralelogramo (p. 823)** Un paralelogramo es un cuadrilátero con dos pares de lados paralelos. Se puede escoger cualquier lado como la *base*. Una *altura* es un segmento perpendicular a la recta que contiene la base, trazada desde el lado opuesto a la base. La *altura*, por extensión, es la longitud de una altura.

**Example**

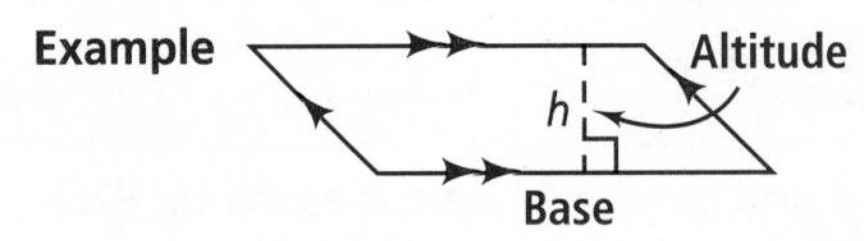


**Parent function (p. 81)** A parent function is the simplest form of a set of functions that form a family.

**Función elemental (p. 81)** Una función madre es la mínima expresión de un conjunto de funciones que forma una familia.

**Example** $y = x$ is the parent function for the functions of the form $y = x + k$.

**Pascal's Triangle (p. 304)** Pascal's Triangle is a triangular array of numbers in which the first and last number is 1. Each of the other numbers in the row is the sum of the two numbers above it.

**Triángulo de Pascal (p. 304)** El Triángulo de Pascal es una distribución triangular de números en la cual el primer número y el último número son 1. Cada uno de los otros números en la fila es la suma de los dos números de encima.

**Example** **Pascal's Triangle**

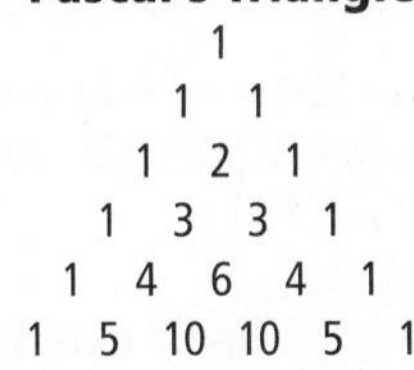

1
1 1
1 2 1
1 3 3 1
1 4 6 4 1
1 5 10 10 5 1

## English / Spanish

**Percentiles (p. 7)** A percentile is a number from 0 to 100 that you can associate with a value $x$ from a data set. It shows the percent of the data that are less than or equal to $x$.

**Percentiles (p. 7)** Un percentil es un número de 0 a 100 que se puede asociar con un valor $x$ de un conjunto de datos. Éste muestra el porcentaje de los datos que son menores o iguales a $x$.

---

**Perfect square trinomial (p. 172)** A perfect square trinomial is a trinomial that is the square of a binomial.

**Trinomio cuadrado perfecto (p. 172)** Un trinomio cuadrado perfecto es un trinomio que es el cuadrado de un binomio.

**Example** $16x^2 - 24x + 9 = (4x - 3)^2$

---

**Period (p. 573)** The period of a periodic function is the horizontal length of one cycle.

**Período (p. 573)** El período de una función periódica es el intervalo horizontal de un ciclo.

**Example**

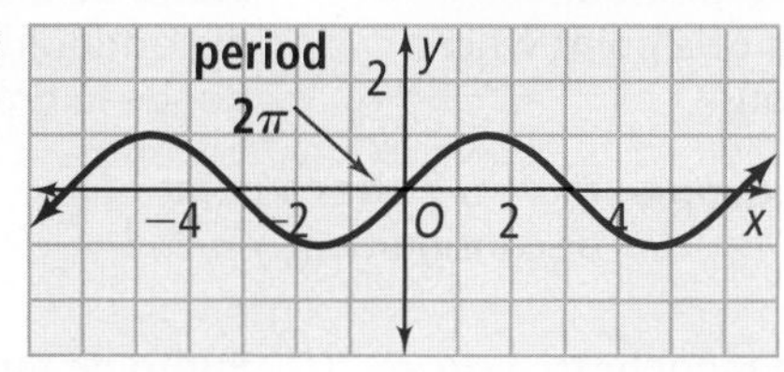


The periodic function $y = \sin x$ has period $2\pi$.

---

**Perimeter of a polygon (p. 809)** The perimeter of a polygon is the sum of the lengths of its sides.

**Perímetro de un polígono (p. 809)** El perímetro de un polígono es la suma de las longitudes de sus lados

**Example**

4 in.

4 in. 3 in.

5 in.

$$P = 4 + 4 + 5 + 3$$
$$= 16 \text{ in.}$$

---

**Periodic function (p. 573)** A periodic function repeats a pattern of $y$-values at regular intervals.

**Función periódica (p. 573)** Una función periódica repite un patrón de valores $y$ a intervalos regulares.

**Example**

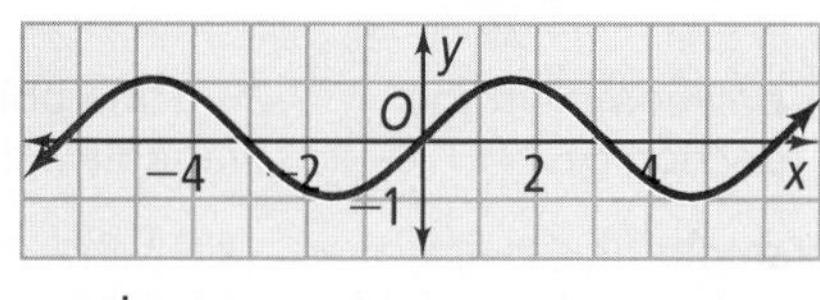


$y = \sin x$

---

**Phase shift (p. 628)** A horizontal translation of a periodic function is a phase shift.

**Cambio de fase (p. 628)** Una traslación horizontal de una función periódica es un cambio de fase.

**Example**

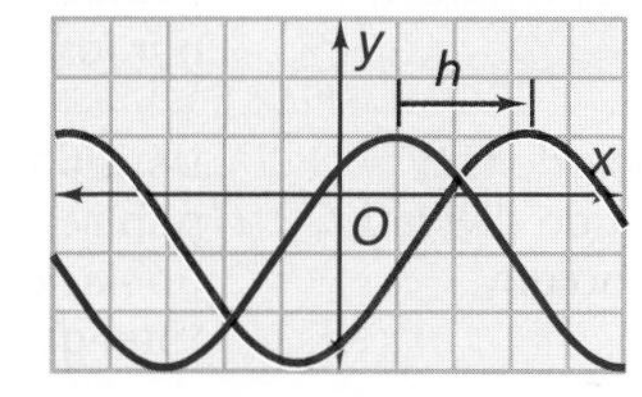


$g(x)$: horizontal translation of $f(x)$
$g(x) = f(x - h)$

| English | Spanish |
|---|---|
| **Pi (p. 858)** Pi ($\pi$) is the ratio of the circumference of any circle to its diameter. The number $\pi$ is irrational and is approximately 3.14159. | **Pi (p. 858)** Pi ($\pi$) es la razón de la circunferencia de cualquier círculo a su diámetro. El número $\pi$ es irracional y se aproxima a $\pi \approx 3.14159$. |

**Example**

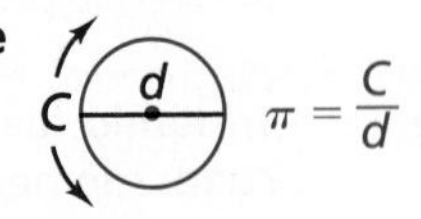


$\pi = \frac{C}{d}$

| English | Spanish |
|---|---|
| **Piecewise function (p. 99)** A piecewise function has different rules for different parts of its domain. | **Función de fragmentos (p. 99)** Una función de fragmentos tiene reglas diferentes para diferentes partes de su dominio. |
| **Point of discontinuity (p. 386)** A point of discontinuity is the $x$-coordinate of a point where the graph of $f(x)$ is not continuous. | **Punto de discontinuidad (p. 386)** Un punto de discontinuidad es la coordenada $x$ de un punto donde la gráfica de $f(x)$ no es continua. |

**Example** $f(x) = \frac{2}{x - 2}$ has a point of discontinuity at $x = 2$.

| English | Spanish |
|---|---|
| **Point of tangency (p. 876)** *See* tangent to a circle. | **Punto de tangencia (p. 876)** *Ver* tangent to a circle. |
| **Polyhedron (p. 774)** A polyhedron is a three-dimensional figure whose surfaces, or *faces*, are polygons. The *vertices* of the polygons are the vertices of the polyhedron. The intersections of the faces are the *edges* of the polyhedron. | **Poliedro (p. 774)** Un poliedro es una figura tridimensional cuyas superficies, o *caras*, son polígonos. Los *vértices* de los polígonos son los vértices del poliedro. Las intersecciones de las caras son las *aristas* del poliedro. |

**Example**

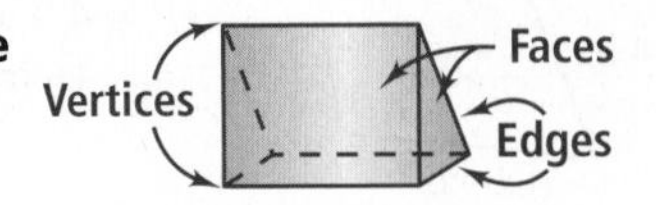


| English | Spanish |
|---|---|
| **Polynomial (p. 239)** A polynomial is a monomial or the sum of monomials. | **Polinomio (p. 239)** Un polinomio es un monomio o la suma de dos o más monomios. |

**Example** $3x^3 + 4x^2 - 2x + 58x \quad x^2 + 4x + 2$

| English | Spanish |
|---|---|
| **Polynomial function (p. 239)** A polynomial in the variable $x$ defines a polynomial function of $x$. | **Función polinomial (p. 239)** Un polinomio en la variable $x$ define una función polinomial de $x$. |

**Example** $P(x) = a_nx^n + a_{n-1}x^{n-1} + \ldots + a_1x + a_0$ is a polynomial function, where $n$ is a nonnegative integer and the coefficients $a_n, \ldots, a_0$ are real numbers.

| English | Spanish |
|---|---|
| **Population (p. 22)** A population is the members of a set. | **Población (p. 22)** Una población está compuesta por los miembros de un conjunto. |
| **Population density (p. 747)** Population density is the number of individuals of a population divided by the total area or volume that they occupy. | **Densidad de población (p. 747)** La densidad de población es el número de individuos de una población dividida por el área total o el volumen total que ocupan. |
| **Power function (p. 325)** A power function is a function of the form $y = a \cdot x^b$, where $a$ and $b$ are nonzero real numbers. | **Función de potencia (p. 325)** Una función de potencia es una función de la forma $y = a \cdot x^b$, donde $a$ y $b$ son números reales diferentes de cero. |

# English

# Spanish

**Principal root (p. 425)** When a number has two real roots, the positive root is called the principal root. A radical sign indicates the principal root. The principal root of a negative number $a$ is $i\sqrt{|a|}$.

**Raíz principal (p. 425)** Cuando un número tiene dos raíces reales, la raíz positiva es la raíz principal. El signo del radical indica la raíz principal. La raíz principal de un número negativo $a$ es $i\sqrt{|a|}$.

**Example** The number 25 has two square roots, 5 and −5. The principal square root, 5, is indicated by $\sqrt{25}$ or $25^{\frac{1}{2}}$.

---

**Probability distribution (p. 29)** A probability distribution is a function that tells the probability of each outcome in a sample space.

**Distribución de probabilidades (p. 29)** Una distribución de probabilidades es una función que señala la probabilidad de que cada resultado ocurra en un espacio muestral.

**Example**

| Roll | Fr. | Prob. |
|---|---|---|
| 1 | 5 | 0.125 |
| 2 | 9 | 0.225 |
| 3 | 7 | 0.175 |
| 4 | 8 | 0.2 |
| 5 | 8 | 0.2 |
| 6 | 3 | 0.075 |

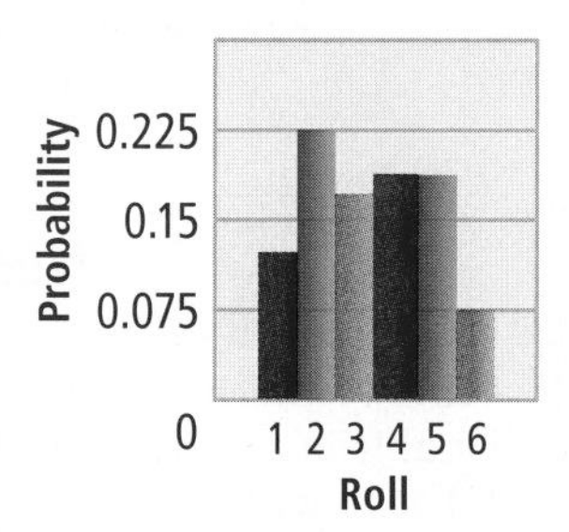


The table and graph both show the experimental probability distribution for the outcomes of 40 rolls of a standard number cube.

## Q

**Quadratic Formula (p. 194)** The Quadratic Formula is $x = \frac{-b \pm \sqrt{b^2 - 4ac}}{2a}$. It gives the solutions to the quadratic equation $ax^2 + bx + c = 0$.

**Fórmula cuadrática (p. 194)** La fórmula cuadrática es $x = \frac{-b \pm \sqrt{b^2 - 4ac}}{2a}$. Ésta da las soluciones a la ecuación cuadrática $ax^2 + bx + c = 0$.

**Example** If $-x^2 + 3x + 2 = 0$, then

$$x = \frac{-3 \pm \sqrt{(3)^2 - 4(-1)(2)}}{2(-1)}$$
$$= \frac{-3 \pm \sqrt{17}}{-2}$$

---

**Quadratic function (p. 151)** A quadratic function is a function that you can write in the form $f(x) = ax^2 + bx + c$ with $a \neq 0$.

**Función cuadrática (p. 151)** Una función cuadrática es una función que puedes escribir como $f(x) = ax^2 + bx + c$ con $a \neq 0$.

**Example**

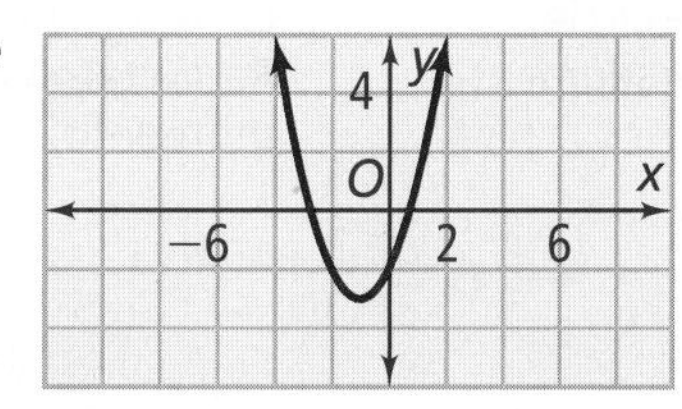


$y = x^2 + 2x - 2$

## English | Spanish

**Quartile (p. 5)** Quartiles are values that separate a finite data set into four equal parts. The second quartile ($Q_2$) is the median of the data. The first and third quartiles ($Q_1$ and $Q_3$) are the medians of the lower half and upper half of the data, respectively.

**Cuartil (p. 5)** Los cuartiles son valores que separan un conjunto finito de datos en cuatro partes iguales. El segundo cuartil ($Q_2$) es la mediana de los datos. Los cuartiles primero y tercero ($Q_1$ y $Q_3$) son las medianas de la mitad superior e inferior de los datos, respectivamente.

**Example** $\{2, 3, 4, 5, 5, 6, 7, 7\}$
$Q_1 = 3.5$
$Q_2$ (median) $= 5$
$Q_3 = 6.5$

## R

**Radian (p. 589)** $\frac{a°}{180°} = \frac{r \text{ radians}}{\pi \text{ radians}}$

**Radián (p. 589)** $\frac{a°}{180°} = \frac{r \text{ radians}}{\pi \text{ radians}}$

**Example** $60° \rightarrow \frac{60}{180} = \frac{x}{\pi}$
$x = \frac{60\pi}{180}$
$= \frac{\pi}{3}$
Thus, $60° = \frac{\pi}{3}$ radians.

**Radical equation (p. 459)** A radical equation is an equation that has a variable in a radicand or has a variable with a rational exponent.

**Ecuación radical (p. 459)** La ecuación radical es una ecuación que contiene una variable en el radicando o una variable con un exponente racional.

**Example** $(\sqrt{x})^3 + 1 = 65$
$x^{\frac{3}{2}} + 1 = 65$

**Radical function (p. 489)** A radical function is a function that can be written in the form $f(x) = a\sqrt[n]{x-h} + k$, where $a \neq 0$. For even values of $n$, the domain of a radical function is the real numbers $x \geq h$. *See also* **Square root function.**

**Función radical (p. 489)** Una función radical es una función quepuede expresarse como $f(x) = a\sqrt[n]{x-h} + k$, donde $a \neq 0$. Para $n$ par, el dominio de la función radical son los números reales tales que $x \geq h$. *Ver también* **Square root function.**

**Example** $f(x) = \sqrt{x-2}$

**Radicand (p. 426)** The number under a radical sign is the radicand.

**Radicando (p. 426)** La expresión que aparece debajo del signo radical es el radicando.

**Example** The radicand in $3\sqrt[4]{7}$ is 7.

**Radius of a circle (p. 855)** A radius of a circle is any segment with one endpoint on the circle and the other endpoint at the center of the circle. *Radius* can also mean the length of this segment.

**Radio de un círculo (p. 855)** Un radio de un círculo es cualquier segmento con extremo en el círculo y el otro extremo en el centro del círculo. *Radio* también se refeiere a la longitud de este segmento.

**Example**

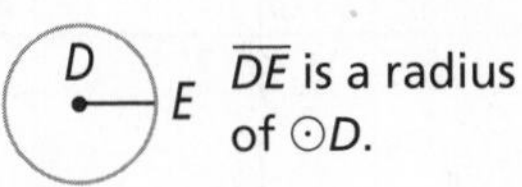

| English | Spanish |
|---|---|

**Random sample (p. 22)** In a random sample, all members of the population are equally likely to be chosen as every other member.

**Muestra aleatoria (p. 22)** En una muestra aleatoria, la probabilidad de ser seleccionado es igual para todos los miembros.

**Example** Let the set of all females between the ages of 19 and 34 be the population. A random selection of 900 females between those ages would be a sample of the population.

---

**Range of a set of data (p. 5)** The range of a set of data is the difference between the greatest and least values.

**Rango de un conjunto de datos (p. 5)** El rango de un conjunto de datos es la diferencia entre el valor máximo y el valor mínimo de los datos.

**Example** The range of the set {3.2, 4.1, 2.2, 3.4, 3.8, 4.0, 4.2, 2.8} is $4.2 - 2.2 = 2$.

---

**Rational equation (p. 401)** A rational equation is an equation that contains a rational expression.

**Ecuación racional (p. 401)** Una ecuación racional es una ecuación que contiene una expresión racional.

---

**Rational exponent (p. 451)** If the *n*th root of *a* is a real number and *m* is an integer, then $a^{\frac{1}{n}} = \sqrt[n]{a}$ and $a^{\frac{m}{n}} = \sqrt[n]{a^m} = (\sqrt[n]{a})^m$. If *m* is negative, $a \neq 0$.

**Exponente racional (p. 451)** Si la raíz *n*-ésima de *a* es un número real y *m* es un número entero, entonces $a^{\frac{1}{n}} = \sqrt[n]{a}$ y $a^{\frac{m}{n}} = \sqrt[n]{a^m} = (\sqrt[n]{a})^m$. Si *m* es negativo, $a \neq 0$.

**Example** $4^{\frac{1}{3}} = \sqrt[3]{4}$

$5^{\frac{3}{2}} = \sqrt{5^3} = (\sqrt{5})^3$

---

**Rational expression (p. 339)** A rational expression is the quotient of two polynomials.

**Expresión racional (p. 339)** Una expresión racional es el cociente de dos polinomios.

---

**Rational function (p. 385)** A rational function $f(x)$ can be written as $f(x) = \frac{P(x)}{Q(x)}$, where $P(x)$ and $Q(x)$ are polynomial functions. The domain of a rational function is all real numbers except those for which $Q(x) = 0$.

**Función racional (p. 385)** Una función racional $f(x)$ se puede expresar como $f(x) = \frac{P(x)}{Q(x)}$, donde $P(x)$ y $Q(x)$ son funciones de polinomios. El dominio de una función racional son todos los números reales excepto aquéllos para los cuales $Q(x) = 0$.

**Example**

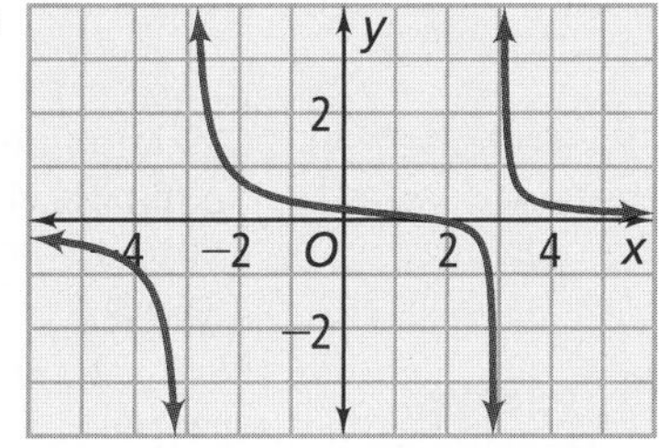


The function $y = \frac{x - 2}{x^2 - 9}$ is a rational function with three branches separated by asymptotes $x = -3$ and $x = 3$.

## English | Spanish

**Rationalize the denominator (p. 435)** To rationalize the denominator of an expression, rewrite it so there are no radicals in any denominator and no denominators in any radical.

**Racionalizar el denominador (p. 435)** Para racionalizar el denominador de una expresión, ésta se escribe de modo que no haya radicales en ningún denominador y no haya denominadores en ningún radical.

**Example** $\frac{1}{\sqrt{2}} = \frac{1}{\sqrt{2}} \times \frac{\sqrt{2}}{\sqrt{2}} = \frac{\sqrt{2}}{2}$

---

**Reciprocal function (p. 376)** A reciprocal function belongs to the family whose parent function is $f(x) = \frac{1}{x}$ where $x \neq 0$. You can write a reciprocal function in the form $f(x) = \left(\frac{a}{x} - h\right) + k$, where $a \neq 0$ and $x \neq h$.

**Función recíproca (p. 376)** Una función recíproca pertenece a la familia cuya función madre es $f(x) = \frac{1}{x}$ donde $x \neq 0$. Se puede escribir una función recíproca como $f(x) = \left(\frac{a}{x} - h\right) + k$, donde $a \neq 0$ y $x \neq h$.

**Example** $f(x) = \frac{1}{2x + 5}$

$p(v) = \frac{3}{v} + 5$

---

**Recursive formula (p. 688)** A recursive formula defines the terms in a sequence by relating each term to the ones before it.

**Fórmula recursiva (p. 688)** Una fórmula recursiva define los términos de una secuencia al relacionar cada término con los términos que lo anteceden.

**Example** Let $a_n = 2.5a_{n-1} + 3a_{n-2}$.
If $a_5 = 3$ and $a_4 = 7.5$, then
$a_6 = 2.5(3) + 3(7.5) = 30$.

---

**Reflection (p. 84)** A reflection flips the graph of a function across a line, such as the *x*- or *y*-axis. Each point on the graph of the reflected function is the same distance from the line of reflection as is the corresponding point on the graph of the original function.

**Reflexión (p. 84)** Una reflexión voltea la gráfica de una función sobre una línea, como el eje de las *x* o el eje de las *y*. Cada punto de la gráfica de la función reflejada está a la misma distancia del eje de reflexión que el punto correspondiente en la gráfica de la función original.

**Example**

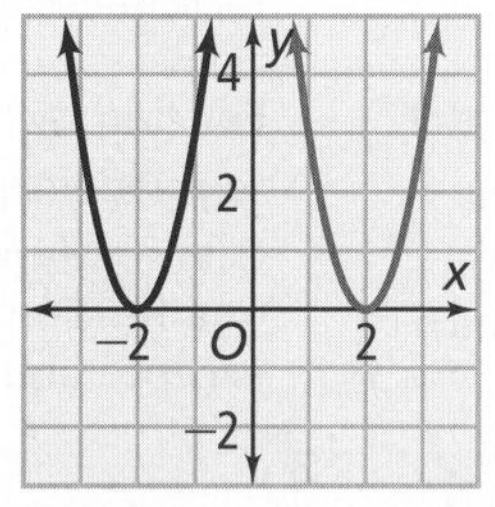


---

**Relative maximum (minimum) (p. 260)** A relative maximum (minimum) is the value of the function at an up-to-down (down-to-up) turning point.

**Máximo (minimo) relativo (p. 260)** El máximo (mínimo) relativo es el valor de la función en un punto de giro de arriba hacia abajo (de abajo hacia arriba).

**Example**

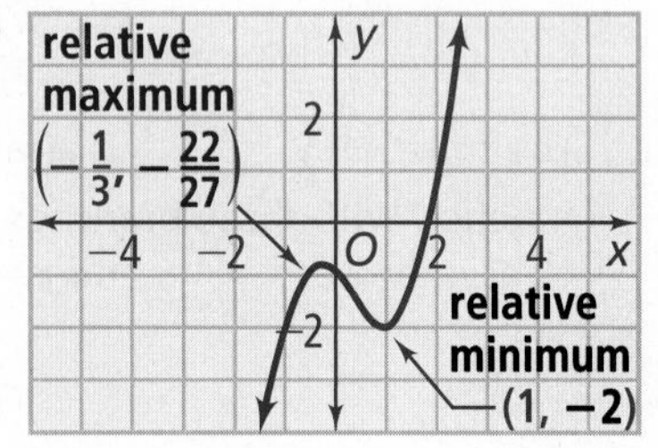

# English

# Spanish

**Removable discontinuity (p. 386)** A removable discontinuity is a point of discontinuity, $a$, of function f that you can remove by redefining $f$ at $x = a$. Doing so fills in a hole in the graph of $f$ with the point $(a, f(a))$.

**Discontinuidad removible (p. 386)** Una discontinuidad removible es un punto de discontinuidad $a$ en una función f que se puede remover al redefinir $f$ en $x = a$. Al hacer esto, se llena un hueco en la gráfica $f$ con el punto $(a, f(a))$.

**Row operation (p. 137)** A row operation on an augmented matrix is any of the following: switch two rows, multiply a row by a constant, add one row to another.

**Operación de fila (p. 137)** Una operación de fila en una matriz ampliada es cualquiera de las siguientes opciones: el intercambio de dos filas, la multiplicación de una fila por una constante o la suma de dos filas.

## S

**Sample (p. 22)** A sample from a population is some of the population.

**Muestra (p. 22)** Una muestra de una población es una parte de la población.

**Example** Let the set of all males between the ages of 19 and 34 be the population. A random selection of 900 males between those ages would be a sample of the population.

**Sample proportion (p. 43)** The ratio $\hat{p}$ compares $x$ to $n$ where $x$ is the number of times an event occurs and $n$ is the sample size. $\hat{p} = \frac{x}{n}$.

**Proporción de una muest7ra (p. 43)** La razón $\hat{p}$ compara $x$ a $n$, siendo $x$ el número de veces que sucede un evento y $n$ el tamaño de la muestra. $\hat{p} = \frac{x}{n}$.

**Example** In a taste test, 120 persons sampled two types of cola; 40 people preferred cola A. The sample proportion is $\frac{40}{120}$, or $\frac{1}{3}$.

**Secant (p. 907)** A secant is a line, ray, or segment that intersects a circle at two points.

**Secante (p. 907)** Una secante es una recta, semirrecta o segmento que corta un cículo en dos puntos.

**Example**

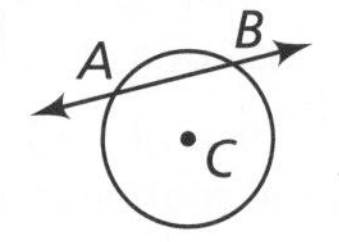


$\overleftrightarrow{AB}$ is a secant of $\odot C$.

**Secant function (p. 641)** The secant (sec) function is the reciprocal of the cosine function. For all real numbers $\theta$ except those that make $\cos\theta = 0$, $\sec\theta = \frac{1}{\cos\theta}$.

**Función secante (p. 641)** La función secante (sec) es el recíproco de la función coseno. Para todos los números reales $\theta$, excepto aquéllos para los que $\cos\theta = 0$, $\sec\theta = \frac{1}{\cos\theta}$.

**Example** If $\cos\theta = \frac{5}{13}$, then $\sec\theta = \frac{13}{5}$.

**Sector of a circle (p. 867)** A sector of a circle is the region bounded by two radii and their intercepted arc.

**Sector de un círculo (p. 867)** Un sector de un círculo es la región limitada por dos radios y el arco abarcado por ellos.

**Example**

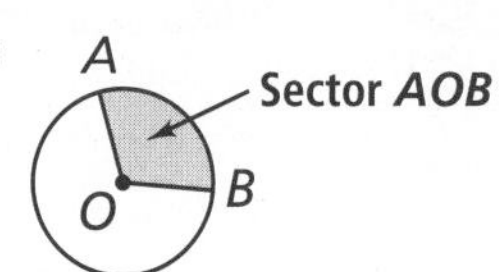

## English | Spanish

**Segment bisector (p. 737)** A segment bisector is a line, segment, ray, or plane that intersects a segment at its midpoint.

**Example**

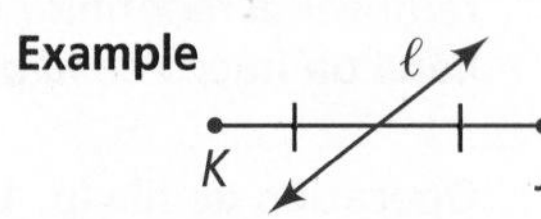


$\ell$ bisects $\overline{KJ}$.

**Bisectriz de un segmento (p. 454)** La bisectriz de un segmento es una recta, segmento, semirrecta o plano que corta un segmento en su punto medio.

**Segment of a circle (p. 868)** A segment of a circle is the part of a circle bounded by an arc and the segment joining its endpoints.

**Example**

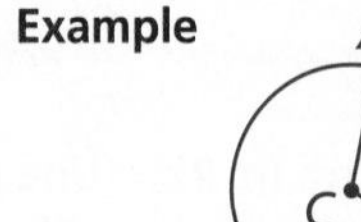


**Segmento de un círculo (p. 868)** Un segmento de un círculo es la parte de un círculo bordeada por un arco y el segmento que une sus extremos.

**Self-selected sample (p. 22)** In a self-selected sample you select only members of the population who volunteered for the sample.

**Muestra de voluntarios (p. 22)** En una muestra de voluntarios se seleccionan sólo a los miembros de la población que se ofrecen voluntariamente para ser parte de la muestra.

**Semicircle (p. 855)** A semicircle is half a circle.

**Example**

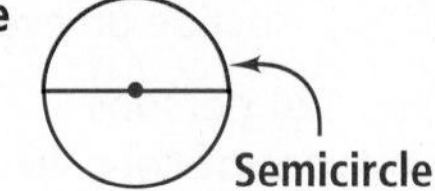


**Semicírculo (p. 855)** Un semicírculo es la mitad de un círculo.

**Sequence (p. 687)** A sequence is an ordered list of numbers.

**Example** 1, 4, 7, 10, . . .

**Progresión (p. 687)** Una progresión es una sucesión de números.

**Series (p. 711)** A series is the sum of the terms of a sequence.

**Example** The series $3 + 6 + 9 + 12 + 15$ corresponds to the sequence 3, 6, 9, 12, 15. The sum of the series is 45.

**Serie (p. 711)** Una serie es la suma de los términos de una secuencia.

**Similar solids (p. 785)** Similar solids have the same shape and have all their corresponding dimensions proportional.

**Example**

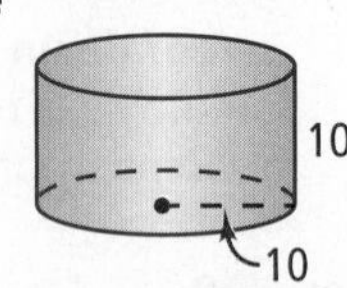


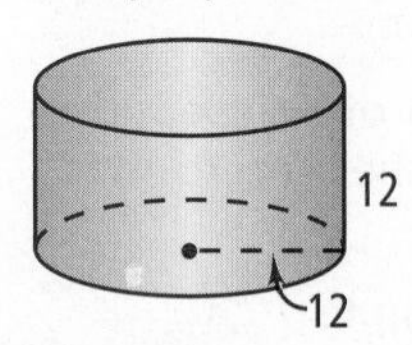


**Cuerpos geométricos semejantes (p. 785)** Los cuerpos geométricos semejantes tienen la misma forma y todas sus dimensiones correspondientes son proporcionales.

## English / Spanish

**Simplest form of a radical expression (p. 433)** A radical expression with index $n$ is in simplest form if there are no radicals in any denominator, no denominators in any radical, and any radicand has no $n$th power factors.

**Mínima expresión de una expresión radical (p. 433)** Una expresión radical con índice $n$ está en su mínima expresión si no tiene radicales en ningún denominador ni denominadores en ningún radical y los radicandos no tienen factores de potencia.

**Sine curve (p. 599)** A sine curve is the graph of a sine function.

**Sinusoide (p. 599)** Sinusoide es la gráfica de la función seno.

**Example**

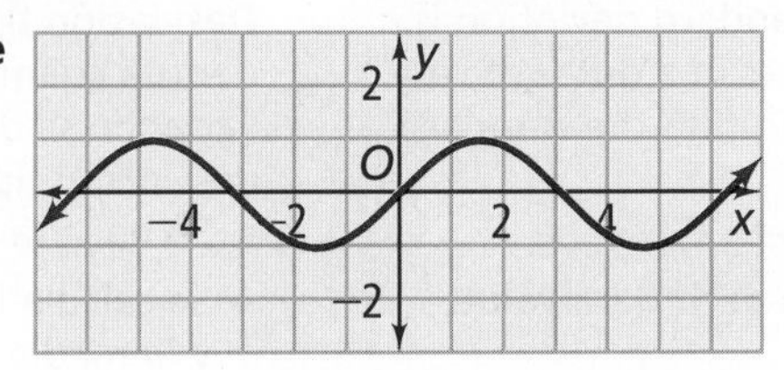


**Sine function, Sine of $\theta$ (pp. 584, 597)** The sine function, $y = \sin \theta$, matches the measure $\theta$ of an angle in standard position with the $y$-coordinate of a point on the unit circle. This point is where the terminal side of the angle intersects the unit circle. The $y$-coordinate is the sine of $\theta$.

**Función seno, Seno de $\theta$ (pp. 584, 597)** La función seno, $y = \sin \theta$, empareja la medida $\theta$ de un ángulo en posición estándar con la coordenada $y$ de un punto en el círculo unitario. Este es el punto en el que el lado terminal del ángulo interseca al círculo unitario. La coordenada y es el seno de $\theta$.

**Example**

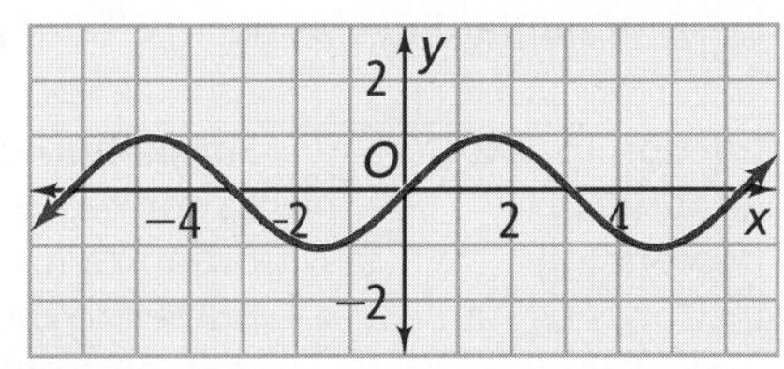


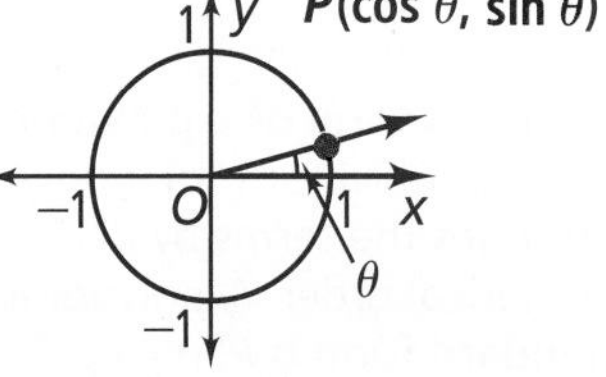


**Slope (p. 73)** The slope of a non-vertical line is the ratio of the vertical change to the horizontal change between points. You can calculate slope by finding the ratio of the difference in the $y$-coordinates to the difference in the $x$-coordinates for any two points on the line. The slope of a vertical line is undefined.

**Pendiente (p. 73)** La pendiente de una línea no vertical es la razón del cambio vertical al cambio horizontal entre puntos. Puedes calcular la pendiente al hallar la razón de la diferencia de la coordenada $y$ y la diferencia de la coordenada $x$ para dos puntos cualesquiera de la línea. La pendiente de una línea vertical es indefinida.

**Example** The slope of the line through points $(-1, -1)$ and $(1, -2)$ is $\frac{-2-(-1)}{1-(-1)} = \frac{-1}{2} = -\frac{1}{2}$.

**Slope-intercept form (p. 75)** The slope-intercept form of an equation of a line is $y = mx + b$, where $m$ is the slope and $b$ is the $y$-intercept.

**Forma pendiente-intercepto (p. 75)** La forma pendienteintercepto de una ecuación lineal es $y = mx + b$, donde $m$ es la pendiente y $b$ es el intercepto en $y$.

**Example** $y = 8x + 2$
$y = -x + 1$
$y = -\frac{1}{2}x - 14$

**Solution of an equation (p. 56)** A solution of an equation is a number that makes the equation true.

**Solución de una ecuación (p. 56)** Una solución de una ecuación es cualquier número que haga verdadera la ecuación.

**Example** The solution of $2x - 7 = -12$ is $x = -2.5$.

| English | Spanish |
|---|---|

**Square root function (p. 489)** A square root function is a function that can be written in the form $f(x) = a\sqrt{x - h} + k$, where $a \neq 0$. The domain of a square root function is all real numbers $x \geq h$.

**Función de raíz cuadrada (p. 489)** Una función de raíz cuadrada es una función que puede ser expresada como $f(x) = a\sqrt{x - h} + k$, donde $a \neq 0$. El dominio de una función de raíz cuadrada son todos los números reales tales que $x \geq h$.

**Example** $f(x) = 2\sqrt{x - 3} + 4$

**Standard deviation (p. 15)** Standard deviation is a measure of how much the values in a data set vary, or deviate, from the mean, $\bar{x}$. To find the standard deviation, follow five steps:
- Find the mean of the data set.
- Find the difference between each data value and the mean.
- Square each difference.
- Find the mean of the squares.
- Take the square root of the mean of the squares. This is the standard deviation.

**Desviación típica (p. 15)** La desviación típica denota cuánto los valores de un conjunto de datos varían, o se desvían, de la media, $\bar{x}$. Para hallar la desviación típica, se siguen cinco pasos:
- Se halla la media del conjunto de datos.
- Se calcula la diferencia entre cada valor de datos y la media.
- Se eleva al cuadrado cada diferencia.
- Se halla la media de los cuadrados.
- Se calcula la raíz cuadrada de la media de los cuadrados. Ésa es la desviación típica.

**Example** {0, 2, 3, 4, 6, 7, 8, 9, 10, 11}
$\bar{x} = 6$
standard deviation $= \sqrt{12} \approx 3.46$

**Standard form of a polynomial function (p. 240)** The standard form of a polynomial function arranges the terms by degree in descending numerical order. A polynomial function, $P(x)$, in standard form is $P(x) = a_n x^n + a_{n-1}x^{n-1} + \ldots + a_1 x + a_0$, where $n$ is a nonnegative integer and $a_n, \ldots, a_0$ are real numbers.

**Forma normal de una función polinomial (p. 240)** La forma normal de una función polinomial organiza los términos por grado en orden numérico descendiente. Una función polinomial, $P(x)$, en forma normal es $P(x) = a_n x^n + a_{n-1}x^{n-1} + \ldots + a_1 x + a_0$, donde $n$ es un número entero no negativo y $a_n, \ldots, a_0$ son números reales.

**Example** $2x^3 - 5x^2 - 2x + 5$

**Standard form of a quadratic function (p. 160)** The standard form of a quadratic function is $f(x) = ax^2 + bx + c$, with $a \neq 0$.

**Forma normal de una función cuadrática (p. 160)** La forma normal de una función cuadrática es $f(x) = ax^2 + bx + c$, con $a \neq 0$.

**Example** is $f(x) = 2x^2 + 5x + 2$

**Standard form of an equation of a circle (p. 222)** The standard form of an equation of a circle with center $(h, k)$ and radius $r$ is $(x - h)^2 + (y - k)^2 = r^2$.

**Forma normal de la ecuación de un círculo (p. 222)** La forma normal de la ecuación de un círculo con un centro $(h, k)$ y un radio $r$ es $(x - h)^2 + (y - k)^2 = r^2$.

**Example** In $(x + 5)^2 + (y + 2)^2 = 48$, $(-5, -2)$ is the center of the circle.

**Standard position (p. 581)** An angle in the coordinate plane is in standard position when the vertex is at the origin and one ray is on the positive $x$-axis.

**Posición estándar (p. 581)** Un ángulo en el plano de coordenadas se encuentra en posición estándar si el vértice se encuentra en el origen y una semirrecta se encuentra en el eje $x$ positivo.

**Example**

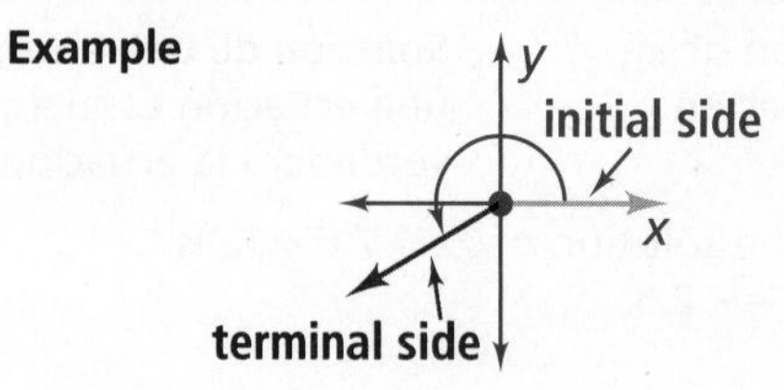

# English

# Spanish

**Step function (p. 99)** A step function pairs every number in an interval with a single value. The graph of a step function can look like the steps of a staircase.

**Función escalón (p. 99)** Una función escalón empareja cada número de un intervalo con un solo valor. La gráfica de una función escalón se puede parecer a los peldaños de una escalera.

**Sum of cubes (p. 266)** The sum of cubes is an expression of the form $a^3 + b^3$. It can be factored as $(a + b)(a^2 - ab + b^2)$.

**Suma de dos cubos (p. 266)** La suma de dos cubos es una expresión de la forma $a^3 + b^3$. Se puede factorizar como $(a + b)(a^2 - ab + b^2)$.

**Example** $x^3 + 27 = (x + 3)(x^2 - 3x + 9)$

**Survey (p. 24)** In a survey, you ask every member of a sample the same set of questions.

**Encuesta (p. 24)** En una encuesta, se le hace a cada miembro de una muestra la misma serie de preguntas.

**Synthetic division (p. 276)** Synthetic division is a process for dividing a polynomial by a linear expression $x - a$. You list the standard-form coefficients (including zeros) of the polynomial, omitting all variables and exponents. You use $a$ for the "divisor" and add instead of subtract throughout the process.

**División sintética (p. 276)** La división sintética es un proceso para dividir un polinomio por una expresión lineal $x - a$. En este proceso, escribes los coeficientes de forma normal (incluyendo los ceros) del polinomio, omitiendo todas las variables y todos los exponentes. Usas $a$ como "divisor" y sumas, en vez de restar, a lo largo del proceso.

**Example**

| $\underline{-3}\rfloor$ | 2 | 5 | 0 | −2 | −8 |
|---|---|---|---|---|---|
| | | **−6** | **3** | **−9** | **33** |
| | 2 | −1 | 3 | −11 | 25 |

$2x^4 + 5x^3 - 2x - 8$ divided by $x + 3$ gives $2x^3 - x^2 + 3x - 11$ as quotient and 25 as remainder.

**Systematic sample (p. 22)** In a systematic sample you order the population in some way, and then select from it at regular intervals.

**Muestra sistemática (p. 22)** En una muestra sistemática se ordena la población de cierta manera y luego se selecciona una muestra de esa población a intervalos regulares.

## T

**Tangent function, Tangent of $\theta$ (pp. 619, 621)** The tangent function, $y = \tan \theta$, matches the measure $\theta$, of an angle in standard position with the $y/x$ ratio of the $(x, y)$ coordinates of a point on the unit circle. This point is where the terminal side of the angle intersects the unit circle. $y/x$ is the tangent of $\theta$.

**Función tangente, Tangente de $\theta$ (pp. 619, 621)** La función tangente, $y = \tan \theta$, empareja la medida $\theta$, de un ángulo en posición estándar con la razón $y/x$ de las coordenadas $(x, y)$ de un punto en el círculo unitario. Este es el punto en el que el lado terminal del ángulo interseca al círculo unitario. $y/x$ es la tangente de $\theta$.

**Example**

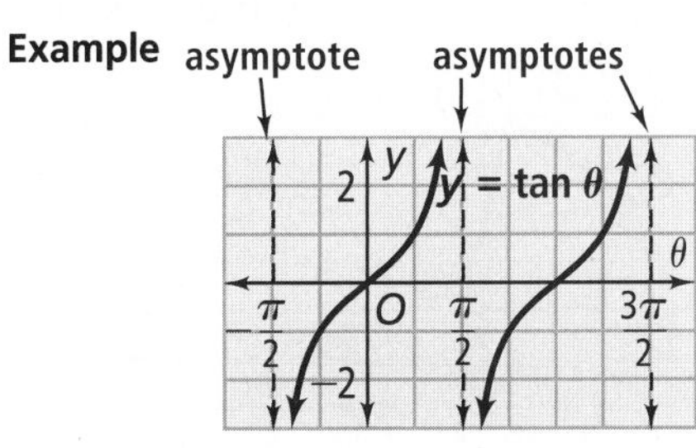


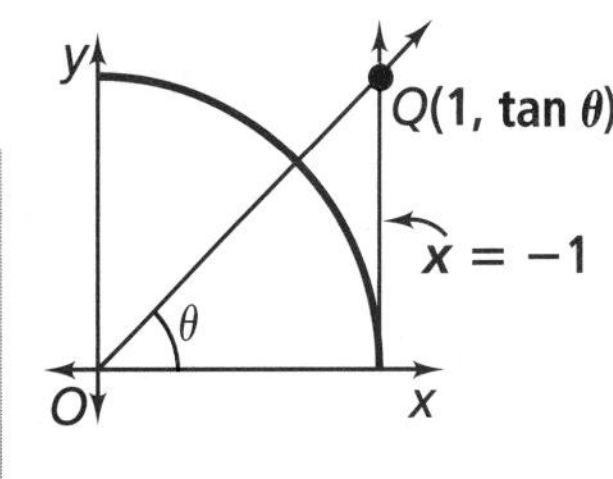

## English | Spanish

**Tangent to a circle (p. 876)** A tangent to a circle is a line, segment, or ray in the plane of the circle that intersects the circle in exactly one point. That point is the *point of tangency*.

**Tangente de un círculo (p. 876)** Una tangente de un círculo es una recta, segmento o semirrecta en el plano del círculo que corta el círculo en exactamente un punto. Ese punto es el *punto de tangencia*.

**Example**

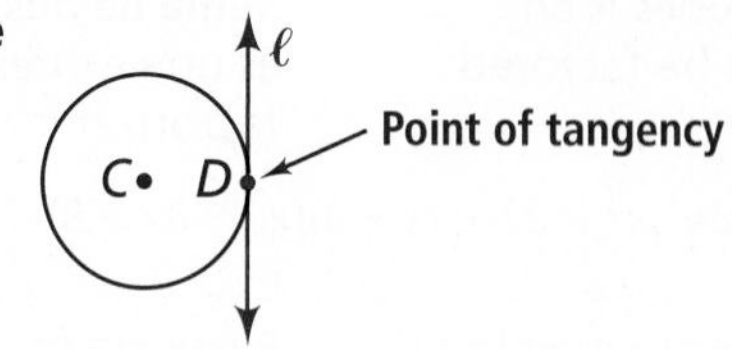


Line $\ell$ is tangent to $\odot C$. Point $D$ is the point of tangency.

**Term of a sequence (p. 687)** Each number in a sequence is a term.

**Término de una progresión (p. 687)** Cada número de una progresión es un término.

**Example** 1, 4, 7, 10, . . .
The second term is 4.

**Terminal side (p. 581)** *See* **Initial side.**

**Lado terminal (p. 581)** *Ver* **Initial side.**

**Test point (p. 102)** A test point is a point that you pick on one side of the boundary of the graph of a linear inequality. If the test point makes the inequality true, then all points on that side of the boundary are solutions of the inequality. If the test point makes the inequality false, then all points on the other side are solutions.

**Punto de prueba (p. 102)** Un punto de prueba es un punto que escoges a un lado del límite de la gráfica de una desigualdad lineal. Si el punto de prueba hace que la desigualdad sea verdadera, entonces todos los puntos en ese límite son soluciones de la desigualdad. Si el punto de prueba hace que la desigualdad sea falsa, entonces todos los puntos del otro lado del límite son soluciones.

**Transformation (p. 81)** A transformation of a function $y = af(x - h) + k$ is a change made to at least one of the values $a$, $h$, and $k$. The four types of transformations are dilations, reflections, rotations, and translations.

**Transformación (p. 81)** Una transformación de una función $y = af(x - h) + k$ es un cambio que se le hace a por lo menos uno de los valores $a$, $h$ y $k$. Hay cuatro tipos de transformaciones: dilataciones, reflexiones, rotaciones y traslaciones.

**Example** $g(x) = 2(x - 3)^2$ is a transformation of $f(x) = x^2$.

**Translation (p. 81)** A translation shifts the graph of the parent function horizontally, vertically, or both without changing its shape or orientation.

**Traslación (p. 81)** Una traslación desplaza la gráfica de la función madre horizontalmente, verticalmente o en ambas direcciones, sin cambiar su forma u orientación.

**Example**

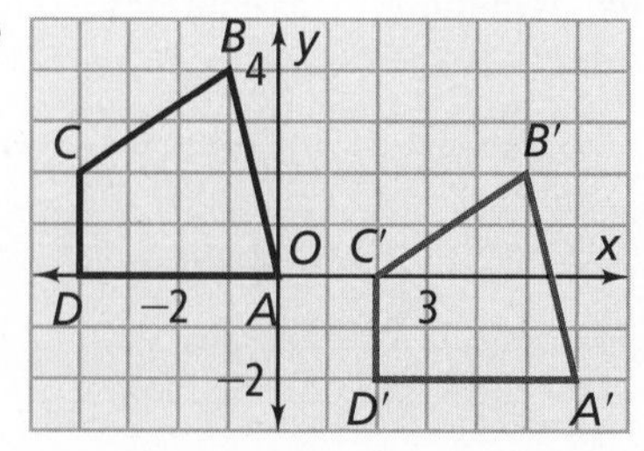

## English | Spanish

**Trapezoid (pp. 832)** A trapezoid is a quadrilateral with exactly one pair of parallel sides, the *bases*. The nonparallel sides are called the *legs* of the trapezoid. Each pair of angles adjacent to a base are *base angles* of the trapezoid. An *altitude* of a trapezoid is a perpendicular segment from one base to the line containing the other base. Its length is called the *height* of the trapezoid.

**Trapecio (pp. 832)** Un trapecio es un cuadrilátero con exactamente un par de lados paralelos, l, as *bases*. Los lados no paralelos se llaman los *catetos* del trapecio. Cada par de ángulos adyacentes a la base son los *ángulos de base* del trapecio. Una *altura* del trapecio es un segmento perpendicular que va de una base a la recta que contiene la otra base. Su longitud se llama, por extensión, la *altura* del trapecio.

**Example**

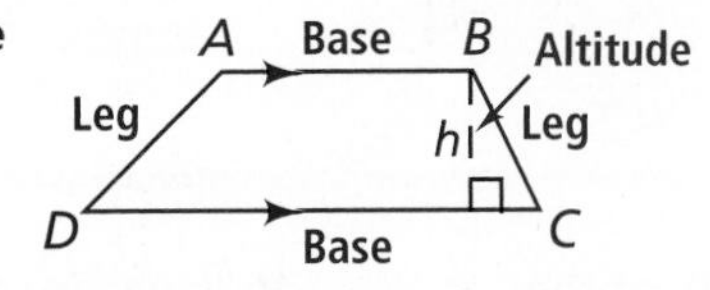


In trapezoid $ABCD$, $\angle ADC$ and $\angle BCD$ are one pair of base angles, and $\angle DAB$ and $\angle ABC$ are the other.

---

**Triangle (p. 825)** A triangle is a polygon with three sides. You can choose any side to be a *base*. The *height* is the length of the altitude drawn to the line containing the base.

**Tríangulo (p. 825)** Un tríangulo es un polígonocon tres lados. Se puede escoger cualquier lado como *base*. La *altura*, entonces, es la longitud de la altura trazada hasta la recta que contiene la base.

**Example**

Altitude

$h$

Base

---

**Trigonometric identity (p. 651)** A trigonometric identity in one variable is a trigonometric equation that is true for all values of the variable for which both sides of the equation are defined.

**Identidad trigonométrica (p. 651)** Una identidad trigonométrica en una variable es una ecuación trigonométrica que es verdadera para todos los valores de la variable para los cuales se definen los dos lados de la ecuación.

**Example** $\tan\theta = \frac{\sin\theta}{\cos\theta}$

---

**Turning point (p. 241)** A turning point of the graph of a function is a point where the graph changes direction from upwards to downwards or from downwards to upwards.

**Punto de giro (p. 241)** Un punto de giro de la gráfica de una función es un punto donde la gráfica cambia de dirección de arriba hacia abajo o vice versa.

## U

**Uniform Distribution (p. 29)** A uniform distribution is a probability distribution that is equal for each event in the sample space.

**Distribución uniforme (p. 29)** Una distribución uniforme es una distribución de probabilidad que es igual para cada suceso en el espacio muestral.

| English | Spanish |
| --- | --- |

**Unit circle (p. 584)** The unit circle has a radius of 1 unit and its center is at the origin of the coordinate plane.

**Círculo unitario (p. 584)** El círculo unitario tiene un radio de 1 unidad y el centro está situado en el origen del plano de coordenadas.

**Example**

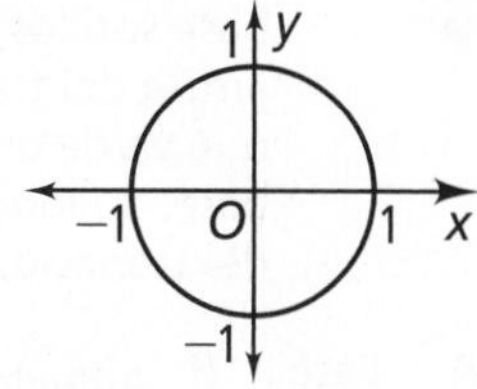


## V

**Variance (p. 15)** Variance is the square of the standard deviation. $\sigma^2 = \frac{\Sigma(x - \bar{x})^2}{n}$

**Varianza (p. 15)** La varianza es el cuadrado de la desviación estándar. $\sigma^2 = \frac{\Sigma(x - \bar{x})^2}{n}$

**Vertex (p. 774)** *See* **polyhedron.** The plural form of *vertex* is *vertices*.

**Vértice (p. 774)** *Ver* **polyhedron.**

**Vertex form of a quadratic function (p. 154)** The vertex form of a quadratic function is $f(x) = a(x - h)^2 + k$, where $a \neq 0$ and $(h, k)$ is the coordinate of the vertex of the function.

**Forma del vértice de una función cuadrática (p. 154)** La forma vértice de una función cuadrática es $f(x) = a(x - h)^2 + k$, donde $a \neq 0$ y $(h, k)$ es la coordenada del vértice de la función.

**Example** $f(x) = x^2 + 2x - 1 = (x + 1)^2 - 2$

**Vertex of a parabola (p. 151)** The vertex of a parabola is the point where the function for the parabola reaches a maximum or a minimum value. The parabola intersects its axis of symmetry at the vertex.

**Vértice de una parábola (p. 151)** El vértice de una parábola es el punto donde la función de la parábola alcanza un valor máximo o mínimo. La parábola y su eje de simetría se intersecan en el vértice.

**Example**

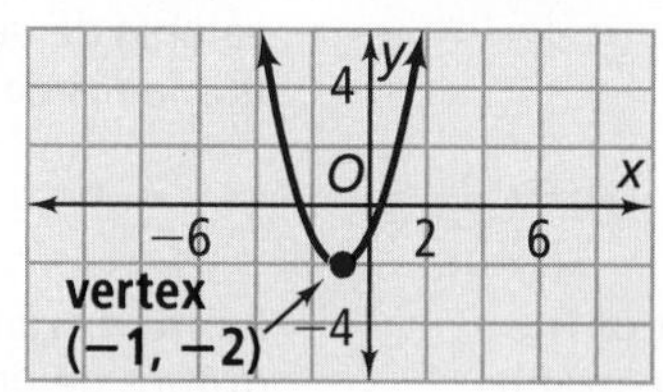


The vertex of the quadratic function $y = x^2 + 2x - 1$ is $(-1, -2)$.

**Vertical compression (p. 84)** A vertical compression reduces all *y*-values of a function by the same factor between 0 and 1.

**Compresión vertical (p. 84)** Una compresión vertical reduce todos los valores de *y* de una función por el mismo factor entre 0 y 1.

**Vertical stretch (p. 84)** A vertical stretch multiplies all *y*-values of a function by the same factor greater than 1.

**Estiramiento vertical (p. 84)** Un estiramiento vertical multiplica todos los valores de *y* por el mismo factor mayor que 1.

## English | Spanish

### X

**$x$-intercept, $y$-intercept (p. 75)** The point at which a line crosses the $x$-axis (or the $x$-coordinate of that point) is an $x$-intercept. The point at which a line crosses the $y$-axis (or the $y$-coordinate of that point) is a $y$-intercept.

**Intercepto en $x$, intercepto en $y$ (p. 75)** El punto donde una recta corta el eje $x$ (o la coordenada $x$ de ese punto) es el intercepto en $x$. El punto donde una recta cruza el eje $y$ (o la coordenada $y$ de ese punto) es el intercepto en $y$.

**Example**

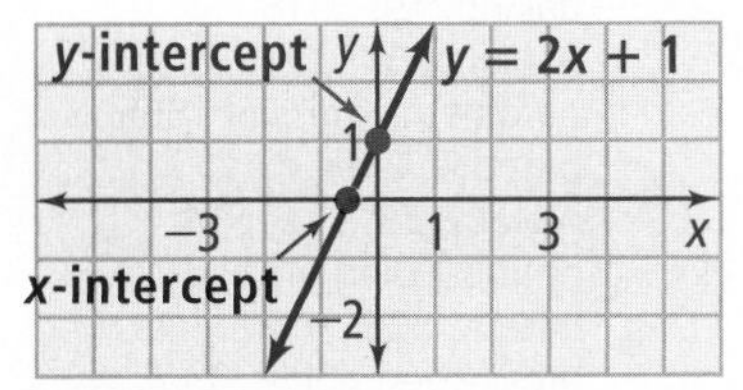


The $x$-intercept of $y = 2x + 1$ is $\left(-\frac{1}{2}, 0\right)$ or $-\frac{1}{2}$

The $y$-intercept of $y = 2x + 1$ is $(0, 1)$ or 1.

### Z

**Zero of a function (p. 178)** A zero of a function $f(x)$ is any value of $x$ for which $f(x) = 0$.

**Cero de una función (p. 178)** Un cero de una función $f(x)$ es cualquier valor de $x$ para el cual $f(x) = 0$.

**Example**

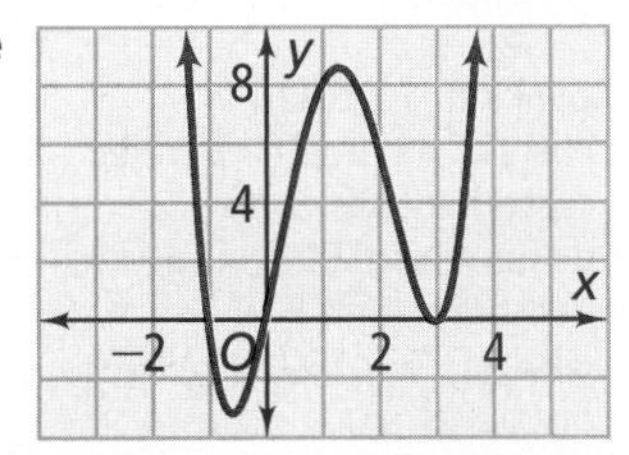


**Zero-Product Property (p. 178)** If the product of two or more factors is zero, then one of the factors must be zero.

**Propiedad del cero del producto (p. 178)** Si el producto de dos o más factores es cero, entonces uno de los factores debe ser cero.

**Example** $(x - 3)(2x - 5) = 0$

$x - 3 = 0$ or $2x - 5 = 0$

**z-score (p. 46)** The $z$-score of a value is the number of standard deviations that the value is from the mean.

**Puntaje $z$ (p. 46)** El puntaje $z$ de un valor es el número de desviaciones normales que tiene ese valor de la media.

**Example** $\{0, 2, 3, 4, 6, 7, 8, 9, 10, 11\}$

$\bar{x} = 6$

standard deviation $= \sqrt{12} \approx 3.46$

For 8, $z$-score $= \frac{8 - 6}{\sqrt{12}} \approx 0.58$

# Index


## A

**absolute value,** 807
**absolute value functions,** 91
**absolute value functions and graphs,** 91–98, 144
**absolute value inequalities,** 105, 149
**Activity Lab**
circles and radians, 873–875
drawing conclusions from samples, 46–49
geometry and infinite series, 720–721
graphing polynomials using zeros, 301–302
margin of error, 42–45
probability distributions, 29–33
proving slope criteria, 839–842
systems with rational equations, 409–412
**addition**
fractions, 337
function operations, 467, 468
percents, 1
of polynomials, 250–255, 330
radical expressions, 441
of rational expressions, 356–362, 419
**algebraic expressions, evaluating,** 53
**algorithms,** 275
**altitude, of a parallelogram,** 823
**ambiguous case, Law of Sines and,** 668–669
**amplitude,** 576, 600
**angle measures,** 672, 673
circles and segment lengths, 906–914, 917
Inscribed Angle Theorem, 900
tangent lines and, 877
**angles**
bisectors, 737
inscribed angles, 897–905, 917
tangent of an angle, 619
of triangles, 663
unit circle and, 581–588, 679
**applications**
academics, 428
acoustics, 549
advertising, 11
agriculture, 39, 177, 866
air pollution, 201
air travel, 320, 419
America's Cup, 502
animating a game, 684
apparent magnitudes of stars, 570
archaeology, 523, 560
architecture, 719
astronomy, 230, 541, 606, 772
athletics, 710
auto loans, 355
auto maintenance, 51
bacteria growth, 563
baking, 195, 518
banking, 346, 710
barometric pressure, 565
baseball, 819
biology, 36, 561, 618
boat building, 431
botany, 523
break-even points, 117
bridges, 300
buoyancy, 754
business, 141, 198, 211, 396
bus travel, 57
calendars, 580
carpentry, 264
ceramics, 626
chemistry, 72, 117, 370, 392, 448, 533
college admissions, 124
communications, 729, 767
commuting, 366, 771
construction, 72, 346, 381, 540, 626
cooking, 104, 326
costs of a gardening project, 806
customer satisfaction, 28
decorating, 759
demographics, 549
design, 764, 792, 802, 871
discounts, 500
distance, 646
earth science, 220, 879
economics, 163, 473
elections, 28
electricity, 430, 500
electronics, 497
energy, 20, 25, 754
engineering, 913
entertainment, 27, 118, 694
estimation, 606
exercise, 359, 691
finance, 134, 695
financial planning, 725
finding the area of a plot of land, 852
fitness, 186
flight, 405
football, 192
forestry, 666
fuel economy, 407
fundraising, 195
game design, 918
games, 772
gardening, 25, 234, 255, 289, 764, 806, 818
gasoline mileage, 384
geography, 596
gift boxes, 803
grades, 12, 72, 395, 407, 429, 713
groceries, 719
health, 579
history, 831
home maintenance, 818
hydraulics, 461
income, 21, 702
industrial design, 871
industry, 408
interest, 509, 510
interior design, 848
investments, 522
landscape design, 863
landscaping, 165, 184, 492, 524, 800
language arts, 580
literature, 792
loan payments, 355
logos, 743
machinery, 230
manufacturing, 41, 131, 158, 514
maximizing profits, 236
medicine, 763
metallurgy, 837
metals, 753
metalwork, 262
meteorology, 11, 17, 18, 550, 800
minimizing costs, 422
money, 111
music, 550, 596, 605
navigation, 677
oceanography, 514
optics, 216
optimal height, 453
packaging, 789, 805
paint, 142
painting, 367
pet care, 820
pets, 863
photography, 909
physics, 165, 181, 184, 198, 232, 329, 371, 438, 439, 466, 497, 523, 561, 659, 678, 730
picture frames, 255
planning a triathlon, 148
platonic solids, 784
playground equipment, 801
population, 514
postage, 100, 101
potential energy, 368
profits, 255
proving a relationship, 336
psychology, 524
recreation, 872
remodeling, 759
resource management, 545
restoring lost data, 52
rockets, 62
rowing, 362
sailing, 667
sales, 472, 475
sales data, 734

satellites, 438, 560
savings, 699
science, 457, 538, 706
seismology, 528, 548
snacks, 141
solar eclipses, 884
sound, 221, 606
space, 557, 558, 560, 594
sports, 39, 133, 201, 408, 514, 676, 745, 838, 864
storage, 407
surveying, 664, 764
swimming, 62
target games, 769, 773
teamwork, 407
technology, 159, 561
television, 904
temperature, 482, 635
testing, 8
tides, 618
tiling, 818
time, 588, 863
track and field, 12
traffic lights, 767
traffic patterns, 772
traffic signs, 465
transportation, 112, 145, 255, 404, 596, 701, 766, 871
urban design, 827
volume, 326, 461
weather, 6, 40, 118, 458
woodworking, 408
zoology, 514

**Arc Addition Postulate,** 856

**arc measures,** 901

**arcs**
chords and, 886–896, 916
circles and, 855–864, 915
inscribed angles, 901
intercept arcs, 592

**area**
of circles and sectors, 865–872, 915
finding, 735
finding the area of a plot of land, 852
of irregular shapes, 815, 826
law of sines and, 660–667, 683
of parallelograms and triangles, 823–831, 850
perimeter and area in the coordinate plane, 809–820, 850
perimeters and areas of similar figures, 755–764, 803
probability and area, 767, 768, 769
of a rectangle, 823
of a segment, 868
of trapezoids, rhombuses, and kites, 832–838, 851
and volumes of similar solids, 785–793, 805

**area ratios,** 758

**arithmetic sequences,** 696–702, 731

**arithmetic series,** 711–719, 732

**assessment**
Chapter Review, 50–51, 143–147, 231–235, 330–335, 418–421, 498–501, 567–569, 679–683, 731–733, 802–805, 850–851, 915–917
Got It?, 4, 5, 6, 7, 8, 16, 17, 18, 23, 24, 25, 35, 36, 37, 56, 57, 58, 59, 64, 65, 66, 67, 68, 74, 76, 77, 78, 82, 83, 84, 85, 86, 92, 93, 94, 95, 103, 104, 105, 106, 110, 111, 112, 113, 114, 119, 120, 121, 122, 127, 128, 129, 130, 135, 136, 137, 138, 139, 152, 153, 154, 155, 156, 160, 162, 163, 170, 171, 172, 173, 174, 178, 179, 180, 185, 186, 187, 188, 189, 194, 195, 197, 204, 205, 206, 213, 215, 216, 217, 218, 223, 225, 226, 227, 240, 242, 243, 244, 250, 251, 252, 256, 257, 258, 260, 261, 265, 267, 268, 269, 274, 275, 276, 277, 278, 283, 284, 285, 286, 296, 297, 304, 305, 314, 315, 316, 317, 322, 323, 324, 326, 340, 341, 342, 343, 347, 348, 349, 350, 351, 356, 357, 358, 359, 364, 365, 366, 367, 368, 377, 378, 379, 380, 381, 386, 388, 389, 390, 391, 402, 403, 404, 426, 427, 428, 432, 433, 434, 435, 436, 441, 442, 443, 444, 445, 450, 451, 452, 453, 454, 455, 459, 460, 461, 462, 463, 468, 470, 471, 478, 479, 480, 481, 483, 489, 490, 491, 493, 494, 505, 507, 508, 509, 511, 516, 517, 518, 520, 526, 527, 529, 530, 536, 537, 538, 542, 543, 544, 545, 546, 547, 554, 555, 556, 557, 574, 575, 576, 577, 582, 583, 584, 585, 590, 591, 592, 593, 598, 599, 600, 601, 602, 611, 612, 613, 614, 620, 622, 623, 629, 630, 631, 632, 633, 634, 642, 643, 644, 645, 652, 654, 655, 656, 661, 662, 663, 664, 671, 672, 673, 688, 689, 690, 691, 697, 698, 699, 704, 705, 706, 707, 712, 713, 714, 715, 716, 723, 724, 726, 737, 738, 739, 741, 742, 748, 749, 756, 757, 758, 759, 766, 768, 769, 775, 776, 777, 779, 780, 785, 787, 788, 789, 794, 796, 797, 810, 811, 812, 813, 814, 815, 824, 826, 832, 833, 834, 844, 845, 856, 857, 858, 860, 866, 867, 868, 877, 878, 880, 881, 882, 887, 889, 891, 892, 898, 900, 901, 907, 908, 910
Open-Ended exercises, 28, 72, 90, 117, 124, 134, 141, 145, 159, 177, 184, 210, 230, 246, 254, 264, 272, 280, 289, 299, 300, 346, 355, 361, 371, 383, 399, 406, 408, 431, 439, 449, 456, 458, 466, 474, 476, 487, 496, 514, 524, 533, 540, 549, 580, 587, 588, 596, 604, 605, 616, 625, 637, 666, 677, 694, 700, 710, 719, 729, 763, 782, 784, 799, 805, 819, 830, 837, 871

**asymptotes**
horizontal asymptotes of rational functions, 389–390
oblique asymptotes, 397–400
vertical asymptotes of rational functions, 387–388


# B


**base, of a parallelogram,** 823

**bases**
base 10 logarithms, 527
change of base formula, 537
exponential equations and, 542, 543
natural base exponential functions, 519

**basic identities,** 651, 652–653

**Big Ideas**
coordinate geometry, 808
data collection and analysis, 2
data representation, 2
equivalence, 150, 238, 338, 424, 504, 572, 686
functions, 54, 150, 238, 338, 424, 504, 572
measurement, 736, 808, 854
modeling, 504, 572, 686
proportionality, 338
reasoning and proof, 854
similarity, 736
solving equations and inequalities, 54, 150, 238, 338, 424
variables, 686
visualization, 736

**bimodal data sets,** 4

**binomial radical expressions,** 440–449, 499

**binomials,** 305, 423

**binomial theorem,** 303–308, 334

**bisectors,** 737

**box-and-whisker plots,** 6–7

**break-even points,** 117


# C


**calculators.** *See* graphing calculators

**capacity, finding,** 789

**centers, finding,** 226

**central tendency, measures of,** 3–4

Index


**Challenge exercises,** 12, 21, 28, 41, 62, 72, 80, 90, 98, 109, 118, 125, 134, 142, 158–159, 166, 177, 184, 192, 202, 211, 221, 230, 247, 255, 264, 272, 281, 289, 300, 308, 321, 329, 346, 354–355, 362, 371, 384, 396, 408, 431, 439, 449, 458, 466, 476, 487, 497, 514, 524, 534, 541, 550, 561, 580, 588, 596, 606, 618, 637, 650, 659, 667, 678, 695, 702, 710, 719, 730, 746, 754, 764, 773, 784, 793, 801, 820, 831, 838, 849, 864, 871–872, 885, 896, 905, 914

**change of base formula,** 537–538

**Chapter Review,** 50–51, 143–147, 231–235, 330–335, 418–421, 498–501, 567–569, 679–683, 731–733, 802–805, 850–851, 915–917

**chords and arcs,** 886–896, 916

**circles**
- Activity Lab, 873–875
- angle measures and segment lengths, 906–914, 917
- areas of circles and sectors, 865–872, 915
- Chapter Review, 915–917
- chords and arcs, 886–896, 916
- circles and arcs, 855–864, 915
- circles and radians, 873–875
- circumscribing a circle, 740, 741
- in the coordinate plane, 222–230, 235
- inscribed angles and, 897–905, 917
- inscribing a regular hexagon, 742
- polygons and, 882
- Pull It All Together, 918
- tangent lines and, 876–885, 916

**circles, area of,** 814

**circumference,** 810, 811

**circumference, of a circle,** 858

**combined variations,** 367–368

**common factors,** 171

**Compare and Contrast exercises,** 19, 27, 39, 71, 88, 97, 107 116, 123, 158, 165, 176, 183, 208, 307, 320, 328, 353, 361, 369, 395, 448, 465, 497, 533, 648, 649, 709, 728, 744, 762, 789, 799, 817

**complex fractions, simplifying,** 351–352

**composition of functions,** 469, 470, 471

**composition of inverse functions,** 483

**compound interest,** 520

**compression,** 153

**Concept Summary**
- exponential functions, 506
- families of exponential functions, 517
- families of logarithmic functions, 530
- families of sine and cosine functions, 632
- fundamental theorem of algebra, 298
- polynomial factoring techniques, 266
- properties of cosine functions, 612
- properties of tangent functions, 621
- slope of a line, 75
- transformations of *f*(*x*), 86

**congruent circles,** 886

**conjectures, making.** *See* Make a Conjecture

**Conjugate Root Theorem,** 284–285

**conjugates, multiplying,** 444

**constructions,** 736, 737–746, 763, 802, 885, 895, 904

**continuously compounded interest,** 520–521

**coordinate geometry,** 808

**coordinate plane**
- circles in, 222–230, 235
- formulas and, 843
- perimeter and area in the coordinate plane, 809–820, 850
- polygons in, 843–849, 851

**corollaries, to Inscribed Angle Theorem,** 899

**cosecant, secant, and cotangent functions,** 641

**cosine equations,** 614

**cosine function,** 610–618, 628–637, 681, 682

**cosines,** 584, 591

**coterminal angles,** 583

**cross sections,** 779–780

**cube root functions,** 493

**cubic functions,** 243, 322, 323–324

**cycles and periods, identifying,** 574


# D


**Data Collection exercises,** 20, 45

**degrees**
- converting between radians and degrees, 590
- determining, 244
- proportion relating radians and degrees, 589–590

**denominators,** 356–358, 445

**density and design problems,** 747–754, 803

**Descartes' Rule of Signs,** 286

**design problems, solving,** 749–750

**diameters, chords and,** 891

**differences,** 244, 440

**dimensional analysis,** 590

**dimensions, determining,** 186

**dimensions, missing,** 824

**discriminants,** 196, 197–198, 237

**distance, finding,** 858, 878

**Distributive Property,** 303–304

**division**
- function operations, 467, 468–469
- of polynomials, 273–281, 332
- of radical expressions, 432–439, 498
- of rational expressions, 347–355, 418

**Division Algorithm for Polynomials,** 275


# E


**elimination method,** 112, 127

**equations.** *See also* inequalities; linear equations, inequalities, and functions; quadratic functions and equations
- equations with two radicals, 463
- exponential and logarithmic equations, 542–550, 556, 569
- inverse relations and functions, 479
- solving, 55–62, 143, 807, 853
- solving equations by completing the square, 188, 189
- solving perfect square trinomial equations, 187
- solving rational equations, 401–408, 421
- solving systems of equations, 110–118, 145
- writing and equation of a circle, 222
- writing in slope-intercept form, 77
- writing the equation of a transformation, 380

**equations and inequalities, solving,** 150, 238, 338, 424

**equivalence,** 150, 238, 338, 424, 504, 572

**equivalent systems, solving,** 113, 128

**Error Analysis exercises,** 10, 11, 21, 40, 61, 62, 71, 72, 79, 80, 90, 97, 117, 124, 132, 142, 164, 166, 177, 184, 191, 200, 210, 220, 229, 255, 263, 272, 281, 288, 289, 300, 308, 320, 327, 346, 355, 361, 370, 395, 406, 407, 429, 438, 439, 448,

457, 466, 474, 486, 496, 513, 522, 540, 548, 559, 560, 561, 578, 587, 596, 604, 625, 636, 647, 665, 676, 693, 701, 708, 718, 728, 730, 752, 753, 762, 771, 782, 791, 817, 847, 862, 870, 884, 894, 903, 912

**Essential Understanding,** 3, 15, 22, 34, 55, 58, 63, 73, 81, 91, 102, 110, 119, 126–127, 135, 151, 160, 169, 178, 185, 193, 203, 212, 222, 239, 250, 256, 265, 273, 282, 295–296, 303–304, 313, 322, 339, 347, 356, 363, 376, 385–386, 390, 401, 425, 432, 440, 450, 459, 467, 477, 488, 505, 515, 525, 535, 542, 553, 573, 581, 589, 597, 610, 619, 628, 641, 651, 660, 670, 687, 696, 703, 711, 722, 737, 747, 755, 765, 774, 785, 794, 809, 823, 832, 833, 843, 865, 855, 876, 886, 897, 906, 909

**estimation,** 763, 764, 819

**Euler's Formula,** 776

**even and odd functions,** 248–249

**explicit formulas,** 687, 688, 699

**exponential and logarithmic equations,** 571

**exponential and logarithmic functions**
- Chapter Review, 567–569
- exploring exponential models, 505–514, 567
- exponential and logarithmic equations, 542–550, 569
- exponential and logarithmic inequalities, 562–566
- logarithmic functions as inverses, 525–534, 568
- natural logarithms, 553–561, 569
- properties of exponential functions, 515–524, 567
- properties of logarithms, 535–541, 568
- Pull It All Together, 570
- using logarithms for exponential models, 551–552

**exponential growth and decay,** 507, 508

**exponential models, exploring,** 505–514, 567

**expressions**
- evaluating, 503, 807
- factoring quadratic expressions, 169–177, 232
- simplifying, 1, 53, 337, 807

**extrapolation,** 317

# F

**factors and factoring,** 423
- factoring perfect-square trinomials, 173
- factoring quadratic expressions, 150, 169–177, 232, 337
- multiplying and dividing rational expressions, 348–349
- polynomial factoring techniques, 266
- polynomials, linear functions, and zeros, 256–264
- solving polynomial equations, 265, 267
- solving quadratic equations, 178–179, 237

**Factor Theorem,** 258

**families of absolute value functions,** 93

**families of exponential functions,** 517

**families of logarithmic functions,** 530

**families of radical functions,** 489

**families of sine and cosine functions,** 632

**finite sequences and series,** 711, 712, 722, 723

**formulas**
- area of a triangle, 660
- change of base formula, 537
- and the coordinate plane, 843
- Euler's Formula, 776
- explicit formulas, 687, 688, 699
- finding the inverse of, 481
- geometric series formula, 724
- quadratic formula, 193–202, 234

**fractions,** 337, 351–352, 685

**function operations,** 467–476, 500

**function rules,** 602

**functions.** *See also* equations; graphs and graphing; linear equations, inequalities, and functions; polynomials and polynomial functions; quadratic functions and equations
- Big Ideas, 54, 150, 238, 338, 424, 504, 572
- cosine function, 610–618, 628–637, 681, 682
- domain and range of, 423
- evaluating, 685
- families of, 81–90, 144
- graphing rational functions, 372–375
- inverse relations and functions, 477–487, 501
- odd and even functions, 248–249
- polynomial functions, 239–247, 330
- polynomials, linear functions, and zeros, 256–264
- rational functions and their graphs, 385–396, 420
- reciprocal function family, 376–384, 420
- sine function, 597–606, 628–637, 680, 682
- tangent function, 619–627, 681

**Fundamental Theorem of Algebra,** 295–300, 334

# G

**general form of the absolute value function,** 95

**general form of the reciprocal function family,** 376

**geometric mean,** 707

**geometric probability,** 765–773, 804

**geometric sequences,** 703–710, 732

**geometric series,** 722–730, 733

**geometric series formula,** 724

**Geometry in 3 Dimensions,** 894

**Get Ready!,** 1, 53, 149, 237, 337, 423, 503, 571, 685, 735, 807, 853

**Golden Rectangle,** 746

**graphing calculator,** 17, 41, 109, 141, 179, 180, 269, 313, 378, 384, 396, 398, 404, 463, 466, 496, 514, 520, 523, 524, 545, 561, 565, 587, 588, 605, 618, 623, 625, 644, 645, 649, 701, 716, 729, 773
- solving square roots and other radical equations, 463, 466

**Greatest Common Factor (GCF),** 171

# H

**Here's Why It Works,** 161, 213

**hexagons,** 742

**horizontal asymptotes of rational functions,** 389–390

**horizontal translations,** 83

# I

**identities, trigonometric,** 651–659, 683

**indirect measurement,** 649

**indirect proof,** 877

**Indirect Reasoning,** 793

**inequalities**
- absolute value inequalities, 105
- exponential and logarithmic inequalities, 562–566
- rational inequalities, 413–417
- solving, 63–72, 143
- solving a quadratic system of, 206
- systems of inequalities, 119–125, 146
- two-variable inequalities, 102–109, 145

**infinite geometric series,** 725, 726
**infinite sequences,** 711
**infinite series,** 711, 720–721, 725, 726
**inscribed angles,** 897–905, 917
**Inscribed Angle Theorem,** 897–898, 899
**intercept arcs,** 592
**interpolation,** 317
**inverse functions, composition of,** 483
**inverse relations and functions,** 477–487, 501, 571
**inverses, logarithmic functions as,** 525–534, 568
**inverse variations,** 363–371, 419
**irregular shapes, area of,** 815, 826
**isosceles and equilateral triangles,** 853

## J

**Justifying Steps exercises,** 72

## K

**Key Concepts**
- Absolute Value Parent Function $f(x) = |x|$, 91
- arc measures, 856
- area of a parallelogram, 823
- area of a rectangle, 823
- area of a segment, 868
- area of a trapezoid, 832
- area of a triangle, 825
- arithmetic sequences, 696
- basic identities, 651
- box-and-whisker plots, 6
- combined variations, 367
- completing the square, 188
- composition of functions, 469
- composition of inverse functions, 483
- converting between radians and degrees, 590
- cosecant, secant, and cotangent functions, 641
- cosine and sine of an angle, 584
- discriminants, 196
- Division Algorithm for Polynomials, 275
- Euler's Formula, 776
- exponential growth and decay, 508
- factoring a difference of two squares, 173
- factoring perfect-square trinomials, 173
- families of radical functions, 489
- the family of absolute value functions, 93
- finding variance and standard deviation, 15
- formulas and the coordinate plane, 843
- function operations, 467
- general form of the absolute value function, 95
- general form of the reciprocal function family, 376
- geometric sequences, 703
- horizontal asymptotes of rational functions, 389
- how multiple zeros affect a graph, 260
- infinite geometric series, 725
- length of an intercepted arc, 592
- logarithms, 525–526
- measures of central tendency, 3–4
- $n + 1$ Point Principle, 314
- natural logarithmic function, 553
- normal distributions, 34–35
- the *n*th root, 425–426
- parabolas, 212–213
- the parent quadratic function, 151
- perimeter, circumference, and area, 809
- point of discontinuity, 386
- polynomial functions, 241
- power functions, 325
- probability and area, 767
- probability and length, 765
- properties of sine functions, 601
- proportion relating radians and degrees, 589–590
- Pythagorean identities, 655
- quadratic formula, 194
- rational exponents, 451
- reciprocal function family, 379
- reflection, stretch, and compression, 153
- rhombuses and kites, 833
- roots, zeros, and *x*-intercepts, 257
- row operations, 137
- samples, 22
- slope-intercept form, 75
- slopes, 73
- solving equations by completing the square, 188
- standard form of an equation of a circle, 222
- standard form of a polynomial function, 240
- study methods, 24
- summation notation and linear functions, 715
- sum of a finite geometric series, 723
- tangent of an angle, 619
- transformations of a parabola, 217
- transforming a circle, 224
- translation of the parabola, 155
- vertical asymptotes of rational functions, 387
- writing and graphing inequalities, 63

**kites,** 808, 832–838, 851

## L

**Law of Cosines,** 670–678, 683
**Law of Sines,** 660–667, 683
**length, and probability,** 765
**lengths, finding,** 860, 889, 910
**Lesson Check,** 9–10, 19–20, 26–27, 38–39, 60–61, 69–71, 78–79, 87–89, 96–97, 107–108, 115–116, 123–124, 131–133, 140–141, 157–158, 163–165, 174–176, 182–183, 190–191, 198–200, 207–209, 219–220, 228–229, 245–246, 253–254, 262–263, 270–271, 279–280, 287–288, 298–299, 306–307, 318–319, 327–328, 344–345, 352–354, 360–361, 369–370, 382–383, 392–394, 405–406, 429–430, 437–438, 446–448, 456–457, 464–465, 473–474, 484–486, 495–496, 512–513, 521–522, 531–533, 539–540, 547–548, 558–560, 577–579, 586–587, 594–595, 603–604, 615–616, 624–625, 635–636, 646–648, 656–658, 664–665, 674–676, 692–693, 700, 708–709, 717–718, 727–728, 743–744, 751–752, 760–762, 770–771, 781–782, 790–791, 798–799, 816–817, 828–829, 835–837, 847, 861–862, 869–870, 883–884, 893–894, 902–903, 911–912
**Lesson Lab**
- the ambiguous case (Law of Sines), 668–669
- exponential and logarithmic inequalities, 562–566
- identifying quadratic data, 167–168
- mathematical induction, 309–312
- partitioning a segment, 821–822
- piecewise functions, 99–101
- summation notation, 13–14

**light waves,** 602–603
**like radicals,** 440
**linear/absolute value systems, solving,** 122
**linear functions**
- and slope-intercept form, 73–80, 143
- summation notation and, 715

**linear inequalities, graphing,** 103
**linear models, using,** 503
**linear-quadratic systems, solutions of,** 203, 204
**linear systems, using a calculator to solve,** 139
**lines,** 75, 839–842
**literal equations,** 59

**loci (sets of points),** 736, 794–801, 805
**logarithmic and exponential functions**
Chapter Review, 567–569
exploring exponential models, 505–514, 567
exponential and logarithmic equations, 542–550, 569
exponential and logarithmic inequalities, 562–566
logarithmic functions as inverses, 525–534, 568
natural logarithms, 553–561, 569
properties of exponential functions, 515–524, 567
properties of logarithms, 535–541, 568
Pull It All Together, 570
using logarithms for exponential models, 551–552
**logarithmic equations,** 546–547
**logarithmic scales,** 527–528, 538
**long division, polynomials and,** 274
**Looking Ahead Vocabulary,** 1, 53, 149, 237, 337, 423, 503, 571, 685, 735, 807, 853

# M

**Make a Conjecture exercises,** 264, 289, 497, 650, 721
**margin of error,** 42–45
**mathematical induction,** 309–312
**mathematical patterns,** 687–695, 731
**matrices, solving systems using,** 135–142, 147
**matrix elements,** 135
**measurements,** 264, 666, 736, 808, 854
**Mental Math,** 465, 549
**midlines, of periodic functions,** 576
**modeling**
Big Ideas, 504, 572
with cosine functions, 613
exponential growth, 508–509
inverse variations, 366
light waves, 602–603
power functions, 326
using linear models, 503
using logarithms for exponential models, 551–552
**More Practice and Problem-Solving Exercises,** 10–12, 20–21, 27–28, 39–41, 61–62, 71–72, 79–80, 89–90, 97–98, 108–109, 117–118, 124–125, 133–134, 141–142, 158–159, 165–166, 176–177, 183–184, 191–192, 200–202, 210–211, 220–221, 229–230, 246–247, 254–255, 263–264, 272, 280–281, 288–289, 299–300, 307–308, 319–321, 328–329, 345–346, 354–355, 361–362, 370–371, 383–384, 395–396, 407–408, 430–431, 438–439, 448–449, 457–458, 465–466, 475–476, 486–487, 496–497, 513–514, 522–524, 533–534, 540–541, 548–550, 560–561, 579–580, 587–588, 595–596, 605–606, 617–618, 625–627, 637, 648–650, 658–659, 666–667, 676–678, 693–695, 701–702, 709–710, 718–719, 729–730, 744–746, 752–754, 762–764, 771–773, 782–784, 791–793, 799–801, 818–820, 829–831, 837–838, 862–864, 870–872, 848–849, 884–885, 894–896, 903–905, 913–914
**Multiple Choice exercise,** 384, 669
**Multiple Representations exercises,** 648
**multiplication**
binomial radical expressions, 443
of binomials, 423
conjugates, 444
function operations, 467, 468–469
of polynomials, 250–255, 330
of radical expressions, 432–439, 498
of rational expressions, 347–355, 418
**multiplicity of a zero, finding,** 260
**multi-step equations, solving,** 56–57

# N

***n* + 1 Point Principle,** 314
**natural base exponential functions,** 519
**natural logarithms,** 553–561, 569
**normal curves,** 36–37
**normal distributions,** 34–41, 51
***n*th root,** 425–426
***n*th roots of *n*th powers,** 427
**numbers, simplifying,** 454

# O

**oblique asymptotes,** 397–400
**odd and even functions,** 248–249
**one-step equations,** 56
**Open-Ended exercises,** 28, 72, 90, 117, 124, 134, 141, 145, 159, 177, 184, 210, 230, 246, 254, 264, 272, 280, 289, 299, 300, 346, 355, 361, 371, 383, 399, 406, 408, 431, 439, 449, 456, 458, 466, 474, 476, 487, 496, 514, 524, 533, 540, 549, 580, 587, 588, 596, 604, 605, 616, 625, 637, 666, 677, 694, 700, 710, 719, 729, 763, 782, 784, 799, 805, 819, 830, 837, 871
**opposite factors,** 342
**order of operations,** 53
**outliers,** 5

# P

**parabolas,** 155, 212–221, 235
**parallel lines,** 739, 839–842
**parallelograms,** 823–831, 850
**parent quadratic function,** 151
**Pascal's Triangle,** 304
**patterns,** 685. *See also* sequences and series
**pentagons,** 813
**percents,** 1
**perfect square trinomial equations, solving,** 187
**perfect-square trinomials, factoring,** 173
**perimeter,** 809–820, 850
**perimeter ratios,** 759
**perimeters and areas of similar figures,** 735–764, 803
**periodic data,** 573–580, 679
**periods, sine curves and,** 599
**perpendicular lines,** 738, 839–842
**phase shifts,** 629
**piecewise functions,** 99–101. *See also* radicals
**points, sets of (loci),** 794–801, 805
**points of discontinuity,** 386–387
**polygons,** 843–849, 851
**polyhedrons,** 774
**polynomial equations,** 265–272, 282–289, 331, 333
**polynomial functions,** 239–247, 257, 297, 330
**polynomial identities,** 290–294
**polynomial models in the real world,** 313–321, 335
**polynomials,** 349–350, 351
**polynomials and polynomial functions**
adding, subtracting, and multiplying polynomials, 250–255, 330
binomial theorem, 303–308, 334
Chapter Review, 330–335
dividing polynomials, 273–281, 332

**polynomials and polynomial functions (*continued*)**
fundamental theorem of algebra, 295–300, 334
graphing polynomials using zeros, 301–302
linear functions and zeros, 256–264, 331
mathematical induction, 309–312
odd and even functions, 248–249
polynomial functions, 239–247, 330
polynomial identities, 290–294
polynomial models in the real world, 313–321, 335
Pull It All Together, 336
solving polynomial equations, 265–272, 331
theorems about roots of polynomial equations, 282–289, 333
transforming polynomial functions, 322–329, 335

**population density,** 748

**postulates, Arc Addition Postulate,** 856

**power functions,** 325, 326

**probability,** 830
geometric probability, 765–773, 804
and length, 765
probability distributions, 29–33

**products,** 432, 434

**proofs,** 62, 221
angle measures and segment lengths, 914
chords and arcs, 894, 895, 896
inscribed angles, 904, 905
Inscribed Angle Theorem, 898
tangent lines, 885

**properties**
change of base formula, 537
combining radical expressions, 432, 434, 440
of cosine functions, 612
of equality, 55
of exponential functions, 515–524, 567
of inequalities, 64–65
of logarithms, 535–541, 568
*n*th roots of *n*th powers, 427
of rational exponents, 453
of sine functions, 601
standard form of a quadratic function, 161
sum of a finite arithmetic series, 711, 712
of tangent functions, 621
Zero-Product Property, 178

**properties of equality,** 55

**proportionality,** 338

**proportions,** 589–590. *See also* ratios

**Pull It All Together,** 52, 148, 236, 336, 422, 502, 570, 684, 734, 806, 852, 918

**Pythagorean identities,** 653, 654, 655

**Pythagorean Theorem,** 853

# Q

**quadratic data, identifying,** 167–168

**quadratic equations,** 178–184, 233, 237, 337, 571. *See also* quadratic functions and equations

**quadratic expressions, factoring,** 337

**quadratic formula,** 193–202, 234

**quadratic functions, graphing,** 237, 423

**quadratic functions and equations**
Chapter Review, 231–235
circles in the coordinate plane, 222–230, 235
completing the square, 185–192, 233
factoring quadratic expressions, 169–177, 232
identifying quadratic data, 167–168
parabolas, 212–221, 235
Pull It All Together, 236
quadratic equations, 178–184, 233
quadratic formula, 193–202, 234
quadratic functions and transformations, 151–159, 231
quadratic systems, 203–211, 234
standard form of a quadratic function, 160–166, 232

**quadratic graphs,** 163

**quadratic systems,** 150, 203–211, 234

**quadrilaterals,** 735, 845

**quartic functions,** 324–325

**quotients, combining radical expressions,** 434

# R

**radian measure,** 589–596, 680

**radians, circles and,** 873-875

**radical expressions and functions**
binomial radical expressions, 440–449, 499
Chapter Review, 498–501
function operations, 467–476, 500
graphing radical functions, 488–497, 501
inverse relations and functions, 477–487, 501
multiplying and dividing radical expressions, 432–439, 498
Pull It All Together, 502
rational exponents, 450–458, 499
roots and radical expressions, 425–431, 498
solving square roots and other radical equations, 459–466, 500

**radicals,** 463, 735

**radius, finding,** 226, 880

**rational equations, solving,** 401–408, 421

**rational exponents,** 450–458, 499, 503

**rational expressions and functions**
adding and subtracting rational expressions, 356–362, 419
Chapter Review, 418–421
graphing rational functions, 372–375, 571
inverse variations, 363–371, 419
multiplying and dividing rational expressions, 347–355, 418
oblique asymptotes, 397–400
Pull It All Together, 422
rational functions and their graphs, 385–396, 420
rational inequalities, 413–417
reciprocal function family, 376–384, 420
simplifying rational expressions, 339–346, 418
solving rational equations, 401–408, 421
systems with rational equations, 409–412

**rational inequalities,** 413–417

**rational numbers,** 53

**rational roots,** 283–284

**Rational Root Theorem,** 282, 283–284

**ratios,** 756, 758, 759. *See also* proportions

**real roots, graphing,** 268

**reasoning and proof, as Big Idea,** 854

**Reasoning exercises,** 7, 12, 18, 20, 21, 23, 27, 30, 31, 37, 39, 40, 53, 59, 60, 67, 70, 72, 74, 76, 80, 85, 89, 90, 92, 98, 104, 106, 108, 109, 113, 123, 128, 129, 132, 138, 152, 158, 159, 163, 168, 172, 176, 177, 180, 183, 184, 188, 195, 197, 200, 201, 206, 208, 211 214, 221, 225, 229, 244, 245, 247, 249, 250, 254, 255, 259, 268, 271, 275, 280, 281, 286, 288, 289, 297, 300, 305, 307, 317, 319,

320, 325, 329, 343, 345, 346, 348, 353, 354, 355, 359, 361, 362, 368, 371, 374, 377, 384, 391, 394, 396, 403, 406, 412, 426, 430, 431, 435, 436, 438, 439, 442, 445, 448, 451, 457, 458, 462, 466, 471, 475, 478, 486, 487, 494, 506, 509, 511, 513, 514, 517, 522, 529, 532, 538, 540, 541, 548, 549, 557, 560, 575, 578, 580, 588, 592, 594, 595, 596, 605, 614, 616, 618, 623, 627, 634, 637, 642, 643, 647, 649, 650, 654, 666, 667, 671, 678, 690, 695, 698, 701, 702, 706, 712, 718, 719, 726, 729, 744, 752, 761, 764, 769, 770, 771, 772, 775, 782, 783, 787, 791, 794, 800, 814, 815, 819, 830, 836, 837, 848, 859, 863, 866, 870, 871, 875, 877, 884, 887, 892, 901, 904, 905, 908, 913, 914

**reciprocal function family,** 376–384, 420

**reciprocal trigonometric functions,** 641–650, 682

**rectangles,** 810, 823

**recursive definitions, of a sequence,** 688, 689–690

**reflection, stretch, and compression,** 153

**reflections,** 84

**relative maximum and minimum,** 260, 261

**Remainder Theorem,** 278

**residuals, plotting and analyzing,** 638–640

**rhombuses,** 832–838, 851

**Richter Scale,** 527

**roots**
- Conjugate Root Theorem, 284–285
- and radical expressions, 425–431, 498
- Rational Root Theorem, 283–284
- roots, zeros, and *x*-intercepts, 257

**row operations,** 137

# S

**samples and surveys,** 22–28, 46–49, 51

**scale factors,** 787, 788, 789

**sectors,** 865–872, 915

**segments**
- angle measures and segment lengths, 906–914, 917
- area of, 868
- finding probability and, 766
- partitioning, 821–822

**sequences and series**
- arithmetic sequences, 696–702, 731
- arithmetic series, 711–719, 732
- Chapter Review, 731–733
- geometric sequences, 703–710, 732
- geometric series, 722–730, 733
- infinite series, 720–721
- mathematical patterns, 687–695, 731
- Pull It All Together, 734

**sets of points (loci),** 794–801, 805

**sine curves,** 599, 600

**sine function,** 597–606, 628–637, 680, 682

**sines,** 584, 591

**skewed data,** 35

**slope criteria, proving,** 839–842

**slope-intercept form,** 73–80, 143, 149

**solids, areas and volumes of,** 785–793, 805

**solutions**
- equations with no solutions, 58
- inequalities without, 66
- of a linear-quadratic system, 203
- systems without unique solutions, 114

**solving equations,** 853

**space figures and cross sections,** 774–784, 804

**square root functions,** 490

**square roots,** 185–186, 424, 459–466, 500, 735

**squares,** 173, 174, 185–192, 233

**squaring numbers,** 807

**standard deviation,** 15–21, 50

**standard form**
- of an equation of a circle, 222
- of a polynomial function, 240
- of a quadratic function, 160–166, 232

**statistics, data analysis and,** 3

**STEM,** 11, 40, 62, 72, 117, 118, 131, 158, 163, 165, 181, 184, 198, 201, 216, 220, 221, 230, 346, 368, 370, 371, 392, 408, 430, 431, 438, 439, 442, 448, 452, 457, 458, 461, 466, 497, 514, 523, 524, 528, 533, 538, 540, 541, 545, 548, 549, 550, 557, 558, 560, 561, 563, 593, 594, 606, 613, 618, 623, 634, 635, 659, 678, 706, 719, 730, 753, 754, 763, 764, 772, 789, 800, 863, 866, 871, 879, 884, 913

**stretch,** 153

**substitution method,** 110–111, 129, 204

**subtraction**
- fractions, 337
- function operations, 467, 468
- percents, 1
- of polynomials, 250–255, 330
- of radical expressions, 441
- of rational expressions, 356–362, 419

**summation notation,** 13–14, 714, 715

**sum of a finite arithmetic series,** 711–713

**sum of a finite geometric series,** 723

**sums, combining radical expressions,** 440

**synthetic division,** 276, 277

**systems**
- quadratic systems, 203–211, 234
- with rational equations, 409–412
- solving systems of equations, 110–118, 145
- solving systems using matrices, 135–142, 147
- systems of inequalities, 119–125, 146
- systems without unique solutions, 114
- systems with three variables, 126–134, 146

# T

**Take Note,** 3–4, 6, 15, 22, 24, 34–35, 55, 63, 64–65, 73, 75, 86, 91, 93, 95, 151, 153, 155, 161, 173, 178, 188, 194, 196, 203, 212–213, 217, 222, 224, 240, 241, 258, 260, 266, 275, 278, 282, 284, 286, 296, 298, 304, 314, 325, 367, 376, 379, 386, 387, 389, 425–426, 427, 432, 434, 440, 451, 453, 467, 469, 483, 489, 506, 508, 517, 525–526, 530, 535, 537, 553, 584, 589–590, 592, 601, 612, 619, 621, 632, 641, 651, 655 660, 661, 670, 696, 703, 711, 715, 723, 725, 755, 765, 767, 776, 786, 809, 823, 825, 832, 833, 843, 856, 858, 860, 865, 868, 876–877, 879, 881–882, 886, 887, 888, 890, 891, 897, 901, 906–907, 919–910

**tangent function,** 619–627, 681

**tangent lines, circles and,** 876–885, 916

**Technical Writing exercises,** 399

Index

Index


**Technology Lab**
- graphing rational functions, 372–375
- graphing trigonometric functions, 607–609
- oblique asymptotes, 397–400
- odd and even functions, 248–249
- plotting and analyzing residuals, 638–640
- polynomial identities, 290–294
- rational inequalities, 413–417
- using logarithms for exponential models, 551–552

**Theorems**
- arc lengths, 860
- area of a circle, 865
- area of a sector of a circle, 867
- areas and volumes of similar solids, 786
- binomial theorem, 303–308, 334
- circumference of a circle, 858
- Conjugate Root Theorem, 284
- Descartes' Rule of Signs, 286
- Factor Theorem, 258
- fundamental theorem of algebra, 295–300, 334
- Inscribed Angle Theorem, 897–898
- law of cosines, 670–671
- law of sines, 661
- perimeters and areas of similar figures, 755
- Rational Root Theorem, 282
- Remainder Theorem, 278
- theorems about roots of polynomial equations, 282–289, 333

**Think About a Plan exercises,** 11, 20, 27, 39, 61, 71, 79, 89, 97, 108, 117, 124, 133, 141, 158, 165, 176, 183, 191, 200, 210, 220, 229, 246, 254, 263, 272, 280, 289, 300, 307, 319, 328, 346, 355, 362, 370, 383, 395, 407, 430, 438, 448, 457, 465, 486, 496, 513, 522, 533, 540, 548, 560, 579, 587, 595, 605, 617, 626, 637, 648, 658, 666, 676, 694, 701, 709, 718, 729, 745, 752, 763, 771, 783, 791, 800, 818, 829, 837, 848, 862, 871, 885, 894, 903, 913

**transformations**
- exponential functions, 515
- identifying, 95
- identifying reciprocal function transformations, 378
- of a parabola, 217
- quadratic functions and, 151–159, 231
- transformations of $f(x)$, 86
- transforming a circle, 224
- transforming polynomial functions, 322–329, 335
- writing the equation of, 380

**translations**
- absolute value functions and graphs, 93
- graphs and graphing, 153, 379
- horizontal translations, 83
- identifying, 149
- sine and cosine functions, 628–637, 682
- translating square root functions horizontally, 490
- translating square root functions vertically, 489
- translation of the parabola, 155
- using to write an equation, 223
- vertical translations, 82

**trapezoids,** 832–838, 851

**triangles,** 660, 661, 662, 663, 669, 808, 812, 823–831, 844, 850

**trigonometric functions**
- the ambiguous case, 668–669
- angles and the unit circle, 581–588, 679
- area and the law of sines, 660–667, 683
- Chapter Review, 679–683
- the cosine function, 610–618, 681
- exploring periodic data, 573–580, 679
- graphing, 607–609
- Law of Cosines, 670–678, 683
- plotting and analyzing residuals, 638–640
- Pull It All Together, 684
- radian measure, 589–596, 680
- reciprocal trigonometric functions, 641–650, 682
- the sine function, 597–606, 680
- the tangent function, 619–627, 681
- translating sine and cosine functions, 628–637, 682
- trigonometric identities, 651–659, 683

**trigonometric identities,** 651–659, 683

**trinomials,** 187, 341

**two-variable inequalities,** 54, 102–109, 145


## U


**unit circle,** 581–588, 679

## V


**variables,** 126–134, 146

**variance and standard deviation, finding,** 15–16

**vertex form,** 154, 156
- completing the square and, 189–190
- converting to standard form, 162
- standard form of a quadratic function, 161
- writing a quadratic function in, 156

**vertical asymptotes of rational functions,** 387–388

**vertical translations,** 82

**visualization,** 736

**Visualization exercises,** 780, 783, 784, 838

**Vocabulary exercises,** 10, 19, 26, 38, 60, 79, 116, 157, 175, 183, 191, 220, 245, 254, 263, 271, 287, 299, 306, 318, 327, 344, 383, 430, 437, 447, 465, 485, 512, 522, 532, 539, 595, 604, 624, 636, 657, 665, 693, 700, 718, 744, 751, 782, 790, 799, 828, 836, 862, 869, 884, 894, 903, 912


## W


**writing**
- absolute value functions, 95
- an equation of a parabola, 218
- equations in slope-intercept form, 77
- exponential equations in logarithmic form, 526
- exponential functions, 511
- inequalities based on graphs, 106
- a polynomial in factored form, 256
- rewriting an exponential function, 518
- rewriting a radical function, 494
- a series in summation notation, 714
- translations of sine and cosine functions, 633
- a trigonometric function, 634
- writing and equation of a circle, 223
- writing and graphing inequalities, 63
- writing a quadratic function in vertex form, 156

writing a system from a matrix, 137
writing equations in slope-intercept form, 149
writing the equation of a transformation, 380

**Writing exercises,** 11, 21, 27, 39, 61, 62, 72, 90, 98, 109, 116, 117, 124, 133, 140, 141, 166, 177, 200, 221, 264, 280, 281, 289, 299, 307, 308, 319, 320, 329, 345, 346, 354, 360, 361, 369, 371, 383, 384, 396, 408, 439, 449, 487, 495, 541, 548, 552, 561, 564, 578, 579, 588, 596, 609, 617, 625, 627, 649, 667, 675, 677, 701, 710, 728, 730, 763, 772, 784, 791, 799, 801, 817, 818, 829, 830, 838, 847, 863, 871, 895, 903

## X

***x*-intercepts,** 257

**Zero-Product Property,** 178

**zeros**
fundamental theorem of algebra, 295–296
graphing polynomials using zeros, 301–302
how multiple zeros affect a graph, 260
linear factors, zeros, and polynomials, 238, 256–264, 331
polynomial functions and, 297
quartic functions and, 324–325
roots, zeros, and x-intercepts, 257
of a transformed cubic function, 323–324

Index

# Acknowledgments

## Staff Credits

The people who made up the High School Mathematics team—representing composition services, core design digital and multimedia production services, digital product development, editorial, editorial services, manufacturing, marketing, and production management—are listed below.

Patty Fagan, Suzanne Finn, Matt Frueh, Cynthia Harvey, Linda Johnson, Roshni Kutty, Cheryl Mahan, Eve Melnechuk, Cynthia Metallides, Hope Morley, Michael Oster, Wynnette Outland, Brian Reardon, Matthew Rogers, Ann-Marie Sheehan, Kristen Siefers, Richard Sullivan, Susan Tauer, Mark Tricca, Oscar Vera, Paula Vergith

**Additional Credits:** Emily Bosak, Olivia Gerde, Alyse McGuire, Stephanie Mosely

## Illustration

**Stephen Durke:** 764, 801, 819, 820, 827, 863, 864, 872; **Jeff Grunewald:** 762, 848; **Phil Guzy:** 769, 772, 793, 858, 862; **Judi Pinkham:** 183; **Rob Schuster:** 126, 133, 165, 262, 264, 277, 396, 408, 465, 694, 695; **Christopher Wilson:** 355.

## Technical Illustration

Aptara, Inc.; Datagrafix, Inc.; GGS Book Services

## Photography

Every effort has been made to secure permission and provide appropriate credit for photographic material. The publisher deeply regrets any omission and pledges to correct errors called to its attention in subsequent editions.

Unless otherwise acknowledged, all photographs are the property of Pearson Education, Inc.

**71** Richard Wahlstrom/Workbook/Jupiter Images/Getty Images; **384** NASA; **541** Jerry Lodriguss/Science Photo Library/Photo Researchers, Inc.; **550** Dave King/©DK Images; **593** Fnalphotos/Dreamstime LLC; **649** Demetrio Carrasco/©DK Images; **783** Sports Bokeh/Alamy; **800** ©matthiasengelien/Alamy; **837** artpartner-images/ Alamy Images; **918** Clive Streeter/©DK Images; **904** Vario Images GmbH & Co.KG/Alamy Images; **909** Melvyn Longhurst/Alamy; **913** dpa/Corbis.